CW01024338

The Management of Construction Health and Safety Risk

Technician Member (Tech IOSH)

This category recognises the qualifications and competence needed by professionals working in a range of operational health and safety roles. To become a Technician, you must have a suitable level of experience in a health and safety role, as well as an IOSH accredited qualification.

Students on a course of study towards Tech IOSH will find this **Essential Health and Safety Guide** particularly useful in developing the knowledge requirements for an IOSH accredited qualification at this level.

RMS Publishing Limited

Suite 3, Victoria House, Lower High Street, Stourbridge DY8 1TA

© RMS Publishing™.

Second Edition October 2007.

Second Edition August 2009 (reprint).

Third Edition January 2012.

Third Edition May 2014 (reprint).

Fourth Edition May 2015.

Fourth Edition April 2016 (reprint).

Cover by Smudge Creative Design.

Printed and bound in Great Britain by CPI Antony Rowe.

Crown Copyright material is reproduced with the permission of the Controller of HMSO and the Queen's Printer for Scotland.

ISBN-13: 978-1-906674-37-3

Contents

Preface   v
Foreword   viii
Figure list   ix
List of abbreviations   xvii

1   Construction law and management   01
     1.1 - Scope, definition and nature of construction activities   03
     1.2 - Consequences of failing to manage health and safety   06
     1.3 - Construction (Design and Management) Regulations (CDM) 2015   08
     1.4 - Sources of external construction health and safety information   17
     Exam practice   19

2   Construction site - hazards and risk control   21
     2.1 - Initial site assessment   23
     2.2 - Appropriate general site control measures   26
     2.3 - Health, welfare and work environment requirements   32
     2.4 - Violence at work   41
     2.5 - Substance misuse at work   42
     2.6 - Safe movement of people on construction sites   44
     Exam practice   54

3   Vehicle and plant movement - hazards and risk control   55
     3.1 - Safe movement of vehicles within a construction environment   57
     3.2 - Driving at work   66
     Exam practice   72

4   Musculoskeletal hazards and risk control   73
     4.1 - Musculoskeletal and work-related upper limb disorders   75
     4.2 - Manual handling hazards and control measures   80
     4.3 - Lifting and moving equipment   90
     Exam practice   110

5   Work equipment - hazards and risk control   111
     5.1 - General requirements for work equipment   113
     5.2 - Hand-held tools   123
     5.3 - Machinery hazards   128
     5.4 - Control measures for machinery hazards   135
     Exam practice   143

6   Electrical safety   145
     6.1 - Hazards and risks associated with electricity   147
     6.2 - Control measures   154
     6.3 - Control measures for working near overhead power lines   166
     Exam practice   167

7   Fire safety   169
     7.1 - Fire initiation, classification and spread   171
     7.2 - Fire risk assessment   177
     7.3 - Fire prevention and prevention of fire spread   181
     7.4 - Fire detection, fire alarm and firefighting equipment   190
     7.5 - Means of escape   194
     7.6 - Evacuation of a construction workplace   196
     Exam practice   198

8	**Chemical and biological health - hazards and risk control**	**199**
	8.1 - Health risks from hazardous substances	201
	8.2 - Assessment of health risks	208
	8.3 - Workplace exposure limits	218
	8.4 - Control measures	222
	8.5 - Specific agents	237
	8.6 - Safe handling and storage of waste	251
	Exam practice	253
9	**Physical and psychological health - hazards and risk control**	**255**
	9.1 - Noise	257
	9.2 - Vibration	265
	9.3 - Radiation	269
	9.4 - Stress	275
	Exam practice	278
10	**Working at height - hazards and risk control**	**279**
	10.1 - Working at height hazards and risks	281
	10.2 - Safe working practices for access equipment and roof work	289
	10.3 - Protection of others	310
	10.4 - Working over or near water	311
	Exam practice	313
11	**Excavation work and confined spaces – hazards and risk control**	**315**
	11.1 - Excavations hazards and assessment	317
	11.2 - Control measures for excavation work	321
	11.3 - Confined spaces hazards and risks	329
	11.4 - Control measures for confined space working	331
	Exam practice	335
12	**Demolition and deconstruction - hazards and risk control**	**337**
	12.1 - Demolition and deconstruction hazards and risk	339
	12.2 - Control measures	344
	12.3 - Pre-demolition, deconstruction or refurbishment surveys	350
	12.4 - Method statements	354
	Exam practice	357
Relevant statutory provisions		**359**
Assessment		**415**
Revision and examination guidance		**451**
Index		**465**

Preface

Publication users

This essential health and safety guide provides an excellent reference for those who have responsibility for or involvement in construction activities. The guide provides an understanding of the health and safety risks affecting this important sector of work and assists those responsible to manage them effectively.

The practical and informative approach of the publication will provide managers, health and safety practitioners and others who work in the construction industry with a perspective of the significance of health and safety risk in construction activities and an understanding of the control measures that can be applied to manage risk. This publication would be particularly useful for clients, designers, principal contractors, principal designers, contractors and site managers. Those working in facilities and event management industries will also find the guide useful, as many of the risks they encounter are similar.

The guide is an excellent source of information for those undergoing the following learning programmes:

- To meet the requirements of the NEBOSH National Certificate in Construction Health and Safety syllabus.

- To develop the knowledge of managers and supervisors working in construction.

- To develop and enhance competency and skills needed for facilities managers.

- To develop and enhance competency and skills needed for those who construct and disassemble temporary structures for outdoor events, music or theatre production and trade or other exhibitions.

Reference is made to the harm that construction hazards may have and the prevalence of injuries they cause in the construction industry. The publication contains an emphasis on practical solutions to construction workplace health and safety issues. Full colour photographs, tables and sample documents are provided to enable an understanding of how these risks can be managed. The publication contains a sample report from a questionnaire that may be used as a basis of a health and safety review for organisations.

Scope and contents

Syllabus

The Essential Health and Safety Guide focuses on construction hazards and related losses, risk control measures and core management of health and safety principles as they relate to construction activities.

The 4th edition of this publication has been thoroughly revised and updated to embrace the November 2014 specification of the syllabus for the NEBOSH National Certificate in Construction Health and Safety award. Though the publication will suit all those interested in the topic in general and studying for other awards, it has been structured to reflect the order and content of the NEBOSH National Certificate in Construction Health and Safety syllabus in particular. In this way, the student studying for this award can be confident that the Essential Health and Safety Guide reflects the themes of the syllabus and forms an excellent Study Book for that purpose. Each element of the Essential Health and Safety Guide has an overview that sets out the learning outcomes of the element, the content and any connected sources of reference and relevant statutory provisions.

All statistics shown throughout this publication are the latest available at time of going to press.

Assessment

In order that users may check their understanding of the topic expressed in the Essential Health and Safety Guide and in particular the syllabus for the NEBOSH National Certificate in Construction Health and Safety award, a number of assessment questions have been included. Any resemblance to NEBOSH examination questions is coincidental; the questions have been created to illustrate the type of question which may be asked at examination to check understanding of the relevant element learning outcomes.

In addition, the publication contains a sample health and safety review questionnaire that may be used as a basis for an evaluation of an organisation's performance. The questionnaire has been produced by NEBOSH as part of their practical assessment of the above award, their origination and copyright is acknowledged. In order to understand how the questionnaire may be used and the type of report produced by candidates studying this award, a completed questionnaire and report is provided.

Revision and examination guidance

There are ways of making study time more effective to give a student the greatest possible chance of success in their exams. This new section has been added to aid students with useful study tips, time management and revision techniques.

Legal requirements

The Essential Health and Safety Guide has at its heart the fact that health and safety should be managed as a risk. However, as one of the risks to a business is the risk of prosecution, care has been taken to relate topics to current legislation. The level of treatment is targeted to cover the interests of those developing their skills in health and safety management and in particular those following a course of study. Legislation is referred to in context in the various elements that comprise the Essential Health and Safety Guide and reflects the certificate level syllabus of the NEBOSH award.

Photographs and users

We have taken particular care to support the text with a significant number of full colour photographs and schematics. They are illustrative of both good and bad working practices and should always be considered in context with supporting text. Readers will find this a useful aid when trying to relate their background and experience to the broad based construction activities that may be encountered.

Where photographs, diagrams and text extracts are known to be drawn from other publications, a clear source reference is shown and RMS wish to emphasise that reproduction of such items within the Essential Health and Safety Guide is for educational purposes only and the original copyright has not been infringed.

Production of the publication

Managing Editor

Ian Coombes, Managing Director ACT, CMIOSH; member of NEBOSH Council, member of NEBOSH Board of Trustees, member of NEBOSH Qualifications and Technical Council and former NEBOSH examiner. Former member of IOSH Professional Affairs Committee and chairman of the Initial Professional Development sub-committee. Member of the Safety Groups UK (SGUK) management committee.

Acknowledgements

RMS Publishing Ltd wishes to acknowledge the following contributors and thank them for their assistance in the preparation of the publication:

Geoff Littley, Principal Consultant ACT, CMIOSH, NEBOSH Diploma, CSPA; experienced health and safety advisor, including manufacturing, NHS Trusts, Local Authorities and transport industries. Lead tutor for NEBOSH Diploma and Certificate level courses, in particular for the NEBOSH National

General Certificate and Construction Health and Safety awards. Provides training and mentor support for Principal Designers.

Barrie Newell, Director ACT, FCIM; Lead Auditor OHAS 18001, former member of the NEBOSH Diploma Panel, current member of the NEBOSH Certificate Panel, former senior manager in the chemical industry with over 20 years' experience in the management of high risk facilities processing highly flammable and toxic chemicals, including HAZOP implementation. Implemented waste management systems including, waste reduction, recycling, reuse, incineration, including energy recovery and disposal to land fill.

Julie Skett, Design and Development Coordinator. Nick Attwood, Kris James, Andy Taylor and Jeff Harper-Smith, layout and formatting.

Publications available from RMS:

Publication	Edition	ISBN
A Study Book for the NEBOSH National Certificate – Unit NGC1 Management of Health and Safety	First	978-1-906674-49-6
A Study Book for the NEBOSH National General Certificate in Occupational Health and Safety	Eighth	978-1-906674-44-1
A Study Book for the NEBOSH Certificate in Fire Safety and Risk Management	Fifth	978-1-906674-32-8
The Management of Construction Health and Safety Risk	Fourth	978-1-906674-37-3
The Management of Environmental Risks in the Workplace	Third	978-1-906674-24-3
The Management of Health and Well-being in the Workplace	First	978-1-906674-14-4
A Guide to International Oil and Gas Operational Safety	First	978-1-906674-19-9
A Guide to International Health and Safety at Work	Fourth	978-1-906674-43-4
Study Books for the NEBOSH National Diploma in Occupational Safety and Health:		
■ (Unit A) Managing health and safety	Fifth	978-1-906674-25-0
■ (Unit B) Hazardous agents in the workplace	Fifth	978-1-906674-26-7
■ (Unit C) Workplace and work equipment safety	Fifth	978-1-906674-27-4
Study Books for the NEBOSH International Diploma in Occupational Safety and Health:		
■ (Unit IA) International management of health and safety	Third	978-1-906674-29-8
■ (Unit IB) International management of hazardous agents in the workplace	Third	978-1-906674-30-4
■ (Unit IC) International workplace and work equipment safety	Third	978-1-906674-31-1
Controlling skin exposure (BOHS)	First	978-1-906674-00-7

Foreword

With the continued poor record of the construction industry in regards to health and safety, it is of the utmost importance to make those within the industry aware of procedures to change both standards and culture.

This essential health and safety guide complements training with a structured approach to give managers and others the tools to allow positive health and safety management within the construction industry.

After many years within the industry, I have seen major improvements but there is always a need for step-change action. This Essential Health and Safety Guide to The Management of Construction Health and Safety Risk will assist construction personnel in achieving such a step-change.

John Lacey, C.F.I.O.S.H., F.S.I.A.. H.F.A.P.S, M.A.S.S.E
IOSH Vice President and Past Chair of the Construction Group.
Has been involved in and led by example construction health and safety,
in both the UK and other areas of the world for over 30 years.

Figure List (including tables and quotes)

Figure Ref   Title and Source   *Page No.*

Element 1
1-1   Number and rate of fatal injury to workers, 1995/96-2014/15. *Source: HSE.*   7
1-2   Appointment of the principal designer and the principal contractor. *Source: CDM 2015 Regulation 5.*   10

Element 2
2-1   Site assessment - previous use. *Source: RMS.*   23
2-2   Site assessment - access. *Source: RMS.*   23
2-3   Roads. *Source: RMS.*   24
2-4   Footpaths. *Source: RMS.*   24
2-5   Railways. *Source: Welsh Highland Railway.*   24
2-6   Waterways. *Source: RMS.*   24
2-7   Commercial properties. *Source: RMS.*   25
2-8   Industrial properties. *Source: RMS.*   25
2-9   Means of access, overhead restrictions. *Source: RMS.*   25
2-10   Safe distance barriers for overhead services. *Source: HSE HSG144.*   25
2-11   Site access. *Source: RMS.*   26
2-12   Site controls - access and roadways. *Source: RMS.*   26
2-13   Misuse of storage. *Source: RMS.*   27
2-14   Loading/unloading. *Source: RMS.*   27
2-15   Site signs. *Source: RMS.*   29
2-16   Steelworks. *Source: RMS.*   29
2-17   Duties of a principal contractor. *Source: CDM 2015 Regulation 13.*   30
2-18   Duties of contractors. *Source: CDM 2015 Regulation 15.*   30
2-19   Good order and site security. *Source: CDM 2015 Regulation 18.*   30
2-20   Unauthorised access. *Source: RMS.*   30
2-21   Perimeter fencing and signs. *Source: RMS.*   30
2-22   Protection of others. *Source: RMS.*   31
2-23   Sanitary conveniences. *Source: RMS.*   31
2-24   Washing facilities. *Source: HSE, HSG150.*   33
2-25   Temporary showers. *Source: RMS.*   33
2-26   Rest rooms and rest areas. . *Source: CDM 2015 Schedule 2.*   34
2-27   Accommodation for clothing. *Source: RMS.*   34
2-28   Rest and eating facilities. *Source: RMS.*   34
2-29   Fresh air. *Source: CDM 2015 Regulation 33.*   34
2-30   Temperature and weather protection. *Source: CDM 2015 Regulation 34.*   35
2-31   Lighting. *Source: CDM 2015 Regulation 35.*   35
2-32   Adverse weather protection. *Source: CDM 2015 Regulation 34(2).*   36
2-33   Temperature at a construction site. *Source: CDM 2015 Regulation 34(1).*   40
2-34   Definition of work related violence. *Source: HSE.*   41
2-35   Slips and trips. *Source: Lincsafe.*   44
2-36   Trip hazards. *Source: Lincsafe.*   44
2-37   Collision with moving vehicles. *Source: RMS.*   45
2-38   Falling materials. *Source: Lincsafe.*   45
2-39   Obstructions. *Source: Lincsafe.*   46
2-40   Public highway works. *Source: RMS.*   46
2-41   Slip resistance surface on steps. *Source: RMS.*   47
2-42   Safe places of construction work. *Source: CDM 2015 Regulation 17.*   48
2-43   Pedestrian vehicle segregation. *Source: HSE, HSG150.*   48
2-44   Prevention of falling objects. *Source: WAH 2005 Regulation 10.*   49
2-45   Outer fencing and inner guarding. *Source: RMS.*   49
2-46   Fencing and guarding at height. *Source: RMS.*   49
2-47   Clothing and footwear. *Source: RMS.*   49
2-48   Safe place of work. *Source: CDM 2015 Regulation 17.*   50
2-49   Guard rails and toe boards. *Source: RMS.*   50
2-50   Access and egress. *Source: CDM 2015 Regulation 17.*   50
2-51   Temperature of indoor places of work. *Source: CDM 2015 Regulation 34.*   50
2-52   Lighting. *Source: CDM 2015 Regulation 35.*   51
2-53   Public highway works safety measures. *Source: RMS.*   53
2-54   Typical work site layout. *Source: TSO, Chapter 8.*   53
2-55   Lane widths and signs. *Source: TSO, Chapter 8.*   53
2-56   Arrangements for work on a footway. *Source: Department of Transport.*   54

Element 3
3-1   Reported injuries due to workplace moving vehicle accidents 2013/14. *Source: HSE.*   57
3-2   Vehicle overturned. *Source: Lincsafe.*   58
3-3   Potential collision with fixed objects. *Source: RMS.*   58
3-4   Vehicles - loading and unloading. *Source: CDM 2015 Regulation 28(5).*   58

3-5	Coupling. *Source: www.trucknetuk.com.*	59
3-6	Tilted LGV cab and prop. *Source: HSE.*	59
3-7	Traffic routes. *Source: CDM 2015 Regulation 27.*	60
3-8	Traffic routes. *Source: CDM 2015 Regulation 27 (3).*	60
3-9	Site entrance to construction site. *Source: HSE, HSG150.*	60
3-10	Traffic routes, supplementary requirements. *Source: CDM 2015 Regulation 27.*	61
3-11	Vehicles - falling into excavations etc. *Source: CDM 2015 Regulation 28(6).*	62
3-12	Roll bar and seat restraint. *Source: RMS.*	62
3-13	Driver protection. *Source: RMS.*	62
3-14	Means of segregation. *Source: Regulation 17(1) of WHSWR 1992.*	63
3-15	Traffic routes. *Source: CDM 2015 Regulation 27.*	63
3-16	Pedestrian crossing point. *Source: HSE, HSG150.*	63
3-17	Segregating pedestrians and vehicles. *Source: RMS.*	63
3-18	No segregation. *Source: RMS.*	64
3-19	Control of vehicle movement. *Source: RMS.*	64
3-20	Fencing and barriers at a distance. *Source: RMS.*	65
3-21	Visual warning on a dumper truck. *Source: RMS.*	65
3-22	Vehicles - safe operation and rules. *Source: CDM 2015 Regulation 28.*	65
3-23	Size of the road risk problem. *Source: RoSPA.*	67
3-24	Road risk. *Source: HSE.*	67

Element 4

4-1	Work related musculoskeletal disorder statistics. *Source: HSE.*	75
4-2	Total cases (prevalence) and new cases (incidence) of MSDs. *Source: HSE.*	75
4-3	Carpal tunnel syndrome. *Source: www.sodahead.com.*	77
4-4	Tenosynovitis. *Source: www.rayur.com*	77
4-5	Tendinitis. *Source: Beth Israel Deaconess Medical Center.*	78
4-6	Epicondylitis. *Source: Myhealth.alberta.ca.*	78
4-7	Poor posture. *Source: Speedy Hire Plc.*	79
4-8	Action to be taken to control WRULD risks. *Source: European Agency for Safety and Health at Work*	80
4-9	Lumber and slipped disc. *Source: NHS*	80
4-10	Manual handling risk assessment. *Source: HSE, Guidance L23.*	82
4-11	Manual handling. *Source: RMS.*	83
4-12	Lifting and lowering. *Source: HSE, Guidance L23.*	84
4-13	Handling while seated. *Source: HSE, Guidance L23.*	85
4-14	Twisting. *Source: HSE, Guidance L23.*	85
4-15	Light weight plastic kerbs. *Source: HSE, COH14.*	85
4-16	Vacuum lift for heavy concrete kerbs. *Source: www.vacuumliftinguk.co.uk.*	86
4-17	Excessive bending to trowel mortar. *Source: HSE, COH01.*	86
4-18	Raised spot board avoids excessive bending. *Source: HSE, COH01.*	86
4-19	Trench block with 'handholds'. *Source: HSE, COH04.*	86
4-20	Mechanical assistance. *Source: RMS.*	87
4-21	Mechanical aids. *Source: HSE, Guidance L23.*	87
4-22	Brick/tile conveyor. *Source: Mace Industries Ltd.*	87
4-23	Basic lifting techniques. *Source: HSE, Guidance L23.*	88
4-24	Sustained posture. *Source: Australia, Comcare.*	89
4-25	Awkward movements. *Source: HSE, HSG60*	90
4-26	Overturning of a fork-lift truck. *Source: HSE, HSG6 – Safety in working with lift trucks.*	91
4-27	Overbalancing of a fork-lift truck. *Source: HSE, HSG6 – Safety in working with lift trucks.*	92
4-28	Poor visibility loading. *Source: RMS.*	92
4-29	Rider operated fork-lift truck (counterbalance type). *Source: RMS.*	93
4-30	Rider operated fork-lift truck (reach type). *Source: RMS.*	93
4-31	Rough terrain counterbalance fork-lift truck. *Source: HSE, HSG6.*	94
4-32	Telescopic materials handler. *Source: HSE, HSG6.*	94
4-33	Side-loading fork-lift truck. *Source: HSE, HSG6.*	94
4-34	Pedestrian-controlled fork-lift truck. *Source: HSE, HSG6.*	94
4-35	Large fork-lift truck. *HSE, HSG6.*	95
4-36	Rough terrain fork-lift truck. *Source: RMS.*	95
4-37	Keys – unauthorised use not controlled. *Source: RMS.*	95
4-38	Pin pad to prevent unauthorised use. *Source: RMS.*	95
4-39	Telehandler. *Source: HSE, HSG6.*	97
4-40	Dumper truck. *Source: RMS.*	97
4-41	Excavator hazards. *Source: RMS.*	97
4-42	Excavator. *Source: RMS.*	97
4-43	Construction platform hoist. *Source: HSE, HSG150.*	98
4-44	Material hoist. *Source: HSS.*	99
4-45	Scissor lift. *Source: HSE, HSG150.*	100
4-46	Safety latch on hook. *Source: Corel Clipart.*	100
4-47	Tower crane. *Source: Dornson.*	101
4-48	Ballast at base of tower crane. *Source: Wolffkran.*	101
4-49	Lifting operation. *Source: RMS.*	102
4-50	Lifting points on load. *Source: RMS.*	102
4-51	Safety latch on hook. *Source: RMS.*	102
4-52	Accessories. *Source: RMS.*	102
4-53	Wheelbarrow. *Source: RMS.*	103
4-54	Sack truck. *Source: RMS.*	103
4-55	Battery-powered pallet truck. *Source: RMS*	103

4-56	Manually operated pallet truck. *Source: RMS*	103
4-57	Gin wheel. *Source: Ambiguous.*	104
4-58	Lifting points. *Source: RMS.*	104
4-59	Lifting operations. *Source: RMS.*	104
4-60	Suitability of work equipment. *Source: PUWER 1998.*	105
4-61	Danger zone – crane and fixed item. *Source: HSE, HSG150.*	105
4-62	Marking of accessories. *Source: RMS.*	106
4-63	Siting and stability. *Source: RMS.*	107
4-64	Crane operation. *Source: RMS.*	107

Element 5

5-1	Air road breakers. *Source: Speedy Hire plc.*	113
5-2	Floor scabbler. *Source: Speedy Hire plc.*	113
5-3	Hand held scabbler. *Source: Speedy Hire plc.*	113
5-4	Lifting sling. *Source: RMS.*	113
5-5	Conveyor. *Source: RMS.*	117
5-6	Electrical isolator with hole for padlock. *Source: RMS.*	117
5-7	Physical isolation of valve. *Source: RMS.*	117
5-8	Multiple (padlock) lock off device. *Source: RMS.*	117
5-9	Inspection and examination. *Source: RMS.*	118
5-10	Air compressor. *Source: Speedy Hire plc.*	119
5-11	Controls and emergency stop. *Source: RMS.*	120
5-12	Controls. *Source: RMS*	120
5-13	Controls. *Source: RMS.*	121
5-14	Disc cutter. . *Source: STIHL.*	125
5-15	Cut off saw. *Source: Draper Tools.*	125
5-16	Belt sander. *Source: Clarke International.*	126
5-17	Cartridge fixing gun. *Source: ITW.*	126
5-18	Pneumatic nail gun. *Source: Bostitch.*	126
5-19	Pneumatic nail gun. *Source: Bostitch.*	127
5-20	Petrol chainsaw. Source: *Mowdirect Garden Machinery.*	127
5-21	Auger drill - entanglement. *Source: STIHL.*	128
5-22	Chop saw - cutting. *Source: Speedy Hire plc.*	129
5-23	Abrasive wheel – abrasion. Source: RMS.	129
5-24	Stabbing and puncture. *Source: Speedy Hire plc.*	129
5-25	Shear. *Source: RMS.*	129
5-26	Crushing. *Source: RMS.*	130
5-27	Impact. *Source: RMS.*	130
5-28	Drawing-in. *Source: RMS.*	130
5-29	Ejection. *Source: RMS.*	130
5-30	Disc saw – ejection. *Source: Water Active, Nov 06.*	130
5-31	Fluid injection. *Source: RMS.*	130
5-32	Summary – machinery hazards. *Source: RMS.*	131
5-33	Abrasive wheel (grinder). *Source: RMS.*	131
5-34	Document shredder. *Source: www.axminster.co.uk.*	131
5-35	Pedestal drill. *Source: RMS.*	132
5-36	Bench cross-cut circular saw. *Source: RMS.*	132
5-37	Hand fed power planer. *Source: Screwfix.*	132
5-38	Spindle moulding machine. *Source: Axminster Power Tool Centre Ltd.*	132
5-39	Compressor. *Source: Atlas Copco.*	133
5-40	Cement mixer. *Source: RMS.*	133
5-41	Plate compactor. *Source: HSS Hire Service Group Ltd.*	134
5-42	Ground consolidation equipment. *Source: RMS.*	134
5-43	Circular saw. *Source: HSS Hire Service Group Ltd.*	134
5-44	Thermoplastic hand marking barrow. *Source: Maxigrip Surfacing Ltd.*	135
5-45	Road Marking Vehicle. *Source: Maxigrip Surfacing Ltd.*	135
5-46	Petrol 110v generator. *Source: RMS.*	135
5-47	Large diesel generator. *Source: RMS.*	135
5-48	Total enclosure fixed guard. *Source: RMS.*	136
5-49	Fixed guard – panel removed. *Source: RMS.*	137
5-50	Fixed guard over fan – mesh too big. *Source: RMS.*	137
5-51	Interlocking guard. *Source: RMS.*	137
5-52	Self adjusting (fixed) guard). *Source: RMS.*	138
5-53	Adjustable (fixed) guard. *Source: BS EN ISO 12100.*	138
5-54	Trip device. *Source: BS EN ISO 12100.*	138
5-55	Trip device on radial drill. *Source: RMS.*	138
5-56	Two-hand control on hedge trimmer. *Source: RMS.*	139
5-57	Notched push-stick. *Source: http://images.google.co.uk/.*	139
5-58	Band saw push-stick. *Source: http://images.google.co.uk/.*	139
5-59	Fixed guard and push-stick. *Source: Lincsafe.*	139
5-60	Information and instruction. *Source: RMS.*	140
5-61	PPE and supervision. *Source: RMS.*	140

Element 6

6-1	A basic electrical circuit. *Source: RMS.*	147
6-2	Basic electrical circuitry. *Source: RMS.*	148
6-3	Electrical equipment near water. *Source: RMS.*	149

6-4	Contact with high voltage buried cable. *Source: RMS.*	149
6-5	Effects of alternating current flowing in the human body. *Source: RMS.*	149
6-6	Used coiled up - risk of overheating. *Source: RMS.*	151
6-7	Max current capacity exceeded. *Source: RMS.*	151
6-8	Worn cable - risk of electrical fire. *Source: RMS.*	151
6-9	Evidence of overheating. *Source: RMS.*	151
6-10	Hazard - fuse wired out. *Source: RMS.*	152
6-11	Continued use of defective equipment. *Source: RMS.*	152
6-12	Hazard - damaged cable insulation. *Source: RMS.*	152
6-13	Hazard - taped joints. *Source: RMS.*	152
6-14	Maintenance of electrical systems. *Source: EWR 1989 Regulation 4.*	153
6-15	Strength and capability of electrical equipment. *Source: EWR 1989 Regulation 5.*	155
6-16	Construction site generator. *Source: RMS.*	156
6-17	Construction site power supply panel. *RMS.*	156
6-18	110v generator. *Source: RMS.*	156
6-19	110v extension lead. *Source: RMS.*	156
6-20	Power supply isolation. *Source: RMS.*	156
6-21	Earth provided to generator. *Source: RMS.*	157
6-22	Earthed distributed equipment. *Source: RMS.*	157
6-23	Plug-foil fuse no earth. *Source: RMS.*	158
6-24	Earthing. *Source: RMS.*	158
6-25	110v centre tapped earth transformer. *Source: RMS.*	159
6-26	110v powered drill. *Source: RMS.*	159
6-27	Residual current device. *Source: RMS.*	160
6-28	Plug-in residual current device. *Source: RMS.*	160
6-29	Double insulated 230V drill. *Source: RMS.*	160
6-30	Double insulation symbol. *Source: HSE, HSG107.*	160
6-31	Work on live conductors. *Source: EWR 1989 Regulation 14.*	161
6-32	Isolation. *Source: EWR 1989 Regulation 12.*	161
6-33	Multi-lock system. *Source: RMS.*	161
6-34	Marking of services. *Source: RMS.*	162
6-35	Maintenance of electrical systems. *Source: EWR 1989 Regulation 4(2).*	162
6-36	Testing frequency. *Source: HSE Note INDG 160L.*	164
6-37	PAT labels. *Source: RMS.*	164
6-38	First aid sign. *Source: RMS.*	165
6-39	Working near overhead power lines. *Source: HSE, HSG150.*	166
6-40	Overhead cable protection on traffic route. *Source: HSE, HSG144.*	167

Element 7

7-1	Fire triangle. *Source: RMS/Corel.*	171
7-2	Illicit smoking. *Source: FSTC Ltd.*	171
7-3	Festoon lighting: an incorrect fixing creates a potential source of ignition. *Source: HSE, HSG168.*	171
7-4	Classification of fires. *Source: RMS.*	173
7-5	Compartment undermined-holes cut. *Source: RMS.*	174
7-6	No fire door fitted. *Source: HSE, HSG168.*	174
7-7	Materials inappropriately stored. *Source: RMS.*	174
7-8	Careless action – hot work. *Source: RMS.*	175
7-9	Misusing equipment – foil fuse, no earth. *Source: RMS.*	175
7-10	Defective electrical equipment. *Source: RMS.*	175
7-11	Potential for deliberate ignition. *Source: RMS.*	175
7-12	Buncefield – run-off from fire hoses. *Source: BBC News.*	176
7-13	Buncefield oil storage depot disaster. *Source: Royal Chiltern Air.*	176
7-14	Misleading fire exit signage, exit no longer available. *Source: HSE, HSG168.*	180
7-15	Welding equipment. *Source: RMS.*	182
7-16	Control arson by external security. *Source: RMS.*	182
7-17	Control arson by housekeeping. *Source: RMS.*	182
7-18	Hot work. *Source: Speedy Hire Plc.*	184
7-19	Secure LPG storage. *Source: HSE, HSG168.*	184
7-20	Gas cylinders for huts, located outside. *Source: RMS.*	185
7-21	Accumulated combustible site rubbish. *Source: HSE, HSG168.*	185
7-22	Flammable liquids classification. *Source: UN, Globally Harmonised System of Classification and Labelling of Chemicals.*	186
7-23	Flammable liquids classification and labelling. *Source: EU, Classification, Labelling and Packing (CLP) Regulations*	187
7-24	Poor storage of flammable liquids. *Source: RMS.*	187
7-25	Storage of flammable materials. *Source: RMS.*	187
7-26	Outdoor storage of flammable liquids. *Source: HSE, HSG51.*	188
7-27	Magnetic door holder linked to alarm. *Source: RMS.*	189
7-28	Door stop with automatic release. *Source: RMS.*	189
7-29	Smoke detector. *Source: RMS.*	190
7-30	Easy operation alarm call point. *Source: RMS.*	190
7-31	Alarm point identified and well located. *Source: RMS.*	190
7-32	Fire point sign. *Source: BCW Office Products.*	192
7-33	Water extinguisher colour coded red by label and sign. *Source: RMS.*	192
7-34	Fire point sign. *Source: Warning Signs Direct.*	192
7-35	Cream colour coded extinguisher. *Source: Low Cost Fire.*	192
7-36	Fire point sign. *Source: Warning Signs Direct.*	192

7-37	Blue colour coded extinguisher. *Source: The Sharpedge.*	192
7-38	Fire point sign. *Source: BCW Office Products.*	192
7-39	Black colour coded extinguisher. *Source: Blazetec Fire Protection.*	192
7-40	Fire point sign. *Source: Midland Fire Ltd.*	193
7-41	Yellow colour coded extinguisher. *Source: Midland Fire Ltd.*	193
7-42	Summary matrix – fire extinguishing media. *Source: RMS.*	193
7-43	Fire escape – hazard of falling on exit due to height from ground. *Source: RMS.*	194
7-44	Maximum travel distances. *Source: HSE, HSG168*	194
7-45	Protected temporary fire escape. *Source: HSE, HSG168.*	195
7-46	Fire escape sign. *Source: RMS.*	195
7-47	Assembly point. *Source: RMS.*	196
7-48	Article 15 of RRFSO 2005. *Source: The Regulatory Reform (Fire Safety) Order (RRFSO) 2005.*	196
7-49	Fire instruction notice. *Source: RMS.*	197
7-50	Fire refuge sign for disabled people. *Source: Safety Selector.*	198

Element 8

8-1	Mould – Aspergillus. *Source: National Geographic.*	202
8-2	Bacteria – Legionella pneumophila. *Source: European hospital.*	202
8-3	Virus – hepatitis C. *Source: National public radio.*	202
8-4	Respiratory system. *Source: BBC.*	209
8-5	Digestive system. *Source: STEM.*	209
8-6	Skin layer. *Source: SHP.*	209
8-7	CLP pictograms. *Source: CLP Regulations.*	213
8-8	Sample GHS chemical labels. *Source: RMS.*	213
8-9	Hazard and precautionary statements table. *Source: CLP.*	213
8-10	Sampling strategy. *Source: RMS.*	216
8-11	Gas detector pump. *Source: Drager.*	217
8-12	Drager short-term detection tubes (before and after). *Source: Drager.*	217
8-13	Personal sampling equipment. *Source: ROSPA OS and H.*	218
8-14	Examples of substances with long-term workplace exposure limits. *Source: HSE. EH40.*	219
8-15	Examples of substances with short-term workplace exposure limits. *Source: HSE. EH40.*	219
8-16	Time weighted average compared with actual concentration. *Source: RMS.*	220
8-17	Regulation 7 (7) of COSHH 2002. *Source: The Control of Substances Hazardous to Health Regulations (COSHH) 2002 (amended).*	221
8-18	Regulation 7 (1) of COSHH 2002. *Source: The Control of Substances Hazardous to Health Regulations (COSHH) 2002 (amended).*	222
8-19	Regulation 12 of COSHH 2002. *Source: The Control of Substances Hazardous to Health Regulations (COSHH) 2002 (amended).*	226
8-20	Working with hazardous substances. *Source: Shutterstock.*	227
8-21	Reduced exposure – bulk supply. *Source: RMS.*	227
8-22	Wall chasing using on-tool extraction. *Source: HSE.*	228
8-23	Extraction unit. *Source: HSE.*	228
8-24	Common elements of a simple LEV system. *Source: HSE, INDG408.*	229
8-25	Captor system on circular saw. *Source: RMS.*	229
8-26	LEV fan and motor. *Source: RMS.*	229
8-27	Flexible hose and captor hood. *Source: RMS.*	229
8-28	Portable self contained unit. *Source: RMS.*	229
8-29	Length of ducting with curves. *Source: RMS.*	230
8-30	Shows a number of ports at the end of one duct - not all ports being used. *Source: RMS.*	230
8-31	Paper filter respirator. *Source: Shutterstock.*	231
8-32	3M filtering face-piece respirator. *Source: RMS.*	232
8-33	Full face canister respirator. *Source: Shutterstock*	232
8-34	Breathing apparatus. *Source: Haxton Safety.*	232
8-35	Gloves. *Source: Speedy Hire plc.*	233
8-36	Protective clothing - gloves. *Source: Haxton Safety.*	233
8-37	Eye and ear protection. *Source: Speedy Hire plc.*	234
8-38	Arc welding visor - UV reactive. *Source: RMS.*	234
8-39	Personal protective equipment. *Source: RMS.*	234
8-40	Schedule 6 medical surveillance. *Source: COSHH ACoP.*	235
8-41	Biological Monitoring Values (BMGVs). *Source: EH40/2005 Workplace exposure limits.*	236
8-42	Person taking lung function test. *Source: www.elitecycling.co.uk*	237
8-43	CO_2 Detector for fixed applications. *Source: Safelinks Ltd.*	240
8-44	CO_2 Portable detector. *Source: Safelinks Ltd.*	240
8-45	Cement burns. *Source: SHP.*	241
8-46	Treatment for leptospira. *Source: Bio-Rad*	242
8-47	Leptospira magnified many times shown on SEM shows spiral shape. *Source: Wikipedia.*	242
8-48	Tension of the spine. *Source: Painting by Charles Bell.*	243
8-49	Asbestos label. *Source: Scaftag.*	244
8-50	Competence to carry out asbestos risk assessments. *Source: HSE ACOP to CAR 2012.*	246
8-51	Examples of uses and locations where asbestos can be found. *Source: RMS.*	247
8-52	Asbestos pipe lagging. *Source: HSE.*	247
8-53	Asbestos insulating board (AIB) *Source: HSE.*	247
8-54	Textured decorative coating. *Source: HSE.*	247
8-55	Window with AIB panel. *Source: HSE.*	247
8-56	Asbestos cement roof sheeting. *Source: HSE.*	248
8-57	Floor tiles containing asbestos. *Source: HSE.*	248
8-58	GHS hazard label - environment. *Source: RMS.*	251

8-59	Environmental hazard. *Source: RMS.*	251
8-60	Measures to control pollution. *Source: RMS.*	252
8-61	Measures to control pollution. *Source: RMS.*	252

Element 9

9-1	Inner ear diagram. *Source: www.echalk.co.uk.*	257
9-2	Rms and peak levels of a sound wave. *Source: RMS.*	257
9-3	Typical noise levels. *Source: RMS.*	257
9-4	Typical noise levels for a range of construction activities. *Source: HSE.*	259
9-5	Noise measurement. *Source: HSE, L108.*	259
9-6	Exposure times. *Source: Australia, SafeWork SA.*	260
9-7	Noise exposure values. *Source: CNWR 2005.*	261
9-8	Noise hazard sign. *Source: RMS.*	261
9-9	Mandatory hearing protection sign. *Source: Stocksigns.*	261
9-10	Basic layout of the main control methods. *Source: RMS.*	262
9-11	Silenced diesel welder. *Source: Speedy Hire Plc.*	262
9-12	Application and limitations of various types. *Source: RMS.*	263
9-13	Ear defenders. *Source: RMS.*	263
9-14	Disposable ear plugs. *Source: RMS.*	263
9-15	Use of circular saw - vibration. *Source: RMS.*	265
9-16	Dumper truck seat, vibration mountings. *Source: RMS.*	266
9-17	Vibration exposure action and limit values. *Source: CVWR 2005.*	267
9-18	UV - from welding. *Source: Speedy Hire Plc.*	269
9-19	Radio mast. *Source: RMS.*	270
9-20	Ionising radiation. *Source: RMS.*	270
9-21	Pest control. *Source: RMS.*	271
9-22	Radon sump. *Source: HSE.*	273
9-23	Control of exposure to ionizing radiation. *Source: IRR 1999 Regulation 8.*	274
9-24	Definition of stress. *Source: HSE.*	275
9-25	Bullying. *Source: CIPD.*	276
9-26	Stress in summary. *Source: RMS.*	278

Element 10

10-1	Working above ground level. *Source: RMS.*	283
10-2	Using a pole to avoid work at height. *Source: HSE, HSG150.*	284
10-3	Avoidance of risks from work at height. *Source: WAH 2005 Regulation 6(5).*	286
10-4	Provision of training. *Source: WAH 2005 Regulation 5.*	288
10-5	Independent tied scaffold. *Source: RMS.*	289
10-6	Independent tied scaffold. *Source: RMS.*	289
10-7	Independent tied scaffold. *Source: HSE, HSG150.*	289
10-8	Putlog scaffold. *Source: HSE, HSG150.*	290
10-9	Putlog scaffold. *Source: RMS.*	290
10-10	Putlog scaffold. *Source: RMS.*	290
10-11	Fans. *Source: RMS.*	290
10-12	Wheels with brakes. *Source: RMS.*	291
10-13	Mobile tower scaffold. *Source: RMS.*	291
10-14	Mobile tower scaffold. *Source: RMS.*	291
10-15	Base plates and sole boards. *Source: Lincsafe.*	292
10-16	Base plate and protection. *Source: RMS.*	292
10-17	Tie through window. *Source: RMS.*	292
10-18	Guardrails and toe boards. *Source: HSE, HSG150.*	293
10-19	Scaffold boards - some defective. *Source: RMS.*	293
10-20	Brick guards. *Source: HSE, HSG150.*	294
10-21	Nets and sheets. *Source: RMS.*	294
10-22	Nets. *Source: RMS.*	294
10-23	Fitting advanced guardrail system. *Source: NASC.*	295
10-24	Competency and training. *Source: WAH Schedule 3 Part 2.*	295
10-25	Means of access. *Source: HASAWA 1974 s2(2)(d).*	295
10-26	Stair access. *Source: RMS.*	295
10-27	Ladder access. *Source: RMS.*	295
10-28	Loading platform. *Source: RMS.*	296
10-29	Loading platform. *Source: RMS.*	296
10-30	Impact protection. *Source: RMS.*	298
10-31	Lighting. *Source: RMS.*	298
10-32	Marking. *Source: RMS.*	298
10-33	Inspection 'Scaftag'. *Source: RMS.*	298
10-34	Mobile elevated work platform (MEWPs). *Source: RMS.*	299
10-35	Mobile elevated work platform (MEWPs). *Source: RMS.*	299
10-36	Use of harness with a MEWP. *Source: HSE, HSG150.*	299
10-37	Scissor lift. *Source: RMS.*	300
10-38	Scissor lift. *Source: HSE, HSG150.*	300
10-39	Ladder as access and workplace. *Source: RMS.*	300
10-40	Improper use. *Source: RMS.*	300
10-41	Correct 1 in 4 angle. *Source: HSE, HSG150.*	301
10-42	Poor storage. *Source: Lincsafe.*	301
10-43	Use of roof ladders. *Source: HSE, HSG150.*	301
10-44	Stepladder. *Source: RMS.*	302

10-45	Three steps clear. *Source: HSE, HSG150.*	302
10-46	Step platform. *Source: HSE, HSG150.*	302
10-47	Incorrect use of a step ladder. *Source: HSE, HSG150.*	302
10-48	Correct use of a step ladder. *Source: HSE, HSG150.*	302
10-49	Trestles and handrail system. *Source: London Tool Hire.*	303
10-50	Ladder staging platform. *Source: Ladder Safety Devices.*	303
10-51	Edge protection and staging platforms. *Source: RMS.*	304
10-52	Mast climbing work platforms. *Source: HSE, HSG150.*	304
10-53	Boatswains chair. *Source: Photo, Pete Verdon.*	305
10-54	Suspended cradle. *Source: Harsco Infrastructure.*	305
10-55	Personal suspension equipment. *Source: RMS.*	306
10-56	Scaffolder using personal fall arrest device. *Source: NASC.*	306
10-57	Safety nets. *Source: RMS.*	307
10-58	Soft fall arrest system. *Source: HSE, HSG150.*	307
10-59	Crash deck assembly. *Source: Bondeck Ltd.*	307
10-60	Passive, collective fall prevention. *Source: Bondeck Ltd.*	308
10-61	Crash deck designed for loading. *Source: Bondeck Ltd.*	308
10-62	Edge protection and access. *Source: RMS.*	309
10-63	Edge protection and roof ladder. *Source: RMS.*	309
10-64	Stair access to roof and edge protection. *Source: RMS.*	310
10-65	Leading edge protection and crawling boards. *Source: RMS.*	310
10-66	Nets, signs and head protection. *Source: RMS.*	310
10-67	Marking. *Source: RMS.*	311
10-68	Barriers, fans and netting. *Source: RMS.*	311
10-69	Prevention of drowning. *Source: CDM 2015 Regulation 26.*	312

Element 11

11-1	Buried services. *Source: RMS.*	317
11-2	Excavation hazards. *Source: RMS.*	317
11-3	Cofferdam. *Source: USA Army Corps Library.*	318
11-4	Pressurised caisson. *Source: YK Times.*	318
11-5	Water in excavation. *Source: RMS.*	319
11-6	Mechanical hazard from excavator. *Source: RMS.*	319
11-7	Using a cable locator. *Source: Allpipe Stoppers*	322
11-8	Marking of services. *Source: RMS.*	322
11-9	Permit to dig. *Source: Reproduced by kind permission of Lincsafe.*	323
11-10	Methods of shoring and battering. *Source: CDM 2015 Regulation 22(1).*	323
11-11	Battering. *Source: RMS.*	324
11-12	Trench box - for shoring. *Source: RMS.*	324
11-13	Close boarded excavation. *Source: BS6031.*	324
11-14	Open sheeting. *Source: BS6031.*	324
11-15	Close sheeting. *Source: RMS.*	324
11-16	Open sheeting. *Source: RMS.*	324
11-17	Access and guardrails. *Source: HSE, HSG150.*	325
11-18	Prevention of falls into excavation. *Source: CDM 2015 Regulation 22(2).*	325
11-19	Materials storage. *Source: RMS.*	326
11-20	Preventing water ingress. *Source: RMS.*	326
11-21	Well point schematic. *Source: W J Groundwater Ltd.*	326
11-22	Well point trench installation. *Source: www.khansahebsykes.com.*	326
11-23	Substances in excavation. *Source: RMS.*	327
11-24	Overloading of excavation by work equipment or material. *Source: CDM 2015 Regulation 22(3).*	327
11-25	Confined space - chamber. *Source: RMS.*	329
11-26	Confined space - sewer. *Source: RMS.*	329
11-27	Confined space - cement silo. *Source: RMS.*	330
11-28	Confined space - open tank. *Source: RMS.*	330
11-29	Example PTW document confined spaces. *Source: HSE Guidance note on permits-to-work.*	332
11-30	Confined space. *Source: HSE, HSG150.*	333
11-31	Entrance to a confined space. *Source: RMS.*	333

Element 12

12-1	Hydraulic demolition jaws. *Source: RMS.*	340
12-2	Hydraulic demolition grapple. *Source: RMS.*	340
12-3	Risk of falling or premature collapse. *Source: RMS.*	341
12-4	Falling materials. *Source: RMS.*	341
12-5	Noise and dust. *Source: Rollaston Council.*	342
12-6	Siting of plant. *Source: RMS.*	342
12-7	Asbestos use in buildings. *Source: HSE, HSG213.*	343
12-8	Building collapse. *Source: The Gazette.*	343
12-9	Demolition or dismantling. *Source: CDM 2015 Regulation 20.*	344
12-10	Doubtful competence of workers. *Source: Lincsafe.*	346
12-11	Use of demolition equipment. *Source: RMS.*	346
12-12	Building structure. *Source: RMS.*	346
12-13	Structural condition and substances. *Source: RMS.*	346
12-14	Hazardous substances. *Source: Scaftag.*	347
12-15	Proximity of other structures. *Source: D Hitchen.*	347
12-16	Demolition exclusion zone. *Source: Adapted from HSE construction sheet No 45.*	348
12-17	Explosives. *Source: CDM 2015 Regulation 21.*	349

12-18	Risk of collision due to close proximity with public road. *Source: HSE, HSG151.*	349
12-19	Dilapidation of a structure. *Source: RMS.*	350
12-20	Competence to carry out asbestos risk assessments. *Source: HSE ACOP to CAR 2012*	351
12-21	Dilapidation of buildings. *Source: RMS.*	352
12-22	Black mould *Source: Premier preservation Ltd.*	352
12-23	Ivy. *Source: Daily Mail.*	352
12-24	Settlement diagonal wall cracking. *Source: diynot.com*	352
12-25	Dry rot - characteristic cuboidal cracking. *Source: Safeguard Europe Ltd.*	353
12-26	Timber damaged by death watch beetle. *Source: Rudders and Paynes Ltd.*	353
12-27	The leaning tower of Pisa, Italy. *Source: Marshaü.*	353
12-28	Demolition - separate entrance for workers and protected pedestrian route. *Source: HSE, HSG151.*	355
12-29	Protection of public. *Source: RMS.*	355
12-30	Disposal of waste. *Source: RMS.*	355

Relevant statutory provisions

RSP-1	GHS hazard pictograms. *Source: RMS*	360
RSP-2	Sample GHS chemical labels. *Source: RMS.*	362
RSP-3	Biohazard sign. *Source: COSHH 2002.*	380
RSP-4	Hazardous properties. Source: Environment Agency, HMR01, What is a Hazardous Waste?	388

List of abbreviations

LEGISLATION

CAOR	Control of Artificial Optical Radiation at Work Regulations 2010
CAR	Control of Asbestos Regulations 2012
CDM	Construction (Design and Management) Regulations 2015
CER	Control of Explosives Regulations 1991
CHIP 4	Chemicals (Hazard Information and Packaging for Supply) Regulations 2009
CNWR	Control of Noise at Work Regulations 2005
CLAW	Control of Lead at Work Regulations 2002
CLP	Classification Labelling and Packaging of Substances (CLP) EC Regulation No 1272/2008
COSHH	Control of Substances Hazardous to Health Regulations 2002
CSR	Confined Spaces Regulations 1997
CVWR	Control of Vibration at Work Regulations 2005
DSEAR	Dangerous Substances and Explosive Atmospheres Regulations 2002
DSE	Health and Safety (Display Screen Equipment) Regulations 1992
EPA	Environmental Protection Act 1990
EWR	Electricity at Work Regulations 1989
FSA	Fire (Scotland) Act 2005
FSECE	Fire Safety (England) Regulations 2010
FSECW	Fire Safety (Employees' Capabilities) (Wales) Regulations 2012
FSSR	Fire Safety (Scotland) Regulations 2006
FAR	Health and Safety (First-Aid) Regulations 1981
HASAWA	Health and Safety at Work etc Act 1974
HWR	Hazardous Waste (England and Wales) Regulations 2005
MAR	Health and Safety (Miscellaneous Amendments) Regulations 2002
MRRA	The Health and Safety (Miscellaneous Repeals, Revocations and Amendments) Regulations 2013
IRR	Ionising Radiations Regulations 1999
LOLER	Lifting Operations and Lifting Equipment Regulations 1998
MHOR	Manual Handling Operations Regulations 1992
MHSWR	Management of Health and Safety at Work Regulations 1999
NCTCR	Notification of Conventional Tower Crane Regulations 2010
NRSWA	New Roads and Street Works Act 1991
PPER	Personal Protective Equipment Regulations 1992
PSSR	Pressure Systems Safety Regulations 2000
PUWER	Provision and Use of Work Equipment Regulations 1998
REACH	Registration, Evaluation, Authorisation and Restriction of Chemicals EC Regulation No 1907/2006
RIDDOR	Reporting of Injuries, Diseases and Dangerous Occurrences Regulations 2013
RRFSO	Regulatory Reform (Fire Safety) Order (RRFSO) 2005
RTA	Road Traffic Act 1988 and 1991
RVCUR	Road Vehicles (Construction and Use) Regulations 1986
RVLR	Road Vehicles Lighting Regulations 1989
SMSR	Supply of Machinery (Safety) Regulations 2008
SSSR	Health and Safety (Safety Signs and Signals) Regulations 1996
TWA	Transport and Works Act 1992
WAH	Work at Height Regulations 2005
WHSWR	Workplace (Health, Safety and Welfare) Regulations 1992

GENERAL

2HC	Two-hand control
3D	Three dimensional
AA	Automobile Association
AC	Alternating Current
ACMs	Asbestos Containing Materials
ACOP	Approved Code of Practice
AIB	Asbestos Insulating Boards
AIDS	Acquired Immune Deficiency Syndrome
APF	Assigned Protection Factor
APS	Association of Project Supervisors
BBV	Blood Borne Virus
BMGV	Biological Monitoring Value
BSI	British Standards Institution
CAD	Computer aided design programmes
CAT	Cable Avoidance Tool
CBI	Confederation of British Industry
CCDO	Scheme for the Certification of Competence of Demolition Operatives
CCTV	Closed Circuit Television
CE	Conformité Européene
CECA	Civil Engineering Contractors Association
CEN	European Standards
CIOB	Chartered Institute of Building
CITB	Construction Industry Training Board
CO_2	Carbon Dioxide
CO	Carbon Monoxide
CONIAC	Construction Industry Advisory Committee
CIRA	Construction Industry Research and Information Association
CLP	Classification, labelling and packaging of chemical substances and mixtures
CPR	Cardio Pulmonary Resuscitation
dB	Decibel
DC	Direct Current
DNA	Deoxyribonucleic Acid
DoC	Declaration of Conformity
DSD	Dangerous Substances Directive
DSE	Display screen equipment
DVLA	Driver and Vehicle Licensing Agency
EC	European Commission
ECITB	Engineering Construction Industry Training Board
EU	European Union
FLT	Fork Lift Truck
FRA	Fire Risk Assessment
GDP	Gross Domestic Product
GHS	Globally Harmonized System of Classification and Labelling of Chemicals
H_2S	Hydrogen Sulphide
HAVs	Hand-arm Vibration Syndrome
HEPA	High Efficiency Particulate Air
HGV	Heavy Goods Vehicle
HIV	Human Immunodeficiency Virus
HML	High, Medium and Low
HSE	Health and Safety Executive
HV	High Voltage
Hz	Hertz
ICE	Institute of Civil Engineers
IET	Institution of Engineering and Technology
IIRSM	International Institute for Risk and Safety Management
IOSH	Institution of Occupational Safety and Health
IP	International protection
IQ	Intelligence Quotient
ISO	International Organization for Standardization
IT	Information Technology
IEE	Institute of Electrical Engineers
LEV	Local Exhaust Ventilation
LFS	Labour Force Survey
LGV	Large Goods Vehicle
LPG	Liquefied Petroleum Gas

LTEL	Long Term Exposure Limit
LV	Low Voltage
mA	MilliAmpere
MCWP	Mast Climbing Work Platform
MDI	Methylene Bisphenyl Di-isocyanate
MDMA	3,4-methylenedioxy-N-methylamphetamine
MEWP	Mobile Elevated Work Platform
MOT	Ministry of Transport test
MSD	Musculoskeletal disorder
MSF	Manufacturing, Science and Finance Union
N_2	Nitrogen
NASC	National Access and Scaffolding Confederation
NEBOSH	National Examination Board in Occupational Safety and Health
NEC	National Exhibition Centre
NNLW	Notifiable Non-Licensed Work
NVQ	National Vocational Qualification
ORSA	Occupational Road Safety Alliance
PAT	Portable Appliance Testing
PPB	Parts Per Billion
PCV	Passenger Carrying Vehicle
PNA	Predicted Noise Attenuation
PPE	Personal Protective Equipment
PPM	Parts Per Million
PTW	Permit-to-work
PVC	PolyVinyl Chloride
RAC	Royal Automobile Club
RCD	Residual Current Device
RMS	Root Mean Square
ROPS	Roll over protection structures
ROSPA	Royal Society for the Prevention of Accidents
RPA	Radiation Protection Adviser
RPE	Respiratory Protective Equipment
RTFLT	Rough Terrain Fork Lift Truck
SDS	Safety Data Sheets
SNR	Single Number Rating
SPF	Sun Protection Factor
STEL	Short Term Exposure Limit
SWL	Safe Working Load
TDI	Toluene Di-isocyanate
TNA	The National Archives
TWA	Time Weighted Average
UK	United Kingdom
UKAS	United Kingdom Accreditation Service
UKCG	UK Contractors Group
UN	United Nations
UN GHS	United Nations' Globally Harmonised System
UNRTDG	UN Recommendations on the Transport of Dangerous Goods
UV	Ultraviolet
VWF	Vibration White Finger
WBV	Whole Body Vibration
WBVS	Whole Body Vibration Syndrome
WEL	Workplace Exposure Limit
WRULD	Work Related Upper Limb Disorder

Construction law and management

Learning outcomes

On completion of this element, candidates should be able to demonstrate understanding of the content through the application of knowledge to familiar and unfamiliar situations. In particular they should be able to:

1.1 Identify the scope, definition and particular issues relating to construction activities.

1.2 Outline the legal, moral and financial consequences of failing to manage health and safety within the construction industry.

1.3 Outline the scope and application of the Construction (Design and Management) Regulations 2015.

1.4 Identify the nature and main sources of external construction health and safety information.

Content

1.1 - Scope, definition and nature of construction activities..3
    Types of work..3
    Range of activities 4
    Meaning of construction terms...5
    Particular construction issues 5
1.2 - Consequences of failing to manage health and safety 6
    General argument...6
    Size of the construction health and safety 'problem' 7
1.3 - Construction (Design and Management) Regulations (CDM) 2015 8
    Scope and application 8
    Duties...9
    Appointment and competence required of relevant parties 12
    Notification of projects 12
    Preparation of pre-construction information 13
    The construction phase plan..14
    Provision of appropriate and relevant information to all parties 15
    Preparation of the health and safety file 15
    Application to domestic clients...17
1.4 - Sources of external construction health and safety information 17
    Sources external to the organisation 17
Exam practice 19

Sources of reference

Reference information provided, in particular web links, is correct at time of publication, but may have changed.

Managing for health and safety, HSG65 third edition 2013, HSE Books, ISBN: 978-0-7176-6456-6
http://www.hse.gov.uk/pubns/priced/hsg65.pdf

Health and Safety in Construction, HSG150, HSE Books, ISBN 978-0-7176-6182-2
http://www.hse.gov.uk/pubns/priced/hsg150.pdf

Managing Health and Safety in Construction, Construction (Design and Management) Regulations 2015, Guidance on Regulations, L153, HSE Books, ISBN: 978-0-7176-6626-3
http://www.hse.gov.uk/pubns/priced/L153.pdf

The Construction (Design and Management) Regulations 2015, Industry guidance for Clients, produced by CONIAC, published by CITB, ISBN: 978-1-85751-389-9
http://www.citb.co.uk/documents/cdm%20regs/2015/cdm-2015-clients-interactive.pdf

The Construction (Design and Management) Regulations 2015, Industry guidance for Principal Designers, produced by CONIAC, published by CITB, ISBN 978-1-8575-1390-5
http://www.citb.co.uk/documents/cdm%20regs/2015/cdm-2015-principal-designers-interactive.pdf

The Construction (Design and Management) Regulations 2015, Industry guidance for Designers, produced by CONIAC, published by CITB, ISBN 978-1-8575-1392-9
http://www.citb.co.uk/documents/cdm%20regs/2015/cdm-2015-designers-interactive.pdf

The Construction (Design and Management) Regulations 2015, Industry guidance for Principal Contractors, produced by CONIAC, published by CITB, ISBN 978-1-8575-1393-6
http://www.citb.co.uk/documents/cdm%20regs/2015/cdm-2015-principal-contractors-interactive.pdf

The Construction (Design and Management) Regulations 2015, Industry guidance for Contractors, produced by CONIAC, published by CITB, ISBN: 978-1-8575-1391-2
http://www.citb.co.uk/documents/cdm%20regs/2015/cdm-2015-contractors-interactive.pdf

The Construction (Design and Management) Regulations 2015, Industry guidance for Workers, produced by CONIAC, published by CITB, ISBN 978-1-8575-1394-3
http://www.citb.co.uk/documents/cdm%20regs/2015/cdm-2015-workers-interactive.pdf

HSE, 'Managing for health and safety' http://www.hse.gov.uk/managing/

HSE's, The Health and Safety Toolbox: How to control risks at work, http://www.hse.gov.uk/toolbox/

Managing contractors - A guide for employers, HSG159, HSE Books,
http://www.hse.gov.uk/pubns/priced/hsg159.pdf

Relevant statutory provisions

Construction (Design and Management) Regulations (CDM) 2015
Health and Safety at Work etc. Act (HASAWA) 1974 - Sections 2, 3, 20-25, 33 and 39-40
Management of Health and Safety at Work Regulations (MHSWR) 1999 - Regulation 5

1.1 - Scope, definition and nature of construction activities

Types of work

BUILDING WORKS

Building works involve most trades within the construction industry such as ground workers, steel erectors, brick layers, carpenters, plasterers, etc. all working closely together with the common goal of creating a new finished building or structure.

RENOVATION

Renovation work involves restoring an existing building or structure to a condition that is representative of its original condition or improved by repair and modernisation using more up-to-date materials and practices. As with new building works, this also involves most of the common trades normally used within the construction industry.

ALTERATION

Alteration works are required when the layout of an existing building, structure or premises no longer suits the use for which it was originally intended. This can include elements of both new building works and renovation works. Alterations can comprise an extension to an existing structure or demolition and removal of sections of the internal structure to make premises more spacious. Alternatively, an alteration may involve dividing the existing structure into smaller, separate sections by the introduction of partition walls of various materials (block-work, brick-work or studding and plasterboard).

MAINTENANCE OF EXISTING PREMISES

Maintenance work is an essential element to ensure that the condition of an existing building, premises or structure does not deteriorate and that it remains in as good a condition as is possible. Work is normally carried out on a regular scheduled basis to deal with issues of wear and tear, but can also be required when a problem suddenly occurs that requires urgent attention, for example, loss of roofing materials following a storm.

Maintenance can be carried out on all components of existing premises, including the building, services, and any final building finish and furnishing.

Occupied premises

Careful planning of maintenance work should be given when the building or premises are occupied. Hazards from paint, dust, falling masonry and excavations should be considered; suitable and sufficient risk assessments should be made and controls implemented.

Unoccupied premises

Unoccupied premises/buildings can pose other hazards, with unstable groundwork, footings, walls, beams supporting floors and roofing. In addition unoccupied buildings are likely to be infested with vermin or suffer intrusion by pigeons in rafters where roof integrity may have failed, presenting the risks of biological hazards.

Again these hazards should be highlighted, suitable risk assessments should be made and controls implemented.

CIVIL ENGINEERING AND WORKS OF ENGINEERING CONSTRUCTION

Civil engineering and engineering works normally relate to heavy construction activities requiring large items of plant and equipment such as cranes and excavators. This work will require specialist knowledge and experience in order to undertake civil engineering activities such as highway construction, bridge construction, piling works, large foundations, large concrete structures, excavations and utility projects. Engineering construction activities include the building of power stations, wind farms, chemical process plant and vehicle assembly plant.

DECOMMISSIONING

Decommissioning is concerned with the preparation necessary to take (permanently or temporarily) a piece of equipment or plant out of use. For example, the decommissioning of an air compressor that requires replacement or a building for a change of use (a warehouse into a manufacturing unit). Decommissioning also applies to taking a production site out of service, for example, a nuclear electrical power generation plant. The decommissioning process will include removal of mechanical, electrical, gas, compressed air, hydraulic, telecommunications, computer or similar services, which are normally fixed within or to a structure. In addition, it will include the safe disposal of any product or waste resulting from decommissioning.

DEMOLITION

The term demolition refers to 'breaking down' or 'removing'. In construction activities, demolition is carried out on buildings and structures that are no longer required or are possibly derelict and unsafe.

Account needs to be taken of potential hazards that may arise from demolition, for example, the risk of premature collapse, presence of live services, asbestos dust and falling debris.

Demolition must be carried out in a well-planned and controlled manner in compliance with a safe system of work. The arrangements for demolition should be written down before the work begins. This safe system of work may be in the form of a safety method statement identifying the sequence required to prevent accidental collapse of the structure.

A safe system of work may include:

- Establishing exclusion zones and hard-hat areas, clearly marked and with barriers or hoardings.
- Covered walkways, to protect pedestrians if materials should fall from above.
- Using high-reach machines for mechanical demolition.
- Reinforcing machine cabs so that drivers are not injured from falling debris.
- Training and supervising site workers, in site rules and incident reporting.

Any project that involves any element of demolition (full or part demolition) falls under the control of the Construction (Design and Management) Regulations (CDM) 2015.

DISMANTLING

The term dismantling refers to taking things apart, often for reuse in another location. In construction, this is applied to parts of buildings and structures that are no longer required where they are located, such as temporary structures used for outdoor events, for example, concert staging or temporary athletic tracks/stadiums. In a similar way to demolition, arrangements for dismantling should be written down before the work begins. The safe system of work may be in the form of a safety method statement identifying the sequence to be followed to prevent accidental collapse of the structure and any temporary supports necessary to maintain stability.

Range of activities

SITE CLEARANCE

Site clearance consists of preparing the site prior to the works being undertaken. This may involve removal of hazardous waste, obstructive trees, unwanted scrub and landscaping. Demolition activities may also be required as part of site clearance prior to construction works beginning. Where there are high levels of contaminants it may also be necessary for ground remediation.

Following completion of construction works site clearance will involve removal of all waste associated with the construction activities to a licensed waste disposal site, for example, brick and timber off-cuts, packaging and spoil. It will also include the removal of all plant and equipment used on the construction project, with the aim of leaving the site in a clean and tidy state ready for its intended use.

EXCAVATION

Excavation consists of digging below ground level to various depths in order to create a cavity that can be used for exposure of buried utility services, trenching for installation of utility services, casting building foundations or ground investigations. Methods of digging used for excavation work include the use of hand tools (pick, fork, shovel), and also by using a mechanical excavator. Major excavations for basements, sub-structures etc., remain as a permanent part in the construction operation.

LOADING, UNLOADING AND STORAGE OF MATERIALS

Construction sites use a host of different materials in the construction process that will require loading or unloading by mechanical or manual means. These can be broken down into materials that are used or removed immediately at site (i.e. excavation spoil, concrete mix, mortar mix) and materials that are stored at site and used or removed at regular intervals as required (bricks, cement, sand, timber, sundries, waste disposal skips). Loading and unloading should be undertaken using the correct procedures that comply with site safe systems of work and wherever possible avoiding the need for manual handling. Storage requirements should be identified and planned for the whole project. This will need to consider security, safe position and suitable ground condition; protection from adverse weather and potential for falls from a height or into an excavation.

SITE MOVEMENTS

Construction sites contain various types of heavy mobile plant and equipment and large numbers of site workers. Construction site projects should be well planned to take into account vehicles moving around the site. In particular, consideration to safe access and egress would include issues of adequacy of space for manoeuvring and ensuring operator visibility. Routes for both vehicles and pedestrians should be provided and be suitably surfaced, clearly defined and separated.

FABRICATION

Fabrication at site can include steel erecting, welding and form-working. Quite often it can involve working at height (where specialist work platforms and fall arrest equipment should be used) and adequate control is essential to prevent the falling of materials and tools. A variety of specialist equipment may be required and only be used by competent persons, for example, welding machine, bolt gun, or nail gun.

DECORATION

Decoration consists of applying various coatings, for example, paints, wallpaper, and artex, necessary to create the final finished appearance to a building or structure. The tools involved with decoration are often handheld and not powered. Various access systems including mobile elevating work platforms are required for this type of work.

CLEANING

Cleaning involves applying water, steam or various abrasive or chemical agents to the surfaces to be treated, for example, walls, windows, floors, fabric. The method of application can require the use of various types of equipment ranging from vacuum cleaners, floor polisher through to high pressure jets. Consideration should be given to the correct disposal of waste materials.

INSTALLATION, REMOVAL AND MAINTENANCE OF SERVICES

Various utility services are required on both existing and new construction sites and are usually buried underground, for example, electricity, gas and water. In new installations this involves a great deal of liaison with the planning authority, utility companies and the designer concerning the route the services will take and will involve excavation with heavy plant, loading and unloading of materials. New services are often connected to their source at a location that is situated outside the construction site boundary. Where this occurs, additional hazards to the general public may be created and suitable precautions will be required. For example, traffic control (by means of signing and lighting) as well as guarding and protection of the public by the use of barriers and warning signs. Removing or maintaining utilities can present other hazards. Utility services should be isolated correctly prior to any work commencing, as this may require involving the utility companies so proactive planning is essential.

LANDSCAPING

Landscaping usually takes place during the final stages of the construction phase when there is little or no construction plant travelling around the site. Landscaping may include altering site levels and the introduction of trees, shrubs, grass turf/seed etc. The works generally consist of loading and unloading of materials, manual handling, and cleaning work (footways and roads). Note that care should be taken to avoid planting trees close to underground services or near to building footings.

Meaning of construction terms

MEANING OF 'EXCAVATION'

CDM 2015 defines 'excavation' as including any earthwork, trench, well, shaft, tunnel or underground working, but does not include the exploration for or extraction of mineral resources or activities in preparation for any place where exploration or extraction is to be carried out.

MEANING OF 'STRUCTURE'

CDM 2015 defines 'structure' as any building, timber, masonry, metal or reinforced concrete structure, railway line or siding, tramway line, dock, harbour, inland navigation, tunnel, shaft, bridge, viaduct, waterworks, reservoir, pipe or pipe-line, cable, aqueduct, sewer, sewage works, gasholder, road, airfield, sea defence works, river works, drainage works, earthworks, lagoon, dam, wall, caisson, mast, tower, pylon, underground tank, earth retaining structure or structure designed to preserve or alter any natural feature, fixed plant and any structure similar to the foregoing.

The definition of structure also includes any formwork, falsework, scaffold or other structure designed or used to provide support or means of access during construction work, and any reference to a structure includes a part of a structure.

Particular construction issues

TRANSITORY NATURE OF WORKERS

The construction industry is characterised by its intermittent, temporary, transitory nature. Generally, building and construction contractors hire a work force on a project basis. Thus, workers in the construction industry are accustomed to travelling from areas where work is not plentiful to fill short-term labour shortages created by expansion and contraction of local construction activity elsewhere.

TEMPORARY NATURE OF ACTIVITIES AND THE CONSTANTLY CHANGING WORKPLACE

Construction sites constantly change through the build phase, as the trades that are associated with the construction vary greatly at each stage. Consideration needs to be given to site induction for new workers as appropriate.

The safe systems of work, risk assessments, site safety procedures and site inductions will need to be updated regularly to suit the most current situation. A construction site will always be an unfamiliar workplace with new hazards and dangers posed as each phase moves to the next.

TIME PRESSURES FROM CLIENTS AND PRINCIPAL CONTRACTORS

Clients have one of the biggest influences on the health and safety of those working on a construction project. Their decisions have substantial influence on the time, money and other resources available for the project. Because of this, the Construction (Design and Management) Regulations (CDM) 2015 make them accountable for the impact their decisions have on health and safety. In the same way, the principal contractor may exert pressure on contractors to fulfil tasks within time limits. This is a natural part of the efficient organisation of a construction activity where a number of contractors work together to achieve the goals. Each activity may depend on the timely completion of another. However, if the time available to complete the overall project becomes limited, possibly due to delays or underestimation of the necessary time for completion of an activity, the principal contractor may put contractors under pressure to complete work on time or early. This can lead to less planning time and the potential for risks to be taken in order to save time.

WEATHER CONDITIONS

For those working outdoors, adverse weather can create numerous problems. Short term exposure to the sun can cause excessive sweating, dehydration and fatigue. There are fears that prolonged exposure can cause skin cancer. Strong wind increases risk when working at height and can cause unexpected movement of loads suspended on cranes. Heavy rain may cause soft ground conditions which can increase problems with site traffic and undermine the stability of scaffolds and excavations. Extreme cold leads to snow and ice which increases the likelihood of slips and falls. It may also increase the risk of brittle failure of equipment.

LEVELS OF NUMERACY AND LITERACY OF WORKERS

Poor levels of literacy and numeracy can significantly impede the progress of workers at a workplace. The level of understanding and critical information retention required, for example, when attending a health and safety induction, can be significantly reduced. Where numbers and the written word are utilised instead of a pictographic approach, then the meaning can be marred regarding written critical safety instructions or directions that may need to be followed could be unintentionally ignored. Weights and measures, dates and times critical to processes could also be misconstrued or overlooked if workers are innumerate.

NON-ENGLISH SPEAKING WORKERS

Regulation 10 of the Management of Health and Safety at Work Regulations (MHSWR) 1999 requires employers to provide information to employees which is comprehensible and relevant, i.e. capable of being understood by the person for whom it is intended.

For employees with little or no understanding of English, or who cannot read English, employers may need to make special arrangements. These could include providing translation, using interpreters, or replacing written notices with clearly understood symbols or diagrams.

Employers need to consider the following with reference to their non-English speaking employees:

- Check that prospective workers have sufficient command of English for their role.
- Check worker understanding of instructions and health and safety related notices.
- If other members of staff are available who can speak the employee's native language, then they may be able to help the employee understand the working culture and environment in the UK.

The employee's previous experience should be determined. This can show whether they have relevant experience to carry out the work required.

1.2 - Consequences of failing to manage health and safety

General argument

There are three good reasons for preventing accidents in the workplace:

MORAL

Injury accidents result in pain and suffering for those affected. Though the actual numbers vary, each year construction activities in the UK typically result in an average of one fatality for each week worked. Clearly, it is important that employers and employees do everything that they can to avoid this.

LEGAL

It is a legal requirement to safeguard the health and safety of employees and others that might be affected by an organisation's operations.

FINANCIAL

Accidents at work cost a great deal of money, especially when damage is added. Costs resulting from construction accidents can be enormous and can be many times larger than could initially be perceived. The effect of an accident on construction work could lead to delays and possibly penalty charges being laid against those causing the delay.

Size of the construction health and safety 'problem'

Although there have been significant reductions in the number and rate of injury over the last 20 years or more, construction remains a high risk industry. The Health and Safety Executive (HSE) report that the Labour Force Survey (LFS) in 2014/15 confirmed that although construction accounted for 5% of the employees in Britain it accounted for 31% of employee fatalities, 10% of the major/specified injures and 6% of the over 7 day absence injuries.

There were 35 fatal injuries to workers in construction in 2014/15, and of these fatalities 11 were to the self-employed. In the previous year there were 46 fatal injuries to workers in construction, and of these fatalities 12 were to the self-employed. This compares with an average of 43 fatal injuries to workers in construction over the previous five years, including an average of 17 to the self-employed. In 2014/15, 24.6% of the total fatal injuries (142 fatal injuries in all industries) to employees were in construction and the industry accounts for the greatest number of fatal injuries of the main industry groups.

The rate of fatal injury per 100,000 construction workers in 2014/15 was 1.62, compared with a five year average for the industry of 2.07. The all industry rate for the period 2014/15 was 0.46 per 100,000 employees.

During 2014/15 the main cause of worker fatalities in construction was falls at 45% (59% in 2012/13). There were four fatal injuries to members of the public in 2014/15 caused by construction activities, the same as the average for the previous five years. This compares with a total of 123 members of the public fatally injured in accidents connected to work in 2014/15.

NUMBER AND RATE OF FATAL INJURY TO WORKERS, 1995/96-2014/15

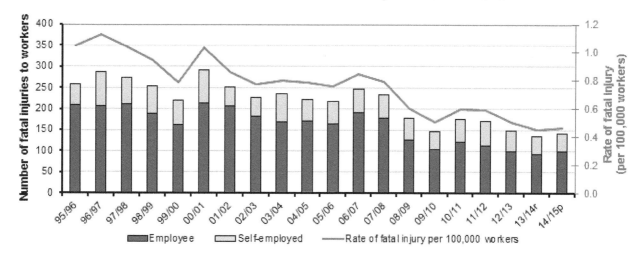

Figure 1-1: Number and rate of fatal injury to workers, 1995/96-2014/15.   *Source: HSE.*

NON-FATAL INJURIES

Between 2012/13 and 2014/15 around 65,000 construction workers in the UK sustained an injury at work and around 25% of these resulted in absence from work of over 7-days.

In 2014/15 provisional figures show over 5,400 reported non-fatal injuries to employees in the construction sector. Reported non-fatal injuries are categorized as either specified, for example fractures, amputations, serious burns, or as resulting in over 7-days off work.

Specified injuries - over 50% of all reported 'specified' injuries in the construction sector are due to either falls from a height or slip, trip or fall on the same level.

INCIDENCE OF ILL-HEALTH

The Labour Force Survey (LFS) estimated average prevalence of 'self-reported illness caused or made worse by current or most recent job for people working in the last 12 months' over the period 2010/11 to 2014/15 was reported to mean 69,000 people were suffering from ill-health in the construction industry. This gave a rate of 3.1% per 100,000 construction workers, which was similar to the all industry average rate of 3.1% per 100,000.

In comparison, the LFS estimated that 1.2 million people who worked in all industries in 2014/15 were suffering from an illness they believed was caused or made worse by work. The total number of new cases for all industry was 516,000 in 2014/15 and for the construction industry it is estimated that there were 31,000 new cases. Around 80% of the new work-related conditions for all industries in 2014/15 were reported in the LFS to be musculoskeletal disorders or stress, depression or anxiety.

The HSE also reported that during 2014/15, of all industry sectors, exposures in the construction industry accounted for the largest proportion (over 40%) of the occupational cancer deaths and cancer registrations. In total, about 3,500 cancer registrations per year in this industry are attributed to the past exposure to asbestos and silica, mostly causing lung cancer and mesothelioma.

Accidents and ill-health are costly to workers and their families. They can also impact significantly on organisations because, in addition to the costs of personal injuries and ill-health, the organisations may incur far greater costs from damage to property or equipment and lost production. The HSE reported that in 2014/15 an estimated 1.7 million working days were lost in the construction industry, 1.2 million due to ill-health and 500,000 due to workplace injuries in the construction industry, making a total of 1.1 days lost per worker. The total for working days lost in all industries was 39.8 million days, 23.5 million due to ill-health and 4.7 million due to workplace injuries. In addition, the HSE reported that in 2014/15 injuries and new cases of ill-health, resulting largely from current working conditions for workers in construction, cost society over £0.9 billion a year. In comparison, the cost for all industries was estimated to be £14.3 billion.

1.3 - Construction (Design and Management) Regulations (CDM) 2015

Scope and application

The Construction (Design and Management) Regulations (CDM) 2015 are intended to focus attention on planning and management throughout construction projects, from design concept onwards. The main aim of CDM 2015 is to integrate health and safety into the management of the project and to encourage everyone involved to work together to:

- Improve the planning and management of projects from the very start.
- Identify hazards early on, so they can be eliminated or reduced at the design or planning stage and the remaining risks can be properly managed.
- Target effort where it can do the most good in terms of health and safety and to discourage unnecessary bureaucracy.

CDM 2015 applies to all 'construction work'. The term 'construction work', as defined in Regulation 2 of CDM 2015, means the carrying out of any building, civil engineering or engineering construction work and includes:

- The construction, alteration, conversion, fitting out, commissioning, renovation, repair, upkeep, redecoration or other maintenance (including cleaning which involves the use of water or an abrasive at high pressure or the use of corrosive or toxic substances), de-commissioning, demolition or dismantling of a structure.
- The preparation for an intended structure, including site clearance, exploration, investigation (but not site survey) and excavation (but not pre-construction archaeological investigations), and the clearance or preparation of the site or structure for use or occupation at its conclusion.
- The assembly on site of prefabricated elements to form a structure or the disassembly on site of prefabricated elements which, immediately before such disassembly, formed a structure.
- The removal of a structure or of any product or waste resulting from demolition or dismantling of a structure or from disassembly of prefabricated elements which immediately before such disassembly formed such a structure.
- The installation, commissioning, maintenance, repair or removal of mechanical, electrical, gas, compressed air, hydraulic, telecommunications, computer or similar services which are normally fixed within or to a structure.

CDM 2015 is divided into five parts:

Part 1	Deals with matters of interpretation and application
Part 2	Deals with specific duties of the client
Part 3	Deals with other health and safety duties and roles
Part 4	Applies to all construction work carried out on construction sites, and covers physical safeguards that need to be provided to prevent danger
Part 5	Deals with enforcement in respect of fire

The Health and Safety Executive's 'Managing safety in construction - Guidance on Regulations' (L153) provides guidance on the legal requirements of CDM 2015. This provides guidance for all duty holders that are given duties by CDM 2015. Further information regarding the full responsibilities of each of the five main duty holders who have duties under CDM 2015 is available in guidance documents produced by the Construction Industry Advisory Committee (CONIAC), which are published and made available free of charge by the Construction Industry Training Board (CITB) on its website. The CONIAC guidance documents also set out, in practical terms, what actions are required of the duty holders to deliver a safe and healthy project. The CONIAC guidance documents include a document to assist workers in understanding what they should expect from duty holders and what is expected of them when working on a construction site.

To help those providing construction services to domestic clients to understand their role there is a series of 'Busy Builder' information sheets, available from the Health and Safety Executive. They contain simple, straightforward guidance for those who run small construction sites. The leaflets also show real examples of good and unacceptable practice on site.

Duties

THE CLIENT

The client is an organisation or individual for whom a construction project is undertaken. This definition includes non-domestic (commercial) and domestic clients. A non-domestic client could be an organisation or individual, for example, a Local Authority, school governors, insurance companies and project originators on private finance initiative projects. Domestic clients are people who have work carried out on their own home or the home of a family member that does not relate to trade or business, whether for profit or not. CDM 2015 makes the client accountable for any adverse effects their decisions and approaches have on health, safety and welfare.

Regulations 4 to 6 of CDM 2015 establish a number of specific duties for clients. Commercial clients must meet these duties in full. However, Regulation 7 of CDM 2015 clarifies how Regulations 4 to 6 of CDM 2015 apply to domestic clients. Regulation 7 of CDM 2015 transfers most of the domestic client's specific duties to other duty holders. Where there is more than one client an agreement can be made that one or more client accepts the duties on behalf of the others.

Clients' duties (other than domestic clients)

The duties of clients (other than non-domestic clients) are to:

a) Make suitable arrangements for managing a project, including the allocation of sufficient time and other resources. Arrangements must be maintained and reviewed throughout the project.

b) Where there is more than one contractor, appoint in writing a principal contractor and a principal designer.

c) Take reasonable steps to ensure designers and contractors are competent.

d) Provide relevant pre-construction health and safety information to designers and contractors.

e) Provide information and instruction as soon as is practicable.

f) Co-operate with others in relation to the project.

g) Take reasonable steps to ensure the principal designer and principal contractor meet their duties.

h) Ensure that a construction phase plan is drawn up by the contractor/principal contractor before the construction phase begins.

i) Ensure that the principal designer prepares a health and safety file for the project and keeps it available for inspection.

j) If the project is classed as notifiable, notify the enforcing authority, which is usually the Health and Safety Executive.

k) Ensure a copy of the notification is displayed in a prominent position at the site for workers to read.

l) Ensure adequate welfare facilities are provided.

m) Ensure the health and safety file is passed on if the client no longer has an interest in the structure to which it relates.

Domestic clients' duties

In the case of domestic clients, the client's duties 'a' and 'c' to 'm' listed above are transferred to the contractor, principal contractor or principal designer (as appropriate).

Domestic clients retain the following duties to:

■ Where there is more than one contractor, appoint in writing a principal designer. If the domestic client fails to appoint a principal designer the designer in control of the pre-construction phase project will be the principal designer.

■ Where there is more than one contractor, appoint in writing a principal contractor. If the domestic client fails to appoint a principal contractor the contractor in control of the construction phase of the project will be the principal contractor.

THE PRINCIPAL DESIGNER

A principal designer is the designer with control over the pre-construction phase of the project. This may be combined with other roles in the project, such as project manager or architect. The principal designer is appointed in writing by the client for projects involving more than one contractor. The principal designer can be an organisation or an individual with sufficient knowledge, skills and experience to carry out the role.

The principal designer's role is to plan, manage and monitor and coordinate the pre-construction phase. For example, any designers appointed should not carry out any work beyond initial design unless the principal designer has confirmed that the client is aware of the duties a client has under CDM 2015.

The principal designer will need to follow the general principles of prevention to identify and eliminate or control risks within the design that affect the health and safety of individuals. It is also their responsibility to ensure that the health and safety file is prepared and handed over to the client at the end of the project.

Principal designers' duties

The principal designers' duties are to:

- Not accept an appointment to a project unless they have the skills, knowledge and experience, and, if they are an organisation, the organisational capability, necessary to fulfil their role in a manner that secures the health and safety of any person affected by the project.
- Plan, manage, monitor and coordinate the pre-construction phase so that it is carried out, so far as is reasonably practicable, without risks to health and safety. In particular when design, technical and organisational decisions are being made or the time to complete stages of work is being estimated.
- Take into account the general principles of prevention, any construction phase plan and any health and safety file.
- Identify, eliminate or reduce foreseeable risks related to the construction work, maintaining/cleaning of the structure or using the structure as a workplace.
- Ensuring designers comply with their duties.
- Ensure coordination and co-operation between all parties working on the pre-construction phase.
- Co-operate with others in relation to the project.
- Assist the client in the provision of pre-construction information, in particular to the principal contractor.
- At the pre-construction phase, prepare a health and safety file and ensure it is reviewed, updated and revised as necessary. On completion of the project the principal designer must pass the health and safety file to the client.
- Liaise and share with the principal contractor information relevant to the planning, management and monitoring of the construction phase and the preparation of the construction phase plan.
- Ensure information or instruction is comprehensible and provided as soon as is practicable.
- When working on a project under the control of another, report to that person anything they are aware of in relation to the project which is likely to endanger their own health or safety or that of others.

THE DESIGNER

A designer is an organisation or individual who, in the course of a business, prepares or modifies a design for a construction project (including the design of temporary works) or arranges for someone under their control to do so.

Typically designers will prepare drawings, design details, specifications, bills of quantities, specification (or prohibition) of articles and substances, as well as the related analysis, calculations and preparatory work for their employees or others under their control to prepare designs relating to a structure or part of a structure.

Designers include architects, structural engineers, building surveyors, landscape architects, interior designers, quantity surveyors, consulting engineers and manufacturing design specialists contributing to or having overall responsibility for any part of a design.

Designers' duties

The designers' duties are to:

- Not accept an appointment to a project unless they have the skills, knowledge and experience, and, if they are an organisation, the organisational capability, necessary to fulfil their role in a manner that secures the health and safety of any person affected by the project (general duties).
- Not commence work unless the client is aware of the duties a client has under CDM 2015.
- Apply the principles of prevention and any pre-construction information when preparing or modifying a design.
- Provide information to the principal designer on residual risks that could not be eliminated by design.
- Ensure appropriate information related to residual risks that could not be eliminated is provided to the principal designer and included in the health and safety file.
- Provide information with the design to assist the client, other designers and contractors.
- Ensure information or instruction is comprehensible and provided as soon as is practicable (general duties).
- Co-operate with others in relation to the project.
- To report to the person in control of the work anything they are aware of in relation to the project which is likely to endanger their own health or safety or that of others.

THE PRINCIPAL CONTRACTOR

The principal contractor is the organisation or individual responsible for planning, managing, monitoring and coordinating the construction phase to ensure, so far as is reasonably practicable, construction work is carried out without risks to health and safety. The principal contractor is appointed in writing by the client for projects involving more than one contractor.

Principal contractors' duties

The principal contractors' duties are to:

- Not accept an appointment to a project unless they have the skills, knowledge and experience, and, if they are an organisation, the organisational capability, necessary to fulfil their role in a manner that secures the health and safety of any person affected by the project.
- Plan, manage, monitor and coordinate the construction phase to ensure that it is carried out, so far as is reasonably practicable, without risks to health and safety. In particular when design, technical and organisational decisions are being made or the time to complete stages of work is being estimate.
- Draw up a construction phase plan and ensure it is reviewed, updated and revised as construction work is carried out.
- Take into account the general principles of prevention.
- Liaise and share with the principal designer information relevant to the planning, management and monitoring of the construction phase and coordination of the pre-construction phase.
- Organise co-operation between contractors.
- Coordinate implementation by the contractors of applicable legal requirements.
- Ensure that employers and self-employed persons apply the principles of prevention and follow the construction phase plan.
- Where the project is notifiable, display the notification details in a prominent place so that workers can read them.
- Prevent unauthorised access to the construction site.
- Provide a suitable site induction.
- Ensure adequate welfare facilities are provided and maintained.
- Provide the principal designer with information relevant to the health and safety file.
- Ensure information or instruction is comprehensible and provided as soon as is practicable.
- Co-operate with others in relation to the project.
- Consult with workers or their representatives on matters which may affect their health, safety or welfare.
- To report to the person in control of the work anything they are aware of in relation to the project which is likely to endanger their own health or safety or that of others.

CONTRACTORS

Contractors are engaged in a project to do construction work, under the control of the principal contractor, where one is appointed. Contractors can be engaged to conduct a range of construction work including specialist construction work, for example, provision of utilities and special trades. In the context of CDM 2015 anyone who directly employs or engages construction workers or manages construction is a contractor. A contractor may be an individual, a sole trader, a self-employed worker or a business that carries out, manages or controls construction work in connection with a business.

In some projects there will be only one contractor, who will liaise with the client and designer(s) and have responsibility for the completion of the construction phase of the project.

Contractors' duties

The contractors' duties are to:

- Not accept an appointment to a project unless they have the skills, knowledge and experience, and, if they are an organisation, the organisational capability, necessary to fulfil their role in a manner that secures the health and safety of any person affected by the project.
- Not start work unless they are satisfied that the client is aware of the duties a client has under CDM 2015.
- Plan, manage and monitor the construction work under their control to ensure that it is carried out, so far as is reasonably practicable, without risks to health and safety.
- Where there is more than one contractor, co-operate with the principal designer or the principal contractor.
- Comply with the construction phase plan.
- Not employ a person who does not have the necessary skills, knowledge, training and experience to work safely and healthily.
- Provide each worker under their control with appropriate supervision, instruction and information so that work can be carried out safely and healthily. The information provided must include:
  - A suitable site induction.
  - Emergency procedures.
  - Information identified by risk assessments.
  - Any other information that the worker ought to be aware of.
- Not commence work unless unauthorised access to the site has been prevented.
- Provide adequate welfare facilities.
- Co-operate with others in relation to the project.
- To report to the person in control of the work anything they are aware of in relation to the project which is likely to endanger their own health or safety or that of others.

Where there is only one contractor, the contractor's duties include duties to:

- Take account of the general principles of prevention. In particular when design, technical and organisational decisions are being made or the time to complete stages of work is being estimate.
- Draw up a construction phase plan prior to setting up a construction site.

Appointment and competence required of relevant parties

Regulation 5 of CDM 2015 states:

> "(1) Where there is more than one contractor, or if it is reasonably foreseeable that more than one contractor will be working on a project at any time, the client must appoint in writing:
>
> (a) A designer with control over the pre-construction phase as principal designer.
>
> (b) A contractor as principal contractor.
>
> (2) The appointments must be made as soon as is practicable, and in any event, before the construction phase begins."

Figure 1-2: Appointment of the principal designer and the principal contractor.   Source: CDM 2015 Regulation 5.

A designer (including principal designer) or contractor (including principal contractor) appointed to work on a project must have the personal skills, knowledge and experience to identify significant risk and manage or control them to an acceptable level. If they are an organisation, they must display the organisational capability, necessary to fulfil the role in a manner that secures the health and safety of any person affected by the project.

Organisational capability is effectively the policies and systems that an organisation has in place to set acceptable health and safety standards which comply with the law, and the resources and people to ensure the standards are delivered. Anyone appointing a designer or contractor must take reasonable steps to assure themselves that the designer or contractor fulfils the conditions regarding skills, knowledge, experience and capability for their role. Reasonableness of the steps necessary to assure this will vary according to the level and complexity of risk, for higher risk more assurance is required.

Designers and contractors must not accept an appointment to a project unless they fulfil the conditions regarding skills, knowledge, experience and capability. This will require them to verify the competence and resources of their own personnel working on the project.

Clients must take reasonable steps to satisfy themselves that designers and contractors fulfil the conditions regarding skills, knowledge, experience and capabilities and the designers and contractors must not accept an appointment unless they do fulfil these conditions.

The principal designer must be a designer and must be formally appointed, in writing, as principal designer by the client. The appointment of a principal designer to a project is only required where there is or is likely to be more than one contractor. As the principal designer is also a designer they must comply with the designer's duties established by CDM 2015 in addition to their duties as a principal designers.

The principal contractor must be a contractor and must be formally appointed, in writing, as principal contractor by the client. The appointment of a principal contractor to a project is only required where there is or is likely to be more than one contractor. As the principal contractor is also a contractor they must comply with the contractor's duties established by CDM 2015 in addition to their duties as a principal contractor.

Notification of projects

CDM 2015 applies to all construction projects. However, construction projects that have a construction phase longer than 30 days **and** more than 20 workers working on the project at any one time **or** involving more than 500 person days of construction work are notifiable to the enforcing authority, which is usually the Health and Safety Executive (HSE).

Notification to the enforcing authority by the client must be in writing as soon as is practicable before the construction phase begins. The notification must contain particulars specified in Schedule 1 of CDM 2015 and this can be carried out by using the form F10 on the HSE's website. The client can request that someone else carry out the notification on their behalf, but they remain accountable for the notification taking place correctly. The client must ensure that an up-to-date copy of the notice is displayed in the site office for workers to read. The client can ask the principal designer, designer, principal contractor or contractor to do this.

Details of information that must be notified to the enforcing authority, set out in Schedule 1 of CDM 2015 is:

- Date of forwarding.
- Exact address of the construction site.
- The name of the local authority where the site is located.
- A brief description of the project and the construction work which it includes.
- Contact details of the client (name, address, telephone number and any e-mail address).
- Contact details of the principal designer (name, address, telephone number and any e-mail address).
- Contact details of the principal contractor (name, address, telephone number and any e-mail address).
- Date planned for the start of the construction phase.
- The time allowed by the client under regulation 4(1) for the construction work.

- Planned duration of the construction phase.
- Estimated maximum number of people at work on the construction site.
- Planned number of contractors on the construction site.
- Name and address of any contractor already appointed.
- Name and address of any designer already engaged.
- A declaration signed by or on behalf of the client that the client is aware of the client duties under CDM 2015.

Preparation of pre-construction information

PURPOSE OF PRE-CONSTRUCTION INFORMATION

Pre-construction information provides information to those bidding for or planning work and for the development of the construction phase plan. Pre-construction information is essentially a collection of information about the significant health and safety risks of the construction project that the principal contractor will have to manage during the construction phase.

The pre-construction information will mainly come from:

- **The client** - the client has the main duty to provide information relevant to health and safety to the principal designer or designer and contractors (including the principal contractor). This could include existing drawings, surveys of the site or premises, information on the location of services, etc. In cases where there is more than one designer, the client might expect the principal designer to help collate the information. In cases where there is only one contractor, it is the responsibility of the client. On projects where there is more than one contractor the client must liaise with the principal designer and then:

  - Ensure that the information is adequate.
  - Take steps to fill any gaps.
  - Provide the information to every designer and contractor.

- **Designers** - must take account of the pre-construction information when preparing or modifying designs.
- **Principal designers** - must assist the client to gather the information. The principal designer should be given information by the client as soon as practicable after their appointment. The principal designer must then assist the client to assess the adequacy of the information and take reasonable steps to fill any gaps.

The pre-construction information serves two main purposes:

1) The pre-construction information plays a vital role in the tender and selection process. Pre-construction information provides the health and safety information needed by designers and contractors who are bidding for work on the project. It enables prospective designers and contractors to be fully aware of the project's health, safety and welfare requirements and take it into account in their tender submissions. The pre-construction information provides a template against which different tender submissions can be measured. The pre-construction information helps the principal designer to advise the client on the provision of resources for health and safety and to assess the competence of prospective principal contractors/contractors.

2) The pre-construction information provides the health and safety information needed by principal designers and principal contractors in planning, managing, monitoring and coordinating the project. In particular, it is used to guide the development of construction phase plan. It can provide a framework for the construction phase plan, allowing the detail of the plan to be added to the framework. The pre-construction information provides may require the plan to be developed in response to the information provided, for example, information provided on risks may require the plan to show how the risks will be managed.

CONTENT OF THE PRE-CONSTRUCTION INFORMATION

Pre-construction information is that which is already in the possession of the client or which could be obtained on the client's behalf. The contents of the pre-construction information will depend on the nature of the project itself. However, the following areas should be considered:

Description of project

- Client brief.
- Key dates of the construction phase.

Planning and management of the project

- Arrangements for planning and managing the construction work.
- Allocation of resources and time.
- Arrangements to ensure coordination and co-operation between parties.
- Site security and welfare.
- Requirements for health and safety of client's employees and customers, including vehicles, permits to work, restrictions and emergency procedures.
- Activities on or adjacent to the site during the works.
- Site delineation and security arrangements.

Managing health and safety hazards on site

a) Safety hazards, including:

- Boundaries and access, including temporary access.
- Restrictions on delivery, storage or removal of materials.
- Adjacent land uses.
- Existing storage of hazardous materials.
- Location of existing services - water, electricity, gas, etc.
- Ground conditions.
- Existing structures - stability, or fragile materials.
- Difficulties and damage to structure, for example, height restrictions or fire damage.

b) Health hazards, including:

- Asbestos, including results of any surveys.
- Existing storage of hazardous materials.
- Contaminated land, including results of surveys.
- Existing structures, hazardous materials.
- Health risks arising from client's activities.
- Materials requiring particular precautions.

INFORMATION IN AN EXISTING HEALTH AND SAFETY FILE

- Asbestos surveys.
- Drawings and plans.
- Safe working loads of floors.
- Key structural items.
- Information regarding maintenance and cleaning.

FORMAT OF THE PRE-CONSTRUCTION INFORMATION

The way the pre-construction information is included in the tender documentation for the construction phase and is structured is essential if responses on health and safety are to be made by prospective principal contractors/contractors.

The information must:

- Be relevant to the project.
- Have an appropriate level of detail.
- Be proportionate to the level of risk.

It is unlikely that information gathered at the initial stages of design will be sufficient for the needs of the whole duration of the project. Information must be collected and added to the pre-construction information as the design progresses.

The construction phase plan

PURPOSE OF THE CONSTRUCTION PHASE PLAN

The purpose of the construction phase plan is to set out how health and safety risks are to be managed during the construction phase. In particular, the plan must cover, the health and safety arrangements for the construction phase, site rules and, if appropriate, how the risks identified in Schedule 3 - 'Work involving particular risks' of CDM 2015 will be managed. For example, risks related to drowning or work near high voltages.

The construction phase plan is developed by the principal contractor and is the foundation on which the health and safety management of the construction work is based. The contents of the construction phase health and safety plan will depend on the nature of the project itself and be proportionate to the risks involved in the project. Many of the items in the construction phase plan reflect the information considered at the pre-construction phase, but with further consideration for the construction phase.

When deciding what information should be included in the plan consideration should be given to:

- Its relevance to the project.
- The level of detail needed to clearly set out the arrangements, site rules and any special measures needed to manage the construction phase.
- The balance of the level of detail and the level and complexity of risk involved in the project.

CONTENT OF THE CONSTRUCTION PHASE PLAN

Description of the project

- A description of the project and programme, which will include details of important dates.
- Details of other parties involved in the project and the extent and location of existing records and plans.

Management of the work

- The management structure and responsibilities of the various parties involved in the project, including the client and other members of the project team, whether based at site or elsewhere.
- The health and safety standards to which the project will be carried out, including health and safety goals.
- These may be set in terms of statutory requirements or high standards that the client may require in particular circumstances.
- Means for informing contractors about risks to their health and safety arising from the environment in which the project is to be carried out and the construction work itself.
- Means to ensure that all contractors, the self-employed and designers to be appointed by the principal contractor are properly selected (i.e. they are competent and will make adequate provision for health and safety).
- Means for communicating and passing information between the project team (including the client and any client's representatives), the principal designer, designers, the principal contractor, other contractors, workers on site and others whose health and safety may be affected.
- Arrangements for reporting and identification of accidents, including passing information to the principal contractor about accidents, ill-health and dangerous occurrences that require to be notified by the HSE under the Reporting of Injuries, Diseases and Dangerous Occurrences Regulations (RIDDOR) 2013.
- Arrangements for the provision and maintenance of welfare facilities.
- Arrangements for health and safety induction and training.
- Arrangements that have been made for consulting and coordinating the views of workers or their representatives.
- Arrangements for site rules and for bringing them to the attention of those affected.
- Arrangements for risk assessments and written systems of work.
- Emergency arrangements for dealing with and minimising the effects of injuries, fire and other dangerous occurrences.
- Arrangements should be set out for the monitoring systems to achieve compliance with legal requirements; and the health and safety rules developed by the principal contractor.

Arrangements for specific site risks

- Arrangements of controls safety risks, including preventing falls, control of vehicles and safety when working with services.
- Arrangements for control of health risks, including removal of asbestos, manual handling, noise and vibration.
- In particular, attention should be given to the arrangements for managing the risks associated with any work that falls within one or more of the categories listed in Schedule 3 of the Regulations.

Provision of appropriate and relevant information to all parties

Relevant information must be provided to appropriate parties to ensure the health and safety of persons affected by the project, and, to assist the persons to whom information is provided under CDM 2015.

In order to perform their duties under CDM 2015, every client must ensure that:

- Every person designing the structure that may be bidding for the work (or who intend to be engaged), is conversant with the project-specific health and safety information needed to identify hazards and risks associated with the design and construction work.
- Every contractor who has been or may be appointed by the client is promptly provided with pre-construction information in accordance with CDM 2015.

The pre-construction information shall consist of all the information in the client's possession (or which is reasonably obtainable), including:

- Any information about or affecting the site or the construction work.
- Any information concerning the proposed use of the structure as a workplace.
- The minimum amount of time before the construction phase which will be allowed to the contractors appointed by the client for planning and preparation for construction work.
- Any information in any existing health and safety file.
- Any information obtained from designers related to risks that could not be eliminated by design.

Preparation of the health and safety file

PURPOSE OF THE HEALTH AND SAFETY FILE

The health and safety file is only required for projects involving more than one contractor. The duty to create a health and safety file is assigned to the principal designer and the appointment of a principal designer is only required where there is or is likely to be more than one contractor involved in the project.

The purpose of the health and safety file is to provide a source of information needed to allow future construction work, alterations, refurbishment and demolition, including cleaning and maintenance, to be carried out in a safe and healthy manner.

Clients, principal designers, designers, principal contractors and other contractors all have legal duties in respect of the health and safety file:

- The principal designer must prepare, review, amend or add to the file as the project progresses, and give it to the client at the end of project.
- Clients, designers, principal contractors and other contractors must supply the information necessary for compiling or updating the file.
- Clients must keep the file to assist with future construction work.
- Everyone providing information should make sure that it is accurate, comprehensible and provided promptly.

PREPARING THE HEALTH AND SAFETY FILE

The principal designer is responsible for ensuring the health and safety file is prepared. Putting together the health and safety file is a task which should ideally be a continual process throughout the project and not left until the construction work is completed.

Early on in the construction project the principal designer may find it useful to discuss the health and safety file with the client.

This will help determine what information the client requires and how the client wishes the information to be stored and recorded.

When the client's requirements are known, procedures may need to be drawn up by the principal designer so that all those who will be contributing to the health and safety file (for example, designers and contractors) are aware of:

- The information that is to be collected.
- How the information is to be collected, presented and stored.

The principal designer may find it useful to detail in the pre-tender stage health and safety plan requirements on how and when the information for the health and safety file is to be prepared and passed on. The principal contractor may also find it useful to include similar procedures in the health and safety plan for the construction phase.

Throughout the project those who carry out design work (including contractors) will need to ensure so far as is reasonably practicable that information about any feature of the structure which will involve significant risks to health and safety during the structure's lifetime are passed to either the principal designer or to the principal contractor.

Providing this information on drawings will allow for amendments if any variations arise during construction. It will also allow health and safety information to be stored on one document, therefore reducing the paperwork.

The principal contractor may need to obtain details of services, plant and equipment which are part of the structure from specialist suppliers and installers, for example, mechanical and electrical contractors and pass this information on.

Contractors have a specific duty in CDM 2015 to pass information for the health and safety file to the principal contractor, who in turn has to pass it to the principal designer. This information could include 'as built' and 'as installed' drawings as well as operation and maintenance manuals.

At the end of the project the principal designer has to hand over the health and safety file to the client. In some cases it might not be possible for a fully developed file to be handed over on completion of the project. This may happen because the construction work was finished rapidly to meet a tight deadline and completion of the health and safety file was impossible. Clearly a common sense approach is needed so that the health and safety file is handed over as soon as practical after a completion certificate or similar document has been issued.

CONTENTS OF THE HEALTH AND SAFETY FILE

The contents of the health and safety file will vary depending on the type of structure and the future health and safety risks that will have to be managed.

Typical information which may be put in the health and safety file includes:

- A brief description of the work carried out.
- Any hazards that have not been eliminated through the design and construction processes, and how they have been addressed (for example, surveys or other information concerning asbestos or contaminated land).
- Key structural principles (for example, bracing, sources of substantial stored energy - including pre or post-tensioned members) and safe working loads for floors and roofs.
- Hazardous materials used (for example, lead paints and special coatings).
- Information regarding the removal or dismantling of installed plant and equipment (for example, any special arrangements for lifting such equipment).
- Health and safety information about equipment provided for cleaning or maintaining the structure.
- The nature, location and markings of significant services, including underground cables; gas supply equipment; firefighting services etc.

■ Information and as-built drawings of the building, its plant and equipment (for example, the means of safe access to and from service voids and fire doors).

Application to domestic clients

Domestic clients are people who have work carried out on their own home or the home of a family member, that does not relate to a trade or business, whether for profit or not. If the work is in connection with the furtherance of a business attached to domestic premises, such as a shop, the client is not a domestic client.

Local Authorities, housing associations, charities, landlords and other businesses may own domestic property, but they are not domestic clients. Similarly, a company formed by independent leaseholders of flats to undertake maintenance of the common parts of a structure is not a domestic client, and will have duties under CDM 2015.

Domestic clients are not required to carry out the duties of commercial clients. The effect of Regulation 7 of CDM 2015 is to transfer most of the domestic clients' duties to other duty holders. Where there is only one contractor, most of the client's duties must be carried out by the contractor in addition to the duties that the contractor already has as a contractor. Similarly, if there is more than one contractor, most of the client duties must be undertaken by the principal contractor in addition to the principal contractor's own duties. As an alternative to this, the client can have a written agreement with the principal designer to carry out most of the client's duties, in addition to the principal designer's duties.

Whilst most of the client's duties are passed on to the contractor, principal contractor or principal designer, domestic clients retain the following duties to:

■ Where there is more than one contractor, appoint in writing a principal designer. If the domestic client fails to appoint a principal designer the designer in control of the pre-construction phase project will be the principal designer.
■ Where there is more than one contractor, appoint in writing a principal contractor. If the domestic client fails to appoint a principal contractor the contractor in control of the construction phase of the project will be the principal contractor.

The role of designers, principal designers, principal contractors and contractors when working on a project for a domestic client, is normally no different to their role when working for a commercial client. They have the same duties and should carry them out in the same way as they would for a commercial client.

Designers and contractors working for domestic clients have to manage their own work and co-operate with and coordinate their work with others involved with the project in order to ensure the health and safety of all involved in the project. The requirements in Schedules 2 (welfare facilities) and Part 4 (Regulations 16-35) of CDM 2015 still apply to the work they do for clients. The client has a specific duty to make arrangements to ensure welfare facilities are provided and, where they control the way in which construction work is carried out, must comply with the requirements of Part 4 as far as they are within the client's control.

1.4 - Sources of external construction health and safety information

Sources external to the organisation

MANUFACTURERS' DATA

Section 6 of the Health and Safety at Work etc. Act (HASAWA) 1974 requires manufacturers to provide information. There are a wide variety of Regulations, for example, the Control of Substances Hazardous to Health Regulations (COSHH) 2002 and the Supply of Machinery (Safety) Regulations (SMSR) 2008, that assist and reinforce this requirement. Where products are delivered to site there should be information readily available related to weight, specialist handling, storage, preservation, where applicable, along with other identified hazardous properties. Manufacturers' data should also provide a source of information regarding the scale of risk related to the use of construction work equipment, in particular with regard to noise and vibration exposure.

LEGISLATION

Details of Acts and Regulations are available from the website of the National Archives (TNA). New statutory instruments are published on the internet within 15 days of the printed publication (http://www.legislation.gov.uk). As the website is a record of current and past legislation care has to be taken to ensure data being viewed has not been amended by subsequent legislation.

Acts and Regulations are prime sources of information; they give the precise legal requirements that are to be complied with. They can, however, be difficult to read without some legal understanding. It is also easy to miss changes and amendments unless an updating service is used.

HSE PUBLICATIONS

HSE Books publishes both HSE approved codes of practice (ACOPs) and HSE guidance documents. While failure to follow an ACOP is not in itself an offence, a defendant would have to show that the steps they took were equally effective. This has the effect of transferring the burden of proof of complying with the ACOP onto the defendant.

This makes ACOPs a particularly important source of information. Guidance notes, and other advisory literature, are persuasive in a court of law. Lists of both priced and free publications are available from HSE Books (http://www.hsebooks.com).

TRADE ORGANISATIONS

The **CITB-Construction Skills** is the sector skills council for construction. It provides initiatives and programmes relating to its sector skills role, providing support and guidance to the construction industry.

Organisations such as the CITB-Construction Skills provide publications, videos/DVDs and CDs to help deliver effective training and development across most subjects within the construction industry. The Construction Industry Research and Information Association were founded in 1960.

In recent times the organisation's name was shortened to **CIRIA.** Today, CIRIA is now known solely by its abbreviated name. CIRIA's mission is to improve the performance of those in the construction and related industries.

CIRIA works with the construction industry, government and academia to provide performance improvement products and services in the construction and related industries and currently engages with around 700 subscribing organisations. Activities include collaborative projects, networking, publishing, workshops, seminars and conferences. Each year CIRIA runs about 40 projects, holds over 90 events and publishes 25 best practice guides.

INTERNATIONAL/EUROPEAN/BRITISH STANDARDS

The British Standards Institute (BSI) provides some high quality advice, which is usually more detailed than that set out in legislation and may express good practice that is more that the legal minimum standard. There is a distinct trend towards linking British Standards with legislation, for example, with the Health and Safety (Safety Signs and Signals) Regulations (SSSR) 1996 and BS 5499-10:2006, which is the British standard that sets out requirements for safety signs. Many other British standards are not linked to specific legislation, but set out good practices that the construction industry should follow, for example, BS 8534:2011 'Construction procurement policies, strategies and procedures. Code of practice'. The BSI has also introduced a health and safety management system standard called 'BS OHSAS 18001:2007 Occupational health and safety management systems'. There is also progressive harmonisation to European Standards (CEN) and the use of CE Marking, standards that conform to European requirements are identified by the addition of EN, for example, BS EN 12649:2008+A1:2011 'Concrete compactors and smoothing machines. Safety'. Similarly, where standards are determined to be applicable internationally they are recognised by the International Organisation for Standardisation and are identified by the addition of ISO, for example, BS EN ISO 19432:2008 'Building construction machinery and equipment. Portable, hand-held internal combustion engine driven cut-off machines. Safety requirements and testing'.

IT SOURCES

There are many information technology sources of information. These include a variety of websites, manufacturers' software and BSI standards. Information via IT is widely available from utility companies, Government Agencies (HSE, EA, etc.), the International Labour Organisation, Local Authorities and the Department of Trade and Industry.

PROFESSIONAL BODIES

Institute of Civil Engineers (ICE)

The ICE was founded in 1818 and was granted a royal charter in 1828. The ICE's declared aim is to 'foster and promote the art and science of civil engineering' and it has 80,000 members worldwide. The ICE is one of the organisations that establish the standards for civil engineering courses run by universities in the UK, and some overseas. The ICE has formed a health and safety expert panel to facilitate best practice in the delivery of health and safety risk management. As part of this process it has established a register for those members who wish to demonstrate a defined level of competency in health and safety within the construction process.

Chartered Institute of Building (CIOB)

With over 42,000 members the CIOB is the international voice of the building professional, representing a body of knowledge concerning the management of the total building process. Chartered Member status, represented by the designations MCIOB and FCIOB, is recognised internationally in the construction industry.

With its increasing international membership and growing profile in the UK, the CIOB makes an influential contribution to the construction industry.

Civil Engineering Contractors Association (CECA)

The Civil Engineering Contractors Association was established in November 1996 at the request of contractors to represent the interests of civil engineering contractor companies registered in the UK. CECA's current membership is in excess of 350 civil engineering companies that range in size from large and well-known national names to the medium and smaller sized companies. CECA members account for 75-80% of the civil engineering workload undertaken in Great Britain. The association establishes annual health and safety priorities that it wishes to achieve, for example, providing representation on strategic health and safety committees and groups, such as Working Well Together SHAD working group.

UK Contractors Group (UKCG)

The UK Contractors Group (UKCG) is an association of contractors operating in the UK. The UKCG has over 30 members, who between them deliver £36 billion of construction turnover - a third of total construction output.

UKCG has two main objectives, to:

1) Promote the interests of the construction industry.
2) Take leadership to raise standards within the industry.

The UKCG works closely with the Confederation of British Industry (CBI) Construction Council on its first objective and with supply chain partners to meet the second. The current main priority is promoting the case for infrastructure investment and working with government to improve the efficiency of public sector construction procurement.

Association for Project Safety (APS)

The APS provides a forum and sets standards of to improve and promote professional practice related to construction health and safety risk management. The APS is a member led organisation, represented through Regional Committees, then through Council to the Board of Directors. Amongst APS members are people involved in the architectural, engineering, health and safety, project management and surveying professions.

Institution of Occupational Safety and Health (IOSH)

Founded in 1945, IOSH is the Chartered body for health and safety professionals. With more than 39,000 individual members, IOSH is the largest professional health and safety organisation in the world. IOSH is the voice of the profession, and lobbies governments on policy and law. IOSH accredit qualifications for their members, provides guidance, develops resources, runs courses and organises events to further health and safety. IOSH has a specific construction group that focuses on health and safety issues that affect the construction industry.

International Institute for Risk and Safety Management (IIRSM)

The IIRSM was established in 1975 as a professional body for health and safety practitioners. It was created to advance professional standards in accident prevention and occupational health throughout the world. Over the last three decades IIRSM has grown from a collective group of UK health and safety professionals to an established international institute in over 70 countries.

Exam practice

1. **Identify** the duties placed upon the principal contractor under the Construction (Design and Management) Regulations 2015. **(8)**

2. (a) **Outline FOUR** of the designer's duties under the Construction (Design and Management) Regulations 2015. **(4)**

    (b) Providing an example in **EACH** case, **outline TWO** ways in which failures on the part of designers to comply with their duties can cause health and safety problems during the construction phase of a project. **(4)**

3. **Outline** the information that could be included within a construction phase plan as required by the Construction (Design and Management) Regulations 2015. **(8)**

4. **Identify** the duties of a non-domestic client for a construction project under the Construction (Design and Management) Regulations 2015. **(8)**

5. (a) **Identify** the criteria that have to be considered for a project to be notifiable to the Health and Safety Executive under the Construction (Design and Management) Regulations 2015. **(2)**

    (b) **Identify** the information that must be notified to the HSE. **(6)**

Please refer to the back of the assessment section for answers.

This page is intentionally blank

Construction site - hazards and risk control

Learning outcomes

On completion of this element, candidates should be able to demonstrate understanding of the content through the application of knowledge to familiar and unfamiliar situations. In particular they should be able to:

2.1 Explain the factors which should be considered when carrying out an initial assessment of a site to identify significant hazards and their risks.

2.2 Explain the appropriate general site control measures needed in setting up and organising a site.

2.3 Identify the health, welfare and work environment requirements on construction sites.

2.4 Explain the hazards and appropriate control measures for violence at work.

2.5 Explain the hazards and appropriate control measures for substance misuse at work.

2.6 Explain the hazards associated with the movement of people on construction sites and the control measures for pedestrians.

Content

2.1 - Initial site assessment..23
   Factors to consider in site assessments..23
2.2 - Appropriate general site control measures...26
   Site planning..26
   Site preparation for specialist activities...29
   Site security and means of protecting the public...30
   Arrangements with client/occupier of premises...31
   Arrangements for site inductions 32
   Working in occupied and unoccupied premises 32
2.3 - Health, welfare and work environment requirements 32
   Provision of health and welfare facilities..32
   Sunlight, inclement weather and extreme temperatures 36
2.4 - Violence at work...41
   Hazards relating to violence at work..41
   Control measures to reduce risks from violence at work...41
2.5 - Substance misuse at work...42
   Types of substances misused at work...42
   Hazards of alcohol and drugs at work 43
   Control measures for the misuse of alcohol and drugs at work 44
2.6 - Safe movement of people on construction sites...44
   Hazards to pedestrians..44
   Control measures for pedestrian hazards 46
   Maintenance of a safe workplace 50
   Working on public highways 52
Exam practice 54

Sources of reference

Reference information provided, in particular web links, is correct at time of publication, but may have changed.

A Guide to Workplace Transport Safety, HSG136, HSE Books, http://www.hse.gov.uk/pubns/priced/hsg136.pdf

Don't mix it - A guide for employers on alcohol at work, INDG240, HSE Books, http://www.hse.gov.uk/pubns/indg240.pdf

Driving at work, managing work-related road safety, INDG382, HSE Books, http://www.hse.gov.uk/pubns/indg382.pdf

Drugs at work - A guide for employers, INDG91 (Rev2), HSE Books, http://www.hse.gov.uk/pubns/indg91.pdf

Managing Health and Safety in Construction, Construction (Design and Management) Regulations 2015, Guidance on Regulations, L153, HSE Books, ISBN: 978-0-7176-6626-3 http://www.hse.gov.uk/pubns/priced/L153.pdf

The Construction (Design and Management) Regulations 2015, Industry guidance for Clients, produced by CONIAC, published by CITB, ISBN: 978-1-85751-389-9

http://www.citb.co.uk/documents/cdm%20regs/2015/cdm-2015-clients-interactive.pdf

The Construction (Design and Management) Regulations 2015, Industry guidance for Principal Designers, produced by CONIAC, published by CITB, ISBN 978-1-85751-390-5

http://www.citb.co.uk/documents/cdm%20regs/2015/cdm-2015-principal-designers-interactive.pdf

The Construction (Design and Management) Regulations 2015, Industry guidance for Designers, produced by CONIAC, published by CITB, ISBN 978-1-85751-392-9

http://www.citb.co.uk/documents/cdm%20regs/2015/cdm-2015-designers-interactive.pdf

The Construction (Design and Management) Regulations 2015, Industry guidance for Principal Contractors, produced by CONIAC, published by CITB, ISBN 978-1-85751-393-6

http://www.citb.co.uk/documents/cdm%20regs/2015/cdm-2015-principal-contractors-interactive.pdf

The Construction (Design and Management) Regulations 2015, Industry guidance for Contractors, produced by CONIAC, published by CITB, ISBN: 978-1-85751-391-2

http://www.citb.co.uk/documents/cdm%20regs/2015/cdm-2015-contractors-interactive.pdf

The Construction (Design and Management) Regulations 2015, Industry guidance for Workers, produced by CONIAC, published by CITB, ISBN 978-1-85751-394-3

http://www.citb.co.uk/documents/cdm%20regs/2015/cdm-2015-workers-interactive.pdf

Health and Safety in Construction (HSG150), HSE Books, ISBN 978-0-7176-6182-2 http://www.hse.gov.uk/pubns/priced/hsg150.pdf

HSE, 'Managing for health and safety' http://www.hse.gov.uk/managing/

HSE, The Health and Safety Toolbox: how to control risks at work http://www.hse.gov.uk/toolbox/ HSE Books, ISBN: 978-0-717665-87-7 http://www.hse.gov.uk/pubns/priced/hsg268.pdf

Safety at Street Works and Road Works: A Code of Practice 2013, HMSO ISBN 978-0-115531-45-3 http://www.gov.uk/government/publications/safety-at-street-works-and-road-works

Safe use of work equipment, ACOP, L22, HSE Books, ISBN 978-0-717666-19-5 http://www.hse.gov.uk/pubns/priced/l22.pdf

The Traffic Signs Manual (Chapter 8: The Traffic Safety Measures and Signs for Road Works and Temporary Situations) Department for Transport, http://www.gov.uk/government/publications/traffic-signs-manual:

Part 1: Design. The current edition is dated 2009 - ISBN 978-0-115530-51-7 http://www.gov.uk/government/uploads/system/uploads/attachment_data/file/203669/traffic-signs-manual-chapter-08-part-01.pdf

Part 2: Operations. The current edition is dated 2009 - ISBN 978-0-115530-52-4 http://www.gov.uk/government/uploads/system/uploads/attachment_data/file/203670/traffic-signs-manual-chapter-08-part-02.pdf

Violence at work - A guide for employers, INDG69, HSE Books http://www.hse.gov.uk/pubns/indg69.pdf

Work at Height Regulations 2005 - A brief guide, INDG401 (rev2), HSE Books, http://www.hse.gov.uk/pubns/indg401.pdf

Workplace health, safety and welfare. Workplace (Health, Safety and Welfare) Regulations 1992, ACOP and guidance, L24, HSE Books, ISBN 978-0-7176-6583-9 http://www.hse.gov.uk/pubns/priced/l24.pdf

Relevant statutory provisions

Construction (Design and Management) Regulations (CDM) 2015

Health and Safety (First-aid) Regulations (FAR) 1981 (as amended)

Health and Safety (Safety Signs and Signals) Regulations (SSSR) 1996

New Roads and Street Works Act (NRSWA) 1991

Personal Protective Equipment at Work Regulations (PPER) 1992

Provision and Use of Work Equipment Regulations (PUWER) 1998

Road Traffic Act (RTA) 1988 and 1991

Workplace (Health, Safety and Welfare) Regulations (WHSWR) 1992

Work at Height Regulations (WAH) 2005 (as amended)

2.1 - Initial site assessment

Factors to consider in site assessments

PREVIOUS/CURRENT USE

The previous and/or current use of a site may present many hazards that need to be identified in an initial assessment before construction work starts. If, for example, it is a 'green field' (undeveloped) site, it may provide public access/right of way to members of the public or a recreation area for children. The site could be private and used for agriculture or grazing of livestock. If a 'brown field' (previously used, developed) site, it could contain occupied or unoccupied buildings/premises. Occupied premises will mean regular traffic on the site whilst unoccupied premises may be in a state of disrepair and dereliction. Any existing premises that are either occupied or unoccupied will, more than likely, be or have been connected to various below ground or overhead services that may require further investigation.

Figure 2-1: Site assessment - previous use.   *Source: RMS.*

Figure 2-2: Site assessment - access.   *Source: RMS.*

HISTORY OF SITE

It is important to take into account the history of a site, as the site may present hazards in the form of asbestos or chemical contamination which requires specialist waste removal and land reclamation services. There may be mineshafts present or other types of underground voids, such as abandoned cellars, manhole chambers or large diameter drains. Action should be taken to make site surveys and obtain current and/or historic plans that may identify any or all of the above circumstances.

AREA OF SITE AND RESTRICTIONS

The location or area of the site should be considered and any possible restrictions noted, for example, there may be trees that are protected and unable to be felled or other natural obstacles that could cause problems to the works. If a site is bounded by a main railway line or other premises, then the available space to store or operate any construction related plant and equipment may be restricted once work begins.

TOPOGRAPHY AND GROUND CONDITIONS

Topography relates to the physical surface conditions of the site and is an important factor to be considered along with the ground conditions below the surface. The landscape may be flat and even or is it made up of banks, dips and hills therefore making any operations on site far more difficult to carry out. The ground conditions may be soft soil, clay or rock, each condition presenting its own individual problems and hazards. The site could have a high water table or be susceptible to becoming flooded or waterlogged.

OTHER (NON-CONSTRUCTION) ACTIVITIES ON SITE

When a site is acquired, it may be necessary for other non-construction activities to be carried out prior to any construction works being authorised to begin. This could be site reclamation and clearance, installation of security fencing, lighting and signs, ground investigations, piling operation, site surveys and installation of essential utilities (power, water and gas). Other non-construction activities usually continue when construction has started, consisting of delivery of plant, equipment or materials, site security and development of a utility network around the site.

NATURE OF SURROUNDINGS

Roads

Roads and highways that surround a site boundary can be a significant source of additional hazard and are a main area for consideration as access to any site is primarily via some form of roadway. Factors such as the type of road (dual carriageway, main road, one-way system, country lane), road speed encountered, volume of traffic (high all day, cyclical, rush hour), type of traffic using the road (agricultural plant, cars, heavy goods vehicles (HGV's), well lit or unlit, and capacity of road (weight, height or width restrictions). It may be that special requests or notifications are to be made with the Local Authority regarding access and site traffic proposals. If the site is within a residential area or in close proximity to a school, permissions or restrictions may be enforced regarding when or if surrounding roadways may or may not be used. In any of the above situations, there is a potential for danger.

Figure 2-3: Roads.   *Source: RMS.*

Figure 2-4: Footpaths.   *Source: RMS.*

Footpaths

Footpaths are a means of providing pedestrians with a safe means of travelling by foot usually alongside a highway. It should be identified how the footpath is used (for example, for a school journey by children or by people queuing for a bus). The risk of injury may be increased at the entrance to a construction site where pedestrians cross the access opening and might encounter heavy site mobile plant or goods vehicles delivering materials to site. Footpaths may also skirt the construction site boundary, where pedestrians may also become at risk due to the activities within the site (for example, falling objects from a scaffold structure, flying objects from cutting, drilling or hammering operations, fumes, dust, chemicals).

Railways

Railways present the hazard of heavy, high speed trains (up to and in excess of 125 mph) that do not have the ability to respond to dangerous circumstances that may arise as other transport modes are able to, i.e. quick emergency stopping, avoidance by changing direction. In addition to these hazards, there may be overhead cables carrying 25,000 volts or rails carrying 750 volts. Work near to railways requires suitable planning, as any clash between a travelling train and site equipment, plant or vehicles could, and most likely would, lead to disastrous consequences. Rail authorities have laid down strict procedures that are to be followed and any party working on railways should be in possession of a 'Personal Track Safety' certificate. High-visibility clothing that is worn on or near to a railway line should be of the correct standard and colour (high-visibility orange). Restrictions on colours worn on or near to a railway should be strictly followed and nothing that is red or green be worn due to the fact that it may be mistaken as a signal by a train driver. Communications should be maintained with the rail authority and notification given of any works being carried out on or near to the railway in order that all issues can be complied with correctly.

Figure 2-5: Railways.   *Source: Welsh Highland Railway.*

Figure 2-6: Waterways.   *Source: RMS.*

Waterways

Waterways located on or near construction sites present a risk of drowning; the water does not have to be fast flowing to cause a worker to get into difficulty. Other factors to consider if waterways are in close proximity to a construction site are: the likelihood of floods occurring, environmental pollution of the waterway, damage to associated wildlife by site activities. Conversely, it is necessary to consider exposure of site staff to hygiene hazards through contaminants or disease (chemical pollutants, Weil's disease) within the waterway.

Waterways are used by a considerable number of boat operators that may be affected by the activities on site (for example, falling objects from a scaffold structure, flying objects from cutting, drilling or hammering operations, fumes, dust, chemicals). Boat operators may equally affect site safety, for example, collision of the boat with a scaffold structure.

Residential/commercial/industrial properties

Construction can take place in local or immediate proximity of residential, industrial or commercial property that may be either unoccupied or occupied and fully operational. Construction traffic will generally add significantly to the normal traffic loading in the area, which may result in congestion, for example, during the 'school run' period and lunch times. This may well be exacerbated by vehicles queuing near the site entrance to gain access. The increase in large goods vehicles (LGV's) in the area will lead to increased engine noise, vehicle exhaust fumes and the risk of collisions with other vehicles, pedestrians. Young children and the elderly may be particularly at risk, as they may choose to weave through semi-stationary traffic and may not be visible to large construction vehicle drivers when they decide to move their vehicles. There are additional risks where work is carried out in commercial property (shops, offices) as the work may take place in busy areas where members of the public and staff are present. In the case of industrial properties (factories, workshops), people may be at work when construction activities take place and the premises can present additional hazards from machinery, plant, equipment, chemicals, etc. being used. Construction workers may not be familiar with the hazards presented, which could increase the risk of personal injury.

Figure 2-7: Commercial properties. *Source: RMS.*

Figure 2-8: Industrial properties. *Source: RMS.*

Schools

Schools are very busy areas and accommodate children of various ages that may have no or little perception of danger or risk and by their nature are often very inquisitive of their surroundings. In addition to children, parents or carers that deliver children to and collect children from the school create pedestrian and vehicular traffic hazards around the immediate area. Children are frequently tempted to try to gain access to construction sites and normally achieve this when site security is poor and consideration has not been given to access through small openings. Sites often underestimate the size of openings, which some small children are able to fit through, particularly when compared with that which is required to restrict adult access.

MEANS OF ACCESS

Access to a construction site should be through a controlled point and requires adequate planning to take into account the surrounding area. Restrictions and hazards relating to safe access to a construction site may include the conditions of the highway from which access is being gained (size, speed, use). The traffic that will operate on the site needs to be considered (size, type, frequency, volume).

Figure 2-9: Means of access, overhead restrictions. *Source: RMS.*

Figure 2-10: Safe distance barriers for overhead services. *Source: HSE, HSG144.*

PRESENCE OF OVERHEAD AND BURIED SERVICES

Overhead services in the form of electricity cables present the obvious risk of electrocution through either making direct contact with the electricity cable or where arcing (discharge by spark 'jumping' to a near earth point) occurs. Overhead cables should be identified prior to site works and the risk factors determined.

Construction sites may involve the use of various pieces of large, mobile plant and equipment (cranes, excavators, etc) and steel scaffold systems near to power supplies. If such equipment is allowed to come too close to an overhead cable it may provide a sufficient level of earth for the power to 'leap', making the particular item of plant live. If this occurs, subsequent 'arcs' are possible to other people or plant within close proximity of the original earth point.

Buried services (electricity, gas, water, etc) are not obvious and the likelihood of striking a service when excavating, drilling or piling is thus increased without a site survey to identify any service present. The results of striking an underground service are varied, and the potential to cause injury or fatality is high. Incidents can include shock, electrocution, explosion and burns from power cables, explosion, burns or unconsciousness from gas or power cables, and impact injury from dislodged stones/flooding from ruptured water mains.

2.2 - Appropriate general site control measures

Site planning

Following an initial site assessment that has identified hazards and risks associated with the works, control measures should be implemented to ensure the safety and well-being of all those who are affected by the construction site and its activities. A plan must be assembled to take into consideration the following factors.

ARRANGEMENTS FOR SITE ACCESS

Access to a construction site must be planned to minimise any hazards identified during the initial assessment. When a suitable location for site access has been identified, this must be controlled at a point or points that are designated as authorised access point/s and the remainder of the construction site boundary must be secure against unauthorised access. Site safety information should be displayed at access points to inform all attendees of contact names, rules and emergency procedures. Barrier systems are normal on complex undertakings, accompanied by procedures for admittance and exit of people and plant. Special rules for site safety induction and issue of any site security identification are often used to maintain control.

Figure 2-11: Site access. *Source: RMS.*

Figure 2-12: Site controls - access and roadways. *Source: RMS.*

ROADWAYS

Public roadways often extend or continue into construction sites and are subject to pedestrian and vehicular traffic. Construction site roads should be subject to site safety rules such as speed limits, safety restraints (seat belts), direction of flow (one-way systems where possible), and there should be segregation of pedestrian and vehicular traffic similar to that used on the public highway. Adequate space should be provided for parking and to allow vehicles and plant to manoeuvre safely and the area should be well lit as required. Vehicles and mobile plant should never be allowed to block roadways or access points as this may prevent emergency vehicles and crews gaining access in the event of a major incident. Site slurry/mud on the road surface that can create skid hazards for site plant and vehicles should not be allowed to accumulate and there should be a system for inspection and cleaning of the surface and vehicles' wheels.

STORAGE

The storage requirements are dependent on the type of material to be stored. Different material types should be stored separately, to avoid cross contamination and the potential for a harmful adverse chemical reaction. If combined storage is permitted, it is advisable that different materials be kept separated for easy identification and retrieval. In addition to authorised access of site operatives, the storage area should be designed to allow safe access by fork-lift trucks and for the use of suitable mechanical lifting aids to eliminate the need for manual handling where possible. Housekeeping should be of a good standard and kept clean and tidy with suitable lighting and ventilation. There should be appropriate fire precautions and provision of correct fire extinguishers.

Storage areas should be restricted to authorised site staff only and have the correct safety information signs that warn of any dangers or mandatory signs enforcing the wearing of personal protective equipment (PPE).

They should be used for solely that purpose and must not be used for any other purposes such as mixing operations or as a rest or smoking area.

Storage of flammable substances

Substances should be stored in such a way that they cannot

- Escape and contaminate personnel or the environment.
- React with other substances causing explosion, fire or toxic fumes.

Requirements for storage

- Store small quantities only in the workplace.
- Small quantities of flammables should be stored in clearly marked flameproof metal containers.
- Non-compatible chemicals should be stored apart.
- Chemicals giving off fumes should be stored and used only with suitable respiratory protection.
- Chemicals should be stored away from sources of heat, possibly refrigerated.
- Bulk storage should be outside away from other buildings and sources of heat, including sunlight.

Features of a bulk flammable substance store

- Single storey, light construction in non-combustible materials.
- Flame proof electrical equipment.
- Door sill and perimeter bunding for containment of up to 110% of the maximum storage container of the chemical. If more than one container is stored, the system must be capable of storing 110% of the biggest container capacity or 25% of the total tank capacity within the bund. Whichever is the greater must be adopted.
- Interceptor pits for spillage.

Figure 2-13: Misuse of storage.   *Source: RMS.*

Figure 2-14: Loading/unloading.   *Source: RMS.*

LOADING/UNLOADING

Construction sites are constantly changing with a variety of tasks all happening at once, including continuous staff, vehicles and material movements around the site. With this in mind, it is very important that any loading and unloading of materials used on the construction site is carried out in its own dedicated area/zone under competent supervision. The delivery of materials or equipment to a construction site should be scheduled and planned to minimise the volume of traffic at site at any one time, and drivers/operators of delivery vehicles given a site specific induction to ensure an awareness of hazards, site safety rules and procedures.

Loading and unloading of materials or equipment should be planned and organised. Materials should not be allowed to be placed too high or to lean over creating a potential risk of collapse with the possible result of major injury or a fatality. A number of people have been killed on construction sites due to carelessness in handling. Generally, loads should be kept small with goods on pallets that are in good repair. Lightweight boxes that offer no strength and can be crushed or bags of free-flowing solid (gravel) should always be palletised and never be stacked on top of each other. Different types of container should be stacked separately.

Loads should not block or be placed near emergency exits, fire points/extinguishers, vehicle routes or block light or visibility. They should be placed on firm, solid ground or floors that are strong enough to provide adequate support. Workers should be trained in the correct way to handle loads and also in the dangers associated with unsafe practices/or incorrect loading methods. Site staff should be instructed never to climb up or stand on top of racking or palletized material.

OFFICES

There should be an office available on site to house first-aid facilities and equipment, emergency procedures, health and safety information, site induction documentation, project notification to the enforcing authority and construction phase health and safety plan (if the Construction (Design and Management) Regulations (CDM) 2015 apply), construction drawings and specifications. General site office equipment and records are also stored in the site office, for example telephone, fax, training records, visitor personal protective equipment and filing facility.

LIGHTING

Adequate lighting should be provided that allows safe access and egress into and around the construction site along roadways, vehicle and pedestrian routes. Special consideration should be made to areas such as scaffold structures, excavations, flammable stores or fuel bunkers/tanks. Signs warning of dangers at site should be clearly lit to allow approaching people advance notice.

SIGNS

The provision of suitable signs is an important factor in making people aware of the hazards and precautions that relate to construction work. The entrance to a construction site should have an information board that provides details of the client, architect, supervisor, contractor and any other important parties. It will also include mandatory health and safety signs such as those requiring the use of hard hats or ear protection. Other information could include a basic site layout plan and details of where to report upon arrival at the site.

REMEDIATION WORKS

Remediation works may need to be carried out prior to the development of a new site or the modification to an existing structure. Remediation can be necessary due to the effects on the site of its prior use, which may lead to contamination of land, water and structures. Former sites that may need remediation include fuel stations, gasworks, chemical storage facilities, industrial factories (for example, wire, rubber and chemical manufacture).

The substances forming the contamination can represent significant health hazards. They may include benzene, hydrocarbons, acids, cyanide and metals, for example, arsenic, nickel, cadmium and chromium.

Remediation work can vary from removal of contaminated soil, for example, with the redevelopment of a brown field site to the identification and establishment of controls for building contaminates, such as asbestos prior to an extension being made to an existing structure. The work may involve removal of hazardous materials left over from prior processes, excavation of contaminated soil, removal of contaminated surface water, cleaning of contaminated soil/water, stabilisation of land, treatment of invasive species of weeds, building temporary bunds to control water runoff and the recovery, movement or protection of human or infected animal remains.

Site preparation/remediation work that involves the removal of topsoil that is contaminated with heavy metals or other hazardous substances will require specific arrangements in relation to personal protective equipment requirements and practices to be carried out. The work is likely to require the provision of gloves, overalls, eye protection and respirators. Additionally, the work will necessitate campaigns of awareness training to ensure good levels of personal hygiene are maintained, with emphasis on ensuring that open cuts are covered with waterproof dressings whenever required.

Consideration will need to be given to specific welfare facilities provision, for example, a decontamination unit may be needed, which has a dirty area where contaminated clothing can be removed after work, an area with a shower or other means of washing and a clean area where normal clothes could be kept while employees are working on site. There should be arrangements in place in order to prevent contamination when eating and smoking. First-aid and emergency decontamination facilities should be located near to the place of work.

PROVISION OF UTILITY SERVICES

The planning of the provision of utility services to the site will involve consideration of the initial needs of the site, further needs as the site becomes established and the long term needs of the client who will take over the site. This may initially involve the use of portable, self-contained services, for example, water stored in a mobile tanker, electricity supplied by generators and portable welfare facilities with contained waste.

As the site develops, demands for utility service may increase and a more robust provision may be required. It may be possible to utilise the services that have to be put in place for the benefit of the client on completion of the construction work or it may be necessary to establish alternative sources. The identification of utility services required for the site should be determined in liaison with local supply companies before work commences, at the planning stage.

Certain utilities, such as gas or fast internet broadband, may not be available. Other services may be limited, such as water supply (particularly pressure), drainage or electrical capacity. Limitations in the water supply may need to be addressed by the provision of storage tanks, particularly if there is an identified need for a water sprinkler system or other firefighting provisions.

Drainage may need to be provided through the use of septic tanks or other means, such as organic reed bed installations. Electrical supply may require the organisation and suitable location of an additional electrical sub-station to increase the capacity of supply.

Site preparation for specialist activities

LIFTING

Lifting operations on construction sites can vary widely dependent upon the size and weight of the load required to be lifted and the lifting equipment required to carry out the lift. Specialist lifting equipment on construction sites is usually either mobile crane or tower crane type.

Prior to undertaking lifting operations with any piece of lifting equipment, vital preparation is required to ensure the safety of all those affected. This includes thorough planning of the lift to include a safe system of work, method statements, risk assessments, permits-to-work (if required) and competent authorised persons assigned to manage the lifting operation.

The ground on which the lifting equipment is to be situated should be firm and level and suitable load spreading decking provided to ensure stability. Depending on the nature and frequency of the lifting operations, it may be necessary and appropriate for the ground to be made up with hardcore or concrete to ensure strength and stability in all weather conditions.

Consideration should also be given to surrounding structures and overhead power cables, ensuring the minimum safe working distances from them. Access to the area below the lifting area should be controlled or restricted to protect people at site from items falling during the lift. The equipment used for the lift must be inspected prior to use and regularly as per the specified frequencies and all test certificates made available.

The Lifting Equipment and Lifting Operation Regulations (LOLER) 1998 are specifically related to mechanical lifting and associated equipment.

PILING

Piling is a method of creating long, straight underground cavities that are used for stabilising/strengthening the ground and providing foundations for a building or structure. This is performed by either using drilling or by compacting force.

The most common method of piling involves the use of a guide 'tube' in which a heavy solid 'driving piece' supported by lifting equipment is released down the guide tube causing the material it strikes to displace upon impact and thus create a cavity when withdrawn. This operation is repeated until the required depth of bore is achieved. Another method involves a steel liner being mechanically 'hammered' into the ground to the required depth.

Preparations for piling works may include identifying buried services, hidden voids, the density of the material being piled and ground stability for equipment, water table levels and any local buildings or structures that may be affected by vibrations. Piling is a very noisy operation and consideration should be given to surrounding areas.

Figure 2-15: Site signs. *Source: RMS.*

Figure 2-16: Steelworks. *Source: RMS.*

STEELWORKS

Steelwork is often used to form the basic 'skeleton' on which a structure is built. The majority of steelwork is designed and manufactured off site and is then assembled using the various pre-fabricated sections and steel beams during the build. Associated activities usually involve working at height with materials that are very heavy and difficult to manoeuvre.

Site preparation involves the creation of large, level concrete surfaces, on which the steelwork stands and is fixed. The erection of steelworks requires thorough planning to include safe systems of work, risk assessments, method statements and permits to work where required.

Where practicable, risks should be eliminated or reduced to the minimum possible level by combating hazards at source (for example, use of mobile elevated work platform for access, cranes for lifting). Any lifting equipment or access equipment should only be used on firm and level ground.

Site security and means of protecting the public

Regulation 13 (4) (b) in Part 3 of CDM 2015 places a duty on the principal contractor to ensure that:

> *"The necessary steps are taken to prevent access by unauthorised persons to the construction site."*

Figure 2-17: Duties of a principal contractor.   *Source: CDM 2015 Regulation 13.*

Regulation 15 in Part 3 of CDM 2015 places a duty on contractors with regard to site security:

> *"(10) A contractor must not begin work on a construction site unless reasonable steps have been taken to prevent access by unauthorised persons to that site."*

Figure 2-18: Duties of contractors.   *Source: CDM 2015 Regulation 15.*

Regulation 18 in Part 4 of CDM 2015 deals with good order and site security, it requires that:

> *"(2) Where necessary in the interests of health and safety, a construction site shall, so far as is reasonably practicable and in accordance with the level of risk posed, either:*
>
> *(a) Have its perimeter identified by suitable signs and be so arranged that its extent is readily identifiable.*
>
> *(b) Be fenced off."*

Figure 2-19: Good order and site security.   *Source: CDM 2015 Regulation 18.*

PERIMETER FENCING

Construction sites must be contained within a perimeter fence. The main purpose of fencing is to keep out unauthorised persons (for example, members of the public including children) and to prevent injury or death.

Perimeter fencing also provides security against theft of materials, plant or equipment from the site. Fences should be adequate and suitable and installed at a reasonable distance from the structure to allow unrestricted movement on site of people and mobile plant, and prevent any activities being undertaken affecting the environment outside the fence. The fence should be regularly inspected to ensure there is no damage, breaks or gaps to allow unauthorised entry. When one piece of fencing is fixed to another, the fixing should face into the protected site, where possible, so as to impede tampering and removal of the fences by unauthorised persons.

Figure 2-20: Unauthorised access.   *Source: RMS.*

Figure 2-21: Perimeter fencing and signs.   *Source: RMS.*

SIGNS

Signs should be fixed at regular intervals on the perimeter fence to warn of the dangers within the site and instruct people to 'keep out'. Quite often, the name of the security company that is responsible for 'out of hours' security will also be displayed with a telephone number for emergency contact or to report any trespass.

SAFE VIEWING POINTS

Members of the public are quite often intrigued by construction sites and can be attracted to the perimeter fence to see for themselves what is going on. This may result in injury from flying particles, dust, fumes or splashes, even though the person is outside the perimeter fence. This can be avoided by arranging for a pre-planned viewing point that consists of a wire mesh panel integrated into the fence that allows members of the public to view the site's activities. The viewing point will be planned and situated in an area that is not exposed to hazards.

MEANS OF SECURING PLANT, CHEMICALS, ETC

Plant, equipment, materials or chemicals should be suitably secured to prevent injury by unauthorised access. Plant should be locked up at all times when not in use and keys held in a secure location (site office, safe). It may be practical to house plant in an additional internal site compound. In order to improve security certain items of heavy mobile plant are provided with steel sheets or shutters fitted around the cab and padlocked in position.

       © RMS

MEANS OF CONTROLLING DANGERS ON PUBLIC HIGHWAYS

Areas that surround a construction site are subject to mud and debris from the tyres and chassis of vehicles that frequent the site, which creates additional hazards to other road users as highway surfaces become slippery and create skid hazards. This can be controlled by the implementation of regular highway cleaning with road sweeper vehicles. Action can also be taken at site exits prior to vehicles leaving the site by routing site traffic through a tyre and undercarriage cleaning system, which assists in preventing mud and debris leaving the site.

Controls need to be in place to avoid vehicles entering the site queuing back onto the public highway; these will include the close monitoring of delivery schedule arrangements. A banksman may be needed to direct the vehicles and other traffic, particularly if the site entrance is restricted and a number of forward and backward movements of delivery vehicles are necessary to enter the site. If work continues in the hours of darkness, additional lighting may be necessary at site entrances and exits to improve the delivery drivers' general perception of hazards and pedestrian visibility.

Arrangements with client/occupier of premises

SITE RULES

Site rules will vary at different sites or premises due to the wide range of activities that may be undertaken. Site rules provide instructions that must be followed by permanent site staff and visitors and also other important information relating to site/location specific hazards. Occupiers of premises or clients may have different standards of site rules and some may enforce them more stringently than others. Contractors should always enforce their own site rules in addition to client/occupier rules.

CO-OPERATION

Co-operation between client, contractor and occupier is a very important factor. The occupier of a premises or site will have a detailed knowledge of any site specific hazards that may or may not be obvious to a contractor undertaking construction works and this may impact upon the works. In addition, the client or occupier has the authority to place controls and restrictions on the site. The contractor should be experienced in the activities that will be carried out and will have assessed any hazards related to the activities that are to be carried out at site. It is vital that all parties co-operate and communicate in order that this knowledge and information can be assessed to determine any new hazards that may arise and to enable appropriate information to be cascaded to other people at risk on the site. Co-operation will also be required where site activities need to be controlled or access restricted or where a shared knowledge is required to undertake a task, for example, decommissioning or removal of machinery.

SHARED FACILITIES

Occupied premises will quite often have various facilities available for existing workers/occupiers, for example, hot and cold water, toilets and rest facilities. It may be acceptable, with the agreement of the party in control of the premises and its facilities, for these to be shared for mutual benefit. CDM 2015 establishes a duty on the client, contractors and the principal contractor to ensure that welfare facilities are provided. Therefore, where CDM 2015 applies and the client occupies the premises where construction work is to take place, it is in the interests of both the client and contractors to agree what facilities are required and what can be made available to the contractors.

Figure 2-22: Protection of others.   *Source: RMS.*

Figure 2-23: Sanitary conveniences.   *Source: RMS.*

First-aid and accidents

It is the duty of the employer (this could be the main contractor), under the Health and Safety (First-Aid) Regulations (FAR) 1981, to provide first-aid provisions and to inform the employees of these arrangements.

These facilities should be in a clean environment, probably sited in a separate site office or portacabin. The Reporting of Diseases and Dangerous Occurrences Regulations (RIDDOR) 2013 require a record of prescribed accidents to be kept on site. All reportable injury accidents and dangerous occurrences must be recorded, deaths being additionally notified by telephone directly to the Health and Safety Executive (HSE).

Protection of other employees/visitors

Construction related activities that are carried out at a client's premises, while the premises are occupied, must take into account the lack of knowledge of construction hazards of the client's employees and visitors using the premises. This lack of knowledge may put them at risk from the hazards. This may require site rules to be amended and be supported by induction, personal protective equipment issue, signs, barriers, lighting or verbal instruction.

Arrangements for site inductions

All new or transferred employees, sub-contractors, including utility suppliers, architects' and surveyors should receive a site induction. This should be tailored to the site concerned and follow a formal structure, with documentation signed and logged.

The following subjects should be covered (as a minimum):

- Welfare provisions (toilets, showers, rest areas).
- Site rules.
- Firefighting equipment and assembly points.
- Use of personal protective equipment (PPE) and any training requirements.
- Traffic management plans.
- Access and egress, for example, signing in and out.

- First-aid provision.
- Permits-to-work and any specific work restrictions.
- Emergency procedures.
- Reporting procedures for incidents, accidents, unsafe conditions, shortcomings in the employer's controls.
- Work procedures.
- Method statements.

Specific hazards and controls:

- Electrical.
- Plant and equipment.

- Hazardous substances.
- Manual handling.

Working in occupied and unoccupied premises

OCCUPIED PREMISES

Careful planning of construction or maintenance work should be taken prior to work commencing on occupied premises. Hazards from paint, dust, falling masonry and excavations should be considered, suitable and sufficient risk assessments should be made and controls implemented. Factors to be considered include establishing controls to segregate contractor workers from the occupier's employees. This may include establishing separate parking, traffic and pedestrian routes. Where this is not possible, particular attention will need to be given to assessing where the contractor - occupier interface presents a risk. Risks will increase when a high volume of the occupier's employees interact with the construction work, such as at the start of work, lunch period and close of work. Where there is a risk from the construction work, such as falls of materials from a height, walkways will need to be covered to protect pedestrians. Arrangements for welfare facilities and first-aid will also need to be determined.

UNOCCUPIED PREMISES

Unoccupied premises/buildings can pose other hazards, with unstable groundwork, footings, walls, beams supporting floors and roofing. In addition, unoccupied buildings are likely to be infested with vermin or suffer intrusion by pigeons in the rafters where roof integrity may have failed; this can increase the risks of biological hazards. Unoccupied premises may have been used by itinerant trespassers sleeping rough and the potential risk of needle stick injuries from discarded syringes will also need to be assessed. Again, these hazards should be highlighted, suitable risk assessments should be made and controls implemented.

2.3 - Health, welfare and work environment requirements

Provision of health and welfare facilities

CDM 2015, Regulation 4, establishes an absolute duty on the client to make suitable arrangements to ensure that Schedule 2 of CDM 2015, regarding welfare facilities, is complied with. The principal contractor also has an absolute duty under Regulation 13 to ensure that Schedule 2 is complied with, throughout the construction phase. A similar, but conditional duty, so far as is reasonably practicable, exists for contractors under Regulation 15, which requires them to ensure welfare facilities are provided for themselves and any other worker under their control.

Generally, on construction sites temporary welfare facilities are provided so that they may be relocated as the build phase of the work is carried out. If the work involves refurbishment or extension to an existing building, separate facilities may be required to segregate construction site workers from the occupiers. This may be a requirement of the contract with the client, but often is necessary to maintain the required number of facilities, such as sanitary facilities, for the extra number of people on site. Other reasons may be to meet specific legal requirements, such as the Control of Asbestos Regulations (CAR) 2012, where there will be a requirement to provide separate washing and clothing facilities for those working with asbestos or its removal. Construction activities may involve workplaces away from the construction site, for example, offices or depots. Where this is the case the health and welfare facilities for these workplaces will need to comply with the Workplace (Health, Safety and Welfare) Regulations (WHSWR) 1992. *For more information see the 'Relevant Statutory Provisions' section.*

DRINKING WATER

Schedule 2 of CDM 2015 requires that an adequate supply of wholesome drinking water must be provided on construction sites.

The supply needs to be accessible. If not provided in the form of a fountain, then drinking vessels must also be provided. The supply outlet from taps should be marked by an appropriate sign to indicate 'suitable for drinking' or 'unsuitable for drinking', as appropriate.

WASHING FACILITIES

Schedule 2 of CDM 2015 requires that suitable and sufficient washing facilities must be provided at readily accessible places on construction sites. This includes showers where they are necessary because of the nature of the work or for health reasons. Where work is particularly dirty or workers are exposed to toxic or corrosive substances, showers may also be necessary.

In addition, washing facilities must be provided:

- In the immediate vicinity of every sanitary convenience.
- In the vicinity of changing rooms required by Schedule 2.

On all sites, a suitable number of wash basins big enough to allow a person to wash their hands, face and forearms should be available. There must be a supply of clean, hot and cold or warm running water, so far as is practicable, soap or other means of cleaning, towels or other means of drying and the rooms that contain these facilities must be kept clean, ventilated, lit and maintained.

Other than facilities for washing hands, forearms and face separate washing facilities must be provided for men and women, unless provided in individual rooms that may be locked from the inside.

SANITARY CONVENIENCES

Schedule 2 of CDM 2015 requires that readily accessible, suitable and sufficient sanitary conveniences must be provided on construction sites. The conveniences must be adequate for the numbers and gender employed, lit, kept clean and maintained in an orderly condition. Separate conveniences for male and female workers must be provided, except where the convenience is in a separate room and the door is capable of being locked from the inside. Provision should be made for regular cleaning and replenishment of consumable toilet items.

Figure 2-24: Washing facilities. *Source: HSE, HSG150.*

Figure 2-25: Temporary showers. *Source: RMS.*

FACILITIES FOR CHANGING CLOTHING

Schedule 2 of CDM 2015 requires that where special clothing must be worn at work or for reasons of health or propriety a person cannot change in another room then suitable and sufficient changing facilities must be provided on construction sites.

Separate facilities or separate use of facilities for male and female workers must be taken into account. The changing rooms must be provided with seating and, where necessary, include facilities to dry work clothing, personal clothing and personal effects.

The changing facilities must be readily accessible to workers, for example, when starting work/completing work and near eating facilities where there is a requirement to remove work clothing. The facilities provided should be sufficiently large to enable the maximum number of workers to use them comfortably and quickly at any one time.

ACCOMMODATION FOR CLOTHING

Schedule 2 of CDM 2015 requires suitable and sufficient accommodation must be provided at readily accessible places to enable workers on construction sites to lock away their personal clothing not worn at work, clothing worn at work that is not taken home and personal effects.

Clothing accommodation must be suitably secure; it must be suitable for the work clothing and would typically be separate from personal clothing where it was necessary to avoid health risks due to contamination or damage. Clothing accommodation should be in a suitable location near to changing facilities and drying facilities for work clothing, personal clothing and personal effects.

REST AND EATING FACILITIES

Schedule 2 of CDM 2015 requires readily accessible, suitable and sufficient rest rooms or rest areas to be provided or made available at readily accessible locations on construction sites. Schedule 2 of CDM 2015 sets out specific requirements that the rest rooms or rest areas must conform to. Rest rooms and rest areas must:

"(b) Be equipped with an adequate number of tables and adequate seating with backs for the number of persons at work likely to use them at any one time.

(c) Where necessary, include suitable facilities for any person at work who is a pregnant woman or nursing mother to rest lying down.

(d) Include suitable arrangements to ensure that meals can be prepared and eaten.

(e) Include the means for boiling water.

(f) Be maintained at an appropriate temperature."

Figure 2-26: Rest rooms and rest areas.   *Source: CDM 2015 Schedule 2.*

Canteens, restaurants etc. may be used as rest facilities providing there is no obligation to buy food.

Figure 2-27: Accommodation for clothing.   *Source: RMS.*   Figure 2-28: Rest and eating facilities.   *Source: RMS.*

SEATING

Suitable seats should be provided for workers who have to stand to carry out their work and occasionally have the opportunity to sit down. Seats should be provided for use during breaks. Rest rooms must have sufficient seats with backrests for the number of workers who may use them at one time. Seats in the work area can be counted as eating facilities provided the place is clean and there is a suitable surface to place food. There should also be facilities for pregnant and nursing mothers to lie down if required.

VENTILATION

Regulation 33 in Part 4 of CDM 2015 requires:

"(1) Suitable and sufficient steps shall be taken to ensure, so far as is reasonably practicable, that every place of work or approach thereto has sufficient fresh or purified air to ensure that the place or approach is safe and without risks to health.

(2) Any plant used for the purpose of complying with paragraph (1) shall, where necessary for reasons of health or safety, include an effective device to give visible or audible warning of any failure of the plant."

Figure 2-29: Fresh air.   *Source: CDM 2015 Regulation 33.*

The principal features of a ventilation system are:

- Provision and maintenance of the circulation of fresh air in every occupied part of a workplace.
- The rendering harmless of all potentially injurious airborne contaminants, for example, welding fumes and gases.

HEATING

Regulation 34 in Part 4 of CDM 2015 requires:

> *"(1) Suitable and sufficient steps shall be taken to ensure, so far as is reasonably practicable, that during working hours the temperature at any place of work indoors is reasonable having regard to the purpose for which that place is used.*
>
> *(2) Where necessary to ensure the health or safety of persons at work on a construction site that is outdoors, the construction site must, so far as is reasonably practicable, be arranged to provide protection from adverse weather, having regard to:*
>
> *(a) The purpose for which the site is used.*
>
> *(b) Any protective clothing or work equipment provided for the use of any person at work there."*

Figure 2-30: Temperature and weather protection.   *Source: CDM 2015 Regulation 34.*

The temperature of workplaces can vary greatly. They may be very cold and exposed, such as at height on a scaffold, or general indoor workplaces at ambient temperature.

The level of heating should be appropriate to provide physical comfort. The nature of the work and the working environment will need to be assessed to achieve the correct level. Several factors should be considered such as personal capability, degree of hot or cold, wind speed and humidity. Whenever possible the individual should be able to adjust their workplace to achieve this objective or be able to use a refuge from time to time against excessive heat or cold weather conditions.

LIGHTING

The basic need is to provide sufficient and suitable light in the circulation areas to allow movement of personnel, materials and equipment between work areas to take place conveniently and in safety. The aim should be to provide conditions that remain comfortable to the eye as it passes from one zone of the workplace to another, and to make available all information relevant (for example, safety signs) to the well-being and safety of the workforce which can be received through the sense of sight. Particular care should be taken when site work is carried out after dark or when work is to be carried out indoors, underground or in any area of confinement not normally accessed by workers.

Each workplace should be assessed in relation to the tasks to be carried out. Increased levels of illuminance should be provided in higher risk locations, for example, where vehicle routes intersect, where pedestrian cross vehicle routes, where there are changes in floor level or where flights of stairs are provided. Luminaires should be carefully positioned to provide good three-dimensional lighting, preventing shadows any avoiding glare by preventing direct sight of the unshielded source. Machinery, which makes fast cyclic movements, should be carefully illuminated to prevent the occurrence of stroboscopic effects. Temporary lighting can be hazardous if not installed correctly and presents the risk of electric shock, fire or explosion.

Sudden changes in lighting levels should not occur between neighbouring zones of the workplace. Levels should be graded to allow time for the eye to adapt. The processes of dark adaptation can take several minutes (more than half an hour in extreme cases) during which time the efficiency of the eye is severely reduced, making accidents more likely.

Differences in the colour characteristics of so-called 'white light' sources are sometimes apparent to the eye and although its ability to colour-adapt is considerable, the occurrence of frequent noticeable changes due to the use of various kinds of sources in the same interior may accelerate the onset of fatigue as well as making fine colour judgments impossible.

Regulation 35 in Part 4 of CDM 2015 requires:

> *"(1) Each construction site and approach and traffic route to that site must be provided with suitable and sufficient lighting, which must be, so far as is reasonably practicable, by natural light.*
>
> *(2) The colour of any artificial lighting provided shall not adversely affect or change the perception of any sign or signal provided for the purposes of health and safety.*
>
> *(3) Suitable and sufficient secondary lighting must be provided in any place where there would be a risk to the health or safety of a person in the event of the failure of primary artificial lighting."*

Figure 2-31: Lighting.   *Source: CDM 2015 Regulation 35*

FIRST-AID FACILITIES

The first-aid facilities required for a particular construction site will depend mainly on the risks of the work being carried out and the number of people affected by the risks. The higher the risks and the number of people affected the more facilities are required.

Where sites are small and only exposed to general construction risks one first-aider and a first-aid box may be adequate. Where the site has a significant number of people exposed to a wide range of risks it may be necessary to provide a number of first-aiders and first-aid boxes and a specific first-aid facility in the form of a first-aid room.

First-aid facilities of this type should contain essential first-aid provision and equipment, including:

- Sink with hot and cold running water.
- Drinking water and disposable cups.
- Soap and paper towels.
- A store for first-aid materials.
- Foot-operated refuse containers, lined with disposable yellow clinical waste bags or a container for the safe disposal of clinical waste.
- An examination/medical couch with waterproof protection.
- Clean pillows and blankets.
- A chair.
- A telephone or other communication equipment.
- A record book for recording incidents attended by a first-aider or appointed person.

Sunlight, inclement weather and extreme temperatures

"Where necessary to ensure the health or safety of persons at work on a construction site that is outdoors, the construction site must, so far as is reasonably practicable, be arranged to provide protection from adverse weather, having regard to:

(a) The purpose for which the site is used.

(b) Any protective clothing or work equipment provided for the use of any person at work there."

Figure 2-32: Adverse weather protection.   Source: CDM 2015 Regulation 34 (2).

SUNLIGHT

Effects of sunlight on workers

The effects of sunlight are mainly caused by the infrared and ultraviolet (UV) rays (radiation) in the sunlight. They can have a number of effects, including heat stress, skin damage and eye damage. The intensity of the infrared and ultraviolet rays that a worker's body receives particularly depends upon the time of year and time of day. Infrared and UV rays are strongest during summer and during the middle of the day.

Heat stress

Sunlight is a form of radiant heat, which can increase the temperature of a worker's body and lead to heat stress. The effects of heat stress on workers is covered separately, later in this section.

Skin damage

Workers whose job keeps them outdoors for a long time, such as construction workers, could get more sunlight on their skin than is healthy for them. The effects of sunlight on the skin mean that, in the short term, mild reddening of the skin can occur. If exposure is sustained or the sunlight is strong, sunburn could develop.

Sunburn develops when the amount of UV exposure is greater than which can be protected against by the melanin in a worker's skin. The lighter a worker's skin, the less melanin it has to absorb UV and protect itself from sunlight exposure. Further exposure to sunlight could lead to the sunburn blistering and the skin to peel.

Longer term problems can arise from prolonged exposure to sunlight. Too much exposure to sunlight speeds up the ageing of the skin, making it leathery, mottled and wrinkled. The most serious effect of prolonged exposure to sunlight is the increased risk of developing skin cancer. Some people are more liable to skin cancers than others. People with white skin are most at risk.

In addition, those at particular risk include people with:

- Fair or freckled skin that does not tan, or goes red or burns before it tans.
- Red or fair hair and light coloured eyes.
- A large number of moles - 50 or more.

Workers of Asian or Afro-Caribbean origin are less at risk. This is because people with naturally brown or black skin have more melanin in their skin cells, which helps to protect the skin from the damaging effects of the UV rays in sunlight.

Eye damage

Sunlight can also damage the eye. Spending a long time in strong sunlight without UV eye protection increases the risk of developing eye damage, including cataracts. Cataracts are a form of eye damage that causes a loss of transparency in the lens of the eye and can cause blurred or misty vision. Another potential effect of the UV in intense sunlight is a painful eye condition, called photokeratitis, also called 'snow blindness'. The condition has the same effect as is caused by arc welding, called 'arc eye'. This is where the UV affects the surface of the eye and surrounding area causing a sunburn like effect that can be very painful. If intense exposure of the eyes to sunlight stops, the effects usually disappear within a couple of days. Workers are only likely to experience this condition if their eyes are exposed to intense sunlight for a sustained period, however, this could happen in some construction work activities, particularly where the sunlight is reflected from the surface of water or snow.

Preventive measures for the effects of sunlight on workers

Preventive measures for the effects of sunlight on workers include:

- Introduce shading from sunlight in areas where individuals are working, particularly if the work causes them to remain in a position exposed to sun for long periods.

- Reschedule work to times of the day when sunlight is less strong.
- Provide more frequent rest breaks in rest areas shaded from sunlight, particularly for midday breaks.
- Educate workers to enable them to be aware of the early symptoms of heat stress.
- Ensure workers keep covered up, clothing made from close woven fabric stops most UV.
- Encourage workers to wear a hat with a brim or a flap that covers the ears and the back of the neck.
- Provide appropriate UV eye protection where workers are exposed to high levels of sunlight that could affect their eyes.
- Use a high factor sunscreen on any exposed skin, use at least Sun Protection Factor (SPF)15.
- Drink plenty of water to avoid dehydration.
- Educate workers to check their skin regularly for any unusual moles or spots and encourage them to see a doctor promptly if they find anything that is changing in shape, size or colour, itching or bleeding.

INCLEMENT WEATHER

Inclement weather is a term used to describe unpleasant weather conditions including storm, rain, high winds, snow and extreme temperatures, for example, very cold, i.e. less than 10°C to below freezing or very hot, i.e. temperatures above 30°C.

Effects of inclement weather on workers

Exposure to inclement weather can have significant effects on a worker's health and safety and those in construction activities can be particularly at risk from the effects. Both very cold and very hot temperatures are a risk to health and one of the fundamental mechanisms by which the body regulates its temperature is by perspiration. Important factors that aid or hinder this process are airflow and humidity. Humidity relates to the moisture content in the air. Air with a relatively high humidity has little capacity to cool the body by 'wicking' away sweat, whereas low humidity can cause dry skin and cracking. In a similar way, if a worker's clothing gets wet the 'wicking' effect can quickly cause significant heat loss in cold conditions. Inclement weather that is wet can therefore have a significant effect on a worker's body temperature and sustained work in wet weather conditions where a worker's footwear becomes wet can lead to conditions like 'trench foot'. In winter, the strength of the wind can significantly affect the air temperature and effectively reduce the ambient temperature by many degrees in exposed workplaces, called wind-chill. This can put individuals at greater risk than in still or sheltered conditions at the same temperature. The effects of extreme temperatures is covered separately, later in this section.

Effects of inclement weather on construction work

In addition to the effects on workers, inclement weather can lead to extremes of temperature and other conditions that can have significant effect on construction work. Extreme temperature effects include very hot and very cold conditions.

In hot conditions construction work sites will become dry and dusty and the ground may become cracked or shrink, particularly in clay soils. This may affect the stability of scaffolds, tower cranes and make site roadways difficult to navigate and cause equipment to overheat or seize. Dust will become airborne easily at relatively low wind speeds (3-4k/hr) and will increase the discomfort of workers, affecting their eyes and exposed skin.

Some dusts are particularly hazardous if they become airborne, such as cement, which are caustic. Dust will also affect visibility and may increase the risk of site vehicle collisions with other equipment, structures or pedestrians.

Cold conditions are often accompanied by rain, snow or ice. Rain will soften the ground and any mud arising will make the site roadways particularly hazardous, increasing the risk of slips to workers and vehicles sliding out of control. Mud may be transferred from site vehicles onto public highways increasing similar risks to road users. The moisture from wet clothing may condense on the inside screens of mobile equipment resulting in poor visibility. Wet conditions may prevent the use of electrical equipment. Water may also transfer from clothing to hands, increasing risks from the operation of electrical equipment, even when indoors. In addition, porous materials that get wet may increase in weight or other materials may become difficult to handle, leading to increased risk of manual handling injuries. Some construction activities, for example work in sewers or excavations, could be affected by flooding that arises due to heavy rainfall in inclement weather.

Severe cold, below zero Celsius, may affect the structural stability of some critical equipment, for example, cranes and lifting accessories exposed to cold and wet weather will have an increased risk of corrosion and brittle failure. All exposed walk surfaces will also be very slippery in wet and low temperature conditions, particularly those on access equipment such as scaffolds, access points to mobile work equipment and the decks of delivery vehicles.

In high winds work may have to be suspended, because loose materials used in construction activities can become mobile in the wind and present a danger. Temporary works structures may become unstable in high winds. Crane operations are likely to be affected and manually handling sheet materials in high winds could result in workers being blown over and falling, with particularly serious consequences where they are working at height.

Visibility may be reduced significantly by snow fall or heavy rain, increasing the risks of collision of site vehicles with other equipment or pedestrians, with the added hazard of water or ice increasing breaking distances and reducing driver directional control. Engine fuels, brake fluids and operational hydraulic oils may freeze, resulting in equipment or brake system failure.

Heavy snow fall will alter the landscape, obliterate walkways and may create ill-defined road routes. Drivers of site vehicles may not see hazards such as trenches or open manholes or underestimate the width of waterways, which when frozen and covered with snow appear much narrower, and may drive their vehicles onto and through the ice.

Preventative measures for inclement weather

Whenever possible outdoor work should be planned to be started and carried out when the weather is temperate, for example, in the spring. Arrangements should be made to monitor weather patterns daily in advance and consider temperature, rainfall, wind speed and direction.

Work areas that may be exposed to severe weather conditions should be sheeted or covered, to provide shelter for workers and protection for the work being conducted. Suitable protective clothing, including footwear, should be provided. Wet conditions may require making available a change of clothing so that wet clothing can be removed and dried. This will necessitate the provision of drying rooms and similar rooms will need to be provided to enable workers to access a warm environment, hot meals and drinks to recover from exposure to inclement weather.

When planning the site layout and its development it is important to establish roads, walkways and drainage of the site. This may require the provision of formal roads and pathways that may be incorporated into the building/structure under construction as the project progresses or they may be set out as a temporary measure.

Make arrangements to improve temporary roads using compacted gravel to reduce the formation of mud, there may also be a need for arrangements to prevent site vehicles transferring mud onto public roads such as water jetting of wheels before the vehicle leaves site. Grit bins should be provided for use where there are gradients for vehicles to navigate or pathways that are likely to be exposed to ice. Check the working temperature of any fluids used in vehicles with manufacture specification for working in low temperature environments. In heavy snow identify traffic routes with markers such as flags and establish a similar scheme to identify high risk areas such as trenches and drains.

Where excavations or other subsurface areas of the site may be affected by heavy rainfall arrangements should be made to limit its ingress and for its removal. This may involve the use of sandbags to prevent water entering areas, sheeting and pumps to remove water. Porous materials that may be affected by wet conditions should be covered or stored indoors. Where possible, arrangements should be made to conduct work involving electrical equipment indoors. Work at a height may have to be suspended in windy conditions and roof work may also be stopped while snow and ice are present.

Excavations, mobile equipment and access equipment, such as scaffolding, may require a formal inspection after the effects of inclement weather.

Wet environments

Preventive measures for wet environments include:

- Providing a sheeted area to protect workers from rain.
- Re-organising work so that it can be conducted indoors while it is raining or ground is wet.
- Establishing areas of made up ground for work to be carried on outside without the need to stand in water or mud.
- Providing suitable breathable fabric waterproof clothing and footwear.
- Providing spare work clothing to enable those affected by wet conditions to change when needed.
- Providing drying facilities for wet clothing, including footwear.
- Encouraging workers to remove wet clothing during rest periods.
- Educating workers to enable them to be aware of the effects of working in wet conditions and its link to cold stress.

Windy environments

Preventive measures for windy environments include:

- Providing a sheeted area to protect workers from wind, for example, sheeting of scaffolds and open areas of partly constructed buildings.
- Giving consideration to suspending high risk outdoor work until the weather improves.
- Re-organising work so that it can be conducted indoors while it is windy.
- Educating workers to enable them to be aware of the effects of working in windy conditions, particularly the wind chill-factor and its link to cold stress.

EXTREME TEMPERATURES

Effects on workers of exposure to extreme temperatures

The effects of excessive exposure to heat is referred to as heat stress and excessive exposure to cold is referred to as cold stress.

Cold stress

In very cold temperatures, the most serious concern is the risk of hypothermia or dangerous overcooling of the body. Another serious effect of cold exposure is frostbite or freezing of the exposed extremities such as fingers, toes, nose and ear lobes. Hypothermia may be fatal in the absence of immediate medical attention.

When surrounding temperatures drop below 18°C body heat is lost. To maintain equilibrium the body adjusts itself by attempting to conserve heat by decreasing the blood flow to the skin's surface areas (ears, nose, fingers and toes) or by increasing heat production through involuntary muscle movement, such as shivering.

The most dangerous and rapid heat loss occurs when clothing is wet, wind is high, surrounding surfaces are cold, or when the body is immersed in cold water. The body can lose 25 to 30 times more heat when in contact with cold wet objects than under dry conditions or with dry clothing.

Cold stress impairs performance of both manual and complex mental tasks. Also, sensitivity and dexterity of fingers lessen in a cold environment. At lower temperatures still, cold affects deeper muscles, resulting in reduced muscular strength and stiffened joints. For all these reasons incidents are more likely to occur in very cold working conditions.

Workers exposed to cold environments are at risk of cold induced injuries occurring in localised areas of the body, for example, frost-nip, chilblain, trench foot, and immersion foot:

- **Frost-nip** is the mildest form of a freezing cold injury, occurs when ear lobes, noses, cheeks, fingers, or toes are exposed to the cold and the top layers of a skin freeze. The skin of the affected area turns white and it feels numb.
- **Chilblains** are a mild cold injury caused by prolonged and repeated exposure for several hours to air temperatures from above freezing, 0°C, to as high as 16°C. In the affected skin area there will be redness, swelling, tingling, and pain.
- **Immersion foot** occurs in workers whose feet have been cold and wet (for example, when wearing boots), but not freezing cold, for days or weeks. It can occur at temperatures up to 10°C. The primary injury is to nerve and muscle tissue. Symptoms include tingling and numbness; itching, pain, swelling of the legs, feet, or hands; or blisters may develop. The skin may be red initially and turn to blue or purple as the injury progresses. In severe cases, gangrene may develop.
- **Trench foot** is 'wet cold disease' resulting from prolonged exposure to cold temperatures in a damp or wet environment from above the freezing point to about 10°C. Depending on the temperature, an onset of symptoms may range from several hours to many days, but the average is three days. Trench foot is more likely to occur at lower temperatures, whereas the immersion foot condition is more likely to occur at higher temperatures and longer exposure times. A similar condition of the hands can occur if a person wears wet gloves for a prolonged period under similar cold conditions as described above. Symptoms are similar to those of immersion foot.

The two most severe cold stress injuries are frostbite and hypothermia.

1) **Frostbite** is caused by exposure to extreme cold or contact with extremely cold objects. It occurs when tissue temperature falls below freezing point. The parts of the body most commonly affected are the face, ears, fingers and toes. Frostbitten skin is white and feels 'wooden' all the way through. In severe cases, gangrene may develop.

2) **Hypothermia** is caused by a decrease in core body temperature to a level at which normal muscle and brain functions are impaired. This occurs when metabolic heat production of the body is not sufficient to replace heat lost by the body to the environment. Maximum severe shivering develops when body temperature has fallen to 35°C.

Lower body temperatures present the following signs and symptoms:

- Persistent shivering.
- Blue lips and fingers.
- Irrational or confused behaviour.

- Reduced mental alertness.
- Poor coordination.
- Poor decision-making.

Hypothermia can occur in relatively mild weather, particularly cool-wet weather, even when physical work is being carried out. It is the most frequent cause of death in water immersion.

Heat stress

In a very hot environment, the most serious concern is heat stroke. In the absence of immediate medical attention, heat stroke may be fatal. Heat stroke fatalities occur every summer. Heat exhaustion, fainting (syncope) and dehydration are less serious types of illnesses that are not fatal, but interfere with a worker's ability to work.

Dehydration can be mild, moderate or severe, depending on how much of your body weight is lost through loss of fluids, for example through perspiration. Two early signs of dehydration are thirst and dark coloured urine.

This is the body's way of trying to increase water intake and decrease water loss. Other symptoms may include dizziness or light-headedness, headache, tiredness, dry mouth/lips and eyes, passing small amounts of urine infrequently (less than three or four times a day).

Dehydration can result in a lack of ability to concentrate, loss of alertness and loss of short term memory. This can lead to an increase in errors that could cause accidents. Dehydration can also lead to a loss of strength and stamina. It is the main cause of heat exhaustion.

Heat exhaustion can occur when the temperature inside the body (the core temperature) rises to anything between the normal 37°C up to 40°C. At this temperature, the levels of water and salt in the body begin to fall, which can cause a person to feel sick, feel faint and sweat heavily. The symptoms of heat exhaustion can develop rapidly.

They include:

- Very hot skin that feels 'flushed'.
- Heavy sweating.
- Dizziness.
- Extreme tiredness (fatigue).
- Feeling sick (nausea).
- Being sick (vomiting).
- A rapid heartbeat.
- Mental confusion.
- Urinating less often and much darker urine than usual.

Heat stroke is far more serious than heat exhaustion. It occurs when the body can no longer cool itself and starts to overheat. When the core temperature rises above 40°C the cells inside the body begin to break down and important parts of the body stop working. If left untreated, it can lead to complications, such as organ failure and brain damage. Severe heatstroke results in death.

Early symptoms of heat stroke include:

- High body temperature.
- Heavy sweating that suddenly stops.
- A rapid heartbeat.
- Rapid breathing (hyperventilation).
- Muscle cramps.

The extreme heat that causes heatstroke also affects the nervous system, which can cause other symptoms such as:

- Mental confusion.
- Lack of coordination.
- Fits (seizures).
- Restlessness or anxiety.
- Problems understanding or speaking to others.
- Seeing or hearing things that are not real (hallucinations).
- Loss of consciousness within half an hour.

Preventative measures for workers exposed to extremes of temperature

When considering preventive measures for exposure to extreme temperatures consideration will need to be given to collective control measures whenever possible, such as the provision of shelter. However, this will often require the provision of other control measures in addition.

> *"(1) Suitable and sufficient steps must be taken to ensure, so far as reasonably practicable, that during working hours the temperature at a construction site that is indoors is reasonable having regard to the purpose for which that place is used."*

Figure 2-33: Temperature at a construction site.   *Source: CDM 2015 Regulation 34(1).*

The Workplace (Health Safety and Welfare) Regulations (WHSWR) 1992 sets out similar requirements to CDM 2015 that apply to all workplaces, for example, site offices and storage depots. The approved code of practice (ACOP) which accompanies WHSWR 1992 states that a temperature of 16°C should be maintained for sedentary work, for example, in site offices, and a temperature of 13°C for work that requires physical effort.

Because these figures are stated in an ACOP, they should be regarded as minimum temperatures for these workplaces and can be used to suggest suitable temperatures to meet CDM 2015 requirements for construction sites.

Cold environments

Preventive measures for cold environments include:

- Provide a sheeted area to protect workers from wind and rain, for example, the sheeting of scaffolding.
- Provide means to bring tools, equipment and materials that need to be handled and have been stored in cold conditions up to a reasonable temperature before use.
- Provide mobile facilities for warming up, and encourage the drinking of warm fluids, such as soup or hot chocolate.
- Introduce more frequent rest breaks.
- Give consideration to suspending work until the weather improves.
- Educate workers to enable them to be aware of the early symptoms of cold stress.

Ensure the personal protective equipment issued is appropriate:

- Clothing should have a high insulation tog rating (but not hinder flexibility for the movements necessary to carry out the tasks required), prevent absorption of water and be suitably fastened to reduce the effects of wind chill.
- The feet should be insulated to avoid loss through conduction.
- The head should be covered to the maximum extent practicable, to avoid excessive heat loss.
- Clothing should be light in colour to prevent heat loss through radiation.

Hot environments

Preventive measures for hot environments include:

- Introduce shading from the heat of the sun in areas where individuals are working, particularly if the work causes them to remain in position for long periods, for example, when doing brick or block work.
- Reschedule work to cooler times of the day.
- Provide more frequent rest breaks and introduce shading to rest areas.
- Provide free access to cool drinking water.
- Encourage the removal of personal protective equipment when resting to help encourage heat loss.
- Educate workers to enable them to be aware of the early symptoms of heat stress.

2.4 - Violence at work

Hazards relating to violence at work

Maintenance and construction activities often need to be completed within a fixed timescale and this can result in increased pressure on workers to work quickly and without error. This may lead to an increase in tension between workers, particularly if one worker perceives another to not be working quickly enough to achieve the final goal.

Such circumstances might result in violent outbursts between co-workers or other contractors. This may include workers being sworn at, threatened or even the use of physical violence.

"Any incident, in which a person is abused, threatened or assaulted in circumstances relating to their work."

Figure 2-34: Definition of work-related violence. *Source: HSE.*

Verbal abuse and threats are the most common types of incident. Physical attacks are comparatively rare. The most common risk factors relating to violence are:

- The position a person holds - a worker may hold a position of authority over another person; how they use this authority and the effects on the person can cause disagreement, resentment and could cause the person to be more aggressive.
- The nature of the work - if a worker is working alone this may lead them to be more at risk of violence. The nature of the work may be dealing with people that are emotionally charged, and this may cause them to react to normal things in an unpredictable way.
- The location of the work - if the worker is working isolated from others this may leave them at risk. Some locations may not be secure and third parties may enter perhaps looking to steal or create damage.
- The time of working - work during late evening and early morning may mean there are less people around and those people that are around who are not workers may be more likely to have violent tendencies. It may also mean there is less supervision and increased irresponsible behaviour, for example, the singling out of a young worker by the more experienced group for teasing or abuse.
- Alcohol and drugs - can make some people more aggressive. Because their perception and behaviour is more unpredictable, it may lead to misunderstandings and violence.
- Visible appearance - violence may arise simply because someone does not like a worker's visible appearance and what this may represent. This can be accentuated if the individual belongs to a minority group and perhaps has a poor understanding of the common language used by co-workers or members of the public.
- The availability of weapons - if weapons, improvised or normal, are available to be used a sudden outburst that may have been verbal could escalate to involve major personal injury because a weapon was available, for example, bricks, knives, hammers, cartridge tools.

DETERMINE THE SIZE OF PROBLEM

Determine the size of the problem by analysing information from various sources.

- Ask workers informally through managers and health and safety representatives.
- Encourage workers to report all incidents and keep detailed records.
- Classify all incidents according to their actual or potential severity of outcome.
- Try to predict what might happen and how violence may arise.

Control measures to reduce risks from violence at work

POLICY

The policy for dealing with violence should be written into the health and safety policy statement so that all employees are aware of it. This will encourage employees to co-operate with the policy and report further incidents.

DETERMINE CONTROLS RELEVANT TO THE RISK

- Identify who might be harmed and how.
- Identify who is most at risk.
- Improve the environment, for example, better seating, lighting.

- Where appropriate, identify potentially violent people in advance.
- Evaluate the risk.
- Check existing arrangements.
- Train workers to recognise early signs of violence and how they can reduce the likelihood with their behaviour.
- Provide information, for example, on relevant incidents.
- Improve security, for example, video cameras; maintain site security and control access and egress.
- Check arrangements for lone workers and consider two workers where risks are high.
- Arrange safe transport or secure car parking for people who work late at night.
- Ensure issue and use of tools and equipment is controlled and stored securely when not required.

MONITOR

Check regularly to see if the arrangements are working by consulting workers and worker health and safety representatives. If violence is still a problem, review work practices and risk controls.

- Ask workers informally through managers and health and safety representatives.
- Encourage workers to report all incidents and keep detailed records.
- Classify all incidents according to their actual or potential severity of outcome.
- Try to predict what might happen and how violence may arise.

DEALING WITH INCIDENTS

If there is a violent incident in the workplace it will be necessary to consider the following:

- Debriefing - victims might need to talk through their experience as soon as possible.
- Time off work - individuals may need differing times to recover.
- Support - in some cases victims might need counselling. Consider a phased return to work.
- Legal help - legal assistance may be appropriate in serious cases.
- Other workers - may need guidance or counselling to help them react appropriately.

2.5 - Substance misuse at work

Types of substances misused at work

Many substances may affect a worker's ability to work safely and they do not have to be taken whilst at work to have an effect. Substances can have a residual effect even when they are taken outside working hours. This can have a significant effect on the health and safety of the worker and those that may be affected by their work. It is imperative that organisations take the issue of substance misuse seriously in order to protect health and safety, especially in high risk activities such as chemical, nuclear, construction and transport etc.

ALCOHOL

Even at low levels of consumption the body is affected by alcohol, reducing reaction time and impeding coordination. It also affects thinking, judgement and mood and can have a significant effect on behaviour when conducting routine work. Whilst large amounts of alcohol in one session can put a strain on the body's functions, in particular the liver, it can also affect muscle function and stamina.

Drinking alcohol raises the drinker's blood pressure and this can increase the risk of coronary heart disease and some kinds of stroke. Regularly drinking smaller amounts also increases the risk of cirrhosis of the liver. The effect of alcohol is not limited to physical effects - people who drink very heavily may develop psychological and emotional problems, including depression.

 Case Study

Brian was a 25 year old male with alcohol related problems. He had been having an increasing number of absences from work, was often late on duty and alcohol was smelt on his breath. The manger discussed the issues with Brian, who agreed that he required help to overcome his excessive drinking and advice from occupational health resulted in Brian being referred for alcohol counselling during the working day. With the full support of the manager, Brian responded well, stopped drinking and his attendance improved. Further follow up by occupational health demonstrated that the early intervention and support provided for Brian prevented his excessive drinking.

LEGAL/ILLEGAL DRUGS

The effects on the workplace of some drugs can be catastrophic if a worker is a regular user and even the casual user may not be fully fit for work after taking a drug the night before or the weekend before work.

Legal drugs

Legal drugs include those that are prescribed by a medical practitioner and those that may be obtained without prescription from a pharmacy. Access to drugs with or without prescription varies in different countries. In some countries opium based drugs, such as codeine or morphine, may be prescribed for pain relief. The depressant effects of this drug when used for short-term use under medical supervision would not normally be a concern related to work; however, in larger doses they may cause a worker to have reduced mental functions that could affect their use of machinery, tools or driving. Antihistamines, used to treat allergic reactions, may cause drowsiness and impaired thinking that can create risks for workers in a number of jobs. Drugs prescribed to treat depression, antidepressants, can also slow reaction speeds and affect activities that require concentration.

Benzodiazepines are a range of drugs that are in wide use to treat insomnia, anxiety and epilepsy. They have a number of common effects that could affect the health and safety of workers, the main ones being drowsiness, dizziness, unsteadiness, confusion, light-headedness and memory loss. Their use should be considered where the work being carried out may be particularly influenced by these effects, for example, work at height, driving or operating mechanical handling equipment or safety critical work like control of a permit-to-work system.

Illegal drugs

Illegal drugs are those that have been classified by the State as requiring control because of the seriousness of their effects. Controls are usually imposed to limit their supply and use, including criminal penalties. There are many types and variants of illegal drugs, some of the common ones include cannabis, depressants and stimulants.

The effects on the individual of using cannabis include:

■ Euphoria.
■ Slow reactions.
■ Poor coordination.
■ Short term memory affected.
■ Distortion in perception of space and time.
■ Drowsiness.
■ Inability to think clearly.
■ Anxiety and depression.

The effects of cannabis can continue for up to three weeks after large consumption.

Depressants include opiates like heroin, opium, morphine and codeine. Opiates begin to affect the central nervous system almost immediately after use. Because the drug suppresses the central nervous system the user experiences 'cloudy' mental function, breathing slows and may reach a point of respiratory failure. They are extremely physically and psychologically addictive drugs.

Stimulants like amphetamines and cocaine and MDMA (3,4-methylenedioxy-N-methylamphetamine) make people feel more lively, awake, energetic, confident and, in the case of MDMA, give a sense of well-being. The effects on the individual will vary depending on the drug, but generally as the drug wears off the person may become anxious, irritable and restless, however, even when they feel desperate for sleep the drug may continue to keep them awake. Finally, exhaustion and often intense mood swings affect the user. The range of adverse health effects include increased heart rate, high blood pressure, high temperature, nausea, chills, sweating, involuntary teeth clenching, muscle cramps and blurred vision.

In the case of MDMA some users report undesired effects like anxiety, agitation and recklessness. In the hours after taking MDMA it causes significant reduction in mental abilities that can last for a week, particularly those affecting memory.

SOLVENTS

Solvents are readily available in the form of paints, varnishes, inks, glues, aerosols, and degreasing agents, particularly in the workplace. Different solvents can affect an individual in different ways, but in particular the central nervous system is readily affected by breathing in solvent vapours. When an individual is exposed to solvent vapours in low concentrations they tend to cause nausea, headache, dizziness and light-headedness.

When higher concentrations of vapours are involved they can cause unconsciousness or death. Long term use can affect the brain, kidneys and liver. The loss of coordination and disorientation from the effects on the central nervous system can lead to workers making errors at work that may affect themselves or others. As with other drugs that affect the central nervous system in a similar way workers that rely on high levels of coordination and concentration, like driving and operating equipment are particularly at risk.

Hazards of alcohol and drugs at work

The regular use of alcohol and drugs is becoming increasingly common in some societies. People who start consuming alcohol or drugs usually have a nil or low dependency and do so for recreational reasons. This however can escalate quickly into abuse when larger quantities of alcohol or drugs are consumed more frequently and consumption becomes habitual. Drugs may be prescribed for a medical condition that a worker requires treatment for or of the controlled type whose general use is illegal, such as cocaine and heroin.

The effects of alcohol or drugs can vary dependent upon the individual's state of health and fitness, and resilience to the chemicals. Alcohol and drugs can remain in the body for a considerable time after consumption and its effects still be present several hours after consumption and, therefore, still affecting the individual when at work.

Effects on health and safety include:

- Poor coordination and balance.
- Perception ability reduced.
- Overall state of poor health including fatigue, poor concentration and stress.
- Poor attitude, lack of adherence to rules.
- Increased risk of violence.
- Increased likelihood of transport incidents.

Legislation, such as the Transport and Works Act (TWA) 1992 and the Road Traffic Act (RTA) 1988 (as amended), specifically prohibit being unfit in specified circumstances through the use of alcohol and drugs. The TWA 1992 prohibits conducting safety critical work and RTA 1988 prohibits driving whilst unfit due to alcohol or drugs.

Control measures for the misuse of alcohol and drugs at work

The use of substances like alcohol and drugs is a personal choice over which employers usually have little or no control when it is conducted in the worker's own time. However, employers should establish a policy to deal with the drugs and alcohol should it start to impact on the worker's performance at work.

Control strategies often start with the identification of safety critical work, where the influence of drugs and alcohol would have a significant effect. It is usual that strategies do not presume use or non-use of alcohol/drugs by those that conduct safety critical work, treating them all equally. In a simple approach, all workers that come on to a construction site might be considered to be in safety critical work. All workers would work to the same rules, which could include prohibiting workers being under the influence of alcohol and drugs while at work, offering them opportunities to talk to someone about how this affects them and carrying out random drugs and alcohol tests. When accidents occur, it is common to consider alcohol and drugs as factors.

It may not always be possible to test an injured party to identify if they caused their own accident by being under the influence of alcohol or drugs, but, for example, it may be possible to test a driver of mobile equipment that ran into someone on site.

2.6 - Safe movement of people on construction sites

Hazards to pedestrians

SLIPS, TRIPS AND FALLS ON THE SAME LEVEL

Slips, trips and falls on the same level are the most common causes of major injuries reported to the Health and Safety Executive (HSE) under the Reporting of Injuries, Diseases and Dangerous Occurrences Regulations (RIDDOR) 2013.

Broken bones are the usual result when the following conditions are present:

- Poorly maintained surfaces - for example, holes in roads, site debris, excavations, insecure ducting or grates, poor re-instatements of roads or walk ways.
- Changes in level caused by temporary road surfaces or reinstatements, excavation covers, heavy plant tracks, ramps, slopes, kerbs, chamber lids or steps not clearly marked.
- Slippery surfaces caused by water, oils, fuels, silt, mud, or mixed compounds, for example, mortar, plaster and render.
- Inappropriate footwear.
- Site rules not followed - for example, running or not taking care when walking on site.
- General obstructions in walkways such as trailing cables, pipes and air hoses.
- Poor standards of housekeeping in the workplace - allowing rubbish to accumulate.
- Adverse weather conditions - for example, high winds, rain, and snow.

Figure 2-35: Slips and trips.   *Source: Lincsafe.*

Figure 2-36: Trip hazards.   *Source: Lincsafe.*

FALLS FROM HEIGHT

Situations that increase the likelihood of this hazard are:

- Inadequate access to and from the workplace, for example, a flat roof.
- Fragile roofs, for example, asbestos cement composite roof panels (particularly if obscured by moss or covered by roofing felt).
- Failure to use roof ladders for sloping roof work.
- Inadequate maintenance of access equipment, for example, worn or damaged ladders.
- Inadequate barriers, for example, no hand rails or edge protection.
- Unprotected trenches, for example, no barriers/fences or designated cross over points.

Stairways represent situations where falls from height, related to movement of people, are more likely. Reasons why this is include:

- Poor design of the staircase.
- Not using handrail, for example, when carrying.
- Slippery condition of the stairs, for example, dust or water.
- Poor maintenance of treads and handrails.
- Obstructions on the stairs, for example, tools or materials.
- Too narrow for volume of people using it or the work to be carried out.
- Inadequate standards of lighting.

COLLISIONS WITH MOVING VEHICLES

Situations that increase the likelihood of this hazard are:

- Restricted space to allow for manoeuvring and passing, for example, where there is a high volume movement of mobile plant and materials.
- Undefined routes to segregate site traffic, for example, people with heavy goods vehicles, excavators, dump trucks or rough terrain vehicles.
- Disregard for site rules concerning site vehicles, for example, speed restrictions, competent operators.
- No or insufficient pedestrian warning devices fitted to vehicles and a general lack of maintenance.
- Poor or unstable ground conditions causing pedestrian to unexpectedly move into the path of the vehicle, for example, loose surface, slippery or sloping ground.

STRIKING BY MOVING, FLYING OR FALLING OBJECTS

When working above ground such as on a scaffold, it is easy to concentrate on protecting people from falling. It is also important to consider precautions to prevent people being struck by moving, flying or falling objects.

Situations that increase the likelihood of this hazard are:

- Stacking materials too high and/or in an unstable state.
- Overloading of materials on scaffolds, roofs or mobile elevated work platforms.
- Lack of use of barriers or mesh screens to prevent materials falling from height or being blown off.
- Unstable workplace structure, for example, insufficient number of scaffold tie points or uneven ground.
- Use of damaged or unsuitable pallets.
- Loose materials stacked at too steep an angle, for example, soil.
- Insecure components or workpiece in moving machinery.
- Products of machining processes not contained, for example, swarf or waste material ejected.
- Free dust from work processes or outside areas blown into the eyes of workers.
- Faulty or inappropriate means of lifting or lowering materials to the workplace.
- Insufficient clearance between people and load when materials are being moved by lift trucks and cranes.
- Unstable loads on vehicles, for example, not correctly supported, tied, secured or shrink wrapped.

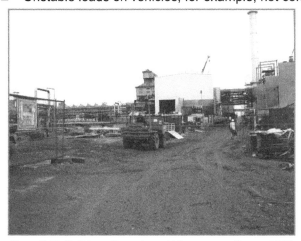

Figure 2-37: Collision with moving vehicles.   *Source: RMS.*

Figure 2-38: Falling materials.   *Source: Lincsafe.*

STRIKING AGAINST FIXED OR STATIONARY OBJECTS

Whilst bumps and bruises are considered by many as 'minor' injuries, they are painful and can be distressing for the sufferer. The following situations could give rise to increased risk.

- Low level or protruding scaffold tubing not correctly protected or highlighted with hi-visibility warning tape.
- Poorly sited machinery and materials.
- Insufficient space for storing tools and materials when working causing poor access and egress.
- Poor lighting.
- Work in enclosed areas.
- Cranes or other lifting devices left with hanging hooks/slings or raised forks.

Treading on sharp items

Sharp objects represent a foot hazard to pedestrians. Construction sites have a large amount of materials moved onto and around them. Sometimes materials, such as sections of trunking (such as may be used to carry electrical wiring) and copper pipe are cut to length and sharp edged off cuts may fall to the ground and be left there. Material can often arrive on site secured by wire binding and when the binding is removed it is often left on the ground, presenting a sharp trip hazard.

In addition, nailed together timber is sometimes used for improvised tasks, and when it is finished with it may be broken apart and discarded, leaving nails protruding. Abandoned broken pallets will present a similar sharps hazard.

HAZARDS TO THE GENERAL PUBLIC CAUSED BY CONSTRUCTION ACTIVITIES

The majority of the general public are attracted to construction activities, including construction activities on public highways, usually out of curiosity for the project underway.

Figure 2-39: Obstructions.   *Source: Lincsafe.*

Figure 2-40: Public highway works.   *Source: RMS.*

The hazards and dangers present at the site are often significantly magnified due to the public's lack of knowledge or awareness of site issues of health and safety. Construction activities on public highways may pose a higher risk due to activities being carried out within the public area resulting in an increased level of public curiosity.

Due to the temporary nature of the majority of construction activities on public highways the working area is often within less secure barrier systems and security is reduced to the vigilance of staff working in the area providing enforcement of site access rules. Items of heavy plant or material deliveries often operate outside the barrier systems that are set up, thus creating increased risk to the public. Works involving scaffold structures on the highway pose an obstruction to members of the public. The risk of impact with scaffold tubes may be a result of not installing ledgers high enough to avoid head injury and the failure to cladding them with foam and high-visibility tape, where pedestrians may be at risk. Unauthorised access to work areas, outside the core working hours, may result in injuries if the site has inadequate access security. Injuries may result from the failure to leave the site safe after work, for example, excavations left unguarded, uncovered and not lit; ladders not removed or secured and mobile equipment not locked or disabled from use.

Control measures for pedestrian hazards

RISK ASSESSMENT

Some or all of the following issues might affect the hazards faced by pedestrians and should be considered when carrying out a risk assessment:

- Weather conditions - particularly snow and ice.
- Lighting - especially at night.
- Surfaces - the presence of holes in the floor or mud.
- Locations where workers need to go that are exposed to surfaces that become covered in environmental grime or slippery growth.

- Drainage.
- Unusually high numbers of people, for example, fitting out and multi-disciplines may be present, for example, plasterers, electricians, plumbers, and carpenters.
- The effectiveness of existing controls - such as barriers.
- Unexpected movements of people - such as shortcuts, entry into restricted areas, emergency evacuation.

SLIP RESISTANT SURFACES

In order to ensure the safe movement of people slip resistant surfaces should be provided:

- On designated walkways.
- On changes of level, such as stairs, steps, ladders, footholds to vehicles.
- On ramps or slopes.
- Where walkways intersect with mobile equipment routes and people may need to stop suddenly.
- In work areas where spills of dry powders are likely.
- Where liquids are decanted or containers filled or stored.
- On access areas used for inspection or maintenance.

Figure 2-41: Slip resistance surface on steps.   *Source: RMS.*

SPILLAGE CONTROL AND DRAINAGE

Many hazards of movement of people relate to slips, some of which are caused by materials and spilt liquids. It is important to establish good spillage control and, where necessary, drainage.

This can involve the use of spill resistant containers for storing substances in, instead of open cans, and provision of drip trays where substances are decanted. Spillage control may involve a change of process in order to avoid spills, for example, using pre-treated materials or enclosed spray containers instead of open pots and brushes.

Spillage controls should include means to control spread and removal of the spill; therefore spill absorbent materials and disposal points need to be provided where they can be readily accessed. This will include storage areas and locations where the substance is used in construction activities. Some construction processes may use large amounts of water that can build-up and present slip hazards.

These should be identified and arrangements made to drain the water to suitable points for collection/containment. This may require the provision of planned drainage on a temporary basis. As some substances may be harmful to the environment drainage may have to be controlled by the use of interceptor pits.

A procedure for spillage response for hazardous liquids should include:

- Raise the alarm and inform emergency services and relevant authorities (for example, Fire Service, Water Company).
- Evacuate all personnel, seal off access from danger area.
- Quickly assess the nature and extent (if possible) of the incident.
- Do not approach the liquid if you do not know what it is.
- Raise first-aid treatment for those who might have been affected.
- Provide bunding or some other form of spillage containment such as sand or special granules to contain the spillage.
- Isolate any ignition sources.
- Keep people away.
- For internal spills with no fire risk, ventilate the area by opening windows and isolate the material by closing doors.
- For external spills, cover drains to prevent the material going into drains and watercourses. Do not wash spillage into drains.
- Issue appropriate personal protective equipment to those involved and competent in carrying out the procedure.
- Ensure safe disposal of the spilled substance and any absorbent material used.

DESIGNATED WALKWAYS

Regulation 17 in Part 4 of CDM 2015, 'Safe places of construction work', requires:

"(1)   There must, so far as is reasonably practicable, be suitable and sufficient safe access to and egress from:

(a) Every construction site to every other place provided for the use of any person whilst at work.

(b) Every place construction work is being carried out to every other place to which workers have access within a construction site.

> (2) A construction site must be, so far as is reasonably practicable, made and kept safe for, and without risks to, the health of a person at work there.
>
> (3) Action must be taken to ensure, so far as is reasonably practicable, that no person uses access to or egress from or gains access to any construction site which does not comply with the requirements of paragraph (1) or (2).
>
> (4) A construction site must, so far as is reasonably practicable, have sufficient working space and be arranged so that it is suitable for any person who is working or who is likely to work there, taking account of any necessary work equipment likely to be used there."

Figure 2-42: Safe places of construction work.   *Source: CDM 2015 Regulation 17.*

The duty to provide a safe place of work relates to such matters as clearly designated and marked walkways that are free of obstruction, the maintenance of floors and staircases, a safe working environment and safe means of access and egress together with the organisation of traffic routes (including pedestrian traffic). The workplace of a construction worker may be some distance from the ground or some distance from the site entrance. Therefore, such things as approach roads, access platforms, and routes through work areas must be considered. Particular thought should also be given to designated walkways for emergency use.

Good site planning should ensure the provision of designated walkways as part of the site layout. For sites that will be used by a significant number of people over a period of time consideration should be made to laying formal concrete walkways for workers, particularly at parts of the site where there will be a high amount of pedestrian traffic - such as entrances, rest facilities and routes through the site.

Effort should be made to segregate pedestrians from site traffic, particularly on approach roads and where vehicles manoeuvre. When arrangements are being made for designated walkways the need for emergency routes and exits need to be considered also. Routes must be clearly indicated and be adequate for the people and hazards present on site.

An important consideration when considering traffic systems for construction sites is the safety interface between pedestrians and traffic.

The routes that people use should be clearly designated and marked via fencing, barriers, crossing points and in the paper format via traffic management plans that are posted in relevant areas and signing in points.

It is a requirement of CDM 2015, Regulation 27, that every construction site be organised in such a way that pedestrians and vehicles can move safely and without risks to health, and that traffic routes are suitable for the persons or vehicles using them, sufficient in number, in suitable positions and of sufficient size.

Figure 2-43: Pedestrian vehicle segregation.   *Source: HSE, HSG150.*

Regulation 17 of CDM 2015 requires that suitable and sufficient access and egress must, so far as is reasonably practicable, be provided. Suitable means such things as designated walkways having no holes or being slippery or uneven.

Measures to control hazards related to designated walkways may include:

- Being kept clean and free from obstructions that may hinder passage.
- Good drainage in wet process areas or wet weather conditions.
- Ramps kept dry and with non-skid surfaces.
- Level, even ground without holes or broken boards.
- Salting/sanding and sweeping of outdoor routes during icy or frosty conditions.
- Steps, corners and fixed obstacles clearly marked.
- Excavations and chambers kept covered when not in use and the edges clearly marked.

FENCING AND GUARDING

Particular attention should be taken to control hazards through the use of fencing and guarding. Fencing of the outer area of a work site, at a suitable distance, will assist in the control of movement of people and vehicles.

In addition, workers and vehicles in the site need protection and in this case inner guarding using barriers may be necessary, for example, to protect the edge of an excavation. It is essential that any fences or guarding (barriers) provided are stable to ensure proper protection is achieved.

Physical barriers should be erected to ensure that there is adequate protection for pedestrians who may be exposed to falls, falling objects and being struck by a moving object such as a vehicle. In addition, where pedestrians may walk into or strike an object, such as a protruding scaffold pole or a ladder the area around the objects should be guarded by means of a barrier.

"Every employer shall, where necessary to prevent injury to any person, take suitable and sufficient steps to prevent, so far as is reasonably practicable, the fall of any material or object."

Figure 2-44: Prevention of falling objects.   *Source: Regulation 10 of Work at Height Regulations (WAH) 2005.*

Figure 2-45: Outer fencing and inner guarding.   *Source: RMS.*

Figure 2-46: Fencing and guarding at height.   *Source: RMS.*

USE OF SIGNS AND PERSONAL PROTECTIVE EQUIPMENT

Signs

Signs must conform to the standards specified in the Health and Safety (Safety Signs and Signals) Regulations (SSSR) 1996. They must be clearly visible and be easily understood. Safety signs should indicate the need to use personal protective equipment, such as hard hats, protective footwear or high-visibility clothing, when entering certain work areas even if people are just visiting or passing quickly through. Some sites may insist on all people who enter the site wearing this equipment, therefore signs are posted at the entrance.

Signs to indicate the presence of a temporary hazard should be used to warn people who might be affected to keep clear of that area. Hazard signs might be used where excavations are present, a change in height occurs or for the demarcation of a hazard area to assist with the provision of diversionary routes, for example, a vehicle unloading area where pedestrians are prohibited.

Figure 2-47: Clothing and footwear.   *Source: RMS.*

Edges of steps, overhead obstructions and cables or pipes laid temporarily across walkways should also be clearly identified with hazard markings.

Personal protective equipment

Head protection

The Personal Protective Equipment at Work Regulations (PPER) 1992 have been amended so that they cover the provision and use of head protection on construction sites.

Employers must ensure that all employees are provided with, and wear, suitable head protection whenever there is a foreseeable risk of injury to the head other than by falling. Head protection provided must fit the person wearing it and be worn properly.

Where employers, self-employed or employees have control over others they must ensure they wear head protection.

Footwear

Risk assessment conducted by the employer or self-employed should consider the possibility of slips, trips and sharp material hazards, and where the decided control of this hazard includes the use of specific footwear this should be arranged. On most construction sites appropriate footwear is important to avoid slips or trips, puncture wounds or injuries from items that are dropped.

If footwear provided has particular properties to deal with hazards related to construction work, such as anti-slip soles or steel mid-plates, this would fall under the requirements of PPER 1992 and the employer should provide them to employees without charge.

High-visibility

On sites where vehicles operate and for street works it is essential that workers are able to be seen, therefore it is essential that high-visibility clothing be used. Though this is not a substitute for the separation of vehicles from people, for the many situations where construction workers work in close proximity to vehicles it will provide valuable assistance in preventing contact.

INFORMATION, INSTRUCTION, TRAINING AND SUPERVISION

The employer, through management, should ensure that rules, policies and procedures are followed and that people do not act irresponsibly. Certain circumstances may require specific information, instruction and training; for example, procedures for use of access equipment or wearing appropriate clothing (for example, head protection or high-visibility jackets).

The Health and Safety at Work etc. Act (HASAWA) 1974 requires employers to provide supervision as necessary. This means that the employer must actively supervise the workplace and the work conducted in it, for example, if high-visibility clothing is required or walkways are to be kept clear this must be supervised. The duty to supervise 'as necessary' requires the supervisor to increase the level of supervision on a needs basis, for example, the higher the risk related to the work or workplace hazard or the more persistent the problem, the greater is the supervision necessary. If a large number of people are to use a route after it has been cleaned the supervisor should make special effort to ensure that it is safe after the cleaning and before use. If an obstruction of a walk route keeps returning, the supervisor will need to put in extra effort to bring it under control.

Maintenance of a safe workplace

CLEANING AND HOUSEKEEPING REQUIREMENTS

Maintenance of a safe workplace may be achieved through the development of a housekeeping procedure. Good housekeeping implies 'a place for everything and everything in its place'. Laid down procedures are necessary for preventing the spread of contamination, reducing the likelihood of accidents resulting in slips, trips, and falls and reducing the chances of unwanted fire caused by careless storage of flammable waste.

Many sites with restricted space work on 'a just in time basis', i.e. materials are delivered as required by the build phase rather than purchased with a view to storage before the build commences.

"(2) A construction site must be, so far as is reasonably practicable, made and kept safe for, and without risks to, the health of a person at work there."

Figure 2-48: Safe place of work.   *Source: CDM 2015 Regulation 17.*

ACCESS AND EGRESS

- Adequate space for easy movement, and safe plant or equipment use.
- No tripping hazards, for example, trailing cables or pipes.
- Guardrails and toe boards where people or materials might fall from floor edges.
- Neat and tidy storage of tools, plant and equipment so that they do not present a hazard to passers-by.
- Identify storage areas.
- Mark areas to be kept clear.
- Pay particular attention to emergency routes.
- Emergency provision, for example, life belts/jackets for work near water.

Figure 2-49: Guard rails and toe boards.   *Source: RMS.*

"(1) There must, so far as is reasonably practicable, be suitable and sufficient safe access to and egress from:

(a) Every construction site to every other place provided for the use of any person whilst at work.

(b) Every place construction work is being carried out to every other place to which workers have access within a construction site."

Figure 2-50: Access and egress.   *Source: CDM 2015 Regulation 17.*

ENVIRONMENTAL CONSIDERATIONS

Heating

"Suitable and sufficient steps must be taken to ensure, so far as is reasonably practicable, that during working hours the temperature at any indoor place of work is reasonable having regard to the purpose to which the place is used."

Figure 2-51: Temperature of indoor places of work.   *Source: CDM 2015 Regulation 34.*

The principal legislation relating to temperature of workplaces on construction sites is Regulation 34 of Part 4 of CDM 2015; this requires a reasonable temperature in any indoor workplace. In addition, the approved code of practice (ACOP) which accompanies the Workplace (Health, Safety and Welfare) Regulations (WHSWR) 1992 states that a temperature of 16°C should be maintained for sedentary (low activity mainly sitting) work, for example, in site offices, and a temperature of 13°C for work that requires physical effort.

Though the WHSWR 1992 do not apply to construction activates the figures used in the WHSWR 1992 ACOP are meaningful minimum standards that should be considered in a construction context. Construction workers can be exposed to a varying degree of conditions and resultant temperatures. The effects of excessive cold or heat can have harmful effects on their health and accidents can result due to fatigue or thermal stress. When work in hot environments is required it will be necessary for workers to be acclimatised gradually. Drinks and the provision of refuge from heat may be necessary to reduce body temperatures.

Where the temperatures cannot be maintained, for example, when working outside, areas should be provided to enable workers who work in cold environments to warm themselves. Practical measures and adequate protection must be provided against adverse conditions, for example, workers may be provided with a sheeted area to work in order to protect them from the rain and wind.

Lighting

Lighting plays an important part in health and safety. Factors to consider include:

- Good general illumination with no glare, especially where there are vehicle movements.
- Regular cleaning and maintenance of lights and windows.
- Local lighting for dangerous processes and to reduce eye strain and fatigue.
- No flickering from fluorescent tubes (it can be dangerous with some rotating machinery).
- Adequate emergency lighting that is regularly tested and maintained.
- Specially constructed fittings for flammable or explosive atmospheres, for example, where paint spraying is carried out.
- Outside areas satisfactorily lit for work and access during hours of darkness - for security as well as safety.
- Light coloured wall finishes improving brightness, or darker colours to reduce glare. For example, arc welding flash.

> *"(1) Each construction site and approach and traffic route to that site must be provided with suitable and sufficient lighting, which must be, so far as is reasonably practicable, by natural light.*
>
> *(2) The colour of any artificial lighting provided must not adversely affect or change the perception of any sign or signal provided for the purposes of health and safety.*
>
> *(3) Suitable and sufficient secondary lighting must be provided in any place where there would be a risk to the health or safety of a person in the event of the failure of primary artificial lighting."*

Figure 2-52: Lighting. *Source: CDM 2015 Regulation 35.*

Care should be taken, in particular where temporary lighting is rigged, to ensure that glare and shadows are minimised. Particular attention should be paid to changes in level, corners and where workers pass between the outside and inside of buildings when darkness occurs.

Noise

Noise can produce a number of types of damage to the ear. Noise levels should be assessed and appropriate controls established. Noise can cause an environmental nuisance to surrounding areas, and can have negative effects on communities in general and wildlife. Controls implemented may include barriers and screens around site boundaries to contain noise produced, the use of equipment that produces lower noise levels and restrictions on operating times to reduce the nuisance dependent upon the sensitivity of the area. ***See also 'Element 9 - Physical and psychological health - hazards and risk control'.***

Dust

General strategies for dust

Dust is a common hazard on construction sites and because it enters the atmosphere can easily escape past site boundaries and then have adverse effects on the environment. The health hazards associated with dusts can vary but usually result in an attack on the respiratory system on humans and other living creatures. Dust can also present significant risk of eye injury and general discomfort.

Other problems are layers of dust settling within the environment, causing damage to vegetation, wildlife habitats and private property. Activities creating dust include external cleaning of buildings, cutting and chasing of masonry and sanding operations.

The area where dust may be created can be watered down to minimise dust transfer into neighbouring premises. Stockpiles of material should be damped down or otherwise suitably treated to prevent the emission of dust from the site.

Stockpiles should be planned and sited to minimise the potential for dust generation. The handling of material should be kept to a minimum and when deposited onto a stockpile it should be from the minimum possible height.

Dust pollution must be minimised during construction activities by:

- The complete screening, if practicable, of the building or structure to be demolished with debris screens or sheets.
- Control of cutting or grinding of materials on the site.
- Mixing of large quantities of concrete or bentonite slurries in enclosed/shielded areas.
- Skips and removal vehicles must be properly covered when leaving the site.
- Materials should be handled in such a way that they do not give rise to excessive dust.
- Watering of rubble chutes shall be undertaken where necessary to prevent dust emission.

It is important to ensure that the area around the site, including the public highway, is regularly and adequately swept to prevent any accumulation of dust and dirt. The use of wheel cleaning facilities and road sweeping equipment may be required.

Any plant used for the crushing of materials must be authorised by a Local Authority under the Environmental Protection Act Part 1 (Prescribed Processes). All work must be carried out in accordance with the conditions of such an authorisation.

Where plant is used to recycle materials, the appropriate licence from the Environment Agency must be obtained. The process operator should notify the Local Authority prior to the movement of the plant on to the site.

Sandblasting

Dust hazards must be minimised during sandblasting by:

- Close-sheeted the work area to reduce dust nuisance from grit. Routine checking is required to ensure that the sheeting remains sound and sealed during sandblasting activities.
- Particular attention should also be given to the working platform to ensure that it is properly sheeted or sealed to contain dust.
- Non-siliceous grit should be used to avoid long term irreversible lung damage from silica dust.
- Proper protection should be provided for any structure painted with lead-based paint.
- In cases where water is used for large scale cleaning and blasting the requirements of the Environment Agency should be followed.
- All grit must be prevented from falling into water courses.

CONTROL MEASURES FOR MAINTENANCE WORK

Some maintenance activities may involve using large pieces of equipment that may compromise access and/or egress routes. It is important that this is taken into consideration during the planning phase of the activity and where required, temporary signage may be displayed.

Barriers may also be required, if there is a need to protect other employees/contractors or the general public from other hazards, for example, noise, fumes, dusts or light (UV from welding).

Temporary lighting will often be required to ensure the work area where maintenance work is to be conducted is sufficiently well lit. This should be installed by a competent electrician, taking into account any risks relating to where it is to be used, such as the potential for flammable or explosive atmospheres.

Competent supervision of the activity is essential to monitor and control any changes to the work, making sure any additional housekeeping is conducted at regular intervals to prevent slips/trips or falls from debris created during the work.

Working on public highways

MEASURES NEEDED TO PROTECT SITE PERSONNEL AND MEMBERS OF THE PUBLIC

It is the responsibility of whoever is in control of construction activities on public highways to sign, light, guard and maintain the works safely. This will require a certain amount of planning to ascertain what procedures need to be implemented and what equipment is required to ensure safety.

Measures to be taken can be found in the document, 'Safety at Street Works and Road Works' that has statutory backing as a code of practice for the New Roads and Street Works Act (NRSWA) 1991 and the Street Works (Northern Ireland) Order.

This code of practice gives guidance on temporary signing, lighting and guarding of construction activities on public highways. Failure to comply with the code of practice may lead to criminal prosecution in addition to any civil proceedings. Further recommendations regarding safety measures at road works can be found in Chapter 8 of the 'Traffic Signs Manual'.

Prior to any works starting, and in order to ensure compliance with current health and safety legislation, an on-site risk assessment must be carried out to ensure a safe system of working is derived in respect of signing, lighting and guarding is in place at all times.

Any signs, lights or guarding equipment must be secured against being blown over or moved out of position by wind or passing traffic. This is usually carried out with the use of sand bags. Hard items should not be used as these can be hazardous if struck by traffic or pedestrians.

Signs should be placed sufficiently far away from the works in order to provide drivers with adequate prior warning of the works. They should not present a hazard to pedestrians if placed in footpaths. Signs should also be of a reflective nature and be monitored to ensure they remain clean and visible.

Any permanent signs or signals that become overridden by the temporary signing, lighting and guarding may require covering over. Consent for this will need to be received from the highway authority.

The placing of signs must consider traffic approaching from all directions, whether it is by two-way traffic or traffic at road junctions.

The working area must also be demarcated with an allowance made for a safety zone (between 0.5m to 1.2m) surrounding the works, and also marked off with cones and lighting as necessary.

The safety zone must never be used as a work area or for storing plant, equipment or vehicles.

When the site is not in use, but signing, lighting and guarding are in place, then arrangements must be in place to ensure regular inspections and any damaged or displaced equipment remedied immediately.

Site vehicles at the works should always operate roof mounted amber beacons if fitted to the vehicles.

Figure 2-53: Public highway works safety measures.   *Source: RMS.*

Hazard warning indicators should not be used at road works as these confuse other road users.

Following completion of a project, all plant, equipment, materials, signs, lights and guarding should be removed immediately.

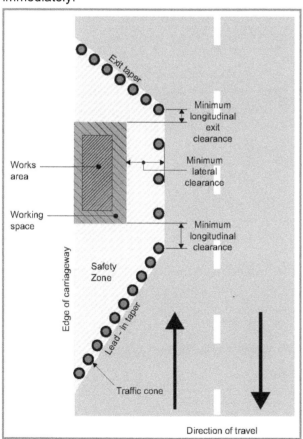

Figure 2-54: Typical work site layout.   *Source: TSO, Chapter 8.*

Figure 2-55: Lane widths and signs.   *Source: TSO, Chapter 8.*

Figure 2-56: Arrangements for work on a footway.   *Source: Department of Transport.*

Exam practice

1. An old factory building has been demolished and the ground cleared ready for the construction of a four story office block. The construction of the office block involves over 40 construction workers employed by the principal contractor being on site at any one time.

    Identify the welfare facilities that should be provided for the 40 construction workers involved in this work. **(8)**

2. A project involves the construction of a concrete structure on a brownfield site, including the installation of drains. **Outline** the topics that site inductions should cover. **(8)**

3. Construction work is about to start on a disused airfield site in a rural location. **Identify** the factors that the principal contractor would have to consider when deciding appropriate first-aid arrangements. **(8)**

4. A disused factory that has stood empty for several years is to be demolished to make way for a new shopping centre.

    (a) **Identify** factors related to the history of the site that should be considered when carrying out the initial site assessment. **(4)**

    (b) **Identify** factors, other than the site history, that should also be considered. **(4)**

Please refer to the back of the assessment section for answers.

Vehicle and plant movement - hazards and risk control

Learning outcomes

On completion of this element, candidates should be able to demonstrate understanding of the content through the application of knowledge to familiar and unfamiliar situations. In particular they should be able to:

3.1 Explain the hazards and control measures for the safe movement of vehicles/plant within a construction environment, including when using public highways as a workplace.

3.2 Outline the factors associated with driving at work that increases the risk of an incident and the control measures to reduce work-related driving risks.

Content

3.1 - Safe movement of vehicles within a construction environment 57
  Hazards from workplace vehicles and plant 57
  Control measures to reduce risks from the movement of vehicles and plant...60
3.2 - Driving at work 66
  Extent of work-related road injuries 66
  Factors that increase risks of a road traffic incident 67
  Managing work-related road safety 68
  Risk assessments for work-related driving 69
  Control measures to reduce work-related driving risks 71
Exam practice 72

Sources of reference

Reference information provided, in particular web links, is correct at time of publication, but may have changed.

A Guide to Workplace Transport Safety, HSG136, HSE Books, http://www.hse.gov.uk/pubns/priced/hsg136.pdf

Driving at work, Managing Work-related Road Safety, INDG382, HSE Books, http://www.hse.gov.uk/pubns/indg382.pdf

Lighting at Work, HSG38, HSE Books, ISBN 978-0-7176-1232-1 http://www.hse.gov.uk/pubns/priced/hsg38.pdf

Safe Use of Vehicles on Construction Sites, HSG144, HSE Books, ISBN 978-0-7176-6291-3 http://www.hse.gov.uk/pubns/priced/hsg144.pdf

Safety at Street Works and Road Works: A Code of Practice 2013, HMSO ISBN 978-0-115531-45-3 http://www.gov.uk/government/publications/safety-at-street-works-and-road-works

Safe use of work equipment, ACOP, L22, HSE Books, ISBN 978-0-717666-19-5 http://www.hse.gov.uk/pubns/priced/l22.pdf

The Traffic Signs Manual (Chapter 8: The Traffic Safety Measures and Signs for Road Works and Temporary Situations) Department for Transport, http://www.gov.uk/government/publications/traffic-signs-manual:

Part 1: Design. The current edition is dated 2009 - ISBN 978-0-115530-51-7 http://www.gov.uk/government/uploads/system/uploads/attachment_data/file/203669/traffic-signs-manual-chapter-08-part-01.pdf

Part 2: Operations. The current edition is dated 2009 - ISBN 978-0-115530-52-4 http://www.gov.uk/government/uploads/system/uploads/attachment_data/file/203670/traffic-signs-manual-chapter-08-part-02.pdf

Workplace Transport Safety - Guidance for Employers, HSG136, HSE Books, ISBN 0-7176-6154-1 www.hse.gov.uk/pubns/priced/hsg136.pdf

Relevant statutory provisions

Construction (Design and Management) Regulations (CDM) 2015

Health and Safety (Safety Signs and Signals) Regulations (SSSR) 1996

New Roads and Street Works Act (NRSWA) 1991

Provision and Use of Work Equipment Regulations (PUWER) 1998 - Part III in particular

Road Traffic Act (RTA) 1988 and 1991

Work at Height Regulations (WAH) 2005 (as amended)

3.1 - Safe movement of vehicles within a construction environment

Hazards from workplace vehicles and plant

There are five main kinds of accidents associated with vehicles; they form a significant part of the accidents that occur in workplace transport operations:

1) Being hit by a moving vehicle.
2) Being hit by a reversing vehicle.
3) Injury caused by a vehicle collapse or overturn.
4) Being hit by a runaway vehicle.
5) Being hit against a vehicle whilst travelling.

HSE state that on average, each year, about 7 workers die as a result of accidents involving vehicles or mobile plant on construction sites and an additional 93 workers are seriously injured. Statistics provided by the Health and Safety Executive (HSE) for 2013/14 show the following injuries occurred as a result of workplace moving vehicle accidents:

		Fatal injury	*Major/specified injury*	*Over 7 day injury*
1	Employee	13	492	999
2	Self-employed	3	27	11
3	Member of the public	6		
	Total	22	519	1010

Figure 3-1: Reported injuries due to workplace moving vehicle accidents 2013/14.   *Source: HSE.*

Statistics provided by the HSE for 2013/14 show that in the construction industry accidents involving being hit by a moving vehicle resulted in 3 fatalities to employees. This represented 23% of all fatal injuries for this type of accident to employees and 7% of the total fatal injuries to employees in construction. In addition, it was reported that in this period in the construction industry there were 55 major/specified injuries to employees involving being hit by a moving vehicle and 53 over 7 day absence injuries. Very few accidents involving movement of vehicles result in minor injury, many result in serious injury, for example, spinal damage, amputation and crush injuries. In addition, accidents relating to the movement of vehicles in the workplace cause damage to plant, equipment, infrastructure and vehicles.

LOSS OF CONTROL

Hazards that can lead to loss of control of workplace vehicles include:

- Slippery surfaces due to contamination of the surface by materials such as oil and dusts, leading to poor traction when steering or braking. Weather conditions such as ice and water can also affect control of the vehicle.
- Potholes and other fracturing of the road surface, along with sudden changes of level, obstructions or kerbs. Contact with these may wrench the steering device from the hand of the driver or suddenly knock the steering in an unintended direction.
- Overloading of vehicles, which can influence their manoeuvrability and braking performance. A counterbalance vehicle, such as a rough terrain fork-lift truck may be overloaded to such an extent that the steering wheels are not sufficiently in contact with the ground. The overloading of vehicles can cause the vehicle to require unusually long braking time or cause it to overbalance on cornering.
- Excessive speed will also affect the performance of brakes and the ability of the driver to manoeuvre the vehicle, leading to loss of control.
- Failure of one of the vehicle controls or critical items can lead to poor or loss of control of the vehicle. A sudden puncture in a pneumatic tyre could make the vehicle difficult to steer. If the conditions of brakes and steering deteriorate, they will perform badly and may cause the vehicle to move suddenly in an unintended direction.

OVERTURNING OF VEHICLES

Various circumstances may cause a construction vehicle to overturn including insecure and unstable loads, manoeuvring with the load elevated, colliding with kerbs and other obstructions, cornering at speed, braking harshly, driving on uneven or soft ground, driving across a slope, under inflated tyres, and mechanical failure.

Causes of vehicles overturning

Possible causes include:

- Overloading/uneven loading of the bucket/forks.
- Driving with load elevated.
- Driving too fast, cornering at excessive speed.
- Sudden braking.
- Hitting obstructions, buildings, structures or other vehicle.

- Driving across slopes.
- Driving too close to the edges of embankments or excavations.
- Driving over debris, holes in the ground, such as drains.
- Mechanical defects that occur because of lack of maintenance.
- Inappropriate or unequal tyre pressures.

COLLISIONS WITH OTHER VEHICLES, PEDESTRIANS AND FIXED OBJECTS

Because construction work involves progressive change by building, altering or demolishing things there is an increased risk of vehicles colliding with other vehicles, pedestrians and fixed objects. A scaffolding or staging may be erected that a driver is not aware of or an excavation appear in a previously available route. The risk of collision is increased by the fact that scaffolds may overhang a vehicle route or power cables may run across the site.

Figure 3-2: Vehicle overturned. *Source: Lincsafe.*

People may unexpectedly appear from a part built or demolished structure or workers intent on the work they are doing may step away from where they are working to collect materials or tools. Other factors are:

- Inadequate lighting.
- Inadequate direction signs.
- Inadequate signs or signals to identify the presence of vehicles.
- Drivers unfamiliar with site.
- Need to reverse.
- Poor visibility, for example, sharp bends, mirror/windscreen misted up.
- Poor identification of fixed objects, for example, scaffold, overhead pipes, doorways, storage materials, corners of buildings/structures.
- Lack of separation of pedestrians and vehicles.
- Lack of safe crossing points on roads and vehicle routes.
- Lack of separate entrance/exit for vehicles and pedestrians.
- Pedestrians suddenly stepping from an exit/entrance into a vehicle's path.
- Poor maintenance of vehicles, for example, tyres or brakes.
- Excessive speed of vehicles.
- Lack of vehicle management, for example, use of traffic control, 'banksman'.
- Environmental conditions, for example, poor lighting, rain, snow or ice.

Figure 3-3: Potential collision with fixed objects. *Source: RMS.*

NON-MOVEMENT RELATED HAZARDS

Loading and un-loading

There is a risk of material falling on a vehicle driver where the vehicle is used to provide materials at a height or to remove materials from delivery vehicles. In addition, when vehicles are being unloaded by hand there is a possibility that the load has shifted and become unstable during transportation. This could mean that the load collapses onto the person unloading when a quantity of it is removed and this could lead to serious injury or death. Some loading and unloading tasks cause people to work at height, which creates the risk that people may fall from a vehicle. This may be more likely if the work is carried out in poor weather conditions, the load or vehicle surface is slippery or where there is no organised means of access to the vehicle. In addition, people loading or unloading may lose awareness of the edge of the load/vehicle when they are paying particular attention to the task they are doing.

> *"No person shall remain, or be required or permitted to remain, on any vehicle during the loading or unloading of any loose material unless a safe place of work is provided and maintained for such person."*

Figure 3-4: Vehicles - loading and unloading. *Source: CDM 2015 Regulation 28(5).*

Securing loads

The hazards relating to securing loads are work at height, slippery surfaces, weather conditions, and manual handling. There is the additional hazard of a badly secured load shifting at some stage in the transport operation. Tasks to secure loads may cause the person to go onto the vehicle in order to fix straps and tighten devices to hold the load. This will present them with the risk of falling from the vehicle or from the load onto the vehicle. The vehicle may be contaminated with dirt, dust, oil or materials spilt from previous loads, which presents a risk of slipping. Load securing equipment will usually have to be placed in position and tightened by the person securing the load; this could expose them to manual handling hazards related to moving things and over-exertion.

Sheeting

Sheeting is the covering of a load with a sheet or net to secure it; to prevent parts of it being disrupted by wind/air movement while being transported and to protect it from the weather. If this is not a mechanised process, it involves the manually unrolling of the sheet over the load and the sides of the vehicle, so that the hazards of height, slips and manual handling exist. Though it may be possible to sheet some vehicles from the ground it is not unusual for the person sheeting to have to gain access to the top of the vehicle and sometimes the top of the load. As with securing the load, this can present risks of falling or slipping. As sheets are designed to be robust they are also quite heavy and it takes a considerable amount of exertion to pull sheets over the load, leading to risk of strains and back injury.

Coupling

The task of coupling a tractor unit to a trailer requires that the tractor unit is reversed towards the front trailer. The '5th wheel' is the connection between the tractor and the trailer. If the 5th wheel jaws are not located properly, this can lead to unexpected movement of the trailer.

Though most accidents during coupling involve drivers or other people being run over, hit or crushed by moving vehicles, a number of non-movement based hazards exist. There is a significant risk of falling during coupling, especially in the dark, as the person coupling may be less able to see slippery surfaces, obstructions or steps.

A particular hazard is that the vehicle trailer could move or overturn. Though the ground may look flat it may be sufficient to cause the trailer to become unstable or move under its own weight.

In addition, during uncoupling the trailer goes from being supported to bearing its own weight, and this can cause the trailer to sink into the ground and overturn.

Figure 3-5: Coupling.   *Source: www.trucknetuk.com.*

Vehicle maintenance work

There are hidden hazards and associated risks with maintenance work from open pits, access gantries, oils and greases and fitting of replacement parts. One of the particular hazards associated with large vehicle maintenance work is the hazard of being crushed by a falling cab that was tilted to gain access to parts of the vehicle for maintenance. Similar hazards exist at the rear of the vehicle where the vehicle has a tipping facility.

Hydraulic ramps and hoists can create crush hazards as they are lowered to the ground or if there is a sudden failure of the hydraulic or mechanical system.

There is an additional hazard that a vehicle or equipment could fall from a lift system, particularly if not located correctly or if the lift system is not raised uniformly. There are many manual handling and posture hazards associated with vehicle maintenance work, from leaning over to reach parts to the movement of large vehicle wheels. The presence of flammable liquids, in the form of fuels, oils and paints present a hazard of fire and explosion.

Electrical hazards are present as portable electric equipment may be used, some operating at mains (230 volt) voltage. Where pneumatic equipment is used it presents the hazard of noise, flying particles and possible injection of air into the body. It may be necessary to work on part of the vehicle at height, for example, to repair the top of a cement transporting and pumping vehicle. This work can present falling hazards that can lead to major injury or death. The hazards are accentuated when working on vehicles that come straight from use and are wet and slippery.

Figure 3-6: Tilted LGV cab and prop. *Source: HSE.*

Control measures to reduce risks from the movement of vehicles and plant

The employer, through its managers, needs to carry out an assessment of risk with regard to the safe movement of vehicles and their loads as part of the overall health and safety policy. This includes the use of vehicles such as dumper trucks, lift trucks, and those used for delivery. Consideration should be given to the following. Design features of the vehicle intended to minimise the consequences of an overturn include rollover protection and seat belts. In addition, features designed to prevent overturning include increasing the width of the wheelbase and lowering the position of the centre of gravity of the vehicles.

SUITABILITY AND SUFFICIENCY OF TRAFFIC ROUTES

The provision and use of safe traffic routes on site for pedestrians and vehicles is an essential component of managing access and egress to the site. Such factors to consider include the size of vehicles, including height, axel weight and the route to be taken should be considered before entry to the site is permitted. Where possible traffic routes should limit or eliminate the need for vehicles to reverse; establishing a one-way system for the site would assist with this. In order for traffic routes to remain suitable for use they need to be maintained so that they are free of obstructions and sufficient clearance for vehicles is available. Traffic routes should be wide enough to allow manoeuvrability and passing. The proximity of pedestrians and other site traffic and their flow through the site is another important consideration when developing a site management plan.

> *(1) A construction site must be organised in such a way that, so far as is reasonably practicable, pedestrians and vehicles can move without risks to health.*
>
> *(2) Traffic routes must be suitable for the persons or vehicles using them, sufficient in number, in suitable positions and of sufficient size.*

Figure 3-7: Traffic routes. *Source: CDM 2015 Regulation 27.*

In order to comply with Regulation 27 (3) of CDM 2015 and to establish good practice for traffic routes it is necessary to ensure that:

> *"(a) Pedestrians or vehicles may use it without causing danger to the health or safety of persons near it.*
>
> *(b) Any door or gate for pedestrians which leads onto a traffic route is sufficiently separated from that traffic route to enable pedestrians to see any approaching vehicle or plant from a place of safety.*
>
> *(c) There is sufficient separation between vehicles and pedestrians to ensure safety or, where this is not reasonably practicable:*
>
> > *(i) Other means for the protection of pedestrians are provided.*
> >
> > *(ii) Effective arrangements are used for warning any person liable to be crushed or trapped by any vehicle of its approach.*
>
> *(d) Any loading bay has at least one exit point for the exclusive use of pedestrians.*
>
> *(e) Where it is unsafe for pedestrians to use a gate intended primarily for vehicles, at least one door for pedestrians is provided in the immediate vicinity of the gate, is clearly marked and is kept free from obstruction."*

Figure 3-8: Traffic routes. *Source: CDM 2015 Regulation 27(3).*

MANAGEMENT OF VEHICLE MOVEMENTS

Many construction sites are complex in nature and require the careful management of vehicles in order to ensure that they are brought onto, move around and leave the site safely.

This can start at the project planning stage as it can cause many problems when a vehicle is brought onto site too early when the site is at an earlier phase and is not ready for it.

Conversely, if it is brought in part way through the project it may be difficult to get it to where it is needed and it may be better to get it to site early.

Where materials are brought to site it may be necessary to manage deliveries so that too many vehicles do not arrive at the site at the same time causing them to back up into the public highway.

Site security arrangements play a significant part in the management of vehicles on site and will assist with controlling vehicles so that they are routed correctly and safely.

Figure 3-9: Site entrance to construction site. *Source: HSE, HSG150.*

It is not uncommon for vehicles to be sent to a site that are too big or too heavy to access the roadways. Site security staff should be trained to identify these to prevent them accessing the site and causing harm. Major vehicle movements, such as a heavy crane may be timed so that the minimum of workers are on site and that it can be conducted easily in a controlled manner.

Banksmen or signallers as they are also known are used to control vehicle movements i.e. reversing and lifting operations. Due to the amount of serious or fatal injuries every year, it is important that they are fully trained and competent. A safe system of work should be adopted with all drivers using standard signals that are easily understood. Drivers should know to stop their vehicle immediately if the banksman disappears from sight. The standard signals are given in the Health and Safety (Safety Signs and Signals) Regulations (SSSR) 1996.

Additional points to consider include:

- Drivers of vehicles that are visiting the premises should be made aware of any local rules and conditions.
- Traffic routes should be clearly marked and signed. These should incorporate speed limits, one-way systems, priorities and other factors normal to public roads.
- Speed limits of 10 or 15 mph are usually considered appropriate, although 5 mph may be necessary in certain situations. It is important to have speed limits that are practicable and effective. Speed limit signs should be posted and traffic slowing measures, such as speed bumps and ramps, may be necessary in certain situations. Monitoring speed limit compliance is necessary, along with some kind of action against persistent offenders.
- Accidents can be caused where vehicles are unsafely parked as they can be an obstruction and restrict visibility. There should be clear entrance and exit routes in parking areas and designated parking areas to allow the loading and sheeting of outgoing transport to be checked safely before leaving the site.
- As far as is practicable pedestrians should be kept clear of vehicle operating areas and/or a notice displayed warning pedestrians that they are entering an operating area.
- Whenever possible separate routes should be provided for pedestrians with designated crossing places and suitable physical barriers at recognised danger spots.
- Clear direction signs and marking of storage areas and buildings should be provided to avoid unnecessary movement, such as reversing.
- Where reversing is required banksmen, also known as signallers, should be used to control vehicle movements.

> *"(4) Each traffic route must be:*
>
> *(a) Indicated by suitable signs where necessary for reasons of health or safety.*
>
> *(b) Regularly checked.*
>
> *(c) Properly maintained.*
>
> *(5) No vehicle is to be driven on a traffic route unless, so far as is reasonably practicable, that traffic route is free from obstruction and permits sufficient clearance."*

Figure 3-10: Traffic routes, supplementary requirements.   *Source: CDM 2015 Regulation 27.*

ENVIRONMENTAL CONSIDERATIONS

Where vehicles operate, environmental conditions such as lighting and adverse weather will make a significant impact on their safe operation by affecting **visibility**. Where reasonably practicable a suitable standard of lighting must be maintained so that operators of vehicles can see to operate their vehicle and can be seen by others. When establishing suitable lighting, it is important to avoid areas of glare or shadow that could mask the presence of a person or vehicle.

Similarly, if vehicles travel from within buildings to the outside it is important that the light level is maintained at a roughly even level in order to give the driver's eyes time to adjust to the change in light. Consideration should be given to adequate lighting on routes taken by vehicles, in loading/unloading/operating areas and where there is a change in level or camber to the road surface. Fixed structure hazards, such as overhead obstructions, edges, and pits should be made as visible as possible with additional lighting and/or reflective strips. If reasonably practicable barriers should be installed to make the hazard more visible and guide the vehicle operator around the hazard at a safe distance.

Roads, gangways and aisles should have sufficient width and overhead clearance for the largest vehicle. Attention should be paid to areas where they might meet other traffic, for example, the entrance to the site. If ramps (speed bumps) are used, a by-pass for trolleys and shallow draft vehicles should be provided. A one-way traffic system should be considered to reduce the risk of collision.

Gradients and changes in ground level, such as ramps and potholes, represent a specific hazard to plant and vehicle operation. Vehicles have a limit of stability dependent on loading and their wheelbase. These conditions could put them at risk of overturning or cause damage to articulated vehicle couplings. Any gradient in a vehicle operating area should be kept as gentle as possible.

Where **changes in level** are at an edge that a vehicle might approach, and there is risk of falling, it must be provided with a robust barrier or similar means to demarcate the edge. Particular care must be taken at points where loading and unloading are conducted.

> *"Suitable and sufficient measures must be taken to prevent any vehicle from falling into any excavation or pit, or into water, or overrunning the edge of any embankment or earthwork."*

Figure 3-11: Vehicles - falling into excavations etc.   *Source: CDM 2015 Regulation 28(6).*

In some circumstances, materials from construction process and mud may contaminate the **surface condition** of the road making it difficult for vehicles to brake effectively. It is important to have a programme that anticipates this with regular cleaning or scarifying of the surface as well as means of dealing with spills. The road surface should be in good condition, free from potholes and obstructions.

Excessive ambient noise levels can mask the sound of vehicles working in the area; therefore additional visual warning should be used, for example, flashing lights. Sufficient and suitable parking areas should be provided away from the main work area and located where the risk of unauthorised use of the work vehicles will be reduced.

MAINTENANCE OF VEHICLES

All vehicles should be well maintained and 'roadworthy' with a formal system of checks and maintenance in place. All construction site vehicles should be maintained to the same good standard as those used on public roads for such critical items as tyres and brakes.

Vehicle maintenance should be planned for at regular intervals and vehicles taken out of use if critical items are not at an acceptable standard. In addition, it is important to conduct a pre-use check of the vehicle. This is usually carried out by the driver as part of their taking the vehicle over for a period of use, such as a work shift or day.

This would identify the condition of critical items and provide a formal system to identify and consider problems that may affect the safety of the vehicle.

Critical items would typically include the following health and safety items:

- Braking systems.
- Cab protection devices, for example, roll over protection structures (ROPS).
- Firefighting equipment.
- Lights and indicators.
- Operational controls.
- Restraint systems, for example, seat belts.
- Safety devices, such as interlocks, guards and panels.
- Steering.
- Tyres, including condition and pressures.
- Vision aids, for example, convex mirrors, CCTV.
- Warning devices and signals.
- Windscreen condition, washers and wipers.

If there is no nominated driver and the vehicle is for general use someone should be nominated to make these checks. A record book or card would usually be used to record the checks and the findings.

DRIVER PROTECTION AND RESTRAINT SYSTEMS

Roll over and restraint systems

In many work vehicle accidents the driver is injured because the vehicle does not offer protection when it rolls over or it does not restrain the driver to prevent them falling out of the vehicle and being injured by the fall or the vehicle falling on them. Vehicles such as dumper trucks, road rollers and rough terrain fork-lift trucks (RTFLT) are examples of equipment that may present this risk. The Provision and Use of Work Equipment Regulations (PUWER) 1998, Part 3, Regulation 26, recognises the importance of this and now set out requirements for equipment to be adapted, where practicable, to provide this protection.

New equipment must now be provided with roll over protection and restraint systems, for example, roll bars and seat/lap belts, where relevant.

For some vehicles, the provision of a cab around the driver will provide protection in the event of a roll over and additional weather, dust and falling materials protection.

Figure 3-12: Roll bar and seat restraint.   *Source: RMS.*   Figure 3-13: Driver protection.   *Source: RMS.*

Protection from falling materials

There is a risk of material falling on a vehicle driver in situations where the vehicle is used to provide materials at a height or to remove materials from delivery vehicles. It is important that suitable protection of the driver be provided by the structure of the vehicle. Protection should also be provided where vehicles work in close proximity to areas where there is a risk from falling materials. This may be by the provision of a frame and mesh above the driver or by the provision of a totally enclosing cab. Safety helmets alone are unlikely to provide sufficient protection, but may be a useful addition where a mesh structure is provided.

Weather conditions

The protection of vehicle drivers from the weather is an important consideration. Protection may be achieved by the provision of a totally enclosing cab around the driver. This will provide protection from wind, rain and cold. However, it can lead to the driver being subject to increased temperatures as the glass in the cab causes heat to be retained. This can lead to discomfort and risk of thermal stress in summer months. The provision of a cab to protect a driver from weather has to be balanced with needs for visibility. There is a risk that when using a cab visibility may be impaired by the structure, windows may mist up or ice form on the window surfaces. The absence of a cab will improve visibility, but expose the driver to weather conditions.

SEGREGATING PEDESTRIANS AND VEHICLES

Means of segregation

"Every workplace shall be organised in such a way that pedestrians and vehicles can circulate in a safe manner."

Figure 3-14: Means of segregation. *Source: Regulation 17(1) of WHSWR 1992.*

"Every construction site shall be organised in such a way that, so far as is reasonably practicable, pedestrians and vehicles can move safely and without risks to health."

"Traffic routes shall be suitable for the persons or vehicles using them, sufficient in number, in suitable positions and of sufficient size."

Figure 3-15: Traffic routes. *Source: CDM 2015 Regulation 27.*

Clearly defined and marked routes should be provided on construction sites for pedestrians and vehicles. These should be provided for access and egress points to work areas, car parks, and vehicle delivery routes. Safe crossing places should be provided where pedestrians have to cross main traffic routes. In buildings where vehicles operate, separate doors and walkways should be provided for pedestrians to get from building to building.

Meshed handrails can be used to channel people into the pedestrian route. Where it is not possible to have a pedestrian route entirely separate from vehicle movement, because of building and structure design, then a raised pedestrian walkway could be considered to help in segregation. Where segregation is by distance or delineation, any traffic route that is used by both pedestrians and vehicles should be wide enough to enable any vehicle likely to use the route to pass pedestrians safely.

Separate gates/doorways should be provided for vehicle entry and blind spots (where vision of the vehicle driver or pedestrian is restricted) should be dealt with by the careful positioning of mirrors on walls, plant, structures or storage materials.

Figure 3-16: Pedestrian crossing point. *Source: HSE, HSG150.*

Figure 3-17: Segregating pedestrians and vehicles. *Source: RMS.*

Measures to be taken when segregation is not practicable

Where pedestrians and vehicle routes cross, appropriate crossing points should be provided and used. Where necessary, barriers or rails should be provided to prevent pedestrians crossing at particularly dangerous points and to guide them to designated crossing places. At crossing places where volumes of traffic are particularly heavy, the provision of suitable bridges or subways should be considered. At crossing points there should be adequate visibility and open space for the pedestrian where the pedestrian route joins the vehicle route.

Where segregation is not practicable and vehicles share the same workplace as pedestrians it is important to mark the work areas as being separate from vehicle routes to warn drivers to adjust their approach and be more aware of pedestrians. This can be carried out by removable barriers or tape to indicate when the vehicle is being given access to a work area.

Figure 3-18: No segregation.   *Source: RMS.*   Figure 3-19: Control of vehicle movement.   *Source: RMS.*

Audible and visual warnings of the presence of the vehicle would also assist. Where vehicles are dominant, but pedestrians need to access the area in which they are working, similar means of warning may be used, but for the opposite reason.

The reversing of large vehicles that have a restricted view can be a particularly high risk to pedestrians sharing the same workplace and should be controlled by the use of a banksman to guide them.

Where segregation is not practicable the use of high-visibility personal protective equipment by pedestrians increases the ability of the driver to see the pedestrian. High-visibility clothing is mandatory on the majority of construction sites. Where it is unavoidable that pedestrians will come into proximity with vehicles, they should be reminded of the hazards by briefings, site induction and signs, so they are aware at all times.

PROTECTIVE MEASURES FOR PEOPLE AND STRUCTURES

It is important to anticipate that drivers of vehicles might misjudge a situation and collide with structures whilst operating vehicles. For this reason, people and vulnerable structures should be provided with barriers that continuously surround them; alternatively posts can be provided at key positions. Particular care should be taken of structures at a height as they may be less obvious to drivers, such as a scaffold spanning a traffic route, pipe bridges, roof trusses or door lintels.

Tall vehicles or those that have tipping mechanisms that can raise their effective height could damage these structures. Though it may not always be possible to protect all structures, such as a doorway, it is important to apply **markings** to make them more visible. In addition, **signs** warning of overhead structures or the presence of vehicles in the area will help increase awareness and avoid collisions. There is a need to alert people to the hazard when working in or near a vehicle operating area. Signs might help and these can be supplemented by **visual and audible warning systems** that confirm the presence of the vehicle. These may be operated by the driver, such as a horn on a dumper truck or automatically, such as an audible reversing signal on a large road vehicle. Visibility can be improved by mounting mirrors at strategic points. Consideration should be given to the provision of high-visibility clothing to pedestrians working within areas where vehicles operate.

Barriers

Moving vehicles, and in particular large plant, have high impact energy when they are in contact with structures or people. It is essential that vehicles be separated from pedestrians and vulnerable structures. Because of the high energy involved the barrier used must reflect the type of vehicle in contact with it. If it is only pedestrians that might contact it a simple portable barrier may be adequate, but if it is heavy plant robust barriers including concrete structures may need to be considered. It is important to identify vulnerable locations that warrant protection, for example, steelwork, formwork, falsework and scaffolds. Barriers are also used to prevent vehicles falling into trenches and other areas below ground where people may be working.

Markings

Any structure that represents a height or width restriction should be readily identified for pedestrians and vehicle drivers. This will include low beams or doorways, pipe bridges, protruding scaffolds and edges where a risk of falling exists. These markings may be by means of attaching hazard tape, painting the structure to highlight the hazard or markings on barriers.

Signs

Signs should be used to provide information, such as height restrictions, and to warn of hazards on site. Signs may be used to direct vehicles around workers at a safe distance.

Figure 3-20: Fencing and barriers at a distance.   *Source: RMS.*

Figure 3-21: Visual warning on a dumper truck.   *Source: RMS.*

Warnings of vehicle approach and reversing

Warnings may be audible or visual or a combination of each. They are used to warn that the vehicle is operating in the area, such as a flashing light on the top of a dumper truck or to warn of a specific movement, such as an audible warning that a large vehicle is reversing.

These are designed to alert people in the area in order that they can place themselves in a position of safety. They do not provide the driver with authority to reverse the vehicle or to proceed in a work area without caution.

"(1) Suitable and sufficient steps must be taken to prevent or control the unintended movement of any vehicle.

(2) Where a person may be endangered by the movement of a vehicle, suitable and sufficient steps to give warning to any person who is liable to be at risk from the movement of the vehicle must be taken by either or both:

    (a) The driver or operator of the vehicle.

    (b) Where another person is directing the driver or operator because, due to the nature of the vehicle or task, the driver or operator does not have full visibility, the person providing directions.

(3) A vehicle being used for the purposes of construction work must, when being driven, operated or towed, be:

    (a) Driven, operated or towed in such a manner as is safe in the circumstances.

    (b) Loaded in such a way that it can be driven, operated or towed safely.

(4) A person must not ride, or be required or permitted to ride, on any vehicle being used for the purposes of construction work otherwise than in a safe place in that vehicle provided for that purpose."

Figure 3-22: Vehicles - safe operation and rules.   *Source: CDM 2015 Regulation 28.*

SITE RULES

It is important to establish clear and well understood site rules regarding vehicle operations. These may have to be communicated to drivers by security staff at the time they visit the site. The rules often stipulate where the driver should be whilst vehicles are being loaded, where the keys to the vehicle should be, obligations not to reverse without permission and what access they have to areas of the site for such things as refreshment. Pedestrians should also know what the site rules are in order to keep themselves safe.

Site rules for pedestrians might include such things as using pedestrian exits/entrances or crossing points, not entering hazardous areas or the need to wear personal protective equipment in hazardous areas, and not walking behind a reversing vehicle.

Where construction sites are made up of or join a highway, such as carriageway repairs on a motorway, it is important to identify who has priority - the vehicle or the worker. Site rules may clarify that once the site boundary is crossed the worker has priority - this has to be clear. The site rules may be reinforced by the provision of additional signs to clarify a speed limit and the nature of the priority of workers.

SELECTION AND TRAINING OF DRIVERS

Only competent persons should be permitted to operate plant or vehicles after they have been selected, trained and authorised to do so, or are undergoing properly organised formal training under competent supervision.

Selection

The safe usage of plant and vehicles calls for a reasonable degree of both physical and mental fitness. The selection procedure should be devised to identify people who have been shown to be reliable and mature enough to perform their work responsibly and carefully. To avoid wasteful training for workers who lack coordination and ability to learn, selection tests should be used. Consideration must be given to any legal age restrictions that apply to vehicles that operate on the public road. A similar approach may be adopted for similar vehicles used on site though the law is not specific on age limitations in such cases. Potential operators should be medically examined prior to employment/training in order to assess the individual's physical ability to cope with this type of work.

They should also be examined every five years in middle age and after sickness or accident. Points to be considered are:

- General - normal agility, having full movement of trunk, neck and limbs.
- Vision - good eyesight in both eyes or corrected by spectacles, is important, as operators are required to have good judgement of space and distance.
- Hearing - the ability to hear instructions and warning signals with each ear is important.

Training

It is essential that immediate supervisors receive training in the safe operation of plant and vehicles and that senior management appreciates the risks resulting from the interaction of vehicles and the workplace. For the operator/driver, safety must constitute an integral part of the skill training programme and not be treated as a separate subject. The operator/driver should be trained to a level consistent with efficient operation and care for the safety of themselves and other persons.

On completion of training they should be issued with a company authority to drive and a record of all basic training, refresher training and tests maintained in the individual's personal documents file. Certification of training by other organisations must be checked.

MANAGEMENT SYSTEMS FOR ASSURING DRIVER COMPETENCE

The trained operator/driver

It should not be assumed that employees who join as trained operators/drivers have received adequate training to operate safely in their new company. The management must ensure that they have the basic skills and receive training in company methods (local practices) and procedures for the type of work they are to undertake. They should be examined and tested before issue of a company driving authority. A copy of the site rules and any internal codes of practice must be given to all internal drivers and to external visitors such as delivery drivers preferably before they arrive at the site.

Testing

On completion of training, the operator/driver should be examined and tested to ensure that they have achieved the required standard. It is recommended that at set intervals or when there is indication of the operator/driver not working to required standards, or following an accident, formal check tests be introduced.

Refresher training

If high standards are to be maintained, periodic refresher training and testing should be considered. A vigorous management policy covering operator training, plant maintenance and sound systems of work, supported by good supervision will reduce personal injury and damage to equipment and materials. This in turn will lead to better vehicle utilisation and increased materials handling efficiency.

Operator/driver identification

Many organisations operate local codes of practice and take great care to confirm the authority they have given to operators/drivers by the provision of a licence for that vehicle and sometimes a visible badge to confirm this.

Access to vehicles should be supervised and authority checked carefully to confirm that the actual class of vehicle is within the authority given. This is important with such things as rough terrain lift trucks that operate differently to a standard counterbalance truck. Where applicable, it is important to be able to confirm that the operator/driver has a suitable licence that allows them to take the plant/vehicle on the public highway.

It is essential that access to keys for vehicles is restricted to those that are competent to operate/drive them; this is not just a practical point but enables compliance with PUWER 1998.

3.2 - Driving at work

Extent of work-related road injuries

The true cost of accidents to any organisation is nearly always higher than just the costs of repairs and insurance claims. This can include personal costs such as ill-health, time in hospital, stress on family members and possible penalty points being imposed on the driver's licences following an incident. There is also the potential for the driver to lose their licence.

Therefore the benefits of managing driving activities through the introduction of policies, risk assessments and developing safe systems for work-related driving is essential. This will ensure compliance with the Health and Safety at Work etc. Act (HASAWA) 1974 and the Management of Health and Safety at Work Regulations (MHSWR) 1999.

The Health and Safety Executive (HSE) provide guidance to assist management in managing driving risk, in the form of the document INDG382 'Driving at work - Managing work-related road safety'. The HSE estimates that up to a third of all road traffic accidents involved somebody who was at work at the time. This may account for over 20 fatalities and 250 serious injuries per week.

> "It has been estimated that between 800 and 1,000 road deaths a year are in some way work-related. Many bosses have ignored this problem in the past, but the Health and Safety Executive has now made it clear that employers have duties under health and safety law to manage the risks faced by their workers on the road."

Figure 3-23: Size of the road risk problem.   Source: RoSPA.

> For the majority of people, the most dangerous thing they do while at work is drive on the public highway.

Figure 3-24: Road risk.   Source: HSE.

Factors that increase risks of a road traffic incident

DISTANCE

Road conditions have improved over the years, which have allowed greater travel distances in shorter periods of time. However the fatigue encountered by drivers often increases due to other drivers' poor performance.

This can be associated with poor or inappropriate training or monitoring of the driver's competence. Large goods vehicle (LGV) drivers' travel distances are regulated by limitations on driving hours. However, there are no similar limits on drivers of smaller vehicles and private cars. When assessing risk of any kind, an important consideration is the frequency and duration of exposure to hazards. It is logical then that the greater the distance of the journey (i.e. the duration of exposure to the hazard) the greater the risk. It is possible that scheduling of routes may extend or reduce the distance that has to be travelled and therefore affect the level of risk significantly.

DRIVING HOURS

If driving hours related to construction activities are excessive the driver is likely to become fatigued, their attention and reaction levels will fall and they are at increased risk of making errors. The hours may be excessive because the driver has been driving too long without a break, their cumulative hours in a day have become too much or their rest period between days has become too little. For some drivers the driving hours is in addition to other work hours, for example, for someone travelling to a meeting these cumulative hours can have a significant effect on fatigue.

Most drivers of commercial vehicles will be fitted with tachometers, which record the time spent driving. These hours are limited by legislation; however, most company car drivers do not have this specific monitoring imposed on them. Therefore, safe systems of work and appropriate training should be given to all drivers concerning the hazards and associated risks with excessive hours. It is important that cumulative hours are monitored and controlled and that breaks are taken at intervals on longer journeys.

The Highway Code recommends that drivers should take a 15 minute break every two hours. The responsibility for monitoring hours and taking breaks is a shared responsibility of both the driver and the employer. Driving hours of goods vehicles over 3.5 tonnes and some passenger vehicles are regulated by European Community rules.

These rules set limits on driver's hours:

- Daily driving limit: 9 hours.
- Maximum driving limit: 4 ½ hours.
- Daily rest period: 11 hours.
- Weekly driving limit: 56 hours.
- Fortnightly driving limit: 90 hours.
- Weekly rest period: 45 consecutive hours.

WORK SCHEDULES

Work schedules that are badly organised can put increased pressure on drivers to be in a place by a given time. This can lead to them being tempted to increase speed and take abrupt action to change lanes to improve their progress. This risky action can lead to higher risk of collision and reduced stopping distances.

Work schedules should take account of periods when drivers are most likely to feel sleepy. The high risk times are 2am to 6am and 2pm to 4pm. Employers should provide drivers with the means to stop and take a break if they feel sleepy, without the fear of recrimination. Where possible, schedules should be organised so that breaks can naturally and easily be taken, with agreed break points if travel is going as planned or if not. Driving to and from the place of employment does not form part of the working day, but may be an accident causation factor if travelling home follows a long working day.

STRESS DUE TO TRAFFIC

Nearly one in three UK drivers report feeling stressed whilst behind the wheel. Driving-related stress is likely to be experienced when the demands of the road/traffic environment exceed the driver's ability to cope with or control that environment. Sometimes driving stress can show itself as a 'road rage'. That is an irrational human mechanism that is activated to protect the sufferer from what they perceive to be actual or potential danger. A person may often resort to irrational behaviour in order to avoid certain situations or events.

Others may perceive the circumstances which aggravate the 'road rage' as being either insignificant or trivial, but to the individual concerned they are 'very real' and 'very relevant'.

WEATHER CONDITIONS

Weather conditions have a significant impact on the risks of driving. Sudden rainfall or snow and fog can lead to poor visibility and sudden breaking. Snow and surface water conditions can increase stopping distances.

Even good weather can have a negative effect as glare from the sun can limit visibility. This is particularly the case in early morning or evening and is most significant during the winter when the sun is lower in the sky for longer.

Managing work-related road safety

POLICY

A road safety policy should be incorporated into the health and safety policy. Whether employers provide vehicles or expect employees to drive their own for work purposes, all employers should have a policy to address the issues.

As part of any driving at work policy, employers should include:

- A requirement that the employee must maintain their vehicle in a roadworthy condition if they are to use their own vehicle for work.
- A requirement that if the vehicle is over three years old, it has a valid MOT certificate.
- A requirement that the employee has a current driving licence.
- A requirement that the employee has appropriate insurance (the employee should present copies of certificates annually for inspection).
- A requirement that the employee informs their line manager of any changes in circumstances such as penalty points, changes in insurer or vehicle used or use of any prescription medication or changes to health that affect their ability to drive safely.
- Assessment of risks.
- The management strategy to plan, organise, control, monitor and review work-related road risk.
- Driver training and competence.
- Taking breaks.
- Breakdown of the vehicle.
- Reporting problems and delays.
- Weather conditions.

SYSTEMS TO MANAGE WORK-RELATED ROAD SAFETY

Competent staff should be trained to manage and implement the work-related road safety policy. These should be developed using the guidance provided by professional organisations that have many years of experience and expertise around this subject, for example, the Automobile Association (AA), the RAC or ROSPA.

Many employers carry out internal assessments of driving skills in addition to the minimum legal requirements. This can be done in-house or carried out by an external assessor. If drivers are being asked to drive minibuses, etc. then employers can require additional qualifications, as proof of abilities.

Some employers offer specific training in safe driving techniques for their employees. It is important that systems are put in place to ensure that driving distances are kept to a minimum, driving hours are controlled and work schedules are organised to reduce pressure on drivers to meet challenging times and in turn reduce undue road risk.

Organisations should have systems in place to respond to inclement weather and enable drivers to take safe decisions about the effects of weather on their driving or journey.

MONITORING PERFORMANCE

It is a legal requirement to monitor health and safety systems to demonstrate compliance. Information which should be considered for effective monitoring includes:

- Legal responsibilities.
- Organisation and structure.
- Competence of drivers.
- Driving hours.
- Reporting of work-related road safety incidents.

Certain road traffic incidents are reportable under the Reporting of Injuries, Diseases and Dangerous Occurrences Regulations (RIDDOR) 2013. Employers should also monitor minor incidents to vehicles and premises.

ORGANISATION AND STRUCTURE

In a large organisation it is likely that various departments within the organisation will have different responsibilities for drivers at work. The despatch department will be responsible for planning journeys; the training department is responsible for driver competence; the human resources department could be responsible for driver selection and checking the validity of driving licences.

The maintenance department is responsible for the upkeep of vehicles and ensuring the roadworthiness of vehicles and the occupational health department is responsible for carrying routine health surveillance of large goods vehicle (LGV) drivers.

It is therefore essential that the structure of the organisation allows for the free and simple interchange of information regarding legal standards and any changes in legislation and/or good practice. Responsibilities of different parts of the organisation should be defined, including the responsibility to co-operate with each other.

LEGAL RESPONSIBILITIES OF INDIVIDUALS ON PUBLIC ROADS

The main responsibilities of individuals who drive on public roads include responsibilities for the vehicle condition, their fitness to drive, their vision and being under the influence of alcohol and drugs.

Vehicle condition

Drivers must:

- Ensure the vehicle and any trailers comply with the full requirements of the Road Vehicles (Construction and Use) Regulations (RVCUR) 1986 and Road Vehicles Lighting Regulations (RVLR) 1989. This may be a shared responsibility with the employer, however, the driver will often be held initially responsible for the vehicle they are driving.

Fitness to drive

Drivers must:

- Report to the Driver and Vehicle Licensing Agency (DVLA) any health condition likely to affect their driving.
- Not begin a journey if tired. Though the cause of tiredness might include work that their employer expects them to do, the driver will have a separate responsibility for driving while tired.

Vision

Drivers must:

- Be able to read (with the aid of vision corrected lenses) a vehicle number plate, in good daylight, from a distance of 20 metres (or 20.5 metres where the old style number plate is used).
- Slow down, and if necessary stop, if dazzled by bright sunlight.
- At night or in poor visibility, not use tinted glasses, lenses or visors if they restrict vision.

Alcohol and drugs

Drivers must:

- Not drink and drive in excess of the legal limit for alcohol.
- Not drive under the influence of drugs or medicine that may affect driving, for example, drugs that might make the driver drowsy.

General

Drivers must:

- Ensure they use all due care and attention for others when in charge of a vehicle.
- Not tow trailers more than their licence permits. Those who passed a car test after 1 January 1997 are restricted on the weight of trailer they can tow.
- Not overload the vehicle or trailer.
- Secure the load and ensure it does not protrude out dangerously.
- Ensure they and other passengers wear a seat belt or suitable restraining device for babies or small children in cars, vans and other goods vehicles if one is fitted (exemptions are allowed for the holders of medical exemption certificates and those making deliveries or collections in goods vehicles when travelling less than 50 metres (approx 162 feet)).

For detailed information refer to the Road Traffic Act (RTA) 1991 and the Highway Code and related legislation refer to www.direct.gov.uk.

Risk assessments for work-related driving

THE RISK ASSESSMENT PROCESS APPLIED TO DRIVING

All work-related driving activity should follow the same principles as risk assessments for any other work activity.

They should be carried out by a competent person with practical knowledge, qualifications and training relating to the work activity being assessed.

Step 1 - Identify the hazards

Hazards will fall into the following categories:

The Driver	Competence, training, qualifications, fitness and health, alcohol and drug use, etc.
The Vehicle	Suitability, condition, safety equipment, ergonomic considerations, the load, security, etc.
The Journey	Route planning, scheduling, time, distance, driving hours, weather conditions, stress, volume of traffic, weather conditions, passengers, etc.

Step 2 - Decide who might be harmed

Obviously the driver, but this might also include any passengers, other road users and/or pedestrians. Consideration should also be given to other groups who may be particularly at risk, such as young or newly qualified drivers and those driving long distances.

Step 3 - Evaluate the risk and decide on precautions

Risks may vary depending on whether driving is carried out at night or in the day, the type of vehicle or driving conditions. Decide the likelihood of the harm and severity (consequence) of any outcome. Consider risk factors such as distance travelled, driving hours, work schedules, traffic levels and weather conditions. Decide on appropriate precautions and once this has been established, decide whether the residual risk is acceptable.

Step 4 - Record the findings and implement them

Significant findings need to be recorded and risk assessments findings should be made available to all drivers.

Step 5 - Review the assessment and update it if necessary

Monitoring and reviewing the assessments to ensure these risks are suitability controlled. Systems should be put into place to gather, monitor, record and analyse about incidents which might effect these risk assessments.

The vehicle and driver's history should also be recorded. Any changes in the route, new equipment and changes in the vehicle specifications should be reviewed and recorded. This will ensure the effectiveness of controlling the risks.

THE DRIVER

The level of risk is particularly affected by the driver's *competency*. If someone is new to driving their skill may be adequate to provide them with a national driving licence but their experience of driving will be low.

Drivers that only drive intermittently also present a high risk as any competence they may have may decay over the time between driving. The driver's competence has to be appropriate to the driving being expected of them; an inexperienced driver driving in heavy traffic in complicated driving settings at night in the winter will present a particularly high risk. Similarly a person that is reasonably experienced in driving their small car may have difficulty when first driving a larger or faster accelerating vehicle. Some drivers will need to adjust to driving slower vehicles and ones with a different centre of gravity.

Driver *fitness* may influence their ability to see well when driving at night, their ability to travel distances without breaks and may put them in a high risk category for heart attack or other type of seizure. Pre-existing *health* conditions such as back injuries and late term pregnancy could influence the driver's ability to concentrate on road conditions. The level of training that the driver has received may affect risk in that if no training is given a driver may have developed bad driving habits and not be aware of them. Refresher driver training may help to reduce risk.

THE VEHICLE

The size, weight, centre of gravity and power of a vehicle will all influence the functioning of the vehicle and therefore the risk that may arise from its use. It is important that the vehicle is *suitable* for the task and the driver. A large, powerful, fast acceleration car may be suitable for a specific task but very unsuitable for an inexperienced driver. The *condition* of the vehicle will have a significant effect on the level of risk. Vehicles that have poor brakes, lights, do not steer well and have poor suspension will represent a high risk in any driving situation. Vehicles with broken or missing mirrors will mean that the driver will not be able to see other road users adequately and will increase the risk when changing lanes.

Much of the *safety equipment* to prevent accidents, such as active braking systems (ABS) should be built into most modern vehicles. Other items may be optional, such as run-flat tyres: these may reduce certain road risks. Other safety equipment is designed to reduce the consequences of accidents and can therefore reduce risk, such as airbags, escape kits, warning triangles and high-visibility vests. The absence of safety critical information, like the height of the vehicle, can have an immediate and significant effect on the level of risk.

Consideration has to be made of the *safety critical information* related to the vehicle, including its height, width, length, weight and load carrying/towing capacity.

Ergonomic considerations have an effect on both comfort and ability to control the vehicle effectively. The comfort issues can increase fatigue, and ergonomic considerations like seat height adjustment can significantly affect the ability of the driver to see out of the vehicle properly.

THE JOURNEY

When evaluating the risk related to journeys it is important to take into account such factors as:

- The *route* being taken - motorways are safer than smaller roads; routes using motorways will be lower in risk.
- *Scheduling* - if the journey is to be made early in the morning there might be an increased level of risk due to tiredness but this may be offset by the reduced level of traffic.
- *Time* allowed for travel - if not enough time is allowed for the journey and normal delays the risk will be higher.
- *Weather conditions* - can rapidly increase risks, conditions such as ice and snow will have a significant effect.

Control measures to reduce work-related driving risks

THE DRIVER

It is the employer's duty to ensure that drivers are competent, fit and in good health and capable of doing their work in a way that is safe for them. Employers must insist that all drivers produce evidence that they have a current licence to drive their vehicle. Without a current licence and/or test certificate the driver's insurance will be invalid.

Regular assessments of driver competence and monitoring the validity of documentation such as insurance and driving licence should be carried out. Large goods vehicle (LGV) drivers and passenger carrying vehicle (PCV) drivers have to maintain a certificate of professional competence by undertaking 35 hours of training every 5 years.

THE VEHICLE

It is the employer's responsibility to ensure that the vehicle fits the purpose for which it is used. It is important that the vehicle is safe and in a fit condition and suitable for the task to be carried out this will include any safety equipment that is required being properly fitted and maintained. Any safety critical information should be displayed within the cab, for example, height or width of the vehicle.

Ergonomics, such as the driver's seat should also be considered; it may require additional support, for example, lumbar cushions. Full body vibration should be considered and air-suspension seats may be required as a precaution.

Ensure safety equipment is used, for example:

- Seat belts, air bags are installed, maintained and used correctly.
- Two-wheeled vehicle users should have appropriate safety helmets and protective clothing.
- Ensure vehicles do not exceed speed limits by fitting trackers to monitor the speed limits.

THE JOURNEY

Journey planning and scheduling is essential in ensuring the safety of employees who drive for work. Investing time in ensuring that journey planning is implemented as a component of the policy, will ensure that where possible, routes are planned thoroughly, schedules are realistic, and sufficient time is allocated to complete journeys safely.

It may be required to plan overnight stopovers (provide hotel accommodation) if the journey time extends due to bad weather or traffic conditions. Delivery schedules should be adjusted so that unrealistic targets are not set.

This will reduce the stress to drivers and will not encourage them to drive too fast for the conditions, or exceed speed limits.

EXCESSIVE DRIVING TIME

It is important to take into account total driving time, both off site and on site, when assessing the maximum hours which should be worked and the frequency of breaks which will be required. In some situations it will be important to consider the non-driving time worked by individuals as well as their driving time in order to control work-related driving risks.

Measures should be put into place to ensure that all drivers' hours of work are controlled in order to avoid excessive working hours. In addition, it will be important to ensure that the duration of time driving is controlled to avoid fatigue. This may involve work rotation or planned breaks. Breaks and rotation should take account of additional fatigue factors like the circumstances the person is driving in or the terrain they are exposed to. Driving in bad weather or on rough terrains will increase fatigue and the need for breaks.

INCIDENT REPORTING

Drivers must be required to record information about all incidents, whether minor or serious, for all journeys. A similar reporting procedure should be in place for reporting significant 'near misses' with emphasis in training on how to recognise, analyse and learn from such events. The data provided should be analysed and any changes or improvements noted. These should be agreed, fed back to those concerned and the policy procedures updated.

Exam practice

1. **Outline** possible control measures for plant, machinery and vehicles used on construction sites. **(8)**

2. (a) **Identify FOUR** reasons why a dumper truck used on a construction site may overturn. **(4)**

    (b) **Outline** practical measures that could be taken to minimise the risk of a dumper truck overturning when used on construction sites. **(4)**

3. Reversing vehicles within a construction site can be hazardous. **Outline** the means by which the risk of accidents from reversing vehicles can be reduced. **(8)**

4. Many construction workers are involved in work-related driving on public roads as part of their work activities. **Outline** the factors associated with this driving that increase the risk of an incident occurring. **(8)**

5. **Outline** the practical measures that could be used to protect pedestrians on a construction site where segregation of people and vehicles is not possible. **(8)**

Please refer to the back of the assessment section for answers.

Musculoskeletal hazards and risk control

Learning outcomes

On completion of this element, candidates should be able to demonstrate understanding of the content through the application of knowledge to familiar and unfamiliar situations. In particular they should be able to:

4.1 Explain work processes and practices that may contribute to musculoskeletal disorders, work-related upper limb disorders and the appropriate control measures.

4.2 Explain the hazards and control measures which should be considered when assessing risks from manual handling activities.

4.3 Explain the hazards and control measures to reduce the risk in the use of lifting and moving equipment with specific reference to manual and mechanically operated load moving equipment.

Content

4.1 - Musculoskeletal and work-related upper limb disorders 75
  Meaning of musculoskeletal and work-related upper limb disorders..75
  Examples of repetitive construction activities 76
  The ill-health effects of poorly designed tasks and workstations 77
  Factors contributing to ill-health conditions 78
  Appropriate control measures...79
4.2 - Manual handling hazards and control measures 80
  Common types of manual handling injury 80
  Assessment of manual handling risks 81
  Avoiding or minimising manual handling risks in construction activities...85
  Efficient movement principles for manually lifting loads 88
4.3 - Lifting and moving equipment...90
  Hazards and controls for mechanically operated load handling equipment...90
  Hazards and control measures for manually operated load handling aids 102
  Requirements for lifting operations..104
  Visual inspection and statutory thorough examination and inspection..109
Exam practice 110

Sources of reference

Reference information provided, in particular web links, is correct at time of publication, but may have changed.

Ergonomics and human factors at work - A brief guide, INDG90 (rev3), HSE Books, http://www.hse.gov.uk/pubns/indg90.pdf

Manual handling at work - A brief guide, INDG143 (rev3), HSE Books, http://www.hse.gov.uk/pubns/INDG143.pdf

Manual Handling, Manual Handling Operations Regulations 1992 (as amended) - Guidance on Regulations (L23), HSE Books, ISBN 978-0-7176-2823-0 http://www.hse.gov.uk/pubns/priced/l23.pdf

Rider-operated lift trucks. Operator training and safe use - ACOP and Guidance, L117, HSE Books, ISBN 978-0-7176-6441-2 http://www.hse.gov.uk/pubns/priced/l117.pdf

Safe use of lifting equipment, Lifting Operations and Lifting Equipment Regulations 1998 - ACOP and Guidance, L113, HSE Books, ISBN 978-0-7176-6586-0 http://www.hse.gov.uk/pubns/priced/l113.pdf

Safe use of Work Equipment (ACOP L22), HSE Books, ISBN 978-0-7176-6619-5 http://www.hse.gov.uk/pubns/priced/l22.pdf

Upper limb disorders in the workplace, HSG60 (second edition 2002), HSE Books, ISBN 978-0-7176-1978-8 http://www.hse.gov.uk/pubns/priced/hsg60.pdf

Working with display screen equipment – A brief guide, INDG36 (rev4), HSE Books, http://www.hse.gov.uk/pubns/indg36.pdf

Work with display screen equipment: Health and Safety (Display Screen Equipment) Regulations 1992 as amended by the Health and Safety (Miscellaneous Amendments) Regulations 2002 - Guidance on Regulations, L26, HSE Books, ISBN: 978-0-7176-2582-6 http://www.hse.gov.uk/pubns/priced/l26.pdf

Relevant statutory provisions

Lifting Operations and Lifting Equipment Regulations (LOLER) 1998

Manual Handling Operations Regulations (MHOR) 1992

Notification of Conventional Tower Cranes Regulations (NCTCR) 2010

Provision and Use of Work Equipment Regulations (PUWER) 1998

4.1 - Musculoskeletal and work-related upper limb disorders

Meaning of musculoskeletal and work-related upper limb disorders

Work-related musculoskeletal disorders (MSD's) are disorders of parts of the body. These are caused by work and working conditions. Disorders can affect the muscles, joints, tendons, ligaments, nerves, bones and the localised blood circulation system. Most work-related MSDs are cumulative disorders, resulting from repeated exposure to high or low intensity loads over a long period of time.

The main areas of the body affected are the back, neck, shoulders and upper limbs, but the lower limbs may also be affected. Some MSDs, such as carpal tunnel syndrome in the wrist, are specific because of their well-defined signs and symptoms. Others are classed as non-specific because only pain or discomfort exists without evidence of a clear specific disorder or occupational disease.

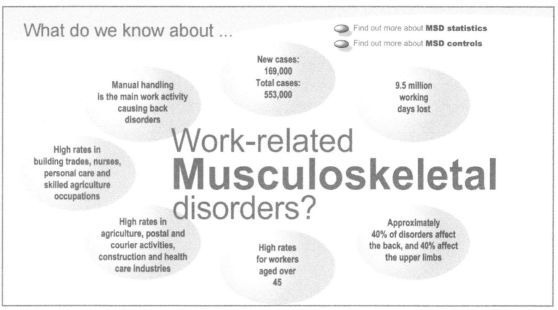

Figure 4-1: Work-related musculoskeletal disorder statistics.   *Source: HSE.*

Work-related upper limb disorder (WRULD's) is a generic term for that group of disorders that affect the neck or any part of the arm from the fingers to the shoulders. Recognised WRULD conditions include carpel tunnel syndrome and tenosynovitis.

Carpal tunnel syndrome is the painful inflammation of the nerves and tendons passing through the carpal bone in the wrist area and affects the whole hand. The syndrome usually affects the thumb, index finger, middle finger and half of the ring finger (but may spread outside these areas). Tenosynovitis is inflammation of the synovial lining of the tendon sheath.

Some tendons are covered by a sheath called the synovium. The synovium makes a tiny amount of oily fluid that lies between the tendon and its overlying synovial sheath, allowing the tendon to move easily. Extended use of the tendon, however, can cause inflammation in the synovial sheath. Symptoms include pain and swelling, usually near where the tendon attaches to the bone.

Figure 4-2: Total cases (prevalence) and new cases (incidence) of MSDs.   *Source: HSE.*

Estimates from the Labour Force Survey (LFS) show that in Great Britain the total number of MSD cases in 2014/15 was 553,000 out of a total 1,243,000 for all work-related illnesses. The number of new cases of MSDs in Great Britain in 2014/15 was 169,000, an incidence rate of 530 cases per 100,000 people. The highest rates of MSDs occurred with construction, agriculture and forestry and transport and storage activities. Construction trades frequently named as high risk are plasterers, bricklayers and joiners. Tasks carried out within construction trades require the use of hand and power tools, involving the use of several body regions, constant movement in awkward positions, and repetitive, forceful, use of the back and upper and lower extremities.

The LFS survey data suggests that despite fluctuations in the incidence rate in recent years, overall the incidence rate of self-reported work-related musculoskeletal disorder has fallen over the period 2001/02 to 2014/15. The LFS reported in 2014/15 that an estimated 9.5 million working days were lost due to MSDs and this represents 40% of all days lost due to work related ill-health. Construction along with agriculture, health and social care and transportation and storage industries all showed elevated rates of musculoskeletal disorders.

The average days lost per case for musculoskeletal disorders was 17 days. This was lower than cases for stress, which were 23 days.

Examples of repetitive construction activities

Anyone who over-uses their back, arms and hands repeatedly may develop a musculoskeletal disorder. Keyboard operators, workers on factory assembly lines, musicians, dressmakers, bricklaying, check out operators and cleaners are examples of workers at particular risk. Those that are involved in repetitive construction activities are particularly at risk of experiencing MSDs and WRULDs. There are a great deal of construction activities that involve repetitive actions, some of these are considered in the following outlines of how the risk presents itself.

DIGGING

Hand digging becomes progressively more difficult and potentially more injurious the deeper below foot level the work is carried out. This is particularly the case if the spoil being removed has to be lifted above waist height for disposal. The use of narrow trenching techniques that can restrict posture significantly will also increase risk of musculoskeletal injuries, fatigue and strain on the limbs.

KERB LAYING

Traditionally, kerbs (in one form or another) have been specified on the majority of roads. The standard components used are principally pre-cast concrete and weigh approximately 67kg. Feature kerbs, stone kerbs or other associated products may be considerably heavier. More recently a number of manufacturers have developed lighter kerbs.

The main hazards associated with the manual handling of kerbs are the weight of the kerb, the repetitive nature of the work and poor posture during the work. These hazards create excessive stress and strain on the body, which can cause damage to muscles and tendons, and in the longer term may lead progressively to more serious musculoskeletal injury.

MOVEMENT AND FIXING OF PLASTERBOARD

Plasterboard is widely used in construction to line internal walls and ceilings. Workers often have to handle the sheets manually and may need to do so in a restricted space, for example, a stairwell. The sheets, which are typically 2.5 metres x 1.25 metres and weigh 32.5kg, are difficult to grip and unwieldy.

The work is physically demanding and the main hazards involve extended reach, and posture flexibility to enable work in a variety of awkward postures, including on raised platforms.

PLACEMENT AND FINISHING OF CONCRETE SLABS

The placement and finishing of concrete slabs will often involve heavy repetitive work and poor posture due to having to work at the level of the worker's feet. The placement and levelling of concrete labs, may involve lifting and repositioning of each slab more than once, putting stain on the fingers, hands and lower back.

BRICKLAYING

Bricklayers are often self-employed and therefore cannot afford to lose time from work. They will carry on working and ignore the warning signs, such as aches and fatigue, which are often a precursor to more serious musculoskeletal injuries. The size of the bricks being laid, the number of bricks they are expected to lay (often several hundred per day) and the relative position of a wall or structure are significant risk factors.

ERECTING/DISMANTLING SCAFFOLDS

The erecting and dismantling of scaffold, by the nature of the work, will involve lifting and placing of materials progressively higher (when erecting) or lower (dismantling). The work involves the need to maintain balance whilst carrying or placing materials, often involving long reaching to position and secure components. The risk of overreach related injuries to the hands, arms and spine is high when working with materials of extended length that are held at one end, such as scaffold boards and poles.

USE OF DISPLAY SCREEN EQUIPMENT

Display screen equipment (DSE) is a device or equipment that has a display screen for graphics, words or numbers. DSE includes both conventional display screens and those used in the latest technologies such as laptops, touch-screens and other similar devices.

Traditional drafting of drawings and plans for construction activities has now been replaced by computer aided design programmes (CAD). CAD systems enable architects to modify and amend drawings as often as is necessary. The designs can be manipulated from any number of elevations and many systems allow the construction of three dimensional models (3D). The designs can be sent electronically to the client for approval, speedily enabling early completion of the work.

Display screen equipment (DSE) users working in design and other similar roles may make many thousands of movements an hour, which will create repeated movement of the fingers. Where the DSE user is not fully proficient in using all fingers to operate the keyboard, many of the movements are centred on a small number of fingers. Where the use of the display screen equipment requires the use of a mouse this can also accentuate the use of a small number of fingers centred on the user's dominant hand. Because of the amount of repeated movements, sometimes without taking breaks, the risks of WRULD are high and the effects are cumulative.

The ill-health effects of poorly designed tasks and workstations

WORK-RELATED UPPER LIMB DISORDERS [WRULD]

Work-related upper limb disorders (WRULD) were first defined in medical literature as long ago as the 19th century as a condition caused by *forceful, frequent, twisting and repetitive movements*. The body will be affected to a varying degree by tasks which involve bending, reaching, twisting, repetitive movements and poor posture.

WRULD is a collective term for a group of occupational diseases that comprise musculoskeletal disorders caused by exposure in the workplace affecting the muscles, tendons, nerves, blood vessels, joints and bursae (a small fluid-filled sac which provides a cushion from injury between bones and tendons and/or muscles around a joint) of the hand, wrist, arm and shoulder.

WRULD include well-known conditions such as tennis elbow, flexor tenosynovitis and carpal tunnel syndrome. It is usually caused by repetitive tasks and movements and aggravated by excessive workloads, inadequate rest periods and sustained or constrained postures. This can result in pain, soreness or inflammatory conditions of soft tissues, such as muscles and the synovial lining of the tendon sheath.

Present approaches to treatment are largely effective, provided the condition is treated in its early stages.

Clinical signs and symptoms are local aching, pain, tenderness, swelling, crepitus (a grating sensation in the joint). Some common WRULDs are:

Carpal tunnel syndrome

CTS occurs when tendons or ligaments in the wrist become enlarged, often from inflammation, after being aggravated. The narrowed tunnel of bones and ligaments in the wrist pinches the nerves that reach the fingers and the muscles at the base of the thumb.

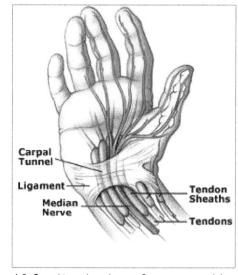

Figure 4-3: Carpal tunnel syndrome. *Source: www.sodahead.com.*

The first symptoms usually appear at night. Symptoms range from a burning, tingling numbness in the fingers, especially the thumb and the index and middle fingers, to difficulty gripping or making a fist, to dropping things.

Tenosynovitis

An irritation of the tendon sheath. It occurs when the repetitive activity becomes excessive and the tendon sheath can no longer lubricate the tendon. As a result, the tendon sheath thickens and becomes aggravated. Symptoms include pain and swelling, usually near where the tendon attaches to the bone.

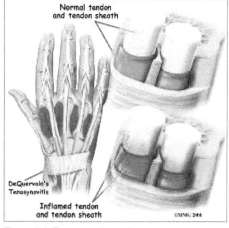

Figure 4-4: Tenosynovitis. *Source: www.rayur.com.*

Tendinitis

Tendinitis involves inflammation of a tendon, the fibrous cord that attaches muscle to bone. It usually affects only one part of the body at a time and lasts a short time. However, in some cases it involves tissues that are continuously irritated. It may result from an injury, activity or exercise that repeats the same movement. Rotator cuff tendinitis is one of the most common causes of shoulder pain.

Peritendinitis

Peritendinitis is an inflammation of the sheath that surrounds a tendon. It can be associated with tendinitis, an inflammation of the tendon itself.

This condition is most commonly seen in overuse injuries, such as those involving continually repeated tasks (for example, data input into a computer) or for those people who do not get enough rest between tasks or following injury. The primary treatment is resting in order to allow the inflamed tissue to heal.

Epicondylitis

Commonly known as 'tennis elbow' or lateral epicondylitis, this is a condition that occurs when the outer part of the elbow becomes painful and tender, usually because of a specific strain, overuse, or a direct impact.

Sometimes no specific cause is found. Tennis elbow is similar to golfer's elbow (medial epicondylitis), which affects the other side of the elbow.

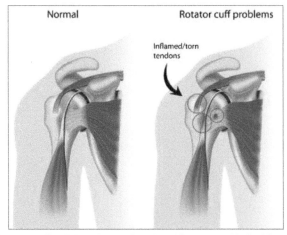

Figure 4-5: Tendinitis. *Source: Beth Israel Deaconess Medical Center.*

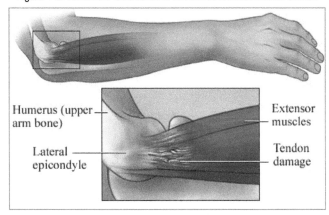

Figure 4-6: Epicondylitis. *Source: Myhealth.alberta.ca.*

HAND ARM VIBRATION SYNDROME (HAVS)

Describes a group of diseases caused by the exposure of the hand and arm to external vibration. The most common is vibration white finger (VWF), in which the circulation of the blood, particularly in the hands, is adversely affected by the vibration. *For further information on HAVS see 'Element 9.2 - Vibration'.*

Factors contributing to ill-health conditions

TASKS

Tasks should be assessed to determine the musculoskeletal health risk factors that arise from them. If the task is *repetitive* in nature, i.e. the same series of operations are repeated in a short period of time, such as ten or more times per minute, then injury may occur to the muscles and ligaments affected. Similarly, work of a *strenuous* nature, such as moving heavy or difficult shaped objects, perhaps in limited space or hot environments, will cause fatigue, strains and sprains.

Whether the worker is able to take appropriate breaks from the task is an important factor. If this is not possible due to technical factors driving completion of an activity, for example, when dealing with continuous pouring of concrete, then this can be a significant factor influencing musculoskeletal ill-health conditions unless the work is designed to provide facilities for work rotation to reduce these effects.

ENVIRONMENT

Working in *extremes of temperature* or handling hot or cold items will make simple work more strenuous. Long hours of work in cold conditions can cause problems with blood circulation. This may increase the likelihood of developing hand arm vibration syndrome, which is a specific work-related upper limb disorder that affects the circulation and nerves in the hand. Eye fatigue will also occur if the *lighting* levels are low, typically below 100-200 lux, or too bright, typically greater than 800 lux. *Glare* can be a significant factor, causing discomfort to the eyes and leading to a person taking up awkward postures to avoid the glare. Reflected light (such as sunlight) on equipment can cause 'glare', for example, on computer monitors, leading to eye strain and the adoption of awkward postures to avoid the glare.

Other lighting factors may need to be considered such as the stroboscopic effects associated with moving machinery. The machine's rotating parts (such as a spindle) can appear to be stationary when viewed under fluorescent lighting which is powered by alternating current (AC).

The risk of injury increases with the *length of time* that a task is carried out. Work for long periods conducting repetitive and strenuous tasks may lead to WRULDs. However, injury may occur over a short period if the work requires a lot of effort.

Working in *uncomfortable positions*, such as working above head height or holding something in the same place for a long period of time, increases the risk of injury. These factors will often be reduced if the worker is able to adjust the conditions to their personal needs. Poor posture can be affected by such workplace environmental factors as:

- The layout and positioning of items on a workstation that might cause a worker to have to reach, twist, bend and stoop, for example, to collect components and assemble them.
- Temporary arrangements where materials and equipment are placed on the floor requiring a worker to kneel and bend to conduct tasks, for example, where a welder might weld material during part of a maintenance task.

Figure 4-7: Poor posture.   *Source: Speedy Hire Plc.*

- Storage placed at a height or low down, for example, causing a worker to stretch or bend to put articles in a cupboard.

EQUIPMENT

Equipment design should take into account the ergonomic *requirements of the user* and, where possible, allow the user to *adjust* any settings to suit their needs. Such things as workbench height and positioning of switches and buttons should be in the operator's easy control. The weight of the equipment should be considered, because excessive weight may put strain on the upper body when it is in use. Equipment should be kept in good working condition so that it is effective with the minimum of effort of the operator, thus reducing the need for extra grip and force.

Appropriate control measures

In managing risks from work-related upper limb disorders a number of changes may need to be made and ergonomic solutions should be given first consideration. This means making the workplace and the work fit the person, rather than making the person adapt to fit the workplace and work. The study of ergonomics is essential to good job design. It is the applied science of equipment design intended to maximise effectiveness by reducing worker fatigue and discomfort. It can be defined as 'the study of the relationship between human beings, the equipment with which they work and the physical environment in which this human-machine system operates'.

Ergonomics is a broad area of study that includes the disciplines of psychology, physiology, anatomy and design engineering. Ergonomics has the human being at the centre of the study where individual capabilities and fallibilities are considered in order to, ultimately, eliminate the potential for human error and harm to effectiveness and efficiency. This includes the minimisation of such things as work-related musculoskeletal disorders that are caused by poorly designed machines, tools, task and workplace.

The aims of ergonomics, therefore, are to design the equipment and the working environment to fit the needs and capabilities of the individual, i.e. fitting the task to the individual, and to ensure that the physical and mental well-being of the individual is being met. This involves the consideration of psychological and physical factors, including the work system, body dimensions, capability, competence and the work environment (layout, noise, temperature and lighting). Individuals, have different physical capabilities due to height, weight, age and levels of fitness. They also have different mental capabilities, memory retention and personalities. All these factors can influence ergonomic choices and the successful matching of the workplace to the individual.

Workstation	*Repetitive movements*
<ul><li>Ensuring that working heights are appropriate for the full range of workers.</li><li>Relocating equipment to provide more space.</li><li>Relocating items that workers have to see clearly within their comfortable range of vision.</li><li>Providing adjustable workstations that allow postures to be varied between standing and sitting.</li></ul>	<ul><li>Mechanising or automating repetitive processes.</li><li>Rotation of workers between tasks with high and low exposures.</li><li>Allowing adequate rest pauses.</li></ul>
Temperature	*Postures*
<ul><li>Avoiding handling or insulating cold items or equipment.</li><li>Directing warm/cool air flow (as appropriate) to the worker to increase thermal comfort.</li></ul>	<ul><li>Relocating equipment or items that must be held to within easy reach.</li><li>Ensuring working heights are at or around waist level.</li><li>Ensuring workplaces and equipment are suitable for the full range of workers' sizes and strengths.</li><li>Providing jigs for re-positioning work pieces.</li><li>Ensuring that items that must be viewed clearly are within the normal visual range.</li></ul>

Hand tools	**Gloves**
■ Providing tools with ergonomically designed handles. ■ Using lighter tools, or providing supports or counterbalances. ■ Ensuring tools are regularly maintained. **Vibration** ■ Using vibration-damped equipment. ■ Ensuring tools are regularly maintained. ■ Limiting exposure to agreed safe limits. **Use of muscular force** ■ Reducing the weight of items. ■ Using jigs or counterbalances to hold items. ■ Using stronger muscle groups to perform the task. ■ Using foot pedals as opposed to hand controls. ■ Using more effective tools that need less muscular power; for example, tools with engines or other mechanical advantage.	■ Providing gloves in a wide range of sizes to fit workers' hands. ■ Providing gloves made from flexible materials. **Mechanical pressure** ■ Providing suitable hand tools as effective substitutes for the use of inappropriate parts of the body. ■ Ensuring that edges on work pieces and equipment items are rounded to distribute pressure during contact with parts of the body. **Organisation of work** ■ Improving work flow to avoid production peaks and troughs through better planning and scheduling. ■ Encouraging better communication and team work. ■ Providing appropriate training.

Figure 4-8: Actions to be taken to control WRULD risks.   *Source: European Agency for Safety and Health at Work.*

4.2 - Manual handling hazards and control measures

Common types of manual handling injury

Around 25% of all injuries reported to enforcing agencies have been attributed to the manual lifting and handling of loads. The injuries arise from such *hazards* as stooping while lifting, holding the load away from the body, twisting movements, frequent or prolonged effort. Injuries can also arise from manually handling heavy/bulky/unwieldy/unstable loads or loads with sharp/hot/slippery surfaces. Other injuries can be caused by workplace space constraints and lack of capability of the individual. Manual handling operations can cause many types of *injury*.

The most common injuries are:

■ Spinal disc herniation.
■ Prolapsed spinal disc.
■ Muscle strain and sprain.
■ Torn or overstretched tendons and ligaments.
■ Rupture of a section of the abdominal wall can cause a hernia.
■ Loads with sharp edges can cause cuts.
■ Dropped loads can result in bruises, fractures and crushing injuries.

DAMAGE TO INTERVERTEBRAL DISC

The spine is made up of individual bones (vertebrae) separated by intervertebral discs. Strain on the disc can cause it to bulge and protrude out between the vertebrae. This is known as a herniated disc. The disc can then press on nearby nerves or the spinal cord. If the fibrous case of the disc collapses the disc can lose its shape and compress - this can cause bones in the spinal column to touch or it can increase pressure on the spinal cord. The above conditions can cause pain and inflammation in the area of the spinal cord where pressure occurs. Pain may also be felt in the area of the body that the part of the spinal cord affected relates to (this condition is called sciatica). The damage to the disc is usually caused by too much pressure being applied to it during lifting and handling operations that involve 'top-heavy' bending. This is where the knees are not bent sufficiently and the head and upper body are bent over, causing the spine to bend in a curved manner (sometimes called stooping). This bending creates a high degree of leverage force on the base of the spine, which leads to the extreme pressure exerted on the disc.

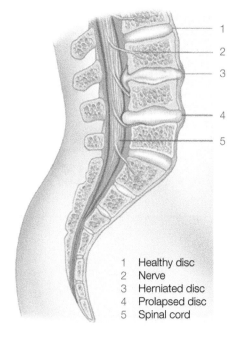

1   Healthy disc
2   Nerve
3   Herniated disc
4   Prolapsed disc
5   Spinal cord

Figure 4-9: Lumber and slipped disc. *Source: NHS.*

The force and therefore pressure on the disc is accentuated by the carrying of heavy loads. Though top-heavy bending is a particular cause of this damage, poor posture due to leaning over for a sustained period could lead to similar damage.

SPRAINS/STRAINS, FRACTURES AND LACERATIONS

The most common injuries that arise from manual handling operations are sprains, strains, fractures and lacerations.

Sprains and strains

Sprains and strains often occur in the back or in the arm and wrists, though injuries in the legs can also occur where the leg has been hyper flexed and where the soft tissues (ligament, tendons and muscles) are overstretched. This can occur through kneeling or handling loads beyond the worker's limit.

- A *sprain* is an injury to a ligament. The ligament is tough fibrous tissue that connects a bone to another bone. Ligament injuries typically involve overstretching or a tearing of this fibrous tissue.
- A *strain* is an injury to either a muscle or a tendon that connects muscles to bones. Depending on the severity of the injury, a strain may be a simple overstretch of the muscle or tendon or it may result in a partial or complete tear. Rupture of the muscles in a section of the abdominal wall can cause a hernia.

Sprains and strains tend to occur when a person's body has been overloaded due to a large steady load being applied, a sudden smaller load being applied without the opportunity of the ligament or tendon to stretch, or a part of the body being forced to move in an unusual way.

This may be because a person is reaching over to an extreme level (sometimes even without picking up a load, as their own body weight may be sufficient to cause damage) or two people picking up a load together in an uncoordinated way. It could also be due to a load slipping that causes someone to move into an awkward position to prevent it falling completely.

Fractures and lacerations

A fracture is a break in a bone, which is usually the result of trauma where the physical force exerted on the bone is stronger than the bone itself. Fractures of the hands and feet are the most likely type of fractures to arise from manual handling work and may be due to the load that is being lifted accidentally being dropped.

Lacerations are often caused by the unprotected handling of loads with sharp corners or edges, or a person's grip slipping when trying to prevent a dropped load.

Assessment of manual handling risks

Musculoskeletal injuries are common in the construction industry. The HSE reports that they typically arise from work that involves:

- Awkward working positions (for example, bending or crouching) or restricted space (for example, working in a roof void).
- Bending and twisting (for example, plastering).
- High job demands or time pressure, which may mean that workers resort to brute force rather than using a mechanical handling solution.
- Lifting, lowering and carrying heavy materials (for example, roof tiles).
- Pushing and pulling objects and equipment (for example, barrows).
- Repetitive movements (for example, tying rebar).
- Working too long without breaks.

The HSE identify that the kinds of activity that are likely to require a manual handling assessment include:

- Asbestos removal.
- Block laying.
- Ceiling fixing.
- Cladding/sheeting.
- Curtain wall installation.
- Diamond drilling/sawing.
- Dry lining.
- Ductwork installation.
- Ground works.
- Mechanical and electrical work.
- Piling operations.
- Plant operation.
- Plastering.
- Pre-cast concrete installation.
- Roads and paving.
- Scaffolding.
- Structural steel work.
- Tunnelling.
- Window installation.

The process of risk assessing includes observing the task as it is actually carried out; recording the factors that contribute to risk; assessing the level of risk that each factor represents (taking account of the circumstances and controls in place); and considering whether the risks are different at different times and for different people.

An employer should:

- *Avoid* the need for hazardous manual handling, so far as is reasonably practicable.
- *Assess* the risk of injury from any hazardous manual handling that cannot be avoided.
- *Reduce* the risk of injury from hazardous manual handling, so far as is reasonably practicable.

FACTORS TO CONSIDER

The Manual Handling Operations Regulations (MHOR) 1992 specify that the four factors to which the employer must have regard, and questions he must consider, when making an assessment of manual handling operations are:

- **L** oad.
- **I** ndividual capability.
- **T** ask.
- **E** nvironment.

Each factor in turn should be assessed to determine whether there is a risk of injury. When this has been completed the information can then be processed giving a ***suitable and sufficient*** risk assessment.

FACTORS	QUESTIONS	Level of Risk: High	Med	Low
Load	Is it: ■ Heavy? ■ Bulky or unwieldy? ■ Difficult to grasp? ■ Unstable, or with contents likely to shift? ■ Sharp, hot or otherwise potentially damaging?			
Individual capability	Does the job: ■ Require unusual strength, height, etc.? ■ Create a hazard to those who have a health problem or are pregnant? ■ Require special knowledge or training for its safe performance? ■ Do clothing and footwear present an increased risk?			
Task	Does it involve: ■ Holding a load at distance from trunk? ■ Unsatisfactory bodily movement or posture? • Twisting the trunk. • Stooping. ■ Excessive movement of load? • Excessive lifting or lowering distances. • Excessive carrying distances. • Excessive pushing or pulling. • Risk of sudden movement of load. • Frequent or prolonged physical effort (repetitive handling). • A work rate imposed by a process. • Insufficient rest or recovery periods.			
Working environment	Are there: ■ Space constraints preventing good posture? ■ Uneven, slippery or unstable floors? ■ Variations in level of floors or work surfaces? ■ Extremes of temperature, humidity or air movement? ■ Poor lighting conditions?			

Figure 4-10: Manual handling risk assessment.   Source: HSE Guidance L23.

The detailed consideration of each factor is necessary to achieve a suitable and sufficient risk assessment. The process of risk assessing includes observing the task as it is actually carried out; recording the factors that contribute to risk; assessing the level of risk that each factor represents (taking account of the circumstances and controls in place), considering if the risks are different at different times and for different people and determining the adequacy of current controls.

The following should be considered when making a risk assessment.

The load

Consideration should be given to:

- The weight of the load. Generally, the heavier the load the higher the risk of injury. Although smaller, lighter loads may require a higher frequency of handling. ***See 'Guidelines for the assessment of manual handling operations' later in this element for more information on risks related to the weight of a load.***

- Where the size, surface texture or nature of a load makes it difficult to grasp this can increase the manual handling risk. For example, it may cause workers to lose their grip and cause loads to be dropped suddenly.
- There is an increased manual handling risk in situations where loads can move unexpectedly while being handled. For example, liquid in a container could move easily and cause the centre of gravity of the weight of the load to move.
- Any loads to be handled that have sharp corners, jagged edges or rough surfaces increase the risk of workers getting cuts when they handle them and may cause the worker to drop the load suddenly.

Figure 4-11: Manual handling.   Source: RMS.

Individual capability

An individual's capability, including their condition and age, could significantly affect their ability to perform a manual handling task safely.

Consideration should be given to:

- The individual's state of health. A worker's fitness and strength can significantly affect their ability to perform a manual handling task safely.
- An individual's physical capability may be affected by their age. Some age groups tend to have reduced physical capability. Age groups particularly at risk include those under 20 years of age and those above 45 years of age.
- Individuals from a vulnerable group, such as a pregnant woman or someone with a pre-existing back injury. These conditions may make them vulnerable to the risk of manual handling injury.

The task

Consideration should be given to:

- If tasks require workers to access things from storage to do their work. Materials, equipment and components in regular use should be stored at waist height to minimise manual handling risks. Storage above or below this height increases manual handling risks and should therefore be used for lighter or less frequently used items.
- Tasks that require workers to do frequent bending, twisting and reaching actions, as these actions can increase the risk of manual handling injury. Similarly, workers who have to carry loads long distances would be at higher risk of manual handling injury.
- Tasks where work routines can creates an increased risk of manual handling injury, for example, fixed postures when holding or supporting loads. There is also an increased risk if work routines require frequent handling of loads.
- Whether fixed breaks are dictated. The needs of workers often vary, therefore fixed breaks are generally less effective in providing timely worker rest and recovery from manual handling work. If workers can take a break from manual handling work as they need them this can reduce the risk of manual handling injury. Usually this would be achieved by a change in work routine rather than a break from all work activities.
- Whether manual handling must be carried out while the worker is seated. In this situation the use of powerful leg muscles to help with lifting a load is prevented and the weight of the worker's body cannot be used as a counterbalance to the load being lifted. This could lead to a higher risk of manual handling injury as the weight of loads that can be handled by a worker who is seated are substantially less than those that can be dealt with while standing.
- Whether team handling is used for tasks that are beyond the capability of one person. Team handling can create additional problems. The proportion of the load carried by each member of the team will vary. Therefore, the load that can be handled by a team will be less than the sum of the loads which each individual could cope with.
- Whether personal protective equipment is used by workers carrying out manual handling activities. The use of personal protective equipment can reduce risk of manual handling injury as it helps workers handling loads to protect their hands and allows them to hold loads close to their body without affecting their own clothes. However, if the use of personal protective equipment restricts movement, this could increase risk of manual handling injury.

The working environment

Consideration should be given to:

- Whether gangways, work space and working areas are adequate to allow room to manoeuvre during manual handling tasks.

- The working environment creates a lack of headroom, for example, caused by poor workstation design or the proximity of adjacent machinery. This could constrict worker movements and cause them to stoop, leading to an increased risk of manual handling injury.
- Whether the work environment is affected by poor housekeeping. Poor housekeeping can mean that there are obstacles on the floor. This could lead to an unstable footing for a worker carrying a load or may cause them to stretch their leg out to step over the obstacle and increase the risk of injury.
- If manual handling tasks involve working on more than one level manual handling risks may be increased, for example, where workers have to use stairs, steps, ladders or ramps during manual handling tasks.
- Whether workbenches are of a uniform height, as this would reduce the need for raising or lowering loads.
- Whether the general working environment is comfortable and suits manual handling activities, for example, suitable and sufficient heating/cooling, ventilation and lighting. Risks of manual handling injuries can be increased if manual handling work is carried out in windy or cold conditions, such as on the roof of an exposed building.

GUIDELINES FOR ASSESSMENT OF MANUAL HANDLING OPERATIONS

Lifting

The MHOR 1992 do not set a specific absolute weight limit requirement for lifting and lowering loads. The following guidelines set out an **approximate** boundary within which manual handling operations are unlikely to create a significant. Work within the guidelines should not require a detailed manual handling risk assessment.

This should manage the risk and enable assessment work to be concentrated where it is most needed, on higher-risk tasks. The guideline figures are not absolute weight limits. They may be exceeded where a more detailed risk assessment shows it is safe to do so. However, the guideline figures should not normally be exceeded by more than a factor of about two.

Figure 4-12: Lifting and lowering.   *Source: HSE Guidance, L23.*

The guideline figures for weight and force will give reasonable protection to nearly all men and between one half and two thirds of women.

The guideline figures are based on the following assumptions:

- The handler is standing or crouching in a stable body position with their back substantially upright.
- The trunk is not twisted during the operation.
- Both hands are used to grasp the load.
- The hands are not more than shoulder width apart.
- The load is positioned centrally in front of the body and is itself reasonably symmetrical.
- The load is stable and readily grasped.
- The work area does not restrict the handler's posture.
- The working environment (heat, cold, wet, condition of floor) and any personal protective equipment used do not interfere with performance of the task.

Carrying

The guideline figures for manual handling operations involving carrying are similar to those given for lifting and lowering. It is assumed that the load is held against the body and is carried no further than about 10 metres without resting. If the load is carried over a longer distance without resting, the guideline figures may need to be reduced.

Where the load can be carried securely on the shoulder (for example, unloading sacks from a lorry) a more detailed risk assessment may show that it is safe to exceed the guideline figure.

Pushing and pulling

Guideline figures for manual handling operations involving pushing and pulling, whether the load is slid, rolled or supported on wheels, are as follows:

- The guideline figure for starting or stopping the load is a force of about 250 newtons (i.e. a force of about 25kg as measured on a spring balance).
- The guideline figure for keeping the load in motion is a force of about 100 newtons (i.e. a force of about 10kg as measured on a spring balance).
- No specific limit is intended as to the distances over which the load is pushed or pulled, provided there are adequate opportunities for rest or recovery.

Handling while seated

The guideline figure for handling operations carried out while seated is given in *figure ref 4-13* and applies only when the hands are within the box zone indicated.

If handling beyond the box zone is unavoidable, a more detailed assessment should be made.

Twisting

The basic guideline figures for lifting and lowering should be reduced if the handler twists to the side during the operation.

As a rough guide, the figures should be reduced by about 10% where the handler twists through 45° and by about 20% where the handler twists through 90° *(see figure ref 4-14)*.

REVIEWING ASSESSMENTS

The assessment should be kept up to date. It should be reviewed whenever there is a reason to suppose that it is no longer valid, for example, because the working conditions or the personnel carrying out the operations have changed.

It should also be reviewed whenever there has been a significant change in the manual handling operations, for example, affecting the nature of the task or load.

Figure 4-13: Handling while seated.   *Source: HSE Guidance L23.*

Figure 4-14: Twisting.   *Source: HSE Guidance L23.*

Avoiding or minimising manual handling risks in construction activities

When avoiding or minimising the risks from manual handling each manual handling operation should be examined. Wherever reasonably practicable, manual handling should be avoided, for example, by redesigning the task to avoid moving the load, by automating the process or mechanising it by using mechanical handling aids.

In some situations, manual handling can be avoided by not handling the load at all. For example, if a heavy load needs to be worked on it might be possible to bring the process to the load, for example, bringing non-destructive testing equipment to where the load is.

Decisions on whether to use automation or mechanisation are best taken at the design stage, or when processes are being updated, as they can involve complex arrangements and capital expenditure, for example, where the process changes from handling raw materials in sacks or bags to bulk delivery, or where storage changes to using gravity or pneumatic transfer systems.

Where risks cannot be avoided, appropriate steps should be taken to minimise the risk of injury to the lowest level reasonably practicable in order to reduce the potential for the creation or further degeneration of MSDs.

Practical measures that may be taken to reduce the risk of injury can be decided by considering the same factors assessed in the risk assessment, the load, individual, task and environment (LITE).

For the purposes of this element measures to avoid or minimise risk are also considered under the headings of design, automation, mechanisation and other considerations.

L OAD

By changing the load by lightening, reducing in size, provision of handles, elimination of sharp edges etc.

Find ways of either avoiding the operation altogether; or using lightweight materials, for example, replacing pre cast concrete kerbs and drainage blocks with plastic equivalents.

Figure 4-15: Light weight plastic kerbs.   *Source: HSE, COH14.*

Alternatively where heavy blocks need to be used provide mechanical aids, such as vacuum lifters or grabs for concrete kerbs and paving.

INDIVIDUAL

Address the individual factors such as selection, provision of information and training, provision of appropriate protective equipment and clothing.

Individuals should be selected according to their capability. Personal factors such as height, build, physical condition, and pre-existing health conditions, such as pregnancy must be considered.

TASK

Consider redesigning the task so that manual handling is eliminated or reduced by mechanisation, reducing carrying distances, team lifting, job rotation and improved technique.

On most sites brick and block laying at ground level involves bending down repeatedly to the stack and mortar spot board as well as to the wall that is being built. The combination of awkward postures and continuous handling can contribute to discomfort and a risk of injury.

Figure 4-16: Vacuum lift for heavy concrete kerbs.
Source: www.vacuumliftinguk.co.uk.

Excessive bending to trowel mortar and lay bricks at ground level can be avoided by raising the height of the spot board as the work proceeds.

Figure 4-17: Excessive bending to trowel mortar.
Source: HSE, COH01.

Figure 4-18: Raised spot board avoids excessive bending.
Source: HSE, COH01.

ENVIRONMENT

Risks can be minimised by improving the working environment, for example, optimum heights of surfaces, improving floor conditions, increasing workspace, improving lighting, avoidance of changes in floor level.

DESIGN

The risks from manual handling may be minimised by the use of good design of the workplace.

This involves placing items where they can be conveniently handled, improving work layouts so that travel distances are minimised and arranging that items can be picked up or put down at a suitable height.

In general, working levels should be waist high, with tools, materials and equipment to be handled placed in front of the worker and within easy reach.

The layout should suit the worker and there should be adequate room to perform the task safely.

Figure 4-19: Trench block with 'handholds'. *Source: HSE, COH04.*

The design of loads can also minimise risks. This could include designing the load to be smaller through concentration of substances contained in it or breaking the load up into suitable sized containers.

It might also mean designing in handles or features that make it easier to grip the load, such as 'sticky grip' areas on plastic sacks.

The HSE explain the benefits of good design in their case study related to trench blocks used for straight runs of foundations.

Large heavy trench blocks were used to build foundations. The combination of block weight and poor posture when working in a restricted space exposed workers to manual handling risks and finger trapping.

Lighter trench blocks (weighing less than 20kg) with handholds were designed and made available in place of the traditional heavier units.

Figure 4-20: Mechanical assistance.　　*Source: RMS.*

The benefits included:

- Lighter blocks help to reduce manual handling risks.
- Handholds make the blocks easier to lift and reduce the risk of finger trapping when lowered into position.
- Blocks had a tongue and groove system, which makes them easier and quicker to install.

AUTOMATION

The opportunities for automation in the construction industry are limited; however automation can include work carried out away from the site in order to prepare materials. When materials are manufactured with features included, pre-assembled or pre-prepared for fixing, it can greatly limit risks from manual handling tasks.

MECHANISATION

This involves the use of handling aids. Although this may retain some elements of manual handling, bodily forces are applied more efficiently.

Examples are:

Levers	Reduces bodily force to move a load. Can avoid trapping fingers.
Hoists	Can support weights, allowing handler to position load.
Trolley, sack truck, truck roller or hoist	Reduces effort to move loads horizontally.
Chutes	A way of using gravity to move loads from one place to another.
Handling devices	Hand-held hooks or suction pads can help when handling a load that is difficult to grasp.

Figure 4-21: Mechanical aids. *Source: HSE, Guidance L23.*

Figure 4-22: Brick/tile conveyor. *Source: Mace Industries Ltd.*

OTHER CONSIDERATIONS

Involving the workforce

Effort should be made to seek contributions from employees and, where applicable, safety representatives or representatives of employee safety.

Training

Employers should ensure that all employees who carry out manual handling operations receive the necessary training to enable them to carry out the task in a safe and healthy manner.

A training programme should include:

- How potentially hazardous loads may be recognised.
- How to deal with unfamiliar loads.
- The proper use of handling aids.
- The proper use of personal protective equipment.
- The importance of good housekeeping.
- Features of the working environments that contribute to health and safety.
- Factors affecting individual capability.
- Good handling techniques.

For training to be effective it should be ongoing, to reflect improved techniques developed by experienced workers, and be supported by periodic refresher training and supervision.

Efficient movement principles for manually lifting loads

LIFTING TECHNIQUES USING KINETIC HANDLING PRINCIPLES

Kinetic lifting is a method of lifting that takes into account the body's characteristics and how it works most effectively. It ensures that lifting is carried out without placing unnecessary strain and pressure on vulnerable body parts.

Figure 4-23: Basic lifting techniques.   *Source: HSE Guidance L23.*

The principles of good lifting and moving techniques have been established for some considerable time. The basic principles are:

- ***Think before lifting/handling.*** Plan the lift. Can handling aids be used? Where is the load going to be placed? Will help be needed with the load? Remove obstructions such as discarded wrapping materials. When a load is to be lifted or lowered a significant distance, consider resting the load midway on a table or bench. This will provide an opportunity for the worker's body to recover and to renew their grip of the load.
- ***Keep the load close to the waist.*** Keep the load close to the body for as long as possible while lifting. Keep the heaviest side of the load next to the body. If a close approach to the load is not possible, before starting to lift it, try to slide the load towards the body before attempting to lift it.
- ***Adopt a stable position.*** The feet should be apart with one leg slightly forward to maintain balance (alongside the load, if it is on the ground). The worker should be prepared to move their feet during the lift to maintain their stability. Avoid tight clothing or unsuitable footwear, which may make this difficult.
- ***Get a good hold.*** Where possible the load should be hugged as close as possible to the body. This may be better than gripping it tightly with hands only.
- ***Start in a good posture.*** At the start of the lift, slight bending of the back, hips and knees is preferable to fully flexing the back (stooping) or fully flexing the hips and knees (squatting).
- ***Don't flex the back any further while lifting.*** This can happen if the legs begin to straighten before starting to raise the load.
- ***Avoid twisting the back or leaning sideways,*** especially while the back is bent. Shoulders should be kept level and facing in the same direction as the hips. Turning by moving the feet is better than twisting and lifting at the same time.
- ***Keep the head up when handling.*** Look ahead once the load has been held securely, not down at the load.
- ***Move smoothly.*** The load should not be jerked or snatched as this can make it harder to keep control and may increase the risk of injury.
- ***Don't lift or handle more than can be easily managed.*** There is a difference between what people can lift and what they can safely lift. If in doubt, seek advice or get help.
- ***Put the load down, then adjust its position.*** If precise positioning of the load is necessary, put it down first, then slide it into the desired position.

POOR POSTURE

Injuries that are received as a result of carrying out manual handling operations need not necessarily arise solely from lifting large, awkward or heavy items. Poor posture can greatly increase the likelihood of suffering manual handling injuries. Postures that are sustained for a period of time or awkward are particularly hazardous. A sustained posture is where part of or the whole body is kept in the same position for a prolonged period. Sustained postures restrict blood flow to the muscles and tendons resulting in less opportunity for them to work well and recover, causing them to fatigue very quickly.

Examples of tasks that frequently lead to sustained posture include:

- Supporting plasterboard sheeting while it is nailed into place.
- Laying a floor.

An awkward posture is where a part of the body is used well beyond its neutral position. A neutral position is where the trunk and head are upright, the arms are by the side of the body, forearms are hanging straight or at a right angle to the upper arm, and the hand is in the handshake position. For example, when a worker's arm is hanging straight down with the elbow by the side of the body, the shoulder is in a neutral position. However, when workers perform overhead work their arms and shoulders are significantly outside the neutral position.

When awkward postures are adopted, because muscles are less efficient at the extremes of the joint range, additional muscular effort is needed to maintain body positions. Awkward postures can also result in friction and compression of soft tissues, leading to injury.

Many construction and maintenance tasks can encourage the worker to take up an awkward posture so they are crouched or bent over for a period of time, for example, painting tasks that require a worker to work at low level. Awkward postures include:

- Posture that is unbalanced or asymmetrical.
- Postures that require extreme joint angles or bending and twisting.
- Squatting while servicing plant or a vehicle.
- Working with arms overhead.
- Bending over a desk or table.
- Using a hand tool that causes the wrist to be bent to the side.
- Kneeling while trowelling concrete or laying carpet.
- Bending the neck or back to the side to see around bulky items pushed on a trolley.

Figure 4-24: Sustained posture. *Source: Australia, Comcare.*

When carrying out an assessment of manual handling tasks that may have poor posture, the following areas and questions should be considered:

Head/neck posture	Does the task involve holding the neck bent or twisted part of the time or more than half of the time?
Back posture	Does the task involve the body being bent forward, sideways or twisted part of the time or more than half of the time?
Shoulder/arm posture	Is one or both of the elbows raised away from the body part of the time or more than half of the time?
Static shoulder and elbows	Is one or both of the shoulders and elbows in a static position (i.e. infrequently moved), for example, for more than 1 hour?
Wrist posture	Is one or both of the wrists bent or deviated a part of the time or more than half of the time?
Hand and finger grip	Is a pinch or wide finger grip being used for a part of the time or more than half of the time?
Static fingers, hand and wrist	Are one or both hands and wrists in a static position (i.e. infrequently moved), for example, for more than 1 hour?

Manual handling operations should be examined to identify those activities that involve poor posture. As with other aspects of manual handling, risks from poor posture should be avoided or minimised by the use of design, automation, mechanisation or other means. Training should be given in manual handling techniques that include good posture.

REPETITIVE MOVEMENTS

Repetitive movements take place when manual handling tasks are made up of a sequence of actions, of fairly short duration, which are repeated over and over again, and which are almost always the same. This requires the same muscle groups to be used repeatedly. Rapid or prolonged repetition may not allow sufficient time for recovery and can cause muscle fatigue. Repeated movements may cause inflammation or degeneration of soft tissues. Many construction tasks have repetitive movements, for example, hammering nails, laying bricks or block, applying plaster, tightening/loosing nuts on scaffold clips digging an excavation using a hand shovel.

This means that many workers may be exposed to the risks from repetitive manual handling movements. It should be remembered that one of the main methods used to reduce the risk of manual handling is to change the load by repackaging it into smaller weights or breaking a bulk load down into smaller batches. This solution avoids the need to lift heavy items. However, it will increase the frequency of manual handling movements and may lead to a significant repetitive movement risk. When carrying out an assessment of manual handling tasks that may have repetitive movements the following areas and questions should be considered:

Repetition	Does the task involve repeating the same motion every few seconds?
	Does the task involve a sequence of movements repeated more than twice per minute?
	Does the task involve more than 50% of the cycle time involved in performing the same sequence of motions?
Force	Does the task require moderate or strong force to be exerted?
Breaks	Does the worker conduct the task continuously, for example, for more than 1 hour?
Work pace	Is it sometimes or often difficult to keep up with the work?

Where manual handling involves a significant amount of repetitive movements, suitable breaks or job rotation should be introduced. Job rotation can enable the work involving repetitive movements to be shared between workers, reducing the effects on any one worker. Mechanical assistance may also be introduced to reduce the effort required to carry out the repetitive movements, which reduces possible effects on the worker. Similarly, the speed required for the repetitive movements may be able to be adjusted so that the effort required over a period of time is reduced and the worker is less likely to become fatigued.

AWKWARD MOVEMENTS

An awkward movement is where a part of the body is moved well beyond its neutral position. Awkward movements include excessive stretching, bending at the waist using the spine and twisting, for example, twisting the spine or wrist.

Whilst standing is considered to be the more suitable posture for lifting, it should also be noted that some awkward movements made in the standing position can increase risk. A twisting motion of the spine of 45 degrees will result in a 10% reduction in lifting capability, while a twisting motion of 90 degrees will result in a 20% reduction.

Figure 4-25: Awkward movements. *Source: HSE, HSG60.*

Awkward twisting movements can also involve twisting the arm or wrist, for example, when using a spanner. When a spanner is used to tighten or loosen a nut the arm and spanner is rotated and can cause the arm and wrist to twist into an awkward position.

Similarly, an awkward twisting movement is created when screws are tightened using a hand powered screw driver. An awkward movement may also involve excessive reaching to get something from a very high storage shelf, reaching behind or reaching to the side. Awkward bending movements often take place where workers do not adopt good lifting techniques, particular where features of the workplace encourage the worker to use a top heavy bending action to remove a load from a low storage place. Awkward manual handling movements present significant risk of injury because they can involve workers in moving loads while putting parts of their body into awkward positions. This combination of factors can lead to sudden injury or cumulative strain of soft tissues. It is important that where it is reasonably practicable awkward movements are avoided, for example, if a power tool was used to tighten or undo nuts it would avoid the awkward twisting movement that using a spanner or screwdriver can cause.

Improved design of workstations and better use of manual handling aids like conveyors may reduce the need for twisting and reaching. It is also important that there are sufficient rest periods or work rotation built into the work activity to allow relief of the muscles likely to be affected.

4.3 - Lifting and moving equipment

Hazards and controls for mechanically operated load handling equipment

FORK-LIFT TRUCKS

Hazards

Although the fork-lift truck (FLT) is a very useful machine for moving materials in many industries, it features prominently in accidents.

Every year many deaths and injuries can be attributed to fork-lift trucks and these can be analysed as follows:

Injuries to driver.	40%.
Injuries to assistant.	20%.
Injuries to pedestrians.	40% of which 80% were fractures with some 60% resulting in injuries to ankles and feet.

Unless preventative action is taken these accidents are likely to increase as fork-lift trucks are increasingly used in the workplace.

As about 45% of the accidents can be wholly or partly attributed to operator error, the need for proper operator training is underlined. There are, however, many other causes of accident including inadequate premises, gangways, poor truck maintenance, lighting etc.

The main hazards related to fork-lift trucks include:

- Overturning:
  - Driving too fast.
  - Sudden braking.
  - Driving on slopes.
  - Driving with load elevated.
- Collisions:
  - With buildings.
  - With pedestrians.
  - With other vehicles.
- Overloading:
  - Exceeding maximum capacity.
- Failure:
  - Load-bearing part (for example, chain).
- Loss of load:
  - Insecure load.
  - Poor floor surface.
  - Sudden starting or stopping of the vehicle.
  - Driving forward down slopes.

How overturning and overloading can occur when using a fork-lift truck is explained in the following sections. It should be noted that fork-lift trucks, unless specifically designed to do so, are not intended for carrying passengers. Many of the hazards outlined for fork-lift trucks, including rough terrain for lift trucks, are equally applicable to other equipment used for load handling and may be seen as generic hazards of mobile mechanically operated load handling equipment.

Overturning

The stability of fork-lift trucks is particularly affected by the forces generated when turning, especially at speed, or if the equipment is tilted sideways, for example, by travelling across an incline or by the wheels running into a pothole or over an obstruction.

The danger of a fork-lift truck being turned on its side is greater with the load in the raised position *(see figure ref 4-26a)*, than in the lowered position *(see figure ref 4-26b)*.

(a)   (b)

Figure 4-26: Overturning of a fork-lift truck. *Source: HSE, HSG6 - Safety in working with lift trucks.*

Over balancing

The mass of a counterbalance fork-lift truck acts as a counterweight so that the load can be lifted and moved without the lift truck overbalancing and tipping forwards *(see figure ref 4-27a)*. However, the fork-lift truck can be overbalanced and tip forward if the fork-lift truck is overloaded.

Overloading may be caused if the load is too heavy *(see figure ref 4-27b)*, if the load is incorrectly placed on the forks so that it is too far forward *(see figure ref 4-27c)*, or if the fork-lift truck accelerates or brakes sharply while carrying a heavy load.

(a)   (b)   (c)

Figure 4-27: Overbalancing of fork-lift truck.   *Source: HSE, HSG6 - Safety in working with lift trucks.*

This may not cause the fork-lift truck to overturn, but the overbalancing can injure the operator and lead to loss of control of steering. Control of steering may be lost because counterbalance fork-lift trucks usually have rear-wheel steering and overbalancing lifts the rear of a counterbalance fork-lift truck from the ground, preventing the steering wheels from contacting the ground properly.

Collisions with other vehicles, pedestrians or fixed objects

People may appear unexpectedly from a part of a building structure or workers intent on their work may step away from where they are working to collect materials or tools. Often the space in workplaces such as construction sites is restricted. Material may be stored at a height because it is large or to maximise the available space.

This in turn leads to restricted visibility, especially at busy junctions where vehicles come together. Loads transported by fork-lift trucks may obstruct the driver's vision and cause them to look to alternate sides of the load in order to see past it. Any of these may lead to collisions with other vehicles and pedestrians or, in the avoidance of these, fixed objects.

When travelling with a load a fork-lift truck should have the forks tilted to cradle the load. If this is not carried out there is a risk that the load may slide from the forks and hit someone or something.

Fork-lift trucks often have a limited or no suspension system to reduce the effects of the wheels going over rough surfaces. This means that the shock of impact with ruts and small bumps can be transmitted readily to the forks and the load, or part of it, may be dislodged and caused to fall.

A fork-lift truck has an open framework that can allow a person to put a part of their body, typically their head or hand, outside the protective structure. Many injuries have occurred to fork-lift truck drivers who, while driving forward with a load obstructing their view, lean out to look round the load and their head strikes a fixed object.

Figure 4-28: Poor visibility loading.   *Source: RMS.*

Loading and unloading

There is a hazard of objects falling on a vehicle driver during loading and unloading operations, particularly where the fork-lift truck is used to load materials at a height or to remove materials from delivery vehicles.

Control measures

Many of the control measures set out for fork-lift trucks would be equally applicable to other mobile work equipment used for load handling and may be seen as generic control measures for mechanically operated load handling equipment.

Traffic routes

The control measures related to traffic routes include:

- Separate routes, designated crossing places and suitable barriers at recognised danger spots.
- Roads, gangways and aisles should have sufficient width and overhead clearance for the largest fork-lift truck.
- Clear direction signs.
- Sharp bends and overhead obstructions should be avoided.
- The ground surface should be in good condition, taking into account a rough terrain fork-lift truck's ability.
- Any gradient in a fork-lift truck operating area should be kept as gentle as possible.

Parking areas

Sufficient and suitable parking areas should be provided away from the main work area. Designated parking areas must be clearly identified. They should be on firm, level ground and located such that they do not obstruct fire points or other traffic routes, especially those for emergency access and exit.

When the fork-lift truck is parked or left unattended the driver should ensure that the mast is tilted slightly forward with the forks resting on the floor, the power is switched off, the brake is applied, and the key removed and returned to a responsible person to prevent unauthorised use.

Protection of personnel

There is a need to alert people to the hazard when working in or near a fork-lift truck operating area. Signs may be used to indicate the general operation of vehicles in the area. These can be supplemented by *visual and audible warning systems* that confirm the presence of a vehicle, such as a flashing light on the top of a fork-lift truck.

Driver protection

In many work vehicle accidents/incidents the driver is injured because the vehicle does not offer protection when it rolls over or it does not restrain the driver to prevent them falling out of the vehicle and being injured by the fall or the vehicle falling on them. Vehicles with open cabs, such as fork-lift trucks, may present this risk.

Where there is a risk of the fork-lift truck overturning, a restraint system should be fitted and would typically involve some sort of adjustable seat-belt.

Selection of equipment

There are many types of fork-lift truck available for a range of activities. There are many situations when specialist trucks such as reach trucks, overhead telescopic or rough terrain trucks are required. Many accidents happen due to the incorrect selection and/or use of fork-lift trucks.

Rider-operated counterbalance fork-lift truck

This type of fork-lift truck has a counterweight to balance the load on the forks. The forks and load project out from the front of the truck. Loads can be raised or lowered vertically and the mast may be tilted forward or backward.

This type of truck is only suitable for use on substantially firm, smooth, level and prepared surfaces. A wide range of attachments is available.

Figure 4-29: Rider operated fork-lift truck (counterbalance type). *Source: RMS.*

Figure 4-30: Rider operated fork-lift truck (reach type). *Source: RMS.*

Rider-operated reach fork-lift truck

This type of fork-lift truck is called a reach truck because the mast is capable of being moved forward (reached out) to pick up the load.

For travelling, the load is reached back and carried within the wheelbase of the fork-lift truck. This allows greater manoeuvrability in areas where space is restricted.

This type of fork-lift truck is only suitable for use on substantially firm, smooth, level and prepared surfaces and is used particularly in warehouses.

Rough terrain counterbalance fork-lift truck

The rough terrain counterbalance fork-lift truck is similar in design to the standard counterbalanced fork-lift truck but is equipped with larger wheels and pneumatic tyres, giving it greater ground clearance.

It has greater ability to operate on uneven and soft ground and is mainly used in the construction industry and in agriculture. It may be used with a range of attachments.

Figure 4-31: Rough terrain counterbalance fork-lift truck. *Source: HSE, HSG6.*

Figure 4-32: Telescopic materials handler. *Source: HSE, HSG6.*

Telescopic materials handler

This form of fork-lift truck is fitted with a boom that is pivoted at the rear of the machine. The boom is raised and lowered by hydraulic rams.

In addition, the boom can be extended or retracted (telescoped) to give extra reach or height. These machines may be two-wheel or four-wheel drive, and have two-wheel, four-wheel or crab steering. They are used mainly in agriculture and the construction industry. A range of attachments may be used with them.

Figure 4-33: Side-loading fork-lift truck. *Source: HSE, HSG6.*

Figure 4-34: Pedestrian-controlled fork-lift truck. *Source: HSE, HSG6.*

Side-loading fork-lift truck

When using a side-loading fork-lift truck the driver is positioned at the front and to one side of the load-bearing deck. The load is carried on the deck of the truck, the mast being traversed out sideways to pick up or set down the load. This type of fork-lift truck is used for stacking and moving long loads such as bales of timber and pipes, and may be fitted with stabilisers for use when picking up or setting down loads.

Pedestrian-controlled fork-lift truck

This type of fork-lift truck has a limited lift height, usually not greater than two metres. It may be electrically or manually powered for lifting and for movement. The operator walks with the truck and controls it with a handle.

Large fork-lift truck

The large fork-lift truck may be either masted or telescopic and is often fitted with a spreader for lifting freight containers. The spreader may be attached to the side or top of the container. These are specialist fork-lift trucks used mainly in container terminals.

When choosing the right fork-lift truck for the job the following factors should be taken into account:

■ Power source - the choice of battery or diesel will depend on whether the truck is to be used indoors or outdoors. Where fork-lift trucks are used indoors, for example, inside large buildings under construction it is preferable to use battery operated lift trucks to avoid the hazard of exhaust gases from diesel trucks.
■ Tyres - solid or pneumatic depending on the terrain.
■ Size and capacity - dependent on the size and nature of loads to be moved.
■ Height of the mast: a large mast may be an advantage with a rough terrain lift truck used outside but may be a disadvantage when used indoors to move materials.

- Audible and/or visual warning systems fitted according to the proximity of pedestrians.
- Protection from risks of falling objects and overturning provided for the operator. Rough terrain might increase the likelihood of overturning loose objects may fall from a load or storage racking.
- Training given to operators must be related specifically to the type of fork-lift truck.
- Provision of a suitable mechanism to prevent unauthorised use, for example, key or electronic pad.

Figure 4-35: Large fork-lift truck.　　　*Source: HSE, HSG6.*

Figure 4-36: Rough terrain fork-lift truck.　　　*Source: RMS.*

Figure 4-37: Keys - unauthorised use not controlled. *Source: RMS.*

Figure 4-38: Pin pad to prevent unauthorised use. *Source: RMS.*

Provision of information

Drivers and supervisors of fork-lift trucks should be familiar with the following information, which should be shown on the truck:

- Name of the manufacturer (or authorised supplier) of the fork-lift truck.
- Model designation.
- Serial number.
- Unladen weight.

- Rated weight carrying capacity.
- Load centre distance.
- Maximum lift height.
- Inflation pressures of pneumatic tyres.

In addition, the functions of all the controls should be clearly marked so that they can be seen from the driver's position.

Operators

No one should be permitted to operate a fork-lift truck or mobile plant unless they have been selected, trained and authorised to do so, or are undergoing properly organised formal training.

Selection of personnel

The safe use of fork-lift trucks calls for a reasonable degree of both physical and mental fitness and of intelligence. The selection procedure should be devised to identify people who have shown themselves reliable and mature during their early years at work.

Training

Training should consist of three stages, the last being the one in which the operator is introduced to his future work environment. This is illustrated by the stages of training of a fork-lift truck operator.

Stage 1 - should contain the basic skills and knowledge required to operate the fork-lift truck safely, to understand the basic mechanics and balance of the machine, and to carry out routine daily checks.

Stage 2 - under strict training conditions closed to other personnel. This stage should include:

- Knowledge of the operating principles and controls.
- Use of the fork-lift truck in gangways, slopes, cold-stores, confined spaces and bad weather conditions as appropriate.
- The work to be undertaken, for example, loading and unloading vehicles or lifting to materials platforms at height.

Stage 3 - after successfully completing the first two stages, the operator should be given further familiarisation and where necessary instruction in the usual place of work for the fork-lift truck.

Testing - on completion of training, the operator should be examined and tested to ensure that he/she has achieved the required standard.

Refresher training - if high standards are to be maintained, periodic refresher training and testing is essential good practice.

Daily checks/pre-use inspection

A checklist for daily checks should include items such as the condition and pressure of tyres, the integrity and proper functioning of lights, horns, brakes, steering and mirrors, the absence of oil leaks and that the seat is securely fixed (with properly functioning and intact restraints where fitted).

The fork-lift truck should also be checked for obvious signs of damage to its bodywork and lifting mechanism, and for the security of any equipment fitted such as liquefied petroleum gas (LPG) cylinders.

If the fork-lift truck is to use attachment accessories, for example, forks or drum grabs, the driver should ensure they are correctly fitted and secured.

Thorough examination of load-bearing parts

The load-bearing parts of fork-lift trucks, for example, the lifting chain, should be thoroughly examined periodically to determine any wear or damage that could affect the integrity of the lifting equipment that forms part of the fork-lift truck.

The Lifting Operations and Lifting Equipment Regulations (LOLER) 1998 specifies that load-bearing parts of fork-lift trucks used only to lift goods must be thorough examinations every 12 months.

Where fork-lift trucks are used to lift people the load-bearing parts must be thoroughly examined every six months.

Summary of controls measures for fork-lift trucks

The control measures for fork-lift trucks include both precautions and procedures and can be summarised as:

- Make someone responsible for fork-lift truck operation.
- Select and train drivers thoroughly.
- Daily fork-lift truck checks.
- Keep keys secure. *Do not leave in the ignition.*
- Maintain and light traffic routes.
- Separate fork-lift trucks and pedestrians.

A vigorous management policy covering operator training, vehicle maintenance and sound systems of work, supported by good supervision will reduce personal injury and damage to equipment and materials. This in turn will lead to better utilisation of plant and increased materials handling efficiency.

TELEHANDLERS

Hazards

Telehandlers are all-purpose machines that can be used for construction site preparation, material handling, scaffold erection, elevated work platforms and for final site clean-up. A telehandler consists of a heavy duty chassis, body and lifting gear on large diameter wheels and deep tread pneumatic traction tyres. Increased power required to cope with the demands of construction sites is transferred through larger drive shafts/wheels and generally larger and heavier duty mechanical ancillary items.

In the case of a telehandler, hazards include moving large hydraulic rams that actuate the front forks or bucket with hydraulic hoses attached that are under high pressure. Materials handling is through various attachments fixed to a boom that enables vertical, horizontal and diagonal reach. Construction sites are finding various uses for telehandlers and, with the different attachments available, greater flexibility is provided for the variety of jobs that may be encountered.

Hazards include the generic hazards of mobile load handling equipment and are similar to that of a rough terrain fork-lift truck. There are various mechanical hazards involved, such as impact, crush, trap, and shear. In addition to these there are non-mechanical hazards such as heat, fumes, chemicals and noise.

Control measures

Control measures should include: use only by competent operators, barriers to segregate pedestrians from machinery to a safe distance, good visibility with the assistance of mirrors, high-visibility clothing for those working nearby, and seat restraints for the operator who should be enclosed in a protective cage that can also act as a guard against contact with moving machinery and the effects of overturning.

Figure 4-39: Telehandler.   *Source: HSE, HSG6.*

Figure 4-40: Dumper truck.   *Source: RMS.*

DUMPER TRUCKS

Hazards

A dumper truck is a general piece of plant consisting of a heavy-duty chassis, body and tipping bucket on large diameter wheels and deep tread, traction tyres, used for transporting materials around a construction site or street works. The equipment is generally used as a large mechanised wheelbarrow.

Hazards include the generic hazards associated with mobile load handling equipment. Specific hazards associated with dumper trucks are the risk of complete 360° rollover, impact with pedestrians or vehicles, trap and crush beneath the tipping bucket as it discharges its contents, falling items or objects from the bucket, high pressure hydraulic lines and tipping over on unstable ground or into excavations. Other hazards include noise, chemicals and fumes emitted from the exhaust of the dumper truck.

Possible causes of a dumper truck overturning include:

- Overloading or uneven loading of the bucket.
- Cornering at excessive speed.
- Hitting obstructions.
- Driving too close to the edges of embankments or excavations.
- Mechanical defects that occur because of lack of maintenance.
- Inappropriate or unequal tyre pressures.
- Driving across slopes.

Control measures

Control measures should include trained, authorised, operatives; maintenance and inspection; segregation of pedestrians to a safe distance by the provision of suitable barriers and signs advising of the dangers of operating plant; stop blocks for tipping into excavations; seat restraints and rollover protection for the operator.

EXCAVATORS

Hazards

Consisting of a heavy duty chassis, fixed or rotating body and digging gear (jib arms and bucket) on large diameter wheels and deep tread, pneumatic traction tyres or caterpillar track system.

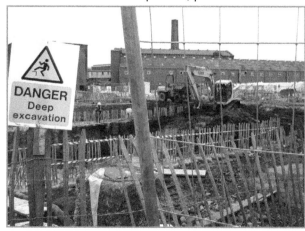

Figure 4-41: Excavator hazards.   *Source: RMS.*

Figure 4-42: Excavator.   *Source: RMS.*

Specific hazards associated with excavators are impact with pedestrians or vehicles by swinging jibs and booms, trap and crush beneath the excavator bucket as it digs into the ground or discharges its contents, falling items or objects from the bucket, high pressure hydraulic lines and tipping over on unstable ground or into excavations.

Other hazards include noise, chemicals and exhaust fumes. The exhaust fumes may find their way into excavations while digging the trench.

Excavation equipment is generally adapted and used for a variety of different purposes that it may not specifically be designed for, including towing/shunting, lifting, loading/unloading transport of articles and equipment. The fact that these are improvised activities increases the risk of injury.

Control measures

Control measures should include trained and authorised operatives; not overloading the bucket; maintenance and inspection; segregation of pedestrians to a safe distance by the provision of suitable barriers and signs advising of the dangers of operating plant; good visibility with the assistance of mirrors where necessary, high-visibility clothing for those working nearby, seat restraints for the operator who should be enclosed in a protective cage that can also act as a guard against contact with moving machinery and the effects of overturning.

LIFTS AND HOISTS

Lifts and hoists are used for transporting people and goods between different levels. They can be found in a variety of buildings/structures, including temporary structures on constructions sites. Small, mobile devices are also used to lift and hoist materials or people.

Lifts are generally lifting equipment that raises the item to be moved from below, often using some form of mechanical or hydraulic mechanism. These include passenger and goods lifts, scissor lifts, vehicle inspection lifts and mobile elevating work platforms (MEWPs). The term 'lift' is often used in common language to describe lifting equipment used to move people in a building, even though the lifting equipment often uses a hoist mechanism.

Hoists are generally lifting equipment that raises the item to be moved from above, often using some form of rope (for example, man-made, artificial fibre or wire rope). These include platform hoists and hand operated gin wheels.

Hazards

In general, the hazards associated with lifts and hoists are the same as with any other lifting equipment.

- The lift/hoist may overturn or collapse.
- The lift/hoist may fail to stop in a safe position at the top, bottom or landing level.
- The lift/hoist can strike who may be near or under the platform or cage.
- As the platform or cage moves, the load, including people, may come into contact with fixed or moving structures and objects, for example, landing level structures.
- The supporting ropes may fail and the platform/cage falls to the ground.
- The load, including people, or part of the load may fall.
- The lift/hoist may fail in a high position.
- People in and around the lift/hoist machinery may get trapped or entangled in moving parts.

Control measures

If lifts and hoist are properly designed, installed and maintained there is relatively little risk from their operation.

All lifts and hoists require:

- Statutory safety devices.
- Holdback mechanisms that operate where the lifting mechanism fails, for example, rope failure.
- Overrun trip to prevent the platform/cage being lifted or lowered beyond a safe limit. For example, overrun trip devices that prevent the platform/cage contacting the lifting gear at the top or being winched over the top of a drum.
- Guards on lift/hoist machinery, for example, to prevent entanglement with the moving parts of the machinery.
- Guards to prevent contact with the car/gage or platform when it is moving.
- Landing gates (securely closed during operation).
- Suitable lighting on all lift/hoist landings to reduce the risk of people tripping or falling.
- The safe working load of the lift/hoist to be clearly marked and visible to the user/operator.

Figure 4-43: Construction platform hoist. *Source: HSE, HSG150.*

In addition, passenger hoists/lifts require more sophisticated controls:

■ Operating controls inside the car/cage.
■ Electromagnetic interlocks on the car/cage doors.
■ The enclosing shaft must be of fire-proof construction, if within a building.

The lift/hoist should be protected by a substantial enclosure to prevent anyone from being struck by any moving part of the hoist or material that falls down the hoist way.

Gates must be provided at all access landings, including at ground level. The gates must be kept shut, except when the platform is at the landing. The controls should be arranged so that the lift/hoist can be operated from one position only, which may be from within the lift/hoist.

If an operator is provided they must be trained and competent. The safe working load of the lift/hoist must be clearly marked and visible to the operator. If the lift/hoist is for materials only there should be a prominent warning notice on the platform or cage to stop people riding on it.

Lifts and hoists that carry people are required to be thoroughly examined every six months and lifts and hoists that only carry goods are required to be thoroughly examined every twelve months.

Alternatively, thorough examination can be at intervals detailed in an examination scheme drawn up by a competent person based on an assessment of risks.

The lift/hoist should be regularly serviced by a reputable maintenance company (approximately every three months).

Figure 4-44: Material hoist.   *Source: HSS.*

The service report provided should relate to the efficient working of the lift/hoist and is not a substitute for the thorough examination. A daily, pre-use check by the user and/or weekly inspection by an engineer should be made to ensure the lift/hoist is in working order. Any remedial work identified to be necessary should receive prompt attention.

Other procedures for the safe operation of lifts and hoists include:

■ Ensuring that unauthorised people cannot open the landing doors to the lift shaft unless the lift is level with the landing floor.
■ Ensuring people are informed not to use the lifts during a fire evacuation, by putting up warning notices at lift landings and around the building, and using the public address system where available.
■ Ensuring that the alarm bell can be activated easily and that the alarm is heard by people who know what to do when it sounds.
■ Ensuring that the entrance to the area containing lifting equipment to raise and lower the platform is secured and locked in order to prevent unauthorised access. The key to this area and the lift/hoist landing doors should be kept in a secure position, controlled by a responsible person and be available at all times to authorised personnel.
■ Procedures for rescuing people trapped in passenger lifts/hoists. Where this is to be carried out by workers, they should be provided adequate training on this procedure. Written rescue procedures should be displayed at appropriate locations.

Additional procedures for hoists controlled by an operator

Only workers who have been trained in the proper use of hoists should be allowed to operate them. The lifting capacity of the hoist must be clearly marked and be visible to the operator and cage-controlled hoists must be equipped with effective warning devices.

Operators should understand that they are prohibited from carrying loads over people and any hoist malfunction should be reported to their supervisor immediately.

Before operation, operators should check that the hoist chains or ropes are of sufficient strength and length to safely lift or otherwise handle the load. On a chain hoist, they should make sure the hook has a safety clip so that if the chain is given slack the hook will not come loose. The oil level on hydraulic hoists should also be periodically checked.

The legislation governing the construction, use and thorough examination of lifts and hoists, is the Lifting Operations and Lifting Equipment Regulations (LOLER) 1998. ***See the 'Relevant Statutory Provisions' section and later in this element for further details.***

SCISSOR LIFTS

Scissor lifts can provide excellent movement of goods to the desired level. They are therefore particularly useful for loading or unloading goods from vehicles and to storage levels in warehouses.

Hazards

Hazards of use of scissor lifts include:

- Crush injuries that may occur as the platform is raised to or past a fixed part of a structure.
- People, equipment or materials falling from the platform.
- The scissor lift may collapse, for example, due to being overload.
- Overturning, for example, due to operating it on particularly uneven ground.
- The sheer effect of the scissor mechanism as it closes.

Controls measures

Before using the scissor lift ensure:

- Whoever is operating it is fully trained and competent.

Figure 4-45: Scissor lift.   Source: HSE, HSG150.

- The scissor lift is fitted with a guard covering the scissor mechanism to a height that is reasonably practicable.
- Anyone in the area is kept clear of the work area.
- That it is not possible to insert a foot or similar part of the body underneath the lifting platform when it is being lowered.
- That there is a safe system of work for the retrieval of items dropped down near the scissor mechanism and for maintenance underneath it.

MOBILE AND TOWER CRANES

Hazards

The principal hazards associated with any lifting operation are:

- **Overturning,** which can be caused by weak support, operating outside the capabilities of the machine, uneven or weak ground (cellars or drains), outriggers not extended, insufficient counter weight, adverse weather and by striking obstructions.
- **Overloading,** by exceeding the operating capacity or operating radii, or by failure of safety devices.
- **Collision,** with other cranes, overhead cables, structures or people.
- **Failure of load-bearing part,** from failure of structural components of the crane itself or an accessory fitted to it. This may be due to overloading or degradation of the load-bearing part due to damage, use (wear) or faults (corrosion).

Figure 4-46: Safety latch on hook. *Source: Corel Clipart.*

- **Loss of load**, from failure of lifting tackle, incorrect hook fittings or poor slinging procedure.
- People in and around the crane may get entanglement or trapped by moving parts.

Factors that will affect all cranes

The factors that can increase the risks from using cranes, which affect all cranes, include:

- Soft or uneven ground conditions.
- Underground voids or cellars that are not capable of bearing the weight of the crane and its load.
- Load-bearing capacity of the crane must be sufficient for the task.
- Adverse weather conditions such as heavy rain, high wind and extremes of temperature.
- Workers or members of the public nearby.
- Insufficient room for the lift.
- Proximity to overhead power lines, buildings or other cranes.
- Tall cranes, for example, construction tower cranes, located near an airport or in a flight path.

Control measures

General requirements for cranes

The main control measures associated with any crane and lifting operation include ensuring that:

- Lifting operations are properly planned by a competent person, appropriately supervised and carried out in a safe manner.
- The ground the crane stands on is it capable of bearing the load; check for underground services and cellars.
- The ground is level, if not, select a crane with hydraulic level adjustment stabilisers.

Figure 4-47: Tower crane. *Source: Domson.*

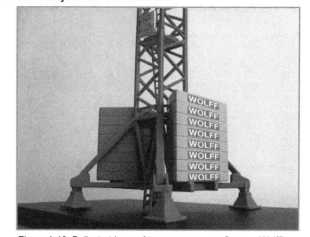

Figure 4-48: Ballast at base of tower crane. *Source: Wolffkran.*

- The load-bearing capacity of the crane is sufficient of for the task.
- The correct procedure is followed when erecting or dismantling any crane.
- The crane is positioned so that there is enough room for the lift and to avoid collision hazards.
- Non-essential people are kept clear of the work area.
- The crane is not operated in adverse weather conditions.
- The structural integrity of the crane is maintained; check for any signs of corrosion.
- A pre-use check is carried out by the operator.
- Lifting equipment is of adequate strength and stability for the load. Stresses induced at mounting or fixing points must be taken into account. Similarly, every part of a load, anything attached to it and used in lifting must be of adequate strength.
- The safe working load (SWL) is clearly marked on lifting machinery, equipment and accessories in order to ensure safe use. Where the SWL depends on the configuration of the machinery, it must be clearly marked for each configuration used and kept with the machinery.
- Passengers are not carried without authorisation, and never on lifting tackle.
- Equipment that is not designed for lifting persons, but which might be used as such, must have appropriate markings to the effect that it is not to be used for passengers.
- Load indicators are fitted. It is preferable that there are two types, a requirement with jib cranes, but beneficial if fitted to all cranes.
- Load/radius indicator is fitted. This shows the radius the crane is working at and the safe load for that radius. It must be visible to the operator.
- Automatic safe load indicator is fitted. This provides a visible warning when the SWL is approached and audible warning when the SWL is exceeded.
- Controls are clearly identified and of the 'hold to run' type.
- Over travel switches are fitted. These are limit switches to prevent the hook or sheave block being wound up to the cable drum.
- Access is provided. Safe access should be provided for the operator and for use during inspection and maintenance/emergency.
- The operating position provides clear visibility of hook and load, with the controls easily reached.
- Lifting tackle - chains, slings, wire ropes, eyebolts and shackles - should be tested before use and thoroughly examined periodically.

See also - 'Requirements for lifting operations' later in this section for more information.

Accessories

Lifting accessories include slings, hooks, chains, eyebolts, shackles, lifting beams and cradles. This equipment is designed with the aim of assisting in lifting items without the need for manual force. Because these accessories are in a constantly changing environment and are in and out of use they need to be protected from damage; a failure of any one item could result in a fatality. For example, lifting eyes need to be correctly fitted, slings have to be used with the correct technique and all equipment must be stored when not in use to prevent damage.

Accessories must be attached correctly and safely to the load by a competent person, and then the lifting equipment takes over the task of providing the necessary required power to perform the lift. As with all lifting equipment, accessories must be regularly inspected and certificated and only used by trained authorised persons.

Figure 4-49: Lifting operation.   *Source: RMS.*

Figure 4-50: Lifting points on load.   *Source: RMS.*

Figure 4-51: Safety latch on hook.   *Source: RMS.*

Figure 4-52: Accessories.   *Source: RMS.*

Hazards and control measures for manually operated load handling aids

WHEELBARROWS

A wheelbarrow is a low-tech fabrication, generally consisting of a shallow hopper style bucket supported on a single wheel at the front and two legs at the rear with handle bars for grip and use when moving. In use, the load being carried is pivoted and supported over the front wheel. There is still a need to manually handle materials when loading and unloading the wheel barrow, with speed of operation and the capacity of the truck governed by the individual that uses the equipment.

Hazards and control measures

Wheel barrows are typically manually driven pieces of equipment and the hazards arising from their use are generally of an ergonomic nature relating to posture and over exertion. Mechanical hazards are restricted to the single wheel of the barrow that only moves when moved by the operator.

Other associated hazards are tripping and falling whilst using the equipment or ejecting the contents of the barrow.

Control measures include indicating a safe working load for the equipment and the provision of information/instruction in the safe loading and use of the equipment for the operator.

SACK TRUCK

A sack truck is a simple fabrication fitted with two wheels on which the load is pivoted and supported when the truck is tilted back and pushed manually. A risk assessment must be made of manual handling operations associated with using equipment of this type. As with the wheelbarrow there is still a need to manually handle materials when using a sack truck.

Hazards and control measures

Sack trucks are typically manually powered and as with the wheelbarrow the hazards arising from their use are generally of an ergonomic nature relating to posture and over exertion through manual handling.

Mechanical hazards are restricted to the wheels of the truck that only move when moved by the operator. Other associated hazards are tripping and falling whilst using the equipment and manual handling back and strain injuries.

Figure 4-53: Wheelbarrow.   *Source: RMS.*   Figure 4-54: Sack truck.   *Source: RMS.*

Control measures include indicating a safe working load for the equipment and the provision of information/instruction in the safe loading and use of the equipment for the operator. A manual handling assessment may be required when using this equipment.

THE PALLET TRUCK

This truck has two elevating forks for insertion below the top deck of a pallet. When the forks are raised the load is moved clear of the ground to allow movement.

This truck may be designed for pedestrian or rider control. It has no mast and cannot be used for stacking. Pallet trucks may be powered or non-powered.

Hazards and control measures

Pallet trucks can be driven both manually or by quiet running electric motor. In addition, some pallet trucks have a lifting mechanism to raise and lower the load.

Hazards include crush from moving loads or momentum of the equipment when stopping, crush and trap in the forks of the equipment, manual handling strain injuries and electricity hazards from battery power points.

Control measures should include trained and authorised operatives; identification of safe working loads; inspection and maintenance; and designated areas for parking the equipment.

Figure 4-55: Battery-powered pallet truck. *Source: RMS.*   Figure 4-56: Manually operated pallet truck.   *Source: RMS.*

MANUALLY OPERATED HOISTS - GIN WHEEL

Gin wheel hoists provide a very convenient way of raising loads. They comprise a pulley wheel and rope suspended from a fixed point, for example, a scaffold. The material to be moved is attached to one end of the rope and is raised by pulling the other end.

Though they are simple pieces of equipment, care is required when assembling and using them. Gin wheels are in wide use on small construction sites, but are being replaced by small electric hoists that use a single wire rope to raise materials.

Hazards

The main hazards are:

■ The loss of the gin wheel and or any load from its fixing point.
■ The loss of load from the hook.

Controls measures

Ensure that the:

■ The gin wheel is securely fixed to the anchorage.
■ A proper hook is being used with a safety catch to secure the load.
■ A safe working platform exists from which the hook can be loaded or unloaded.

Figure 4-57: Gin wheel. *Source: Ambiguous.*

Requirements for lifting operations

CONTROL OF LIFTING OPERATIONS

Under Regulation 8 of the Lifting Operations and Lifting Equipment Regulation (LOLER) 1998 employers have a duty to ensure that every lifting operation involving lifting equipment for the purposes of lifting or lowering of a load is organised safely.

This will include ensuring the following:

■ Lifting operations to be properly planned by a competent person.
■ Provision of appropriate supervision.
■ Work is to be carried out in a safe manner.

STRONG, STABLE AND SUITABLE EQUIPMENT

Strength

Regulation 4 of LOLER 1998 requires every employer shall ensure that:

■ Lifting equipment is of adequate strength and stability for each load, having regard in particular to the stress induced at its mounting or fixing point.
■ Every part of a load and anything attached to it and used in lifting it is of adequate strength.

When assessing whether lifting equipment has adequate strength for the proposed use, the combined weight of the load and lifting accessories should be taken into account. It is important to consider the load, task and environment in order to match the strength of the lifting equipment to the circumstances of use. For example, if the environment is hot or cold this can affect the lifting capacity of the lifting equipment. In order to counteract this effect equipment with a higher rated safe working load may be needed.

Figure 4-58: Lifting points.   *Source: RMS.*

Figure 4-59: Lifting operations.   *Source: RMS.*

If the load to be lifted is a person, equipment with a generous capacity above the person's weight should be selected in order to provide an increased factor for safety. If the load is likely to move unexpectedly, because of the movement of an animal or liquids in a container, this sudden movement can put additional forces on the equipment and may necessitate equipment with higher strength to be selected. When lifting a load that is submerged in water, the initial lifting weight will be misleading because the load will be supported by the water. When the load emerges from the water the support will no longer be available and this sudden increase in weight can put additional stress on the crane and its lifting accessories.

When conducting the lifting task the lifting accessories may be used in such a way that may reduce its lifting capacity below its stated safe working load; sharp corners on a load and 'back hooking' can have this effect. In these circumstances accessories with a higher rated safe working load may be required.

It is essential to remember that in a lifting operation the equipment only has an overall lifting capacity equivalent to the item with the lowest strength. For example, in a situation where a crane with a lifting capacity of 50 tonnes is used with a hook of 10 tonnes capacity and a wire rope sling of 5 tonnes capacity this would give an overall maximum lifting strength/capacity of 5 tonnes.

Stability

A number of factors can affect the stability of lifting equipment, for example, wind conditions, slopes/cambers, stability of ground conditions and how the load is to be lifted. Lifting equipment must be positioned and installed so that it does not tip over when in use. Anchoring can be achieved by securing with guy ropes, bolting the structure to a foundation, using ballast as counterweights or using outriggers to bring the centre of gravity down to the base area. Mobile lifting equipment should be sited on firm ground with the wheels or outrigger feet having their weight distributed over a large surface area. Care should be taken that the equipment is not positioned over cellars, drains or underground cavities, or positioned near excavations. Sloping ground should be avoided as this can shift the load radius out or in, away from the safe working position. In the uphill position, the greatest danger occurs when the load is set down. This can cause the mobile lifting equipment to tip over. In the downhill position, the load moves out of the radius and may cause the equipment to tip forwards.

Suitability

Lifting equipment, and any accessories used for lifting, are pieces of work equipment under the Provision and Use of Work Equipment Regulations (PUWER) 1998.

Regulation 4 of PUWER 1998 states:

> *"Every employer shall ensure that work equipment is used only for operations for which, and under conditions for which, it is suitable in order to avoid any reasonably foreseeable risk to the health and safety of any person."*

Figure 4-60: Suitability of work equipment. *Source: PUWER 1998 Regulation 4.*

Most lifting equipment and lifting accessories will also fall within the scope of the European Union Machinery Directive, as implemented by the UK Supply of Machinery (Safety) Regulations. Such equipment must have been subject to conformity assessment, be appropriately CE marked and accompanied by a Declaration of Conformity (DoC) before being placed on the market or brought into use. This includes lifting equipment whose only source of power is directly applied human effort, for example, manually operated chain blocks and car jacks. The DoC, which must accompany the new product, is an important document, which should be retained by the user. The DoC may avoid the need for an initial thorough examination before first use in those cases where the safety of the equipment does not depend on the conditions of its installation or assembly. In order for lifting equipment to be suitable it must be of the correct type for the task, have a safe working load limit in excess of the load being lifted, and have the correct type and combination of lifting accessories attached.

Lifting equipment used within industry varies and includes mobile cranes, static tower cranes and overhead travelling cranes. The type of lifting equipment selected will depend on a number of factors including the weight of the load to be lifted, the radius of operation, the height of the lift, the time available, and the frequency of the lifting activities. This equipment is often very heavy, which means its weight can cause the ground underneath the equipment to sink or collapse. Other factors like height and size may have to be considered as there may be limitations in site roads that are located between structures or where overhead restrictions exist. Careful consideration of these factors must be made when selecting the correct crane. Selecting lifting equipment to carry out a lifting activity should be done at the planning stage, where the most suitable equipment can be identified that is able to meet all of the lifting requirements and the limitations of the location.

POSITIONED AND INSTALLED CORRECTLY

Lifting equipment must be positioned or installed so that the risk of the equipment striking a person is as low as is reasonably practicable.

Similarly, the risk of a load drifting, falling freely or being unintentionally released must also be considered and equipment positioned to take account of this. All nearby hazards, including overhead cables and uninsulated power supply conductors, should be identified and removed or covered by safe working procedures such as locking-off and permit systems.

The possibility of striking other lifting equipment or structures should also be examined.

Detailed consideration must be given to the location of any heavy piece of lifting equipment due to the fact that additional weight is distributed to the ground through the loading of the equipment when performing a lift.

Figure 4-61: Danger zone - crane and fixed item. *Source: HSE, HSG150.*

Surveys must be carried out to determine the nature of the ground, whether soft or firm, and what underground hazards are present such as buried services or hollow voids.

If the ground proves to be soft, then this can be covered using timber, digger mats or hard core to prevent the equipment or its outriggers sinking when under load. The surrounding environment must also be taken into consideration and factors may include highways, railways, electricity cables, areas of public interest. The area around where lifting equipment is sited should be securely fenced, including the extremes of the lift radius, with an additional factor of safety to allow for emergency arrangements such as emergency vehicle access or safety in the event of a collapse or fall.

Where practicable, lifting equipment should be positioned and installed such that loads are not carried or suspended over areas occupied by people. Where this is necessary appropriate systems of work should be used to ensure it is carried out safely.

If the operator cannot observe the full path of the load an appointed person (and assistants as appropriate) should be used to communicate the position of the load and provide directions to avoid striking anything or anyone.

VISIBLY MARKED (SWL)

The safe working load (SWL) must be clearly marked on lifting machinery, equipment and accessories in order to ensure safe use. Where the SWL depends on the configuration of the machinery, it must be clearly marked for each configuration used and kept with the machinery.

Accessories must be marked with supplementary information that indicates the characteristics for its safe use, for example, safe angles of lift.

Equipment designed for lifting people must be clearly marked as such and equipment which is not designed for lifting persons, but which might be used as such, must have appropriate markings to the effect that it is not to be used for lifting people.

Figure 4-62: Marking of accessories.   *Source: RMS.*

PLANNED, SUPERVISED AND CARRIED OUT IN SAFE MANNER BY COMPETENT PEOPLE

Regulation 8 of LOLER 1998 requires that every employer shall ensure that every lifting operation involving lifting equipment is:

- Properly planned by a competent person.
- Appropriately supervised.
- Carried out in a safe manner.

The type of lifting equipment that is to be used and the complexity of the lifting operations will dictate the degree of planning required for the lifting operation.

Planned

The plan should address the risks identified by the risk assessment and identify the resources required, the procedures and the responsibilities so that any lifting operation is carried out safely. The plan should ensure that the lifting equipment remains safe for the range of lifting operations for which the equipment might be used.

The type of lifting equipment that is to be used and the complexity of the lifting operations will dictate the degree of planning required for the lifting operation.

Planning combines two parts:

1) Initial planning to ensure that lifting equipment is provided which is suitable for the range of tasks that it will have to carry out.
2) Planning of individual lifting operations so that they can be carried out safely with the lifting equipment provided.

Factors that should be considered when formulating a plan include:

- The load that is being lifted - weight, shape, centres of gravity, surface condition, lifting points.
- The equipment and accessories being used for the operation and suitability - certification validity.
- The proposed route that the load will take including the destination and checks for obstructions.
- The team required to carry out the lift - competencies and numbers required.
- Production of a safe system of work, risk assessments, permits to work.
- The environment in which the lift will take place - ground conditions, weather, local population.
- Securing areas below the lift - information, restrictions, demarcation and barriers.
- A suitable trial to determine the reaction of the lifting equipment prior to full lift.
- Completion of the operation and any dismantling required.

Supervised

It is important that someone takes supervisory control of lifting operations at the time they are being conducted.

Although the operator may be skilled in lifting techniques, this may not be enough to ensure safety, because other factors may influence whether the overall operation is conducted safely, for example, people may stray into the area.

The level of supervision necessary is influenced by the nature of the work and the competence of those involved in using the equipment and assisting with the lifting operation. The supervisor of the lifting operation must remain in control and stop the operation if it is not carried out satisfactorily.

Figure 4-63: Siting and stability. *Source: RMS.*

Carried out in a safe manner

Lifting equipment and accessories should be subject to a pre-use check in order to determine their condition and suitability. In addition, care should be taken to ensure the lifting accessories used are compatible with the task and that the load is protected or supported such that it does not disintegrate when lifted.

Lifting operations should not be carried on where adverse weather conditions occur, such as fog, poor lightning, strong wind or where heavy rainfall makes ground conditions unstable. It is important that measures be used to prevent lifting equipment overturning and that there is sufficient room for it to operate without contacting other objects.

Figure 4-64: Crane operation. *Source: RMS.*

Lifting equipment should not be used to drag loads and should not be overloaded. Special arrangements need to be in place when lifting equipment not normally used for lifting people is used for that purpose, for example, de-rating the working load limit, ensuring communication is in place between the people being lifted and the operator, and ensuring the operation controls are manned at all times.

General rules for safe operation of a crane

Always	Ensure the lift is planned and supervised by a competent person and operators/slingers are trained and competent
Always	Select the right appliance and lifting accessories for the job
Always	Site the crane on solid stable ground away from structures or overhead cables
Always	Ensure the appliance is stable when lifting, for example, not outside lifting radius and that outriggers are correctly positioned
Always	Use correct slinging methods
Always	Protect sling from sharp edges - pack out and lower onto spacers
Always	Ensure the sling is securely attached to the hook
Always	Ensure load is lifted to correct height and moved at an appropriate speed
Always	Use standard signals that are understood by those involved in the crane operation - refer to the Health and Safety (Safety Signs and Signals) Regulations (SSSR) 1996
Never	Use equipment if damaged (check before use) - for example, stretched or not free movement, worn or corroded, outside inspection date
Never	Exceed the safe working load
Never	Lift with sling angles greater than 120 degrees
Never	Lift a load over people
Never	Drag a load or allow sudden shock loading

Rules should be established for when a crane operator takes over a crane and before use of the crane. For example, before taking over a mobile crane the driver must always check around the crane, and check the pressure of tyres, the engine for fuel, lubrication oil, water and the compressed air system.

All controls, such as lifting equipment clutches and brakes, should be tested to see that all lifting ropes run smoothly and safe load indicators function correctly. The following are examples of specific safe operating rules for a *mobile crane*.

The operator must:

- Always understand the signalling system and observe the signals of the appointed signaller/'banksman'.
- Never permit unauthorised persons to travel on the crane.
- Never use the crane to replace normal means of transport or as a towing tractor.
- Always check that the crane is on firm and level ground before lifting and that spring locks/outriggers are properly in position.
- Never overload the crane. Always keep a constant watch on the load radius indicator.
- Always ensure movements are made with caution. Violent handling produces excess loading on the crane structure and machinery.
- Always make allowances for adverse weather conditions.
- Never cause loads to swing. Always position the crane so that the pull on the hoist rope is vertical.
- Always ensure that the load is properly slung. A load considered unsafe should not be lifted.
- Always ensure that all persons are in a safe position before any movement is carried out.
- Always make certain before hoisting that the hook is not attached to any anchored load or fixed object.
- Never drag slings when travelling.
- Always ensure that the jib, hook or load is in a position to clear any obstruction when the crane is slewing (swinging in a sideways or circular motion), but the load must not be lifted unnecessarily high.
- Always drive smoothly - drive safely. Remember that cranes are safe only when they are used as recommended by the makers. This applies in particular to speciality cranes.
- Always be on the lookout for overhead obstructions, particularly electric cables.
- Never tamper with or disconnect safe load indicators.
- Always stop the crane if the hoist or jib ropes become slack or out of their grooves, and report the condition.
- Always report all defects to the supervisor and never attempt to use a crane with a suspected serious defect until it has been rectified and certified by a competent person that it is not dangerous.
- Always make sure the crane is safe when leaving it unattended: ensure that the power is off, the engine stopped, the load unhooked, and the hook is raised up to a safe position.
- Always ensure special devices (for example, magnets and grabs) are used only for the purpose intended and in accordance with the instruction given.
- Always keep the crane clean and tidy.
- Always park the crane safely after use, remember to apply all brakes, slew locks, and secure rail clamps when fitted. Some cranes, however, particularly tower cranes, must be left to weather vane and the manufacturer's instructions must be clearly adhered to. Park the crane where the weather vaning jib will not strike any object. Lock the cabin before leaving the crane.

Competent people

The Health and Safety at Work etc. Act (HASAWA) 1974 places a duty on employers to their employees for the provision of information, instruction, training and supervision as is necessary to ensure, so far as is reasonably practicable, the health and safety at work of the employees. In addition to this general duty, a further duty exists under the Provision and Use of Work Equipment Regulations (PUWER) 1998. Employers must ensure that any person who uses a piece of work equipment has received adequate training for purposes of health and safety, including training in the methods which may be adopted when using work equipment, and any risks which such use may entail and precautions to be taken.

Drivers/operators of cranes and other lifting appliances, including others involved in lifting operations (for example, those that direct the movement of the load), must be adequately trained, experienced and aged 18 years or over. The only exception is when under the direct supervision of a competent person for training requirements.

There are various appointments with specified responsibilities in order to ensure the safety of lifting operations on site. These are as follows:

Competent person	Appointed to plan the operation
Load handler	Attaches and detaches the load
Authorised person	Ensures the load safely attached
Operator	Appointed to operate the equipment
Responsible person	Appointed to communicate the position of the load (banksman)
Assistants	Appointed to relay communications

Crane operators and slingers should be fit and strong enough for the work. A safe system of work, including safety rules, should be developed and communicated to all those involved. Circumstances differ from site to site and additional rules should be added to cover different circumstances, equipment and conditions. Training should be provided for the safe operation of the particular equipment. In particular, crane operators should receive systematic training similar to the approach used to train fork-lift truck operators, discussed earlier in this element.

Typically this would include 3 stages:

Stage 1 - should contain the basic skills and knowledge required to operate the crane safely, to understand the basic mechanics and balance of the machine, and to carry out routine daily checks.

Stage 2 - under strict training conditions in an area which workers not involved in the training and other people that may be harmed are excluded.

This stage should include:

- Knowledge of the crane operating principles and controls.
- Use of the crane in likely work conditions and doing the type of work to be undertaken, for example, loading and unloading vehicles.
- On completion of training, the crane operators should be examined and tested to ensure that they have achieved the required standard.

Stage 3 - after successfully completing the first two stages, crane operators should be given further familiarisation and where necessary instruction in the usual place of work for the crane operators.

SPECIAL REQUIREMENTS FOR LIFTING EQUIPMENT FOR LIFTING PERSONS

Regulation 5 of PUWER 1998 requires every employer to ensure that lifting equipment for lifting persons:

- Is such as to prevent a person using it being crushed, trapped or struck or falling from the carrier.
- Is such as to prevent so far as is reasonably practicable a person using it, while carrying out activities from the carrier, being crushed, trapped or struck or falling from the carrier.
- Has suitable devices to prevent the risk of a carrier falling.
- Is such that a person trapped in any carrier is not thereby exposed to danger and can be freed.

In addition, every employer shall ensure that if the risk described above cannot be prevented for reasons inherent in the site and height differences:

- The carrier has an enhanced safety coefficient suspension rope or chain.
- The rope or chain is inspected by a competent person every working day.

Special arrangements need to be in place when lifting equipment not normally used for people is used for that purpose, for example, de-rating the working load limit, ensuring communication is in place between the people and operator, and ensuring the operation controls are manned at all times. Lifting equipment for lifting people is subject to specific requirements for statutory examination.

Visual inspection and statutory thorough examination and inspection

Statutory requirements to conduct examinations and inspections of lifting equipment are set out in Regulation 9 of the LOLER 1998. Used lifting equipment must be thoroughly examined before being put into service for the first time by a new user. This does not apply to new lifting equipment (unless its safety depends on installation conditions) or equipment that conforms to European Community requirements and has been certified as being examined within the previous 12 months. Suppliers of used lifting equipment are obliged to certify that a thorough examination has been carried out. Where the safety of lifting equipment depends on the installation conditions, for example, a tower crane, it must be thoroughly examined prior to first use, after assembly and on change of location in order to ensure that it has been installed correctly and is safe to operate.

Lifting equipment exposed to conditions causing deterioration that is liable to result in dangerous situations is to be thoroughly examined by a competent person:

- At least every 6 months - lifting equipment for lifting persons and lifting accessories.
- At least every 12 months - other lifting equipment.
- In either case, in accordance with an examination scheme.
- On each occurrence of exceptional circumstances liable to jeopardise the safety of the lifting equipment.

Regulation 10 of LOLER 1998 requires that where a defect is discovered that represents a danger to people it must be notified immediately to the employer responsible for conforming to LOLER 1998. In addition, a written report containing information specified in Schedule 1 of LOLER 1998 must be produced and provided as soon as is practicable. The report is to be signed by the competent person carrying out the thorough examination. Where defects are notified, the employer must ensure the equipment is not used until the defect is rectified.

Regulation 11 of LOLER 1998 concerns the keeping of information in relation to examinations and specifies that any report written by a competent person, following an examination, must be kept available for inspection for the period of validity of the report.

Regulation 9 of LOLER 1998 requires that where appropriate to ensure health and safety, inspections must be carried out at suitable intervals between thorough examinations. Similar to thorough examinations, Regulation

10 of LOLER 1998 requires that the person carrying out the inspection must notify the employer if defects that represent a danger to people are discovered and, in any case, as soon as practicable make a record of the inspection in writing. Examinations and inspections must ensure that the good condition of equipment is maintained and that any deterioration can be detected and remedied in good time.

Exam practice

1. A welfare unit is to be lifted from the vehicle trailer it is being delivered on to its location on the construction site. **Outline** what the person appointed to have overall control of this operation would have to ensure so that lifting operations are conducted safely. **(8)**

2. A 100 metre long section of a footpath in a residential area with a speed limit of 30mph is to have the kerbstones replaced.

    (a) **Identify** the hazards that could affect the health and safety of the employees involved in this process. **(4)**

    (b) **Outline** the control measures that could be put into place to reduce the risk. **(4)**

3. **Identify** factors relating to the condition of lifting accessories that could form part of a pre-use checklist. **(8)**

4. **Identify** the requirements for thorough examinations of lifting equipment to be carried out to meet the requirements of the Lifting Operations and Lifting Equipment Regulations (LOLER). **(8)**

5. **Identify** the measures that should be taken to reduce the risk of a rough terrain fork-lift truck overturning. **(8)**

6. Manual handling operations during construction activities can cause injuries.

    (a) **Identify TWO** types of injury that may be caused by the incorrect manual handling of loads. **(2)**

    (b) With reference to the work environment related to construction manual handling activities, **outline** means of reducing the risk of injury during manual handling operations. **(6)**

Please refer to the back of the assessment section for answers.

Work equipment - hazards and risk control

Learning outcomes

On completion of this element, candidates should be able to demonstrate understanding of the content through the application of knowledge to familiar and unfamiliar situations. In particular they should be able to:

5.1 Outline general requirements for work equipment.

5.2 Outline the hazards and control measures for hand-held tools, both powered and non-powered.

5.3 Describe the main mechanical and non-mechanical hazards of machinery.

5.4 Explain the main control measures for reducing risk from common construction machinery hazards.

Content

5.1 - General requirements for work equipment 113
  Scope of work equipment 113
  Suitability as it relates to provision of equipment..113
  Requirement to restrict the use and maintenance of equipment...115
  Information, instruction and training 115
  Equipment to be maintained and maintenance conducted safely...116
  Visual inspection and statutory thorough examination and inspection...118
  Importance of operation and emergency controls, etc. 119
  Responsibilities of users 123
5.2 - Hand-held tools..123
  Hand tools...123
  Common portable power tools used in construction 124
  Suitability for location..128
  Procedures for defective equipment...128
5.3 - Machinery hazards...128
  Main mechanical and non-mechanical hazards 128
  Hazards presented by a range of equipment 131
5.4 - Control measures for machinery hazards...135
  Machinery guarding 135
  The principles, merits and limitations of protection methods..136
  Application of protection methods to a range of equipment 141
  Basic requirements for guards and safety devices..142
Exam practice 143

Sources of reference

Reference information provided, in particular web links, is correct at time of publication, but may have changed.

Buying new machinery, INDG271 (rev1), HSE, http://www.hse.gov.uk/pubns/indg271.htm

BS EN ISO 12100:2010 'Safety of machinery. General principles for design. Risk assessment and risk reduction' (formerly BS EN 292), British Standards Institution ISBN 978-0-5807-4262-0

Chainsaws at work, INDG317 (rev2), HSE, http://www.hse.gov.uk/pubns/indg317.pdf

Personal Protective Equipment at Work Regulations 1992 (as amended) - Guidance on Regulations, L25 (second edition 2005), HSE Books, ISBN 978-0-7176-6139-3 http://www.hse.gov.uk/pubns/priced/l25.pdf

Safe use of vertical spindle moulding machines - Information Sheet (Woodworking Sheet No. 18), HSE, http://www.hse.gov.uk/pubns/wis18.pdf

Safe use of woodworking machinery - ACOP and guidance, L114 (second edition 2014), HSE Books, ISBN 978-0-7176-6621-8 http://www.hse.gov.uk/pubns/priced/l114.pdf

Safe Use of Work Equipment - ACOP and guidance, L22 (fourth edition 2014), HSE Books, ISBN 978-0-7176-6619-5 http://www.hse.gov.uk/pubns/priced/l22.pdf

Supplying new machinery, INDG270 (rev1), HSE, http://www.hse.gov.uk/pubns/indg270.pdf

Relevant statutory provisions

Personal Protective Equipment at Work Regulations (PPER) 1992

Provision and Use of Work Equipment Regulations (PUWER) 1998

Supply of Machinery (Safety) Regulations (SMSR) 2008

5.1 - General requirements for work equipment

Scope of work equipment

The Provision and Use of Work Equipment Regulations (PUWER) 1998 are concerned with most aspects relating to work equipment. The regulations define work equipment as any machinery, appliance, apparatus, tool or assembly of components that are arranged so that they function as a whole. The term embraces many types of hand tool, power tool and machinery. It also extends to lifting accessories, such as a chain sling.

HAND TOOLS

Common hand tools include trowels, spades, hammers, chisels, planes, screwdrivers.

POWER TOOLS

Common power tools use electric power (battery or 110 volts), diesel or petrol and include various drills, and piling hammers, road breakers, chain and circular saws, bench saws, floor saws, cartridge nail guns.

MACHINERY

In common with power tools, machinery is usually powered by diesel, petrol fuel or compressed air. Examples include:

- Air compressor.
- Scabblers.
- Mobile elevating work platforms (MEWP's).

- Cranes.
- Excavator.
- Rough terrain fork-lift truck (RTFLT).

Not work equipment:

- Livestock.
- Substances.

- Structural items (buildings).
- Private car.

Figure 5-1: Air road breakers.   *Source: Speedy Hire plc.*

Figure 5-2: Floor scabbler.   *Source: Speedy Hire plc.*

Figure 5-3: Hand held scabbler.   *Source: Speedy Hire plc.*

Figure 5-4: Lifting sling.   *Source: RMS.*

Suitability as it relates to provision of equipment

PROVISION OF WORK EQUIPMENT REGULATIONS (PUWER) 1998

PUWER Regulation 4 - Suitability of work equipment

PUWER 1998, Regulation 4, sets out the following requirements related to the suitability of work equipment:

"(1)   Every employer shall ensure that work equipment is so constructed or adapted as to be suitable for the purpose for which it is used or provided.

(2)   In selecting work equipment, every employer shall have regard to the working conditions and to the risks to the health and safety of persons which exist in the premises or undertaking in which that work equipment is to be used and any additional risk posed by the use of that work equipment.

(3)   Every employer shall ensure that work equipment is used only for operations for which, and under conditions for which, it is suitable.

(4)   In this regulation, 'suitable' means suitable in any respect which it is reasonably foreseeable will affect the health or safety of any person."

Suitability should consider:

- Its initial integrity.
- The place where it will be used.
- The purpose for which it will be used.

Integrity - is equipment safe through its design, construction or adaptation? Sharp edges should be removed, 'home made' tools constructed properly and equipment adapted to do a specific task.

Place - is equipment suitable for different environments (risks), for example, wet or explosive environments? Account must be taken of the equipment causing a problem - for example, a petrol generator used in a confined space or a hydraulic access platform used in a location with a low roof.

Use - is equipment suitable for the specific task? A hacksaw being used to cut metal straps that secure goods to a pallet (instead of a purpose designed tool); the use of a ladder to do work at a height (instead of a scaffold or other access platform); exceeding the safe working load of a crane or fork-lift truck, a swivel chair used as a means of access to a shelf.

CONFORMITY WITH RELEVANT STANDARDS, CE MARKING

Section 6 of the Health and Safety at Work etc. Act (HASAWA) 1974 requires those involved in the supply (including design and manufacture) of equipment to ensure that it is safe and healthy, so far as is reasonably practicable. This will require them to take account of all relevant standards.

PUWER Regulation 10 - Conformity with community requirements

PUWER 1998, Regulation 10, sets out the following requirements related to conformity of work equipment:

"(1) Every employer shall ensure that an item of work equipment has been designed and constructed in compliance with any essential requirements, that is to say, requirements relating to its design or construction in any of the instruments listed in Schedule 1 (being instruments which give effect to Community directives concerning the safety of products).

(2)   Where an essential requirement is applied to the design or construction of an item of work equipment, the requirements of Regulations 11 to 19 and 22 to 29 shall apply in respect of that item only to the extent that the essential requirement did not apply to it.

(3)   This Regulation applies to items of work equipment provided for use in the premises or undertaking of the employer for the first time after 31st December 1992."

Work equipment provided for use after 31 December 1992 must conform with legislation made in the UK in response to EC directives relating to work equipment. Only those directives listed in Schedule 1 of PUWER 1998 are to be considered and then only those that have been translated to UK law.

Examples relate to:

- The amount of noise emitted from a variety of equipment (for example, construction equipment or lawn mowers).
- Electro-medical equipment.
- Simple pressure vessels.
- Machinery safety. *See also 'Supply of Machinery (Safety) Regulations (SMSR) 2008' in the Relevant Statutory Provisions section.*
- Personal protective equipment.

Directives, and in turn, UK regulations, tend to contain details of 'essential health and safety requirements' and a system whereby compliance may be demonstrated. Compliance is usually demonstrated by the attachment of a CE (Conformité Européene) mark and the manufacturer/supplier holding an EC declaration of conformity.

FIT FOR PURPOSE

Equipment used for any activity must be suitable to fulfil the exact requirements of the task. This means considering the ergonomic requirements *(see following paragraph)*, strength, durability, power source, portability, and protection against the environment, range of tasks to be carried out and the frequency and duration of use. Equipment that is designed to perform a specific task must only be used for that task and not adapted for other tasks not considered in the manufacturer's design and instructions. An example of this is where a portable battery operated drill is rotated by hand or the back/butt of the drill is used as a hammer, clearly a task not meant for this equipment. Equipment used in these types of situation identifies a lack of forethought in the planning stage of a project when the correct equipment should have been sought and used. The equipment may be used indoors or outdoors where consideration must be given to the dangers of damp, water and electricity or explosive atmospheres within confined spaces. The grade of equipment should be industrial or commercial type for work activities and not the type of equipment designed for personal use at home. Whenever equipment is required, the full capacity and limitation requirements should be identified and it should be confirmed that the equipment provided can cope with the demands/limitations placed upon it. For example, construction sites use 110 volt supply and it is important that workers only use equipment that suits this power supply.

ERGONOMIC CONSIDERATIONS

Ergonomic considerations involve the study of person-equipment interface, with an emphasis on adjustability of the machinery and equipment. The aim is to suit a variety of individual sizes and positions in order to provide the most comfortable position possible. In considering the ergonomic factors of a task that requires equipment to be used, it is essential to include the operator's individual attributes, and how they affect and may be affected by the process. Factors might include posture when seated or standing, height of the workstation, how the equipment may be adjusted and frequency of the task being performed. It is essential that ergonomic considerations form an active part at the planning stage of a process to ensure the correct equipment is obtained and the reactive effects of poor ergonomics eliminated.

Requirement to restrict the use and maintenance of equipment

PUWER 1998, Regulation 7, sets out the following requirements to control specific risks related to work equipment:

"(1) Where the use of work equipment is likely to involve a specific risk to health or safety, every employer shall ensure that:

(a) The use of that work equipment is restricted to those persons given the task of using it.

(b) Repairs, modifications, maintenance or servicing of that work equipment is restricted to those persons who have been specifically designated to perform operations of that description (whether or not also authorised to perform other operations).

(2) The employer shall ensure that the persons designated for the purposes of sub-paragraph (b) of paragraph (1) have received adequate training related to any operations in respect of which they have been so designated."

For example, in view of the specific risks, it would be appropriate to restrict the use of a nail gun, circular saw or mobile elevated work platform to those competent and authorised to use it. In the same way, maintenance of an abrasive wheel (replacement of a grinding wheel) or a rough terrain fork-lift truck (replacement of load-bearing components) should be restricted.

Information, instruction and training

INFORMATION AND INSTRUCTION

Whenever equipment is provided and used in the workplace there is a requirement to ensure that all operators are given adequate information and instruction in order that they can use the equipment safely. The issues covered should include the safe operation of the equipment and also the capacities and limitations of the equipment. Specific information must be given on the particular hazards of equipment, and instruction and training given on how to implement, use and maintain control measures correctly.

PUWER Regulation 8 - Information and instruction

PUWER 1998, Regulation 8, sets out the following requirements with regard to information and instruction:

"Every employer shall ensure that all persons who use work equipment have available to them adequate health and safety information and, where appropriate, written instructions pertaining to the use of the work equipment.

Every employer shall ensure that any of his employees who supervises or manages the use of work equipment has available to him adequate health and safety information and, where appropriate, written instructions pertaining to the use of the work equipment, information and, where appropriate, written instructions on:

(a) The conditions in which and the methods by which the work equipment may be used.

(b) Foreseeable abnormal situations and the action to be taken if such a situation were to occur.

(c) Any conclusions to be drawn from experience in using the work equipment."

TRAINING

PUWER Regulation 9 - Training

PUWER 1998, Regulation 9, sets out the following requirements with regard to training:

"Every employer shall ensure that all persons who use work equipment have received adequate training for purposes of health and safety, including training in the methods which may be adopted when using the work equipment, any risks which such use may entail and precautions to be taken.

Every employer shall ensure that any of his employees who supervises or manages the use of work equipment has received adequate training for purposes of health and safety, including training in the methods which may be adopted when using the work equipment, any risks which such use may entail and precautions to be taken."

Training may be needed for existing staff as well as inexperienced staff or new starters (including temporary staff), particularly if they have to use powered machinery. The greater the danger, the better the training needs to be. For some high risk work such as driving fork-lift trucks, using a chainsaw and operating a crane, training should be carried out by specialist instructors. Remember that younger people can be quite skilful when moving and handling powered equipment, but they may lack experience and judgment and may require closer supervision to begin with.

Examples:

- **Users** - how to carry out pre-use checks, report defects, only to use equipment for the purpose designed.
- **Maintenance** - safe isolation, acceptable replacement parts and adjustments in accordance with manufacturer's manuals.
- **Managers** - be aware of the hazards and controls and maintain effective supervision.

In addition, where the use of work equipment is likely to involve a specific risk to health and safety the employer must provide those restricted to repair, modify, maintain or service the equipment with adequate training.

Equipment to be maintained and maintenance conducted safely

EQUIPMENT TO BE MAINTAINED

Procedures for defective equipment

Under section 7 of the HASAWA 1974 and Regulation 14 of the Management of Health and Safety at Work Regulations (MHSWR) 1999, employees have a duty to and should notify any shortcomings in the health and safety arrangements, even when no immediate danger exists, so that employers can take remedial action if needed. The duties placed on employees do not reduce the responsibility of the employer to comply with his own duties. Regulation 5 of PUWER 1998 requires equipment to be maintained. With duties being placed upon both the employer and the employee to ensure the use of safe equipment, when identified in the workplace, faulty equipment should be isolated until such a time it can be repaired by a competent person.

PUWER Regulation 5 - Maintenance

PUWER 1998, Regulation 5, sets out the following requirements with regard to the maintenance of work equipment: *"Every employer shall ensure that work equipment is maintained in an efficient state, in efficient working order and in good repair."*

In order to achieve this, a system of maintenance should be in place that includes regular adjustment, replacement of parts and testing. Maintenance logs, where they exist, must be kept up to date.

MAINTENANCE TO BE CONDUCTED SAFELY

PUWER Regulation 22 - Maintenance

No one should be exposed to undue risk during maintenance operations. In order to achieve this equipment should be stopped and isolated as appropriate before work starts. If it is necessary to keep equipment running then the risks must be adequately controlled. This may take the form of controlling running speed, range of movement or providing temporary guards. Consideration must be given to other legislation, such as Electricity at Work Regulations (EWR) 1989, during the assessment of risks involved in maintenance work.

Maintenance hazards

The principal sources of hazards are associated with maintenance work on:

- Heavy plant.
- Crushers.
- Cranes.
- Concrete pumps.
- Storage tanks.
- Large hoists and lifts.

Typical hazards associated with maintenance operations

Mechanical	Entanglements, machinery traps, contact; shearing traps, in-running nips, ejection, unexpected start up
Electrical	Electrocution, shock, burns
Pressure	Unexpected pressure releases, explosion
Physical	Extremes of temperature, noise, vibration, dust
Chemical	Gases, vapours, mists, fumes, etc
Structural	Obstructions and floor openings
Access	Work at heights, confined spaces

Typical accidents

- Crushing by moving machinery.
- Falls.
- Asphyxiation.
- Electrocution.
- Explosions.
- Burns.

One or more of the following factors causes maintenance accidents:

- Lack of perception of risk by managers/supervisors, often because of lack of necessary training.
- Unsafe or no system of work devised, for example, no permit-to-work system in operation, no facility to lock off machinery and electricity supply before work starts and until work has finished.
- No coordination between workers, and communication with other supervisors or managers.
- Lack of perception of risk by workers, including failure to wear protective clothing or equipment.
- Inadequacy of design, installation, siting of plant and equipment.
- Use of contractors with no health and safety systems or who are inadequately briefed on health and safety aspects.

Maintenance to be conducted safely

Isolation

This does not simply mean switching off the equipment using the stop button. It includes switching the equipment off at the start button and switching off the isolator for the equipment. In new workplaces, individual equipment isolators should be provided; i.e. each piece of equipment has its own isolator near to it. One isolator should not control several items of equipment as it is then impossible to isolate a single piece of equipment on its own.

Figure 5-5: Conveyor.   *Source: RMS.*

Figure 5-6: Electrical isolator with hole for padlock. *Source: RMS.*

Lock out and tag out

Isolation alone does not afford adequate protection, because there is nothing to prevent the isolator being switched back on, or removed fuses being replaced inadvertently while the person who isolated the item in the first place is still working on the equipment. To ensure that this does not happen, the isolator needs to be physically locked in the off position (typically using a padlock, the key to be held by the person in danger).

Multiple lock out devices are often used where multiple trades are carrying out work on the same equipment or plant; they are designed to carry a number of isolation padlocks for the different people working on the equipment; the equipment cannot be energised until all the padlocks are removed, thereby protecting the last worker on the job. It is also a good idea to sign *'do not switch on...'* or tag on the equipment at the point of isolation.

Figure 5-7: Physical isolation of valve.   *Source: RMS.*

Figure 5-8: Multiple (padlock) lock off device.   *Source: RMS.*

Summary of control measures

- Plan work in advance - provide safe access, support parts of equipment which could fail.
- Use written safe systems of work, method statements or permit-to-work systems as appropriate.
- Plan specific operations using method statements.
- Use physical means of isolating or locking off plant.

- Systems of working should incorporate two-man working for high risk operations.
- Integrate safety requirements in the planning of specific high risk tasks.
- Prevent unauthorised access to the work area by using barriers and signs.
- Ensure the competence of those carrying out the work.
- Ensure the availability and use of appropriate personal protective equipment (PPE) - gloves, eye protection.
- Prevent fire or explosion - thoroughly clean vessels that have contained flammable solids or liquids, gases or dusts and check them thoroughly before hot work is carried out.

Visual inspection and statutory thorough examination and inspection

INSPECTION

PUWER Regulation 6 - Inspection

PUWER 1998, Regulation 6, sets out the following requirements with regard to the inspection of work equipment:

"Every employer shall ensure that work equipment exposed to conditions causing deterioration which is liable to result in dangerous situations is inspected:

(a) At suitable intervals.

(b) Each time that exceptional circumstances which are liable to jeopardise the safety of the work equipment have occurred, to ensure that health and safety conditions are maintained and that any deterioration can be detected and remedied in good time.

Every employer shall ensure that the result of an inspection made under this regulation is recorded and kept until the next inspection under this regulation is recorded."

Figure 5-9: Inspection and examination. *Source: Industrial Safety Inspections.*

Equipment must be inspected on a regular basis in order to confirm the condition that it is in. The inspection required may be a regular visual inspection or daily pre-use check carried out by the operator. The person using equipment, who should be confirmed as competent, should carry out operator checks prior to the use of any equipment. Operator checks should include guards, cables, casing integrity, cutting or machine parts and safety devices such as cut-outs.

The requirements of Regulation 6 of PUWER 1998 extend to inspections that are more significant and address a list of identifiable health and safety critical parts. For example, the main items on a *dumper truck* that should be the subject to periodic inspection include: the provision and condition of roll over protection and driver restraints (for example, seat belts); the condition of the bodywork and seats; the condition of the tyres; the effectiveness of the braking system, steering and warning devices; the performance of the bucket release and tilt mechanisms; the integrity of fuel, oil and hydraulic systems and the legibility of labels and signs.

Similarly, the main items for regular (for example, weekly) inspection of a 360° wheeled *excavator* include: hydraulic systems; wheels and tyres; windscreens and other windows; brakes and steering; the condition of bodywork and seats (including any seat belts); lights and visual warning devices; the condition of mirrors and other rear view equipment and the proper functioning of the controls.

An inspection sheet should be used to control the inspection process. The purpose of an inspection sheet is to record deterioration of specific parts, abuse and misuse, also to ensure that all items are considered at the time of inspection, by serving as an aide memoir. The results of the inspection will confirm whether or not a piece of equipment is in a safe enough condition to use. Other regulations, such as the Lifting Operations and Lifting Equipment Regulations (LOLER) 1998 require and set certain statutory inspection requirements. Note also that Regulation 6(5) of PUWER 1998 has been amended by the Work at Height Regulations (WAH) 2005 to include 'work equipment to which Regulation 12 of the WAH 2005 applies'. *See also 'Work at Height Regulations (WAH) 2005' in the Relevant Statutory Provisions section.*

THOROUGH EXAMINATION

PUWER 1998 does not contain a general requirement for the thorough examination of all work equipment. However, specific requirements exist in the Lifting Operations and Lifting Equipment Regulations (LOLER) 1998 regarding such equipment as MEWPs, cranes and accessories.

LOLER 1998 essentially sets out requirements for thorough examination under four situations:

1) When lifting equipment is first 'supplied', i.e. used for the first time by that employer.
2) When certain equipment is 'installed' and its safety is dependent on installation conditions, for example, a tower crane.
3) Periodically, during the lifetime of the equipment.
4) Following exceptional circumstances.

The periodic thorough examination must be:

■ In the case of lifting equipment for lifting persons or an accessory for lifting, at least every 6 months.
■ In the case of other lifting equipment, at least every 12 months.
■ In either case, in accordance with an examination scheme determined by a competent person.

Where a defect is discovered that represents a danger to people it must be notified immediately to the employer responsible for compliance with LOLER 1998. In addition, a written report containing information specified in Schedule 1 of LOLER 1998 must be produced and provided. Where defects are notified, the employer must ensure the equipment is not used until the defect is rectified.

See also 'Element 4 - Requirements for regular visual inspection and statutory requirements for the thorough examination and inspection of lifting equipment' for further information.

There is also a legislative requirement for the thorough examination of pressure systems under the Pressure Systems Safety Regulations (PSSR) 2000.

A pressure system is, as defined in the PSSR 2000, as follows:

■ A system comprising one or more pressure vessels of rigid construction, and any associated pipework and protective devices.
■ The pipework with its protective devices to which a transportable gas container is or is intended to be connected.
■ A pipeline and its protective devices.

A pressure vessel is generally considered to be one that operates at a pressure greater than atmospheric pressure, for example, steam boilers and air receivers.

PSSR 2000 requires that a competent person draw up a written scheme of examination for the pressure system and that thorough examinations are carried out in accordance with the written scheme.

Adequate records of thorough examinations, repairs, modifications etc., should be kept at the premises where the equipment is used.

Figure 5-10: Air compressor.   *Source: Speedy Hire plc.*

Importance of operation and emergency controls, etc.

OPERATION AND EMERGENCY CONTROLS

PUWER Regulation 14 - Controls for starting or making a significant change in operating conditions

PUWER 1998, Regulation 14, sets out the following requirements with regard to operating controls for work equipment:

"(1) Every employer shall ensure that, where appropriate, work equipment is provided with one or more controls for the purposes of:

(a) Starting the work equipment (including re-starting after a stoppage for any reason).

(b) Controlling any change in the speed, pressure or other operating conditions of the work equipment where such conditions after the change result in risk to health and safety which is greater than or of a different nature from such risks before the change.

(2) Subject to paragraph (3), every employer shall ensure that where a control is required by paragraph (1), it shall not be possible to perform any operation mentioned in sub-paragraph (a) or (b) of that paragraph except by a deliberate action on such control."

Paragraph (1) does not apply to re-starting or changing operating conditions as a result of the normal operating cycle of an automatic device.

Any change in the operating conditions should only be possible by the use of a control, except if the change does not increase risk to health or safety. Examples of operating conditions include speed, distance, height, angle, pressure, temperature and power. The controls provided should be designed and positioned so as to prevent, so far as possible, inadvertent or accidental operation. Buttons and levers should be of appropriate design, for example, including a shroud or locking facility. It should not be possible for the control to 'operate itself' because of the effects of gravity, vibration, or failure of a spring mechanism.

For most equipment used in construction activities, the controls should be of the 'hold to run' type, as it is not generally appropriate to leave it in an active condition without operator attention. This will also provide a higher standard of safety, ensuring that the operator is in immediate control of such equipment as MEWPs, cranes, excavators and other high hazard equipment.

PUWER Regulation 15 - Stop controls

PUWER 1998, Regulation 15, sets out the following requirements with regard to stop controls for work equipment:

"(1) Every employer shall ensure that, where appropriate, work equipment is provided with one or more readily accessible controls the operation of which will bring the work equipment to a safe condition in a safe manner.

(2) Any control required by paragraph (1) shall bring the work equipment to a complete stop where necessary for reasons of health and safety.

(3) Any control required by paragraph (1) shall, if necessary for reasons of health and safety, switch off all sources of energy after stopping the functioning of the work equipment.

(4) Any control required by paragraph (1) shall operate in priority to any control, which starts or changes the operating conditions of the work equipment."

The primary requirement of this regulation is that the action of the control should bring the equipment to a safe condition in a safe manner. This acknowledges that it is not always desirable to bring all items of work equipment immediately to a complete or instantaneous stop, for example, to prevent the unsafe build-up of heat or pressure or to allow a controlled run-down of large rotating parts.

The regulation is qualified by 'where necessary for reasons of health and safety'. Therefore, accessible dangerous parts must be rendered stationary. However, parts of equipment which do not present a risk, such as suitably guarded cooling fans, do not need to be positively stopped and may be allowed to idle.

PUWER Regulation 16 - Emergency stop controls

The function of an emergency stop control device is to provide a means to bring a machine to a rapid halt. It is provided in such circumstances where it would be of benefit and should be readily available to the operator and/or others. It should be easy to operate and clearly discernible from other controls.

PUWER 1998, Regulation 16, sets out the following requirements with regard to emergency stop controls for work equipment:

"(1) Every employer shall ensure that, where appropriate, work equipment is provided with one or more readily accessible emergency stop controls unless it is not necessary by reason of the nature of the hazards and the time taken for the work equipment to come to a complete stop as a result of the action of any control provided by virtue of regulation 15(1).

(2) Any control required by paragraph (1) shall operate in priority to any control required by Regulation 15(1)."

Emergency stops are intended to affect a rapid response to potentially dangerous situations and they should not be used as functional stops during normal operation. Emergency stop controls should be easily reached and actuated. Common types are mushroom-headed buttons, bars, levers, kick plates, or pressure-sensitive cables.

Figure 5-11: Controls and emergency stop.   *Source: RMS.*

Figure 5-12: Controls.   *Source: RMS.*

PUWER Regulation 17 - Controls

PUWER 1998, Regulation 17, sets out the following general requirements for controls fitted to work equipment:

"(1) Every employer shall ensure that all controls for work equipment shall be clearly visible and identifiable, including by appropriate marking where necessary.

It should be possible to identify easily what each control does and on which equipment it takes effect. Both the controls and their markings should be clearly visible.

As well as having legible wording or symbols, factors such as the colour, shape and position of controls are important.

(2) Except where necessary, the employer shall ensure that no control for work equipment is in a position where any person operating the control is exposed to a risk to his health or safety.

(3) Every employer shall ensure where appropriate:

(a) That, so far as is reasonably practicable, the operator of any control is able to ensure from the position of that control that no person is in a place where he would be exposed to any risk to his health or safety as a result of the operation of that control, but where or to the extent that it is not reasonably practicable.

(b) That, so far as is reasonably practicable, systems of work are effective to ensure that, when work equipment is about to start, no person is in a place where he would be exposed to a risk to his health or safety as a result of the work equipment starting, but where neither of these is reasonably practicable.

(c) That an audible, visible or other suitable warning is given by virtue of Regulation 24 whenever work equipment is about to start.

(4) Every employer shall take appropriate measures to ensure that any person who is in a place where he would be exposed to a risk to his health or safety as a result of the starting or stopping of work equipment has sufficient time and suitable means to avoid that risk."

Figure 5-13: Controls.   Source: RMS.

Warnings given in accordance with Regulation 17(3)(c) should be given sufficiently in advance of the equipment actually starting to give those at risk time to get clear. As well as time, suitable means of avoiding the risk should be provided.

This may take the form of a device by means of which the person at risk can prevent start-up or warn the operator of his/her presence.

Otherwise, there must be adequate provision to enable people at risk to withdraw, for example, sufficient space or exits. Circumstances will affect the type of warning chosen.

PUWER Regulation 18 - Control systems

PUWER 1998, Regulation 18, sets out the following requirements with regard to control systems for work equipment:

"(1) Every employer shall:

(a) Ensure, so far as is reasonably practicable, that all control systems of work equipment are safe.

(b) Are chosen making due allowance for the failures, faults and constraints to be expected in the planned circumstances of use.

(2) Without prejudice to the generality of paragraph (1), a control system shall not be safe unless:

(a) Its operation does not create any increased risk to health or safety.

(b) It ensures, so far as is reasonably practicable, that any fault in or damage to any part of the control system or the loss of supply of any source of energy used by the work equipment cannot result in additional or increased risk to health or safety.

(c) It does not impede the operation of any control required by Regulation 15 or 16."

Failure of any part of the control system or its power supply should lead to a 'fail-safe' condition (more correctly and realistically called 'minimised failure to danger'), and not impede the operation of the 'stop' or 'emergency stop' controls. The measures, which should be taken in the design and application of a control system to mitigate against the effects of failure, will need to be balanced against the consequences of any failure, and the greater the risk, the more resistant the control system should be to the effects of failure.

STABILITY

PUWER Regulation 20 - Stability

PUWER 1998, Regulation 20, sets out the following requirements with regard to stability of work equipment:

"Every employer shall ensure that work equipment or any part of work equipment is stabilised by clamping or otherwise where necessary for purposes of health or safety."

Most machines used in a fixed position should be bolted or otherwise fastened down so that they do not move or rock during use.

This is particularly important where the equipment is tall relative to its base or has a high centre of gravity, for example, a pedestal mounted abrasive wheel, platform hoists and tower cranes.

LIGHTING

PUWER Regulation 21 - Lighting

PUWER 1998, Regulation 21, sets out the following requirements with regard to lighting for work equipment:

"Every employer shall ensure that suitable and sufficient lighting, which takes account of the operations to be carried out, is provided at any place where a person uses work equipment."

Local lighting may be needed to give sufficient view of a dangerous process or to reduce visual fatigue.

MARKINGS AND WARNINGS

PUWER Regulation 23 - Markings

PUWER 1998, Regulation 23, sets out the following requirements with regard to markings on work equipment:

"Every employer shall ensure that work equipment is marked in a clearly visible manner with any marking appropriate for reasons of health and safety."

There are similarities between Regulation 23 and 24 covering markings and warnings. Certain markings may also serve as a warning, for example, the maximum working speed, maximum working load or maximum reach.

PUWER Regulation 24 - Warnings

PUWER 1998, Regulation 24, sets out the following requirements with regard to warnings on work equipment:

"Every employer shall ensure that work equipment incorporates any warnings or warning devices which are appropriate for reasons of health and safety. Warnings given by warning devices on work equipment shall not be appropriate unless they are unambiguous, easily perceived and easily understood."

Warnings and warning devices are introduced following the implementation of markings and other physical measures, where appropriate risks to health and safety remain. Warnings are usually in the form of a notice, sign or similar. Typically, warnings are positive instructions (hard hats must be worn), prohibitions (no naked flames) and restrictions (do not heat above 60°C). Warning devices are active units that give out either an audible or visual signal, usually connected to the equipment in order that the warning operates only when a hazard exists. Warning devices are also used where the equipment is mobile. A flashing light can warn of the presence of a dumper truck and an audible device may warn of a vehicle reversing or a concrete pump about to start.

CLEAR UNOBSTRUCTED WORKSPACE

Construction (Design and Management) Regulations (CDM) 2015

Regulation 17 - Safe place of work

CDM 2015, Regulation 17, sets out the following requirements with regard to a safe place of work, including when using work equipment:

"(1) There must, so far as is reasonably practicable, be suitable and sufficient safe access to and egress from:

(a) Every construction site to every other place provided for the use of any person whilst at work.

(b) Every place construction work is being carried out to every other place to which workers have access within a construction site.

(2) A construction site must be, so far as is reasonably practicable, made and kept safe for, and without risks to, the health of a person at work there.

(3) Action must be taken to ensure, so far as is reasonably practicable, that no person uses access to or egress from or gains access to any construction site which does not comply with the requirements of paragraph (1) or (2).

(4) A construction site must, so far as is reasonably practicable, have sufficient working space and be arranged so that it is suitable for any person who is working or who is likely to work there, taking account of any necessary work equipment likely to be used there."

Workrooms should have enough free space to allow people to get to and from workstations and to move within the room with ease. Where work equipment, such as a circular saw, is used in a workplace care should be taken to ensure that adequate space exists around the equipment to ensure it is not overcrowded and does not cause risk to operators and those passing by the equipment when it is operating. It is important that the workspace allocated for users of work equipment is maintained clear and unobstructed.

Obstructions could lead to slips, trips and falls, which could also involve contact with the equipment or moving parts of the equipment. Material being readied to be worked on, material worked on and any scrap material should not be allowed to build-up in the workspace.

Material such as dust, scraps of wood or metal can quickly build-up as the equipment is used. Scrap material must be removed from the workspace at suitable intervals, so that it does not build-up and obstruct the workspace. Good control of the input, output and processing of material is essential.

Responsibilities of users

Management of Health and Safety at Work (MHSWR) Regulation 1999, Regulation 14 - Employees' duties

MHSWR 1999, Regulation 14, sets out the following requirements with regard to employees' duties, including use of work equipment:

"Every employee shall use any machinery, equipment, dangerous substance, transport equipment, means of production or safety device provided to him by his employer in accordance both with any training in the use of the equipment concerned which has been received by him and the instructions respecting that use which have been provided to him by the said employer in compliance with the requirements and prohibitions imposed upon that employer by or under the relevant statutory provisions."

Employees have a duty under Section 7 of the HASAWA 1974 to take reasonable care for their own health and safety and for that of others who may be affected by their acts or omissions and to co-operate with the employer to enable him to comply with statutory duties for health and safety. This includes the appropriate use of work equipment. The duty under Section 7 is further accentuated by the duties expressed in Regulation 14 of MHSWR 1999 to use equipment in accordance with training and instructions.

Supporting the Section 7 of HASAWA 1974 duty to co-operate with the employer employees have a duty under Regulation 14 of MHSWR 1999 to:

"Inform his employer or any other employee of that employer with specific responsibility for the health and safety of his fellow employees:

(a) Of any work situation which a person with the first-mentioned employee's training and instruction would reasonably consider represented a serious and immediate danger to health and safety.

(b) Of any matter which a person with the first-mentioned employee's training and instruction would reasonably consider represented a shortcoming in the employer's protection arrangements for health and safety, in so far as that situation or matter either affects the health and safety of that first mentioned employee or arises out of or in connection with his own activities at work, and has not previously been reported to his employer or to any other employee of that employer in accordance with this paragraph."

This would mean that if a user of work equipment, for example, a crane operator, found that the equipment was not working safely or had missed a scheduled thorough examination that they were aware it required they must report this to their employer. The duties placed on employees do not reduce the responsibility of employers to comply with their own duties.

5.2 - Hand-held tools

Hand tools

HAZARDS AND MISUSE OF HAND TOOLS (NON-POWERED)

Anyone who uses a non-powered hand-held tool (hand tool) may be at risk of injury, either accidentally, through misuse or equipment failure. There is a range of risks from using hand tools, many of the hazards can affect the user of the hand tools and those passing or working nearby.

For example:

- Noise induced hearing loss from cutting or impact tools.
- Respiratory disease from inhalation of dust from sanding.
- Eye injury from material thrown off from chiselling.
- Punctures and cuts caused by sharp equipment such as knives, chisels, saws, planes and screwdrivers.
- Heat-producing equipment, such as blowtorches, can cause burns and permanent scarring.
- Hammers are basic tools, but they are also notorious for causing thumb and finger injuries.

Misuse includes using the wrong tool for the job, for example, a hammer to drive home a screw, rather than a screwdriver, or a file, which is brittle, as a lever.

CONTROL MEASURES FOR HAND TOOLS

Hammers

The following checklist will help to avoid incidents with hammers:

- Check the condition of the hammer - avoid split, broken or loose handles and worn or chipped heads. Heads should be properly secured to the handles.
- Grip the handle firmly.
- Hold the hammer at the end of the handle.
- Hit the surface squarely with the hammer.
- Use the whole arm and elbow.
- Place the work against a hard surface.
- Work in a natural position.
- Check area is clear around you before swinging the hammer.
- Practice good hammering technique.

Files

These should have a proper, well designed handle. The file should be held firmly in one hand with the fingers of the other hand used only to guide the file. The material being filed should be firmly held in clamps or a vice.

File strokes should be made away from the user. Take care to avoid the file slipping on the surface of the material causing sudden forward movement of the user. Files must never be used as a lever - they are very brittle and will shatter easily. They should only be cleaned by using a cleaning card and not by striking them against a solid object as this can also cause the file to shatter.

Chisels

Choose a chisel large enough for the job, so the blade is used rather than only the point or corner. Never use chisels with dull blades - the sharper the tool, the better the performance. Chisels that are bent, cracked, or chipped should be discarded. The cutting edge should be sharpened to the correct angle. Do not allow the head of cold chisels to spread to a mushroom shape - grind off the sides regularly. Use a hand guard on the chisel and hit the chisel squarely. Chisels should not be used as a lever as they may break suddenly.

Screwdrivers

A screwdriver is one of the most commonly used and abused tools. The practice of using screwdrivers as punches, wedges, or levers should be discouraged as this practice dulls blades and may cause injury if the blade fractures or slips in use. Screwdrivers should be selected so the tip fits the screw. When working on electrical equipment screwdrivers must be equipped with insulated handles and blades. Screwdrivers with split handles or damaged tips should be taken out of use and discarded safely.

Spanners

Avoid spanners with splayed or damaged jaws. Use ring spanners or sockets where possible, as these are less likely to slip. Discard safely any spanners that show signs of slipping. Ensure enough spanners of the correct size are available. Do not improvise by using pipes, etc., as extensions to the handle. Where necessary use penetrating oil to loosen tight nuts.

Knives

Knives cause more disabling injuries than any other hand tool. The risks are that the hands may slip from the handle onto the blade or that the knife may strike the body or the free hand. Use knives with handle guards if possible. Make sure that the cutting stroke is always away from the body. Return the knife to a safe place and ensure it is sheathed before conducting other tasks, like moving a sack that the user has opened. Do not hold a knife with an open blade while carrying other things. Knives must be kept sharp and in their holders or sheaths when not in use.

Dirty or oily knives should be wiped clean to avoid the user's grip slipping. To clean the blade wipe with a towel or cloth with the sharp edge turned away from the wiping hand. Horseplay of any kind involving a knife (throwing, 'fencing', etc.) must not be tolerated. Where there is a potential for a flammable atmosphere to be present use alloy or bronze tools to prevent sparks.

Common portable power tools used in construction

PNEUMATIC DRILL/CHISEL

Pneumatic drills or chisels are used commonly where heavy duty tasks are performed such as penetrating tarmac or concrete surfaces. This equipment is usually very heavy and labour intensive, resulting in manual handling hazards and risks. The pneumatic energy is usually delivered through mobile industrial compressors that are capable of supplying adequate power.

Hazards

The compressor is a separate piece of equipment that introduces its own specific hazards. Perhaps the most obvious hazard is the drill or chisel piece which, when operating, presents a risk of impact injury to the feet of users, and others nearby. During normal operation, the drill or chisel tool produces high intensity noise from contact with the surface. Other noise includes the exhausting of the pneumatic pressure from the internal drive of the equipment as the tool operates. The noise sources are located very close to the user's ears, are at a level that is damaging to the ear and require the user to wear hearing protection. The operation of the chisel produces the hazard of flying debris in the form of dust and fragments that pose the risk of abrasion, cuts or eye damage.

Control measures

In order to control this risk the surface may be damped down and protective goggles worn by the user. The energy produced by the compressor is converted into vibration. Vibration introduces the risk of injuries, such as hand arm vibration syndrome (HAVS), with possible long term effects, including damage to the nervous system beginning at the fingertips. Precautions for vibration include using well maintained equipment, using equipment with lower vibration levels, taking frequent breaks or job rotation, exercise to improve circulation and warm the hands and seeking suitable personal protective gloves. There are risks associated with high pressure air lines becoming broken or damaged resulting in pipes lashing freely. Equipment should always be inspected as safe to use with certification for pressure lines. Screens can be used as a final measure to protect others at the location where the equipment is used.

ELECTRIC DRILL

Electric drills are used for penetrating various materials and in construction are usually of a medium to heavy-duty nature. This equipment involves rotating shafts and tool bits, sharp tools, electricity and flying debris.

Hazards

Hazards include shock and electrocution leading to possible fatalities; however, this potential is reduced by using 110 volt or battery operated equipment. Other hazards include puncture, entanglement, ejection of materials and parts of the drill, noise and dust.

Control measures

Control measures include using only equipment that is suitable for the task, ensuring equipment is tested and inspected as safe to use, suitable shut off and isolation measures, goggles, hearing protection. It is important to check that drill bits are securely and centrally held in the drill chuck. Care should be taken to ensure the drill bits are kept sharp as injuries can occur when the rotating drill bit gets stuck in the material being drilled and the drill is caused to kick and rotate in the user's hands.

DISC CUTTER

Hazards

Disc cutter saws consist of a petrol motor providing power to a circular cutting disc. Disc cutters are used for cutting grooves into surfaces. Hazards associated with disc cutters include cuts from the rotating blade, entanglement with rotating parts, ejection of material, noise, vibration, fire, inhalation of fumes and dust.

Control measures

Goggles must be worn when operating this equipment. Due to the velocity of the flying debris they must be grade 1 impact resistant and totally enclose the eye region of the face. The area being cut into may be damped down to minimise the production of dust clouds into the atmosphere.

Vacuum attachments are available that make their operation almost dust-less when working correctly.

Dust masks must also be worn when using this equipment. Sparks arising from cutting operations can result in a fire. In order to control this risk good housekeeping practice is essential, including removing sources of fuel from the work area.

Figure 5-14: Disc cutter. *Source: STIHL.*

Misuse of this equipment must be prevented through training and supervision, including using the side of the cutting disc, using over worn discs, using the incorrect disc for the material being cut, leaving the cutter with the disc still spinning and not wearing the appropriate personal protective equipment (PPE). The disc, when spinning, may lead to cuts of cables, hands and legs; entanglement with rotating parts; noise and hearing damage.

CUT OFF SAW

Cut off (chop) saws consist of a motor providing power to a circular cutting disc. Cut off saws are normally powered by electricity, however petrol motors are available. The saws have a motorised disc or saw blade, which has an enclosed guard. This is mounted on a counter sprung or a pneumatic arm which is operated by pulling down onto the materials to be cut.

They are usually used to cut brick, stone, timber, steel, aluminium, plastic and wood into manageable lengths.

Hazards

Hazards associated with these saws are cuts, entanglement, electric shock, fire, inhalation of fumes, dusts, noise, vibration, ejection of material, such as metal shavings or small off-cuts.

Figure 5-15: Cut off saw. *Source: Draper Tools.*

Control measures

Only trained and competent workers should use this equipment due to the hazards; the saw should be fitted with a method of locking-off the equipment to prevent unauthorised use. The saw should be fitted with an adjustable fixed or self-adjusting guard to enclose the blade. Goggles and protective clothing must be worn to prevent injuries from flying debris or dusts/fumes from harming the human body. In order to control the risk of fire from the sparks ejected when cutting some materials good housekeeping practice is essential, including removing sources of fuel from the work area. The equipment should be isolated from the mains supply prior to changing any cutting discs or replacing saw blades.

SANDER

Hazards

Sanding equipment is available in a variety of sizes from hand held equipment to large industrial machines. Sanders are used to provide a smooth finished surface, using a mechanical abrasive action.

Sanding operations are carried out on a wide variety of materials including wood, minerals such as marble and man-made fibres. The main hazards associated with the sanding process are vibration and noise.

Also, harm can be caused by the inhalation of respirable particles from dust. Where organic materials such as wood are being processed, fire may result from overheated surfaces or explosion from dust by-products. Associated hazards may include electrocution if supply cables are damaged by hand held sanders, particularly if the sander is placed on the ground whilst still rotating.

Figure 5-16: Belt sander.   *Source: Clarke International.*

Other risks include trips from trailing leads, cuts from sharp surfaces and strains or sprains from manual handling of process materials.

Control measures

When using sanding equipment, suitable personal respiratory protective equipment (RPE) is required to protect the user from dust exposure. Where possible, local exhaust ventilation equipment should be used to minimise dust in the atmosphere. In order to protect against vibration injuries, the operator should be given regular breaks and the equipment maintained at intervals, including the renewal of sanding media to prevent the need for over exertion by the operator. Where tools like sanders are held in the hand, suitable hand protection will also reduce injuries from vibration, cuts and manual handling. Pre-use inspections by the operator and regular thorough examinations should be carried out to identify potential electrical problems. Care should be taken to ensure that power leads do not create tripping hazards and they are positioned so that the likelihood of mechanical damage is minimised.

CARTRIDGE AND PNEUMATIC NAIL GUNS

Guns for nails and other fixings are used in many activities in construction including carpentry, steelwork, plastering and surveying. Power sources range from battery power, electrical low voltage, pneumatic and explosive cartridge. They are used for shooting nails or pins into materials in order to secure a section.

Pneumatic guns may be operated by a pressurised changeable cylinder or compressor fed supply. Pneumatic guns usually provide a continuous supply of fixings from a belt or other type of magazine. Explosive cartridge guns are available in single cartridge manual change or fast loading format, the latter often being used to fix roofing and decking to steelwork. Some fixing guns operate using a fuel cell and small linear combustion engine, the controlled combustion/explosion providing the energy to drive the fixing into the material.

Figure 5-17: Cartridge fixing gun.   *Source: ITW.*

Figure 5-18: Pneumatic nail gun. *Source: Bostitch.*

Hazards

The puncture hazard of fixings fired from the gun is the main hazard and can affect the user and people in the area where the gun is used. There is a significant risk of flying debris from fixing operations and impact/puncture injuries to eyes or hands are likely from the flying debris and fixings released incorrectly from the gun. The noise produced is high intensity impact noise and represents a significant hazard; it may also be amplified by the material it is vibrating through.

Vibrations produced by the use of this equipment, which is grasped in the hand, may present a risk of causing HAVS in sustained use. The high pressure air used with some fixing guns creates a hazard of injection of air into the body.

Figure 5-19: Pneumatic nail gun.   *Source: Bostitch.*

The explosive cartridges used with some fixing guns can present an explosive hazard coupled with the hazard of ejection of cartridge materials.

Control measures

It is important users of these guns are trained to keep their hands away from the firing zone. This may be assisted by using clamps and other devices instead of the user's hand to hold materials in position prior to fixing. Impact resistant goggles or face protection must be worn when using the gun.

Personal hearing protection must be worn at all times due to the risk of hearing damage from the high intensity impact noise. Equipment must be maintained to reduce vibration levels and operators instructed to take regular rest breaks and report any prolonged numbness to fingers or hands to their supervisor.

Procedures should be in place to ensure there is a safe zone around and behind the fixing area. The lowest power explosive cartridge or air pressure capable of making the fixing should be used, to avoid fixings passing through material being fixed. Arrangements should be in place to deal with 'miss-fires' and jams of fixings within the gun. Where explosive cartridges are used, strict control must be placed over the storage and issue of the cartridges.

CHAINSAW

Chainsaws are predominately used in arboreal work, for tree felling, logging and pruning. In construction activities this may be part of remediation/site preparation work or final ground works before handover to users of a building or structure.

Hazards

Chainsaws are potentially dangerous pieces of equipment that can cause major injuries and even death if not used correctly. Injuries can occur to the head from 'kickback' of the blade. This is where a chain tooth at the upper tip of the guide bar cuts into wood without cutting through it, the chain becomes stuck and the bar is driven up in an arc toward the operator. Injuries to the legs can result from inadvertent follow through when cutting horizontally.

Injury can also result if the chain breaks during operation due to poor maintenance or attempting to cut inappropriate materials.

Figure 5-20: Petrol chainsaw.   *Source: Mowdirect Garden Machinery.*

The potential for eye injuries from wood chipping is also high. Other hazards include falls from a height, falling branches/trees, sawdust and exhaust gas inhalation. As the equipment used is often powered by a petrol engine there is a risk of fire. In addition, parts of the motor may get hot presenting a risk of burning to the skin of the operator. Health hazards include potential back problems from poor posture whilst working with extended reach. Chainsaws also expose users to high levels of noise and hand-arm vibration, which can lead to hearing loss and conditions such as vibration white finger.

Control measures

The Approved Code of Practice supporting Regulation 9 of the Provision and Use of Work Equipment Regulations (PUWER) 1998, regarding training, sets a minimum standard for competence of people using chainsaws in tree work. All employees using chain saws should receive adequate and appropriate training and have obtained a relevant certificate of competence or a national competence award. The Health and Safety Executive (HSE) information leaflet 'Chainsaws at work' (INDG317) advises that chainsaw users should have regular refresher/update training to ensure they work to industry best practice and maintain their levels of competence. The suggested intervals for such training are: occasional users - every two to three years; full-time users - every five years. Maintenance schedules are essential for safe use and protection against ill-health from excessive noise and vibration. The saw must be maintained in its manufactured condition with all the safety devices in efficient working order and all guards in place. It should be regularly serviced by someone who is competent to do the job. Chainsaw users should report any damage or excessive wear from daily checks. Suitable PPE is essential to protect the user from hazards. PPE selected should be suitable for chainsaw work and whenever possible hand, arm and legs should be protected by PPE lined with cut prevention webbing that jams and stops the chain on contact, this must comply with European standards for suitability of use with chainsaws, 'Protective clothing for users of hand-held chain saws' - BS EN 381. Head and face protection should also be of a suitable quality for protection against chainsaw contact. Equipment must be maintained to reduce vibration levels and operators instructed to take regular rest breaks and report any prolonged numbness of their fingers or hands to their supervisor.

Suitability for location

In explosive or flammable atmospheres only correctly rated anti-spark hand-held tools should be used. Electrical tools, for example, drills should be totally enclosed to prevent sparks from the motor igniting and causing explosions in flammable atmospheres. These tools are made from an alloy metal know commonly as 'gun metal' which do not cause sparks when in contact with other metals. A good example of this is fuel tanks on cars and petrol pumps. It should be remembered that petrol driven portable power tools are popular in construction activities as they can be used where no electrical supply is available. This makes them useful for use on large open construction sites, particularly in the first phases of the construction activities, including site surveying, clearance and preparation. However, they will not be suitable for use in confined areas where the exhaust gases could build-up. The carbon monoxide created as a product of combustion would make them unsuitable in cellars, sewers and many indoor areas. Electrical equipment may be unsuitable for use in particularly adverse wet weather conditions, working in or near water or where water from processes may fall onto or be transferred by hand to the equipment.

Procedures for defective equipment

With duties being placed upon both the employer and the employee to ensure the use of safe equipment, when faulty equipment, including hand-held tools, is identified in the workplace it should be isolated until such a time it can be repaired by a competent person. It is important that replacement hand-held tools are readily available to encourage people to stop using defective equipment when it is identified and the defective equipment to be removed from use. Under section 7 of the HASAWA 1974 and Regulation 14 of MHSWR 1999 employees have a duty to notify any shortcomings in the health and safety arrangements where there is a danger, and should do this even when no immediate danger exists. This is to enable employers to take remedial action if needed. The duties placed on employees do not reduce the responsibility of employers to comply with their own duties. A formal procedure should be in place to anticipate this need for reporting shortcomings; it should particularly take account of the need to report defects in hand tools.

Under Regulation 5 of the PUWER 1998: *"Every employer shall ensure that work equipment is maintained in an efficient state, in efficient working order and in good repair."* Regulation 6 of PUWER 1998 lays down requirements for inspecting work equipment to ensure that health and safety conditions are maintained and that any deterioration can be detected and remedied in good time.

5.3 - Machinery hazards

Main mechanical and non-mechanical hazards

To meet requirements of the syllabus, machinery hazards are discussed in this section.

'Control of hazards' is considered in 'Application of protection methods to a range of equipment'; see section '5.4 - Control measures for machinery hazards'.

Mechanical and other hazards identified in BS EN ISO 12100 Part 1 are described as follows.

MECHANICAL HAZARDS

Entanglement

The mere fact that a machine part is revolving can constitute a very real hazard of entanglement. Loose clothing, jewellery, long hair, etc. increase the risk of entanglement.

Figure 5-21: Auger drill - entanglement. *Source: STIHL.*

Examples of entanglement hazards include couplings, drill chucks/bits, flywheels, spindles, shafts (especially those with keys/bolts) and rotating tools like abrasive wheels.

Friction and abrasion

Friction burns and encountering rough surfaces moving at high speed, as found in a sanding machine, grinding wheel or conveyor belt, can cause abrasion injuries.

Figure 5-22: Chop saw - cutting.   Source: Speedy Hire plc.

Figure 5-23: Abrasive wheel - abrasion.   Source: RMS.

Cutting

Saw blades, knives and even rough edges, especially when moving at high speed, can result in serious cuts and even amputation injuries. The dangerous part can appear stationary due to the stroboscopic effect under certain lighting conditions. Examples of cutting action hazards include saws, slicing machines, abrasive cutting discs and chainsaws.

Shear

When two or more machine parts move towards/past one another a 'trap' is created. This can result in a crush injury or even an amputation. Examples of shearing action hazards include scissor lifts, platform hoists passing a landing and guillotines.

Stabbing and puncture

The body may be penetrated by sharp pieces of equipment, or material contained in the equipment. Examples of stabbing and puncture hazards include fixing materials such as nails fired from a nail gun or a drill bit which could puncture the hand when operating the drill.

Impact

Impact is caused by objects that strike the body, but do not penetrate it. They may cause the person or part of the person to be moved, sometimes violently, resulting in injury. For example, a person could be struck by the jib of a crane/excavator or materials on a hoist.

Figure 5-24: Stabbing and puncture.   Source: Speedy Hire plc.

Figure 5-25: Shear.   Source: RMS.

Crushing

Crushing is caused when part of the body is caught between either two moving parts of machinery or a moving part and a stationary object.

Examples of crushing hazards include the platform of a hoist closing together with the ground or an overhead beam or the folding arms of a MEWP.

Figure 5-26: Crushing.   *Source: RMS.*

Figure 5-27: Impact.   *Source: RMS.*

Drawing-in

When a belt runs round a roller an 'in-running nip' is created between the moving parts, in the direction of travel of the belt. This inward movement draws in any part of the body presented to it. Examples of drawing-in hazards are the rollers of a surface roller, chain drives of a fork-lift truck lifting mast, V-belts on the drive from a motor to the drum of a cement mixer or the spindle of a drill.

Figure 5-28: Drawing-in.   *Source: RMS.*

Figure 5-29: Ejection.   *Source: RMS.*

Ejection

When pieces of the material being worked on or components of the machinery are thrown or fired out of the equipment during operation, they represent an ejection hazard. Ejection hazards include parts of a shattered grinding wheel, waste metal turnings, and dust from a grinder/disc saw or a nail from a nail gun.

Injury by compressed air or high pressure fluid injection

Injection of fluids through the skin may lead to soft tissue injuries similar to crushing. Air entering the blood stream through the skin may be fatal. Examples of high pressure fluid injection hazards include leaking hydraulic lift systems, diesel injectors, spray painting, compressed air jets for blast cleaning the outside of a building and a high pressure lance for cutting concrete.

Figure 5-30: Disc saw - ejection. *Source: Water Active, Nov 06.*

Figure 5-31: Fluid injection.   *Source: RMS.*

OTHER (NON-MECHANICAL) HAZARDS

Machinery may also present other hazards. The nature of the hazard will determine the measures taken to protect people from them.

The various sources of non-mechanical hazards include the following:

- Electricity - electric shock and burns.
- Hot surfaces - burns and source of ignition.
- Noise and vibration - noise induced hearing loss; vibration white finger.
- Biological - viral and bacterial.
- Chemicals that are toxic, irritant, flammable, corrosive, explosive.

- High/low temperatures - burns to hands.
- Ionising and non-ionising radiation - nausea, vomiting, death.
- Access - slips, trips and falls; obstructions and projections.
- Manual handling - work-related upper limb disorders.

SUMMARY OF MACHINERY HAZARDS

Mechanical		Non-mechanical
Entanglement	for example, auger drill, drilling machine	Electricity
Friction and abrasion	for example, grinding wheel	Hot surfaces/fire
Cutting	for example, sharp edges of circular saw	Noise
Shear	for example, scissor lift mechanism	Vibration
Stabbing and puncture	for example, nail gun	Noise/vibration
Impact	for example, moving arm of an excavator	Chemicals
Crushing	for example, folding arms of MEWP	Radiation
Drawing in	for example, rollers of a surface roller	Access
Injection	for example, high pressure hydraulic oil system	Manual handling
Ejection	for example, disc cutter - dust and particles	Extremes of temperature

Figure 5-32: Summary - machinery hazards. *Source: RMS.*

Hazards presented by a range of equipment

OFFICE MACHINERY

Photocopier

The hazards of a photocopier are drawing-in, hot surfaces, fumes, toner dust, electrical, manual handling, noise and glare. These hazards are more likely to be encountered by people who carry out unauthorised maintenance work.

Document shredder

The main hazards of a document shredder are drawing-in, cutting or crushing, also cuts from paper handling and electrical dangers.

Although these machines are well designed and, therefore guarding is adequate, care has to be taken to ensure that loose clothing such as ties and scarves do not get caught in the blades. If the equipment is fitted with an interlock, there should be regular inspections to ensure that the device has not moved out of adjustment or has been overridden. Unauthorised electrical repairs should not be carried out.

Figure 5-33: Abrasive wheel (grinder). *Source: RMS.*

Figure 5-34: Document shredder. *Source: www.axminster.co.uk.*

WORKSHOP MACHINERY

Bench-top grinder

Bench-top grinders are typically found in workshops and are suitable for indoor use. Bench-top grinders are used for sharpening of tool bits (drills, chisels and blades), shaping steel, and de-burring cut steel components.

The hazards of bench-top grinders include friction and abrasion from contact with the moving abrasive wheel, entanglement, drawing-in and possible ejections when parts of the wheel or work piece break and sparks are thrown off. Other hazards are electricity, heat and noise.

Pedestal drill

The hazards in setting up a pedestal drill include failure to remove the chuck-key (which will be ejected if the equipment is stated) and failure to secure the guard to drive pulleys. Hazards when the pedestal drill is in use include entanglement, puncture and flying waste metal (swarf).

Bench-mounted circular saw

Cutting is the main hazard of a bench-mounted circular saw. Other hazards include electricity, noise, sawdust, splinters and musculoskeletal disorders related to posture and materials handling.

Figure 5-35: Pedestal drill.   *Source: RMS.*

Figure 5-36: Bench cross-cut circular saw.   *Source: RMS.*

Hand fed power planer

The hazards of a hand fed power planer include noise, cuts and severs, dust, impact from flying debris, fire and electrocution.

Spindle moulding machine

Spindle moulding machines are widely used in woodworking activities for the high speed machining of timber, multi-spindle machines allow machining on all four sides. Typical products include squared stock, tongued and grooved boarding, skirting board, etc.

Virtually all these machines produce noise levels in excess of 85dB and noise levels up to 105dB have been recorded at the in-feed operator's position. It is known that many operators of spindle moulding machines are exposed to noise levels well in excess of 85dB even when the machines are provided with noise enclosures. Hazards include noise, cuts, entanglement and risk of fire.

Figure 5-37: Hand fed power planer. *Source: Screwfix.*

Figure 5-38: Spindle moulding machine. *Source: Axminster Power Tool Centre Ltd.*

CONSTRUCTION SITE MACHINERY

Compressor

Pneumatic compressors are a source of power for a variety of portable equipment used in construction activities. Tools that can source power from compressors include drills and chisels, saws, nail guns, mixing equipment and plasterer's surface scotchers.

Whilst this list of tools is not exhaustive, the principle remains the same in that power is delivered through a high pressure airline to the tool and converted into mechanical power.

Figure 5-39: Compressor. *Source: Atlas Copco.*

Pneumatic compressors are typically large pieces of mobile plant that attach to the towing bar of a road going works vehicle. When at site, a compressor is free standing, only attached to the tool by the pressure airline.

Hazards arise from the fuelling of the plant (normally diesel) where contact with the skin can occur, splashes into eyes, inhalation of fumes and the possible risk of fire where hot temperatures are involved. In operation, the compressor produces exhaust gases from the motor which may, in addition to the fuel, require an assessment in compliance with the Control of Substances Hazardous to Health Regulations (COSHH) 2002.

The exhaust gases are a particular hazard in confined areas. Noise and vibration at high levels may be produced from the compressor although these levels may vary dependent upon the effectiveness of the soundproofing material incorporated into the plant in addition to the condition of the equipment and frequency of maintenance programmes that may exist. This equipment also involves pressure lines that provide a hazard of injection and trip hazard.

Cement mixer

Cement mixers are portable construction plant used for mixing a variety of aggregates and cement used in the construction process. The main benefit of this equipment is removing a significant volume of the manual labour aspect of the mixing process although a significant amount of labour intensive activities remain.

The equipment consists of a motor (electric, petrol or diesel) linked through a gear box and drive shaft to a rotating drum that incorporates internal mixing blades to aid the mixing process.

The assembly may vary from a complete unit that pivots on a central bar or a two part system where the mixer is seated onto a plinth or stand and pivots forward to enable emptying of the drum when the mixture is complete.

Figure 5-40: Cement mixer. *Source: RMS.*

Hazards arise when the source of power is electricity as water is used in the mixing process and the equipment is used outdoors, which presents a risk of electrocution. In order to control this risk, a low voltage power supply should be used, with suitable heavy duty cable and cable covers when there is a risk of running over them with vehicles or plant. Used with a residual current protection device a good level of protection can be obtained.

When the fuel source is diesel or petrol there is a risk of fire, which increases during refuelling operations when the exhaust system may still be hot or people may be smoking in the close vicinity of the equipment. The rotating drum and drive shaft poses an entanglement risk with personal protective equipment and other tools. If covers are removed they can expose drive belts or gearing with the associated risk of drawing in.

Operatives loading mixers should be warned of the dangers of shovels and trowels becoming caught in the mixer blades and snatching the hand tool out of the operatives hand with force, which may result in personal injury to limbs and muscles.

Loading the mixer is a manual task which can result in injury from repetitive, twisting motion when emptying shovels or gauging buckets into the mixer. Slip and trip hazards may arise from spilt material or material placed ready to be used. The fumes from the diesel/petrol motor, dusts involved in the mixing process and wet cement present a health hazard.

Often the mixing activity is a slow process; operatives tend to leave the mixer running alone until the mix is ready. If the equipment is left running and unattended there is a risk of unauthorised access to the mixer and injuries to third parties. As the mixing process proceeds there is a likelihood of build-up of materials on the floor, leading to a risk of slips and trips and a possibility of falling onto the moving equipment.

Plate compactor

Plate compactors are simple machines used for consolidating aggregates or loose materials. They are also used for securing block paviors into position by applying a heavy downward force through a flat plate where the force is increased by the vibrating motion.

They operate on the principle of a motor that rotates a cam through a drive belt which provides the vibration force. Upon first appearances from a distance, operators would appear to look as though they are operating a lawn mower as the equipment is walked up and down the surface to be compacted, with the vibration providing the drive, assisted by the operator.

Hazards arise from the source of power, typically petrol, which has associated fire risks that are increased when refuelling is carried out when the exhaust system is still hot.

This equipment, because of its purpose, has to be heavy which brings a risk of manual handling strain injuries when loading or unloading from a vehicle. Additional hazards include noise, vibration and manual handling.

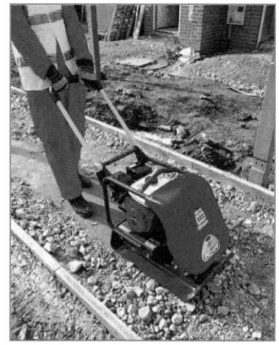
Figure 5-41: Plate compactor. *Source: HSS Hire Service Group Ltd.*

Ground consolidation equipment

Ground consolidation equipment serves the same purpose as a plate compactor.

However, a plate compactor is generally for lighter duty than the large types of ground consolidation equipment such as man riding rollers or manual rollers.

This heavy duty type of equipment requires competence and authorisation in order to use it on site. Ground consolidation equipment moves at a greater speed than lighter duty equipment and its power drives the equipment directly through the roller wheel.

Figure 5-42: Ground consolidation equipment. *Source: RMS.*

The potential harm from the drawing in/crush hazards are high, a drawing in/crush sustained from a piece of this plant could more easily lead to a major injury or fatality.

Portable circular saw

A portable circular saw is a powerful tool that can cross cut and rip timber. It is a versatile piece of equipment used for small woodworking tasks.

Commonly the blade can cut to a depth of 55mm (2in). The main hazards relate to cuts from the blade, which revolves at high speed.

Typical other hazards are electric shock from damaged cables, cuts or injury from flying waste materials and dust. Vibration, noise and poor posture are also hazards.

Figure 5-43: Circular saw. *Source: HSS Hire Service Group Limited.*

Road-marking equipment

Road marking usually involves the application of a hot plastic based substance to the surface of a road. The equipment used will often have its own supply of fuel in the form of liquefied petroleum gas (LPG). This is used to maintain the marking substance at a suitable working temperature in a holding vessel.

Direct hazards from the equipment include the hazard of drawing in/crush involving the wheels of the equipment, contact with the hot marking substance and potential overheating of the marking substance leading to a fire. Other hazards include exhaust gases and falls from the equipment.

Figure 5-44: Thermoplastic hand marking barrow. *Source: Maxigrip Surfacing Ltd.*

Figure 5-45: Road Marking vehicle. *Source: Maxigrip Surfacing Ltd.*

Electrical generators

Diesel/petrol powered electrical generators are used for powering portable power tools and other construction equipment. Smaller generators are often used to power road breakers; large versions may be used to provide electricity for site welfare arrangements. They may be equipped with 230V and 110V sockets or provide electricity to a 415 volt distribution system. The main hazards are electrocution, hot surfaces, fire, noise and asphyxiation from carbon dioxide and carbon monoxide present in the exhaust gases. Other hazards include risks related to handling the fuel and, where they are portable, manual handling hazards related to moving them into the position needed.

Figure 5-46: Petrol 110v generator. *Source: RMS.*

Figure 5-47: Large diesel generator. *Source: RMS.*

5.4 - Control measures for machinery hazards

Machinery guarding

OBJECTIVE OF MACHINERY GUARDING

- To prevent workpeople from coming into contact with dangerous parts of machinery.
- To prevent physical injury from power driven and manually operated machines.
- To enable machines to be operated safely without interference with production.

PUWER REGULATION 11 - DANGEROUS PARTS OF MACHINERY

PUWER 1998, Regulation 11, sets out the following requirements with regard to dangerous parts of machinery:

"(1) Every employer shall ensure that measures are taken in accordance with paragraph (2) which are effective:

    (a) To prevent access to any dangerous part of machinery or to any rotating stock-bar.

    (b) To stop the movement of any dangerous part of machinery or rotating stock-bar before any part of a person enters a danger zone.

(2) The measures required by paragraph (1) shall consist of:

    (a) The provision of fixed guards enclosing every dangerous part or rotating stock-bar where and to the extent that it is practicable to do so, but where or to the extent that it is not.

    (b) The provision of other guards or protection devices where and to the extent that it is practicable to do so, but where or to the extent that it is not.

    (c) The provision of jigs, holders, push-sticks or similar protection appliances used in conjunction with the machinery where and to the extent that it is practicable to do so.

(d) The provision of information, instruction, training and supervision as is necessary.

(3) All guards and protection devices provided under sub-paragraphs (a) or (b) of paragraph (2) shall:

(a) Be suitable for the purpose for which they are provided.

(b) Be of good construction, sound material and adequate strength.

(c) Be maintained in an efficient state, in efficient working order and in good repair.

(d) Not give rise to any increased risk to health or safety.

(e) Not be easily bypassed or disabled.

(f) Be situated at sufficient distance from the danger zone.

(g) Not unduly restrict the view of the operating cycle of the machinery, where such a view is necessary.

(h) Be so constructed or adapted that they allow operations necessary to fit or replace parts and for maintenance work, restricting access so that it is allowed only to the area where the work is to be carried out and, if possible, without having to dismantle the guard or protection device.

(4) All protection appliances provided under sub-paragraph c) of paragraph (2) shall comply with sub-paragraphs (a) to (d) and (g) of paragraph (3).

(5) In this regulation - 'danger zone' means any zone in or around machinery in which a person is exposed to a risk to health or safety from contact with a dangerous part of machinery or a rotating stock-bar; 'stock-bar' means any part of a stock-bar which projects beyond the headstock of a lathe."

Regulation 11(2) gives the measures that an employer should take to fulfil the duty under Regulation 11(1) a combination of measures may be necessary to satisfy Regulation 11.

When deciding on the appropriate level of safeguarding, risk assessment criteria (likelihood of injury, potential severity of injury, numbers at risk) need to be considered both in relation to the normal operation of the machinery and other operations such as maintenance, repair, setting, tuning, adjustment etc. Regulation 11(3) (c) applies to the maintenance of guards and protection devices and will include those which are not attached to the machine itself, for example, perimeter fences.

The principles, merits and limitations of protection methods

HIERARCHY OF MEASURES FOR DANGEROUS PARTS OF MACHINERY

When considering control measures for dangerous parts of machinery the following hierarchy can be considered:

■ Prevent access to dangerous parts by means of **F** ixed guard (preferably fully enclosing).

■ When the above is not practicable protect by other guards (**I** nterlock, **A** utomatic) or safety devices (for example, **T** rip device).

■ When the above is not practicable protect by using safety appliances (for example, push stick or jig).

The various guards and safety devices can be summarised as follows:

F ixed	*I* nterlock	*A* utomatic (including self-closing)	*T* rip devices

FIXED GUARDS

A fixed guard/fence must be fitted such that it cannot be removed other than by the use of specialist tools which are not available to operators of the equipment.

A fixed guard may be designed to enable access by authorised personnel for maintenance or inspection, but only when the dangerous parts of the machine have been isolated.

A common example of a fixed guard is shown in **figure ref 5-48**. Not all fixed guards are of solid construction, some are made of mesh.

The holes in a mesh guard are of sufficient size to allow air circulation to cool the drive belt, but small enough to prevent the finger of the hand from penetrating the mesh and result in injury from the belt.

Figure 5-48: Total enclosure fixed guard. *Source: RMS.*

Distance (fixed) guard

Fixed guards do not always completely cover the danger point but place it out of normal reach. The larger the opening (to feed in material) the greater must be the distance from the opening to the danger point. A tree shredding machine uses a fixed distance guard design to prevent operators reaching the dangerous part of the machine when in use.

Merits of fixed guards

- Create a physical barrier.
- Require a tool to remove.
- No moving parts - therefore they require very little maintenance.
- Can be designed to enable visibility through clear panels or mesh.
- Suitable for adverse environments.

Limitations of fixed guards

- Do not disconnect power from the machine when not in place. Therefore the machine can be operated without guard being.
- May cause problems with visibility for inspection.
- If enclosed, may create problems with heat.
- May not protect against non-mechanical hazards, such as dust/fluids, which may be ejected.

Figure 5-49: Fixed guard - panel removed. *Source: RMS.*

Figure 5-50: Fixed guard over fan - mesh too big. *Source: RMS.*

INTERLOCKING GUARDS

An interlocking guard is similar to a fixed guard, but has a movable (usually hinged) part, so connected to the machine controls that if the movable part is in the open/lifted position the dangerous moving part at the work point cannot operate. This can be arranged so that the action of closing the guard activates the working part (to speed up work efficiently); for example, the front panel of a photocopier or the gates of a platform hoist. Interlocked guards are useful if operators need regular access to the danger area. Everyday examples of interlocking guards are those found on domestic equipment such as dish washers, microwave cookers and automatic washing machines. In ***figure ref 5-51***, the electrical interlock is positioned halfway down the right hand side of this panel.

The panel is made from transparent material to allow easy visual checks of the products that are manufactured by this equipment.

Merits of interlocking guards

- Connected to power source, therefore the machine cannot be operated with guard open.
- Allow regular access.

Limitations of interlocking guards

- Have moving parts therefore need regular maintenance.
- Can be over-ridden.
- If interlock is in the form of a gate, a person can step inside and close the gate behind them (someone else could then re-activate the machine).

Figure 5-51: Interlocking guard. *Source: RMS.*

- Dangerous parts of machinery may not stop immediately the guard is opened, therefore, a delay timer or brake might need to be fitted as well. For example, the drum on a spin drier does not stop instantly, and therefore a delay is fitted to prevent the door being opened until the drum is stationary.

SELF-ADJUSTING GUARD

Self-adjusting guards are guards that are fixed to the machine that have moving parts, which close themselves over the dangerous parts as an integral part of the operation of the machine. They prevent accidental access by the operator, but allow entry of the material to the machine in such a way that the material forms part of the guarding arrangement itself. For example, a hand held circular saw.

Merits of self-adjusting guards

- Close over the dangerous parts to provide protection without the need of the operator to do anything.

Limitations of self-adjusting guards

- May obscure visibility when in use.
- Are vulnerable to damage in the operation of the equipment.

Figure 5-52: Self-adjusting (fixed) guard.　　　*Source: RMS.*　　　Figure 5-53: Adjustable (fixed) guard.　*Source: BS EN ISO 12100.*

ADJUSTABLE GUARD

Adjustable guards are a fixed guard that incorporates an adjustable element to accommodate a range of positions and size of dangerous parts of the machinery. When adjusted it remains set in position for the duration of a particular operation. For example, the crown guard of a bench circular saw or a pedestal drill chuck/drill bit guard.

Merits of adjustable guards

- Can be adjusted by operator to provide protection.
- Protects operator where size or position of dangerous parts vary.

Limitations of adjustable guards

- Are reliant on the operator to adjust to the correct position.
- May obscure visibility when in use.

SENSITIVE PROTECTIVE EQUIPMENT/TRIP DEVICE

Sensitive protective equipment (sometimes called a trip device) comprises a sensitive rod, cable or other mechanism, which causes the device to activate a further mechanism which either stops or reverses the machine. It is important to note that this is not classed as a guard. A guard is something that physically prevents access to the hazard whereas sensitive protective equipment detects the person in the danger zone and responds to this, for example, a pressure sensitive mat.

Merits of sensitive protective equipment

- Can be used as an additional risk control measure.
- Can minimise the severity of injury.

Limitations of sensitive protective equipment

- Can be over-ridden.
- May not prevent harm from occurring.

- May cause production delays and increase stress in users with false 'trips'.

Figure 5-54: Trip device. *Source: BS EN ISO 12100.*　　　Figure 5-55: Trip device on radial drill.　　　*Source: RMS.*

TWO-HAND CONTROL (2HC) DEVICE

They provide a level of protection where other methods are not practicable, helping to ensure the operator's hands remain outside the danger area. A two-hand control is a device that requires both hands to operate it, the controls must be operated simultaneously and help to assure that both hands are kept away from the dangerous parts. '2HC' devices protect only the operator. An everyday example of use of two hand controls are those fitted to a hedge trimmer.

Merits of two hand control devices

- Ensures both of the operator's hands are out of danger area when the machine is operated.

Limitations of two hand control devices

- Only protects the operator from harm.
- May limit speed of operation with delays if controls are not pressed at exactly same time.

HOLD-TO-RUN

The principle of this device is that the operator has to 'hold' a button, stick or foot pedal to 'run' a piece of equipment.

Figure 5-56: Two-hand control on hedge trimmer. *Source: RMS.*

A common application of this device is on a domestic lawn mower or hedge trimmer. It is essential that the hold-to-run device, which when released stops the machine, is located far enough away from the danger area to prevent the operator getting access to the moving parts without releasing it.

Merits of hold-to-run devices

- Ensures the operator is out of the danger area when the machine is operated.
- Provides distance between operator and hazard.

Limitations of hold-to-run devices

- Only protects the operator from harm.
- There may be residual movement of dangerous parts once the device has been released.

JIGS, HOLDERS AND PUSH-STICKS

When the methods of safeguarding mentioned above are not practicable then protection appliances such as jigs, holders and push-sticks must be provided. They will help to keep the operator's hands at a safe distance from the danger area. There is no physical restraint to prevent the operator from placing their hands in danger.

Figure 5-57: Notched push-stick. *Source: http://images.google.co.uk/.*

Figure 5-58: Band saw push-stick. *Source: http://images.google.co.uk/.*

Merits of protection appliances

- Provide distance between operator and hazard.
- Inexpensive and easily replaced if damaged.
- May be shaped to suit work being carried out.

Limitations of protection appliances

- Harm may still occur from other non-mechanical hazards.
- Some designs can be awkward to use and may result in a lack of control.
- Continuing adjustments have to be made for example, when using different sizes of wood.
- Failure of protection appliance (for example, breaking or kickback) may present additional hazard to operator.

Figure 5-59: Fixed guard and push-stick. *Source: Lincsafe.*

EMERGENCY STOP CONTROLS

The function of an emergency stop control device is to provide a means to bring a machine to a rapid halt. It is provided in such circumstances where it would be of benefit and should be readily available to the operator and/or others. It should be easy to operate and clearly discernible from other controls. Emergency stop controls should be easily reached and actuated. Common types are mushroom-headed buttons, bars, levers, kick plates, or pressure-sensitive cables. Emergency stops are intended to effect a rapid response to potentially dangerous situations and they should not be used as functional stops during normal operation.

Merits	Limitations
■ Removes power immediately.	■ Does not prevent access to the danger area.
■ Equipment has to be reset after use.	■ May be incorrectly positioned.
■ Prevents accidental restarting of the equipment.	

PERSONAL PROTECTIVE EQUIPMENT (PPE)

The Personal Protective Equipment at Work Regulations (PPER) 1992 governs the provision of PPE. PPE is a last resort and should only be relied upon when other controls do not adequately control risks. The use of machinery presents a number of mechanical hazards and care has to be taken that PPE is not used in situations where they present an increased risk of entanglement or drawing in to machinery, such as might happen with loose overalls and gloves.

Main examples are:

- Eye protection (safety spectacles/glasses, goggles and face shields) - protection for the eyes and face from flying particles, welding glare, dust, fumes and splashes.
- Head protection (safety helmets or scalp protectors i.e. bump caps) - protection from falling objects, or the head striking fixed objects.
- Protective clothing for the body (overalls) - protection from a wide range of hazards, specialist clothing for chain saw hazards.
- Gloves (chain mail gloves and sleeves) - protection against cuts and abrasions when handling machined components, raw material or machinery cutters.
- Footwear (steel in-soles and toe-caps) - protection against sharp objects that might be stood on or objects dropped while handling them.
- Ear protection for noisy machine operations.

Merits

- Easy to see if it is being worn.
- Provides protection against a variety of hazards.

Limitations

- Only protects the user.
- May not give adequate protection.
- May pose additional hazards, for example, gloves becoming entangled.

INFORMATION, INSTRUCTION, TRAINING AND SUPERVISION

PUWER 1998 requires every employer to ensure that all persons who use work equipment and any of his employees who supervises or manages the use of work equipment have available to them adequate health and safety information and, where appropriate, written instructions and appropriate training pertaining to the use of the work equipment.

This includes information and, where appropriate, written instructions that are comprehensible to those concerned on:

- The conditions in which and the methods by which the work equipment may be used.
- Foreseeable abnormal situations and the action to be taken if such a situation were to occur.
- Any conclusions to be drawn from experience in using the work equipment.

Figure 5-60: Information and instruction. *Source: RMS.*

Figure 5-61: PPE and supervision. *Source: RMS.*

Similarly, PUWER 1998 requires employers to ensure that all persons who use work equipment and any of his employees who supervises or manages work equipment have received training in any risks which such use may entail and precautions to be taken.

It is a requirement of both the HASAWA 1974 and PUWER 1998 Regulation 11 that supervision is provided as necessary. This will require extra supervision for new, inexperienced or less capable users of equipment.

Merits

- Easy to reach a wide audience on a variety of subjects.
- Can be applied immediately and adapted to suit specific needs of the user.

Limitations

- Supervision may not prevent contact with the hazard.
- Relies on the person concerned to follow the instruction.
- May be misunderstood.
- Supervision is needed to a sufficient degree to ensure health and safety, and a high degree of supervision may be required for some equipment.

Application of protection methods to a range of equipment

To meet the requirements of the syllabus, protection methods are discussed in this section. Specific *hazards* of the equipment listed are covered in section *'5.3 - Machinery hazards'*.

OFFICE MACHINERY

Photocopier

Because access to the moving parts by the user are likely to be required to remove paper jams the use of interlocking guard is appropriate for these access panels. Fixed guards may also protect some dangerous parts inside the panels, such as heating elements. Appropriate additional precautions are to avoid loose clothing i.e. ties, signage for hot components, well ventilated/suitable extraction, gloves, training in good practice when removing paper jams etc.

Shredder

Appropriate precautions are the use of interlocking guards that identify the removal of the shredding element of the equipment from the shredded paper collection area. Where the shredder has a large opening to the moving parts of the shredder to feed material in, it may be necessary to protect this with sensitive protective equipment that will detect the presence of the user's hand or clothing.

WORKSHOP MACHINERY

Bench grinder

Control measures include an adjustable fixed guard that is fitted over as much of the grinding wheel as is practicable, a work-piece rest, trained and competent users, high impact resistant goggles, respiratory protective equipment (depending on task) and personal hearing protection.

Pedestal drill

Appropriate precautions for pre-use are:

- Drive pulley entanglement prevented by isolation from power when adjusting speeds.
- Check that chuck key is removed before use.

Appropriate precautions during use are:

- Interlocking guard to cover the drive pulley and belts.
- Adjustable (fixed) guard provided round the chuck and drill bit, face shield/goggles for protection from flying metal pieces from the cutting process (swarf).
- Prevent entanglement - close fitting clothing, control of long hair and removal of jewellery.
- Puncture prevented by jigs or clamping devices.

Bench-mounted circular saw

Appropriate precautions are:

- Guarding for crown and front of the saw, and for the part of the saw below the bench.
- Riving knife fitted at rear of the saw above the bench.
- Use of jigs/holders or push sticks where appropriate.
- Need for a table extension to ensure distance of at least 1.2m between edge of saw and end of table if another person assistants at the back of the bench.

Hand fed power planer

Appropriate precautions are:

- Use of a suitable bridge guard, adjusted according to the operation being undertaken.
- Use clamps to secure to a stable platform.
- Keep tools sharp and clean.

Spindle moulding machine

No single type of guard or other safety device can deal adequately with the variety of work that can be carried out on a spindle moulding machine. Each job must be considered individually to provide the most effective protection. Guidance is contained in the HSE Information Sheet (Woodworking Sheet No. 18) 'Safe use of vertical spindle moulding machines'. It is essential that users of this equipment are properly trained. General precautions include an effective brake to stop the cutter block rotating when it is running down, ensuring the gap between the spindle and table is kept to a minimum, use guards to cover the cutters as much as possible, otherwise use jigs and work holders. Provide extraction of wood dust.

CONSTRUCTION SITE MACHINERY

Compressor

Appropriate precautions are:

- Over-pressure relief valve.
- Pressure gauge.
- Hose couplings fitted with pins or chains.
- Hose couplings inspected as part of daily plant inspection.
- Noise control equipment fitted to compressor.

Cement mixer

Fixed guards must be provided around drive mechanisms. Motor covers should be closed when in use. Operators should be warned of the dangers of shovels and trowels becoming caught in the mixer blades when charging. Electrical hazards are reduced by the use of low voltage (110 volts) power (or residual current circuit breaker if 230 volt supply), with suitable heavy duty protected cable. If petrol or diesel driven, equipment should be allowed to cool (for example, exhaust system) before refuelling, no smoking should be observed. Other controls include manual handling training, good housekeeping of spilt materials, and avoidance of exposure to dust and fume.

Plate compactor

Appropriate precautions are:

- Use a remote-control rather than a hand-guided compactor to reduce risks from hand-arm vibration.
- Take regular breaks to reduce exposure or rotate use among several people.
- A safe system of work for handling this equipment may be required, which could include a hoist on site vehicles and a trolley to manoeuvre around the site.

Ground consolidation equipment

Control measures include segregation of pedestrians and plant using barriers, warning signs and close supervision.

Portable circular saw

Appropriate precautions include provision and use of fixed and self-adjusting guards. Precautions also include ensuring material being cut is held firm to prevent movement on contact with the saw blade and during the cutting process. Support of the material being cut is advisable to prevent excess side pressure on the blade, particularly on completion of the cut. Care should be taken to ensure the blade has stopped revolving and self-adjusting guard covers the blade before putting the saw down. Eye and hearing PPE should be worn to reduce the risk of noise induced hearing loss and eye injuries from the waste wood cuttings. Portable mounted saws should be fitted with suitable local exhaust ventilation equipment, where possible. Respiratory protection may also be necessary particularly when cutting hardwoods. Regular rest breaks should be taken for hand held equipment to reduce the effects of vibration on the user.

Road-marking equipment

This equipment requires special training and authorisation for its safe use. Where this equipment is being used, barriers, warning signs and lighting is to be used, in addition to supervision. When this equipment is being used it is normally a requirement to have refuelling facilities available on site. When this is the case suitable isolation from sources of heat should be ensured, with only authorised operatives allowed to carry out refuelling activities.

Electrical generators

Diesel or petrol generators should always be used outdoors to prevent the risk of carbon monoxide accumulation. They should not be sited below scaffolds or near trenches where people are working, because there is a continuous risk of build-up of carbon dioxide whilst the compressor is running. They should never be refuelled when hot and noise limiting covers should remain closed when in use. The compressor must be installed and maintained by a competent person. The compressor must be of sufficient capacity for the total load required (electrical motors typically require three times their rated wattage on start-up). This should be taken into account before selection and use.

Basic requirements for guards and safety devices

PUWER 1998 REGULATION 11 - EFFECTIVE GUARDS AND DEVICES

PUWER 1998, Regulation 11, paragraph 3 sets out the following requirements with regard to guards and devices: *"All guards and protection devices provided under sub-paragraphs (a) or (b) of paragraph (2) shall:*

*(a) Be **suitable** for the purpose for which they are provided.*

(b) Be of **good construction**, sound material and adequate strength.

(c) Be **maintained** in an efficient state, in efficient working order and in good repair.

(d) Not give rise to any increased risk to health or safety.

(e) Not be **easily bypassed** or disabled.

(f) Be situated at **sufficient distance** from the danger zone.

(g) Not unduly **restrict the view** of the operating cycle of the machinery, where such a view is necessary.

(h) Be so constructed or adapted that they allow operations necessary to fit or replace parts and for maintenance work, restricting access so that it is allowed only to the area where the work is to be carried out and, if possible, without having to dismantle the guard or protection device."

COMPATIBILITY WITH PROCESS

Compatibility with the material being processed - this is particularly important in the food processing industry where the guard material should not constitute a source of contamination of the product. Its ability to maintain its physical and mechanical properties after coming into contact with potential contaminants such as cutting fluids used in machining operations or corrosive agents used in cement processing machinery is also very important.

In selecting an appropriate safeguard for a particular type of machinery or danger area, it should be borne in mind that a fixed guard is simple, and should be used where access to the danger area is not required during operation of the machinery or for cleaning, setting or other activities. As the need for access arises and increases in frequency, the importance of safety procedures for removal of a fixed guard increases until the frequency is such that interlocking should be used.

ADEQUATE STRENGTH

Guard mounting should be compatible with the strength and duty of the guard. In selecting the material to be used for the construction of a guard, consideration should be given to the following:

- Its ability to withstand the force of ejection of parts of the machinery or material being processed, where this is a foreseeable danger.
- Its ability to provide protection against hazards identified. In many cases, the guard may fulfil a combination of functions such as prevention of access and containment of hazards. This may apply where the hazards include ejected particles, liquids, dust, fumes, radiation, noise, etc. and one or more of these considerations may govern the selection of guard materials.

MAINTAINED

All guards must be maintained in effective order to perform their function. This will require a planned approach to checks on guards and work such as checking the security of fixed guards.

ALLOW FOR MAINTENANCE WITHOUT REMOVAL

Its weight and size are factors to be considered in relation to the need to remove and replace it for routine maintenance. If a guard has to be removed in order to carry out maintenance work, it increases the risks for maintenance workers and also increases the chances that the guard will not be replaced. This is especially the case if a piece of equipment has a history of regular break down.

NOT INCREASE RISK OR RESTRICT VIEW

Any guard selected should not itself present a hazard such as trapping or shear points, rough or sharp edges or other hazards likely to cause injury. Power operated guards should be designed and constructed so that a hazard is not created or restrict the view of the process or machine by the user.

NOT EASILY BY-PASSED

Guards or their components must not be easily by-passed, in particular by operators. There is always a temptation to do so when under production or similar pressures. When positioning such protective devices as interlock switches; it is best to locate them away from the operator and preferably within the guard.

Exam practice

1. The Provision and Use of Work Equipment Regulations 1998 require that work equipment used in hostile environments is inspected at suitable intervals.

   Identify the items on a 360° tracked excavator that should be subject to inspection. **(8)**

2. **Outline** practical control measures for reducing the risk to employees when using a bench mounted electrical powered circular saw on site. **(8)**

3.   **Outline** the control measures that should be used to reduce risks when cutting concrete kerbstones with a petrol disc cutter. **(8)**

4.   **Identify** ways in which accidents can occur from the use of cartridge-operated nail guns on a construction site. **(8)**

5.   (a)   **Identify** and **give an example for each** of **FOUR** mechanical hazards of construction machinery. **(4)**

     (b)   **Outline** the advantages and limitations of using a fixed guard to protect people from mechanical hazards of construction machinery **(4)**

Please refer to the back of the assessment section for answers.

Electrical safety

Learning outcomes

On completion of this element, candidates should be able to demonstrate understanding of the content through the application of knowledge to familiar and unfamiliar situations. In particular they should be able to:

6.1   Outline the principles, hazards and risks associated with the use of electricity in the workplace.

6.2   Outline the control measures that should be taken when working with electrical systems or using electrical equipment.

6.3   Outline the control measures to be taken when working near or underneath overhead power lines.

Content

6.1 - Hazards and risks associated with electricity 147
   Principles of electricity 147
   Risks of electricity 148
   High risks associated with electricity 153
6.2 - Control measures..154
   Selection and suitability of equipment for use in construction activities 154
   Electrical systems on site 155
   Advantages and limitations of protective systems...158
   Use of competent persons..161
   Use of safe systems of work...161
   Inspection and maintenance strategies 162
   Emergency procedures following an electrical incident..165
6.3 - Control measures for working near overhead power lines 166
   Control measures 166
Exam practice 167

Sources of reference

Reference information provided, in particular web links, is correct at time of publication, but may have changed.

Avoidance of danger from overhead electrical lines, GS6 (fourth edition), HSE Books, http://www.hse.gov.uk/pubns/gs6.pdf

Avoiding danger from underground services, HSG47 (third edition 2014), HSE Books, ISBN 978-0-7176-6584-6 http://www.hse.gov.uk/pubns/priced/hsg47.pdf

Electrical safety and you - A brief guide, INDG231 (Rev1), HSE Books, http://www.hse.gov.uk/pubns/indg231.pdf

Electricity at Work - Safe Working Practices, HSG85 (third edition 2013), HSE Books, ISBN 978-0-717665-81-5 http://www.hse.gov.uk/pubns/priced/hsg85.pdf

Guidance on Safe Isolation procedures: www.select.org.uk/downloads/publications/Select%20-%20Safe%20Isolation%20Procedures.pdf

Maintaining Portable and Transportable Electrical Equipment, HSG107 (third edition 2013), HSE Books, ISBN 978-0-7176-6606-5 http://www.hse.gov.uk/pubns/priced/hsg107.pdf

Memorandum of guidance on the Electricity at Work Regulation 1989, HSR25 (second edition 2007), HSE Books, ISBN 978-0-717662-28-9 http://www.hse.gov.uk/pubns/priced/hsr25.pdf

Safe use of vehicles on construction sites (HSG144), HSE Books, ISBN 978-0-7176-6291-3 http://www.hse.gov.uk/pubns/priced/hsg144.pdf

Relevant statutory provisions

Electricity at Work Regulations (EWR) 1989

Health and Safety (First-aid) Regulations (FAR) 1981 (as amended)

Reporting of Injuries, Diseases and Dangerous Occurrences Regulations (RIDDOR) 2013

6.1 - Hazards and risks associated with electricity

Principles of electricity

Electricity is a facility that we have all come to take for granted, whether for lighting, heating, as a source of motive power or as the driving force behind the computer. Used properly it can be of great benefit to us, but misused it can be very dangerous and often fatal.

Electricity is used in most industries, offices and homes and our modern society could now not easily function without it. Despite its convenience to the user, it has a major danger. The normal senses of sight, hearing and smell will not detect electricity. Making contact with exposed conductors at the domestic supply voltage, 230V can be lethal.

Unlike many other workplace accidents, the actual number of electrical notifiable accidents is small. However, with a reported five fatalities and over 500 accidents involving direct contact with electricity each year, the severity is high. Accidents are often caused by complacency, not just by the normally assumed ignorance. It must be recognised by everyone working with electricity that over half of all electrical fatal accidents are to skilled/competent persons.

In order to avoid the causes of electric injury, it is necessary to understand the basic principles of electricity, what it does to the body and what controls are necessary.

BASIC CIRCUITRY

The flow of electrons through a conductor is known as a current. Electric current flows due to differences in electrical 'pressure' (or potential difference as it is often known), just as water flows through a pipe because of the pressure behind it.

Differences in electrical potential are measured in volts. In some systems the current flows continually in the same direction. This is known as direct current (DC). However the current may also constantly reverse its direction of flow. This is known as alternating current (AC). Most public electricity supplies are AC.

The UK system reverses its direction 50 times per second and it is said to have a frequency of 50 cycles per second or 50 Hertz (50Hz). DC is little used in standard distribution systems but is sometimes used in industry for specialist applications. Although there are slight differences in the effects under fault and shock conditions between AC and DC it is a safe approach to apply the same rules of safety for the treatment and prevention of electric shock.

Figure 6-1: A basic electrical circuit. *Source: RMS.*

As a current passes round a circuit under the action of an applied voltage it is impeded in its flow. This may be due to the presence in the circuit of resistance, inductance or capacitance, the combined effect of which is called impedance and is measured in ohms.

RELATIONSHIP BETWEEN VOLTAGE, CURRENT AND RESISTANCE

There is a simple relationship between electrical pressure (Volts), current (measured in amperes or milliAmperes) and resistance (measured in Ohms) represented by Ohm's law:

Voltage *(V)* = current *(I)* multiplied by the circuit resistance *(R)*. Therefore, $V = I \times R$ or $I = \dfrac{V}{R}$

Hence, given any two values the third can be calculated. Also, if one value changes the other two values will change accordingly. This basic electrical equation can be used to calculate the current that flows in a circuit of a given resistance. This will need to be carried out to determine, for example, the fuse or cable rating needed for a particular circuit.

Resistance in a circuit is dependent on many factors. Most metals, particularly precious metals (silver, gold and platinum), allow current to pass very easily. These have a low resistance and are used as electrical conductors. Other materials such as plastics, rubber and textiles have a high resistance and are used as electrical insulators.

Similarly, the current that will flow through a person who touches a live conductor can be calculated by using Ohm's law, where the current flowing through the person can be calculated as follows:

Current = $\dfrac{\text{Voltage}}{\text{Resistance}}$ or $I = \dfrac{V}{R}$

Figure 6-2: Basic electrical circuitry.   *Source: RMS.*

If the person is on a dry concrete floor, resistance in the body will only be about 2,000 ohms and the resistance in the floor about 4,000 Ohms, therefore, the combined resistance would be 6,000 ohms.

Presuming the person is in contact with a live electrical supply at 230 volts the current flowing through the person in this fault condition can be calculated.

$$I = \frac{V}{R} = \frac{230 \text{ volts}}{2,000 + 4,000 \text{ ohms}} = 0.038 \text{ amperes}$$

The current flowing through the person will then be about 0.04 amperes or 40mA (40 milliAmperes). This could result in a fatal shock. *(See figure ref 6-2).*

Two terms appear in common usage in relation to electricity and electrical circuits - 'live' and 'dead'. A 'live' electrical circuit is one carrying an electrical current. Once the 'live' electrical circuit has been disconnected from its power sources it is described as 'dead', a 'dead' electrical circuit. No electrical current flows through a 'dead' electrical circuit.

Risks of electricity

ELECTRIC SHOCK AND ITS EFFECT ON THE BODY

The term electric shock is used to describe the unwanted or undesirable exposure to electricity at a detectable level. Electric shock results from the current flowing through the body interfering with muscle and central nervous system functions. *(For further details of the effects, see the section on 'Current').*

Other consequences of contact with electricity are:

- Electrical burns   -   resulting from the heating effect of the current which burns the body tissue.
- Electrical fires   -   caused by overheating or arcing apparatus in contact with a fuel.
- Explosions   -   from sparks in a flammable atmosphere.
- Secondary injuries   -   falling from a ladder.

Direct/indirect electrical shock

Direct shock

Direct shock relates to when a person makes contact with a charged or energised conductor that is intended to be charged or energised. In these circumstances the electrical system is operating in its normal or proper condition. This may occur when someone is working on equipment where conductors are exposed and in the live condition.

Indirect shock

Indirect shock relates to when a person makes contact with a conductor or exposed conductive parts, for example, the casing of apparatus that is normally safe to touch but which, under fault conditions, could become dangerously live.

Conductive parts of equipment that may become live in a fault condition include the conducting casing of equipment and trunking around electrical cables. For example, where the casing of equipment has a poor connection to earth and a fault occurs on the equipment, the casing may become live.

Common causes of electric shock

- Work on electrical circuits by unqualified persons.
- Work on live circuits.
- Replacement of fuses and light bulbs on supposedly dead circuits.
- Working on de-energised circuits that could accidentally be re-energised.
- Using electrical equipment in a wet environment.

FACTORS INFLUENCING SEVERITY

Factors influencing severity of the effects of electric shock on the body

The factors influencing the severity of the effects of electric shock on the body include the following:

- Voltage.
- Frequency.
- Duration.
- Impedance/resistance.
- Current and current path.

The severity of electric shock or the amount of current which flows for a given voltage will depend on the frequency of the supply voltage, on the level of the voltage which is applied and on the state of the point of contact with the body, particularly the moisture condition.

Figure 6-3: Electrical equipment near water.   *Source: RMS.*

Figure 6-4: Contact with high voltage buried cable. *Source: RMS.*

Current

The current that flows through the body provides the energy to do the harm, the more current flowing the more harm likely to be done. The body can tolerate small levels of current flowing through it, but as the level increases the current is able to have a greater effect on the body, in particular the muscles. As such, low currents tend to influence only the smaller muscles and the larger muscles need a larger current to influence them.

The effects on the muscles will be felt as pain and will cause the muscles to spasm. Therefore, small muscles in the hand may contract causing the hand to close or at higher current flow larger muscles in the chest and the diaphragm muscle may contract restricting breathing, leading to **respiratory failure**.

The heart, being made of large muscles, requires a significant current to affect it. When the heart is affected by the current flow its normal beat may be disrupted. This can cause the muscles of the heart to spasm and stop working, leading to **cardiac arrest**, or the heart may attempt to beat but does this in a discordant manner, causing the effect known as **fibrillation**.

It should be remembered that the level of current necessary to cause harm to the body is much less than that required to run most equipment and is in mA rather than Amperes.

Effects of current flowing in the human body

Current (mA)	Length of time	Likely effects
0 - 1	Not critical	Threshold of feeling. Undetected by person.
2 - 15	Not critical	Threshold of cramp. Independent loosening of the hands no longer possible.
16 - 30	Minutes	Cramp-like pulling together of the arms, breathing difficult. Limit of tolerance.
31 - 50	Seconds to minutes	Strong cramp-like effects, loss of consciousness due to restricted breathing. Longer time may lead to fibrillation.
51 - 500	Less than one heart period (750 ms)	No fibrillation. Strong shock effects.
	Greater than one heart period	Fibrillation. Loss of consciousness. Burn marks.
Over 500	Less than one heart period	Fibrillation. Loss of consciousness. Burn marks.

Figure 6-5: Effects of alternating current flowing in the human body.   *Source: RMS.*

Voltage

Voltage is the driving force behind the flow of electricity, somewhat like pressure in a water pipe influences the amount of water that flows. The correct name for this term is potential difference, as a voltage is the measure of the difference in electrical energy between two points. Any electrical charge that is free to move about will move from the higher energy to the lower one, taking a quantity of that energy difference with it.

Frequency

The frequency of current flow in an alternating current supply, such as the mains supply on a construction site or in an office block, operates at 50 cycles per second in the UK. This frequency is close to that of the heart when functioning normally. It can have the effect of disrupting the operation of the heart causing it to beat in a discordant manner, to fibrillate.

Duration

For an electric shock to have an effect a person needs to be in contact with the current for sufficient time. At low current levels the body tolerates the current so the time is not material, however, at higher current levels, for example, 50 mA, the person has to remain in contact for sufficient time for the heart to be affected, in the order of milliseconds. In general, the longer a person is in contact with the current the more harm may be caused.

Resistance

The amount of resistance in a circuit influences the amount of current that is allowed to flow, as explained previously, by Ohm's law. It is possible for a person to be in contact with a circuit and to present sufficiently high resistance that very little current is allowed to flow through their body. The example shown in *figure ref 6-2* illustrates this.

It should be noted that the level of current is also dependent on the voltage; at high voltages an enormous amount of resistance is needed to ensure current flow will remain at a safe level. The human body contributes part of the resistance of the circuit, and the amount it contributes depends on the current path taken and other factors such as personal chemical make-up (a large portion of the body is water), dryness and thickness of skin, and any clothing that is being worn, such as shoes and gloves.

Current path

The effect of an electric shock on the body is particularly dependent on the current path through the body. Current has to flow through from one point to another as part of a circuit. If the flow was between two points on a finger the effect on the body would be concentrated between the two points.

If the current path is between one hand and another, across the chest, this means the flow will pass through major parts of the body, such as the heart, and may cause fibrillation or cardiac arrest. In a similar way, a contact between hand and foot (feet) can have serious effects on a great many parts of the body, including the heart. These two current paths tend to be the ones leading to fatal injuries. However, a current path from hand to foot down the one side of the body may not affect the heart and therefore may not be fatal.

Although many people may experience shock from 230 volts this may not be fatal if they were, for example, standing on or wearing some insulating material. This may be a matter of fortune and, as a rule; protection should not be relied on.

ELECTRICAL BURNS

When an electric current passes through a material, the resistance to the flow of electrons dissipates energy, usually in the form of heat. If the material is human tissue and the amount of heat generated is sufficient, the tissue may be burnt. The effect is similar to damage caused by an open flame or other high-temperature source of heat, except that electricity has the ability to burn tissue well beneath the skin, including internal organs.

External burns

Direct

When electrical current makes contact with the skin of a person, it becomes part of the electrical circuit. This can cause the point of entry and exit of the electrical current flowing through the person's body to reach a high temperature creating immediate tissue damage and charring. As the outer layer of skin is burnt the resistance decreases and so the current will increase.

The point of entry tends to be limited to small areas and will often appear sunken or hollowed, whereas the exit wound is more extensively damaged and open. Whilst there are likely to be burn marks on the skin at the points of entry and exit there may also be deep seated burning below immediately below the skin, which is painful and slow to heal.

Indirect

If while working on live equipment the system is short-circuited by, for example, an un-insulated spanner touching live and neutral this will result in a large and sudden current flow through the spanner. This current will cause the spanner to melt and may throw molten metal out from the points of contact. When this molten metal contacts the parts of a person in the vicinity of the spanner, for example, the hands or face, serious burns can take place as the molten metal hits and sticks to the person. With high voltages and the very low resistance of the spanner very large currents can flow. This rapid discharge of energy that follows contact with high voltages not only causes the rapid melting of the spanner, but does so with such violent force that the molten particles of metal are thrown off with huge velocity.

It is not necessary to have high voltages to melt a spanner in this way - it can also occur with batteries that have sufficient stored energy, such as those on a fork-lift truck. There are many experiences of people suffering similar injury when servicing batteries due to a metal object falling out of their overall top pocket across the terminals of a battery.

Internal burns

The severity of the damage caused internally by electrical burns will depend upon the pathway the current follows. In the human body the pathways of least resistance being firstly blood vessels, nerves, bone marrow, muscle, then skin, tendon, fat, and finally bone. The current flowing through the body can cause major burns to internal organs and bone marrow as it passes through them. The current flow will cause deep seated burning within the body, which is painful and slow to heal.

ELECTRICAL FIRES

Common causes

Much electrical equipment generates heat or produces sparks and this equipment should not be placed where this could lead to the uncontrolled ignition of any substance.

The principal causes of electrical fires are:

- Wiring with defects such as insulation failure due to age or poor maintenance or physical damage.
- Overheating of cables or other electrical equipment through overloading with currents above their design capacity.
- Incorrect fuse rating.
- Poor connections due to lack of maintenance or unskilled personnel (for example, cables not secured by a cable grip inside a drill casing).

Electrical equipment may itself explode or arc violently and it may also act as a source of ignition of flammable vapours, gases, liquids or dust through electric sparks, arcs or high surface temperatures of equipment.

Other causes of fire are due to heat created by poorly maintained or defective motors, heaters and lighting. When extension leads are used coiled up they can rapidly overheat and may also cause a fire.

Figure 6-6: Used coiled up - risk of overheating. *Source: RMS.*

Figure 6-7: Max current capacity exceeded. *Source: RMS.*

Figure 6-8: Worn cable - risk of electrical fire. *Source: RMS.*

Figure 6-9: Evidence of overheating. *Source: RMS.*

WORKPLACE ELECTRICAL EQUIPMENT INCLUDING PORTABLE ELECTRICAL EQUIPMENT

Conditions and practices likely to lead to electrical accidents

Unsuitable equipment

- Unsuitable apparatus for the duty or the conditions.
- Misuse.
- Failure to follow operating instructions.
- Wrong connection of system - supply phase, neutral or earth reversed.
- Wrong voltage or rating of equipment.

Inadequate maintenance

- Inadequate maintenance of the installation and the equipment.
- Wrong or broken connection to portable apparatus.
- Inadequate earthing.
- Poor maintenance and testing.
- No defect reporting system.

Figure 6-10: Hazard - fuse wired out. *Source: RMS.*

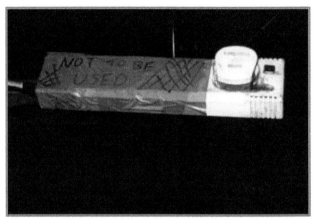

Figure 6-11: Continued use of defective equipment. *Source: RMS.*

Use of defective apparatus

- Faulty cables, notably extension leads.
- Plugs and sockets.
- Damaged plug or socket.
- Protection devices, such as fuses or circuit breaker, incorrect rating, damaged or missing.
- Overloaded leading to damage or over-heating.
- Short circuit leading to damage, overheating or movement.
- Isolation procedures or systems of work wrong.
- Bad circuit connections.

General

- Lack of competence.
- Poor access, lighting and emergency procedures.
- No work planning, for example, permit-to-work.

Figure 6-12: Hazard - damaged cable insulation. *Source: RMS.*

Figure 6-13: Hazard - taped joints. *Source: RMS.*

SECONDARY EFFECTS OF CONTACT WITH ELECTRICITY

These occur where the injury results from the flow of electricity through the body's nerves, muscles and organs and causes abnormal function to occur. Muscular spasm may be severe, particularly if the leg muscles are affected, causing a person to be thrown several metres. Injuries may result from dislocation, impact with surrounding objects or fall from a height. In addition, a tool may be dropped causing such injuries as burns or impact injury to the user or others nearby.

High risks associated with electricity

USE OF POORLY MAINTAINED ELECTRICAL EQUIPMENT

Regulation 4 of the Electricity at Work Regulations (EWR) 1989 sets out requirements for the maintenance of electrical systems.

"All systems shall at all times be of such construction as to prevent, so far as reasonably practicable, such danger. As may be necessary to prevent danger, all systems shall be maintained so as to prevent, so far as reasonably practicable, such danger."

Figure 6-14: Maintenance of electrical systems. *Source: EWR 1989 Regulation 4.*

Many deaths and injuries result from poorly maintained electrical equipment and fires started by faulty electrical appliances. Around 1,000 electrical accidents at work are reported to the Health and Safety Executive each year, of these, seven people die of their injuries.

All electrical equipment should be maintained at appropriate intervals (HSE Guidance 'Maintaining portable and transportable electrical equipment' (HSG107) gives some advice on user checks, inspection and test intervals) to ensure it is safe and in good repair.

In particular, managers (and others, such as landlords) responsible for electrical equipment maintenance should ensure:

■ Equipment is maintained in a safe condition.
■ Information is available to equipment users to ensure safety.
■ Safe procedures for inspection and testing are used.
■ Records of inspection and testing are maintained.

WORK NEAR OVERHEAD POWER LINES

Contact with live overhead power lines kills a significant number of people and causes serious injuries every year. A high proportion - about one third - of inadvertent line contacts prove fatal. Overhead power lines may be confused with telephone lines, which can lead people not to identify the risk from contact. Lines may be hard to see at night or against a dark or very bright background. Power lines carry electricity at between 230 and 400,000 volts, even contact with a 230 volt line can kill. They are not normally covered in insulation so direct contact can easily be made. Contact can lead to current passing through a person, and the item that contacted the line, on a path to earth. Rubber-soled shoes would not provide protection from current flow and shock. Actual contact with a power line is not necessary to result in electric shock; a close approach to the line conductors may allow an arc to take place. The risk of arcing increases as the line voltage increases.

Many construction occupations may require workers to perform their job tasks near overhead power lines. Scaffold erectors, truck drivers, excavation equipment operators, tree service workers, mobile material handling equipment operators, tower crane operators and others find themselves carrying out their work in the vicinity of live overhead power lines. They may not be trained to recognise the dangers of electrocution if their bodies, equipment, tools, work materials or vehicles come near to an overhead power line.

CONTACT WITH UNDERGROUND POWER CABLES DURING EXCAVATION WORK

Underground power cables are present in most locations that excavations are conducted, in the high street, on construction or re-development sites and even in the country. Their location may be marked, not identified or not known of at all. Their presence is not obvious when conducting a visual site survey and so the likelihood of striking a power cable when excavating, drilling or piling is increased. The results of striking an underground power cable can include shock, electrocution, explosion and burns. As with overhead power lines, any underground service should be treated as live until confirmed dead by a power authority. Maps showing the location of underground power cables need to be taken as an indication of their location not as 'pin-point' accuracy, which means that careful testing needs to take place until indicated power cables are located. Even then some degree of caution needs to be taken in case unmarked power cables are encountered.

WORK ON MAINS ELECTRICAL SUPPLIES (230 VOLT)

Mains electricity supplies can be treated complacently because of their prevalence and their relatively low voltage, however a number of deaths occur each year of people working on mains electricity supplies.

WORK ON LIVE AND DEAD ELECTRICAL SUPPLIES

It is never absolutely safe to work on live electrical equipment. There are few circumstances where it is necessary to work live, and this must only be done after it has been determined that it is unreasonable for the work to be carried out dead. Even if working live can be justified, many precautions are needed to make sure that the risk is reduced 'so far as is reasonably practicable'. As discussed previously, each year about 1,000 accidents at work involving electric shock or burns are reported to the Health and Safety Executive, of these, seven people die of their injuries. Some of the high risk work associated with these deaths involves work on live electrical supplies. Work on live electrical supplies represents a high risk because the conductors being worked on are live and others nearby may also be live. In this situation there is a significant risk that tools used in live work could contact the different conductors or that a circuit is made between a live conductor and the frame of the equipment, causing a short circuit.

Additionally, when working on a live conductor the tool used and worker could provide an easy path for the current to pass to earth. The resultant shock of the current passing through the worker's body could lead to fatal injuries. Non-fatal shocks can cause severe and permanent injury, including burns and fractures. In addition, there is a risk of explosive vaporisation of metal conductors when they are accidentally short circuited by non-insulated tools.

In construction activities, electrical work may involve work on dead electrical circuits that may become live unexpectedly. This could be due to changes made to the electrical circuitry during the progress of construction work, causing a dead circuit to become unexpectedly energised.

USE OF ELECTRICAL EQUIPMENT IN WET ENVIRONMENTS

Use of electrical equipment in wet conditions increases the risk of harm because the wet conditions increase the conductivity of surrounding surfaces. Where a fault exists on electrical equipment in a wet environment it may not be necessary to make direct contact with it to receive an electric shock, the wet substance may act as a conductor making a circuit between the faulty equipment and the person. These conditions may exist where, for example, a plasterer plasters a wall around a faulty light socket or a pressure water cleaner has a damaged cable lying in the water run-off from the cleaning operation.

USE OF ELECTRICAL EQUIPMENT IN FLAMMABLE/EXPLOSIVE ENVIRONMENTS

The failure to use correctly rated electrical equipment (international protection (IP) rating) in areas where explosive atmospheres exist or may exist may result in ignition of flammable dust, gases or vapours with explosive results. The spread of ignited material to other areas where fires might be initiated, far from the original source of ignition, may also result in additional explosions, propagating the fire to adjacent areas. This will result in damage to property and individuals within the vicinity, resulting in severe burns, physical damage to the body and hearing/sight sensory organs.

6.2 - Control measures

Selection and suitability of equipment for use in construction activities

PROTECTION OF CONDUCTORS

Conductors, whether live, neutral or earthed require protection from accidental or deliberate contact, interference, misuse or even abuse. This is often in the form of electrical insulation. Electrical *insulators* are materials that do not readily conduct electricity. Some common insulator materials are glass, plastic, rubber, air, and wood. Where conductors that are insulated are exposed to a higher risk of damage they may be further protected by a metal casing, which provides re-enforcement around the insulation, or ducting which provides a protective location for it to be placed.

CABLES AND LEADS

Insulation appropriate to the environment should be used to give resistance to abrasion, chemicals, heat and impact. The insulation must be in good condition. Flexible, multi-strand cables are required for portable tools and extension leads. Cables must be secured by the outer sheath at their point of entry into the apparatus, including plugs. The individual conductor insulation should not show through the sheath and conductors must not be exposed. Extension leads must be fused.

Temporary wiring should be used in compliance with standards and properly secured, supported and mechanically protected against damage. Taped joints in cables are not allowed and proper line connectors must be used to join cables. Connectors should be kept to a minimum to reduce earth path impedance.

Many cables are set up on a temporary basis, but these improvised arrangements can get left for a considerable time. Care should be taken to identify true short term temporary arrangements and those that warrant full longer term arrangements, such as being placed in trunking for better protection.

Conductors across roads or pedestrian ways should be covered to protect them from damage. Where they are to cross a doorway this is usually best carried out by taking it around the door instead of trailing it across the floor.

Overhead cables likely to be hit by vehicles or persons carrying ladders, pipes etc. should be highlighted by the use of appropriate signs.

Regular visual inspection should be made for deterioration and cuts. This is best identified by using the technique of systematic bending of short sections of cable by hand, progressing along the length of the cable.

Cuts will be opened by this process revealing the conductor, kinks or bend damage (particularly near to the point of entry into apparatus), exposed conductors, overheating or burn damage, trapping damage, insulation embrittling or corrosion.

STRENGTH AND CAPABILITY OF EQUIPMENT

Regulation 5 of the Electricity at Work Regulations (EWR) 1989 sets out requirements for strength and capability of electrical equipment.

> *"No electrical equipment shall be put into use where its strength and capability may be exceeded in such a way as may give rise to danger."*

Figure 6-15: Strength and capability of electrical equipment.   *Source: EWR 1989 Regulation 5.*

Strength and capability in this context has a wide meaning. This includes the requirement that any electrical equipment needs to be capable of standing normal and fault currents without failure.

In order for equipment to remain safe when subjected to sustained fault conditions it may require the inclusion of protective devices which detect the fault and break the circuit containing the fault.

It is also important to ensure that all electrical equipment is suitable for what it is used for in terms of its strength and capability. For example, if it is to be used for outdoor work on a construction site in conditions that it might get wet, equipment providing protection from the ingress of water must be selected. Many tools are designed and provided for use in a domestic situation and they may not be suitable for use in the more arduous conditions of a construction site, for example, cable entry grips may be more secure and outer protection of cables thicker on equipment designed for construction work.

The British Standard BS 7671, the Institute of Electrical Engineers (IEE) 17th edition requirements, Chapter 13 - 'Fundamental principles for safety' - specifies the following needs to ensure electrical installations are appropriate and safe: *"Good workmanship and proper materials shall be used. Construction, installation, inspection, testing and maintenance shall be such as to prevent danger. Equipment shall be suitable for the power demanded and the conditions in which it is installed. Additions and alterations to installations shall comply with Regulations. Equipment which requires operation or attention shall be accessible."*

The Institution of Engineering and Technology (IET) was formerly known as the Institute of Electrical Engineers (IEE).

The Low Voltage (Safety) Regulations place a duty on the supplier of equipment to ensure that equipment using between 50 and 100 volts ac is safe. Construction of the equipment, including flexible cables and cords, must be to European Union (EU) accepted good engineering practice standards. The Low Voltage (Safety) Regulations are deemed satisfied if the equipment bears a recognised standard mark, certificate or other acceptable authorisation. Supply of unsafe equipment or components is prohibited.

Electrical systems on site

PLANNING AND INSTALLATION OF A PROGRESSIVELY EXTENDING ELECTRICAL SYSTEM ON SITE

Electricity in construction brings numerous hazards that require stringent planning and control systems. Prior to starting construction activities, at the planning stage consideration must be given to factors including buried services, electricity sub-stations or proximity to overhead cables. A site may have existing buildings and tests must be made to determine whether existing services are live or dead. At the planning stage, a full site survey will include identifying the location of any electrical sources or conductors.

Planning also provides the ideal opportunity to ensure that where electricity is involved, the correct measures are implemented to control risk. This may include location of plant, planning cable runs or ducts, whether high or low voltage is required, control features when in use (switch panels, isolation, and lock off), protection devices (earthing arrangements, trip switches, residual current devices, panel housings, warnings and instructions). Maintenance should play a key part in the planning stage, with consideration given to access, isolation, lock-off and security.

When construction activities start heavy mechanical plant will be introduced that may operate in close proximity to sources of electricity. Safe systems should be introduced to include ensuring that sufficiently safe distances are maintained from overhead cables to prevent electrical 'arc' (discharge) from the uninsulated cables.

Safe systems may include permits-to-work, 'goal post' type visual barriers, information for site workers and signs. There may be activities that involve explosive atmospheres that require intrinsically safe equipment to be used (for example, work is sewers or chambers).

Most industrial installations work on high voltage systems due to increased consumption of electricity during the many different processes. Owing to economic advantages, industrial sites commonly include their own dedicated power sub-stations that operate at voltages typically in ranges of 11kV. This high voltage is then transformed down into values more commonly in the range of 415v. When working with high voltage circuitry, staff must be 'high voltage' trained and work under a permit-to-work system.

It is essential that the planning and installation of electrical systems reflect not only the power needs but the lighting needs of the site as well. The plan should include anticipated needs or demand as the site changes, for example, extending provision as a structure is built or orderly withdrawal of provision as a structure is demolished. Planning should ensure power is available at key points as close to where work is carried out that requires it, thus minimising the need for extension cables to run for long distances. Planning should take account of where it is not practicable to provide a permanent system and where local power generation is more suitable. In this case the same planning is required to ensure the system provided is adequate for the demands. In some cases this will require the provision of a quantity of small generators to ensure the right amount of power is available where it is needed.

Figure 6-16: Construction site generator. *Source: RMS.*

Figure 6-17: Construction site power supply panel. *Source: RMS.*

If work is to be conducted in someone else's building that is occupied and power is to be obtained by adapting the system within the building, consideration has to be given to the effects on the host's power supply of this additional demand. Care should be taken to ensure that power is drawn from agreed points and at agreed, safe voltages. Where practicable systems provided for construction work should run at 110V or lower and should be set into place at the earliest safe opportunity; in many cases this can be integrated into ground works that is planned for the site. If systems are to be left in place at the end of the work, and they do not form part of the system for the structure constructed, care should be taken to identify them on plans and if they are to be left 'dead' they should be checked to ensure this is the case.

Figure 6-18: 110v generator. *Source: RMS.*

Figure 6-19: 110v extension lead. *Source: RMS.*

PERMIT-TO-WORK PROCEDURES AND REQUIREMENTS

A permit-to-work is an official, documented safe system of work that is used for controlling high risk activities. Implementation is required prior to work beginning to ensure that all precautions are taken and are securely in place to prevent danger to the workforce. When managed correctly, a permit-to-work prevents any mistakes or deviations through poor communication; by stating the specific requirements of the task. For electrical systems, a permit-to-work is typically used for those rated at or in excess of 230v or where there is more than one point or means of isolation. The authorised person issues the permit-to-work and will sign the document to declare that all isolations are made and remain in place throughout the duration of the task. In addition to this, the authorised person will make checks to ensure that all controls to be implemented by the acceptor are in place before work commences.

Figure 6-20: Power supply isolation. *Source: RMS.*

The acceptor of the permit-to-work assumes responsibility for carrying out the work on the electrical system. The acceptor signs the document to declare that the terms and conditions of the permit-to-work are understood and will be complied with fully at all times by the entire work team. Compliance with a permit-to-work system includes ensuring the required safeguards are implemented and that the work will be restricted to only the equipment stated within the document.

Items included in the electrical permit-to-work are:

■ Permit issue number.
■ Authorised person identification.
■ Points at which isolation is made.
■ Test procedure and confirmation of dead circuitry.
■ Warning information sign locations.
■ Earth connection points.
■ Details of the work to be carried out.
■ Signature of authoriser.
■ Signature of acceptor.
■ Signature for works clearance/extension/handover.
■ Signature for cancellation.

Other precautions include risk assessments, method statements, and personal protective equipment.

REQUIREMENTS FOR TEMPORARY ELECTRICAL SUPPLIES

The supply of electricity on a construction site will normally be provided by one or both of the following:

■ A public supply from the local electricity company.
■ A site generator, where public supply is not practical or economic.

Public supply

The public supply company will require the installation of a suitable facility for the incoming cables to be connected to. The facility may be a temporary structure or a permanent substation which may be required for the site development. The supply will be connected to isolation switch gear, monitoring equipment and in accordance with the supplier requirements for earthing.

Generators

Where generators are required, these will either be petrol or diesel powered and will need to be sited to reduce the effects of noise and emissions on the site workers or others on neighbouring facilities. Generating equipment should be installed by a competent person in accordance with BS7375:2010; a code of practice that gives recommendations for the distribution of electricity on construction sites.

The sites covered in the standard are areas where any of the following take place:

■ Construction work of new buildings.
■ Repair, alteration, extension, demolition of existing buildings or parts of existing buildings.
■ Engineering works.
■ Earthworks.
■ Work of similar nature.

If the generator is rated above 55 volts AC, it must be earthed and the effectiveness of the earth checked by a competent person. Generators that operate at or below 55 volts AC do not require an earth. Not all portable generators available have a centre tapped earth output of 110 volts, giving 55 volts at point of use *(see also 'Element 6.2 - Reduced low voltage systems')*. This is common with generators with dual voltage output selection. Where there is a site distribution system the metal framework of the generator should be connected to a common earth.

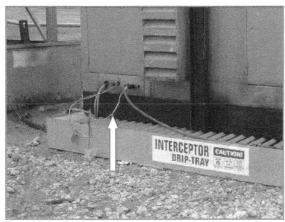

Figure 6-21: Earth provided to generator.　　*Source: RMS.*

Figure 6-22: Earthed distribution equipment.　　*Source: RMS.*

Electrical contractors should not switch on the electricity until they have a written request from the main contractor or the main contractor's agent; the circuits have been fully inspected and tested and are safe to use.

When the electricity is switched on, the main contractor is legally responsible for making sure that everyone working on site is aware of any live circuits in an area. They are also responsible for making sure that their electrical subcontractors use safe isolation procedures before working on any circuits that could possibly be live. The electrical subcontractor has the same duty and responsibility to use safe isolation practices when required.

Advantages and limitations of protective systems

FUSES

This is a device designed to automatically cut off the power supply to a circuit within a given time when the current flow in that circuit exceeds a given value. A fuse may be a rewirable tinned copper wire in a suitable carrier or a wire or wires in an enclosed cartridge.

In effect it is a weak link in the circuit that melts when heat is created by too high a current passing through the thin wire in the fuse case. When this happens the circuit is broken and no more current flows. A fuse usually has a rating in the order of Amperes rather than milliAmperes which means it has **limited usefulness in protecting people from electric shock.** The fuse will operate (break the circuit) relatively slowly if the current is just above the fuse rating. Using too high a fuse means that the circuit will remain intact and the equipment will draw power. This may cause it to overheat leading to a fire or if a fault exists the circuit will remain live and the fault current may pass through the user of the equipment when they touch or operate it.

The following formula should be used to calculate the correct rating for a fuse:

Current (amperes (A)) = $\dfrac{\text{Power (watts (W))}}{\text{Voltage (volts (V))}}$

For example, the correct fuse current rating for a 2 kilowatt kettle on a 230 volt supply would be:

$\dfrac{2{,}000 \text{ W}}{230 \text{ V}}$ = 8.69 amperes

Typical fuses for domestic appliances are 3, 5, and 13 ampere ratings. The nearest fuse just above this current level is 13 amperes.

	Typical examples of power ratings are:	*Suitable fuses at 230 Volts:*
Computer processor	350 watts	3 amperes
Electric kettle	1,850 - 2,200 watts	13 amperes
Dishwasher	1,380 watts	13 amperes
Refrigerator	90 watts	3 amperes

Limitations of fuses

A fuse is:

- A weak link in the circuit that melts slowly when heat is created by a fault condition. However, this usually happens too slowly to protect people.
- Easy to replace with wrong rating.
- Often needs a tool to replace.
- Easy to override by replacing a fuse with one of a higher rating or putting in an improvised 'fuse', such as a nail, that has a high rating.

Figure 6-23: Plug-foil fuse no earth.   *Source: RMS.*

Figure 6-24: Earthing.   *Source: RMS.*

Advantages of fuses

- Offers a good level of protection for the equipment.
- Very cheap and reliable within its limits.

EARTHING

A conductor called an earth wire is fitted to the system; it is connected at one end to a plate buried in the ground and the other end connected to the metal casing of the equipment. If for any reason a conductor touches the casing so that the equipment casing becomes 'live' the current will flow to the point of lowest potential, the earth. The path to this point (earth) is made easier as the wire is designed to have very little resistance. This *may prevent electric shock* provided it is used in association with a correctly rated fuse, or better still a residual current device (RCD), and no one is in contact with the equipment at the time the fault occurs. It should be remembered that earthing is provided where the casing can become live. If the equipment is designed so that this cannot be the case, such as double insulated equipment where the user touches non-conducting surfaces, earthing of the equipment is no advantage. In summary, earthing provides a path of least resistance for 'stray' current and provides protection against indirect shock.

ISOLATION OF SUPPLY

Isolation of an electrical system is an excellent way of achieving safety for those that need to work on or near the system; for example, isolation of a power supply into a building that is to be refurbished or isolation of plant that is to be maintained. In its simplest form it can mean switching off and unplugging a portable appliance at times it is not in use. Care must be taken to check that the isolation has been adequate and effective before work starts; this can include tests on the system. It is also important to ensure the isolation is secure; 'lock off' and 'tag out' systems will assist with this.

REDUCED AND LOW VOLTAGE SYSTEMS

One of the best ways to reduce the risk from electricity is to reduce the voltage. This is frequently achieved by the use of a transformer (step down) which will reduce the voltage. A common reduction is from the mains voltage of 230V to 110V. Normally, transformers that are used to reduce voltage are described as 'centre tapped to earth'. In practice this means that any voltage involved in an electrical shock will be 55V.

Using the earlier example of Ohms law, if the voltage is 230V then:

$$I = \frac{V}{R} = \frac{230 \text{ volts}}{2,000+4,000 \text{ ohms}} = 0.038 \text{ amperes or 38 mA}$$

However, if a centre tapped to earth transformer is used then:

$$I = \frac{V}{R} = \frac{55 \text{ volts}}{2,000+4,000 \text{ ohms}} = 0.009 \text{ amperes or 9 mA}$$

Reference to *figures 6-2 and 6-5* will clearly show how this *reduces the effects of electric shock* on the body.

Figure 6-25: 110V centre tapped earth transformer. *Source: RMS.*

Figure 6-26: 110V powered drill. *Source: RMS.*

An alternative to reduction in voltage by means of a transformer is to provide battery-powered equipment; this will commonly run on 12V to 24V, but voltages may be higher. The common method is to use a rechargeable battery to power the equipment which eliminates the need for a cable to feed power to the equipment and gives a greater flexibility of use for the user, for example, for drills and power drivers.

RESIDUAL CURRENT DEVICE

A residual current device (RCD) is an electro-mechanical switching device that automatically isolates the supply when there is a difference between the current flowing into a device and the current flowing from the device.

Such a difference might result from a fault causing current leakage, with possible fire risks or the risk of shock current when a person touches a system and provides a path to earth for the current.

RCDs can be designed to operate at low currents and fast response times (usually 30 mA and 30 milliseconds) and thus they *reduce the effect of an electric shock*. Though they do not prevent the person receiving an electric shock they are very sensitive and operate very quickly and reduce some of the primary effects of the shock.

It is still possible for a person to receive injury from the shock, not least some of the secondary injuries referred to earlier. But the use of this type of device means the fault current should be isolated before sustained shock, and therefore before fibrillation, occurs. The equipment needs to be de-energised from time to time in order to be confident it will work properly when needed. This can easily be carried out by a simple test routine before use, as equipment is plugged into the RCD.

Summary of the features of an RCD

A residual current device is:

- Rapid and sensitive.
- Difficult to defeat.
- Easy and safe to test and reset.
- Not able to prevent shock, but reduces the effect of a shock.

Figure 6-27: Residual current device.   *Source: RMS.*

Figure 6-28: Plug-in residual current device.   *Source: RMS.*

DOUBLE INSULATION

This is a common protection device and consists of a layer of insulation around the live electrical parts of the equipment and a second layer of insulated material around this, commonly the casing of the equipment. Since the casing material is an insulator and does not conduct electricity, equipment having this type of protection does not normally have an earth wire.

To make sure that the double insulation is not impaired, it must not be pierced by conducting parts such as metal screws. Nor must insulating screws be used, because there is the possibility that they will be lost and will be replaced by metal screws. Any holes in the enclosure of a double Insulated appliance, such as those to allow ventilation, must be so small that fingers cannot reach live parts.

Each layer of insulation must be sufficient in its own right to give adequate protection against shock. Equipment which is double insulated will carry the symbol shown in *figure ref 6-30*. Double insulated equipment has two layers of insulating material between the live parts of the equipment and the user. If a fault occurs with the live parts and a conductor touches the insulating material surrounding it no current can pass to the user, therefore, *no shock occurs.*

Figure 6-29: Double insulated 230V drill.   *Source: RMS.*

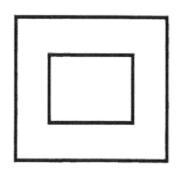

Figure 6-30: Double insulation symbol. *Source: HSE, HSG107.*

Use of competent persons

It is particularly important that anyone who undertakes electrical work is able to satisfy the requirements of the Health and Safety at Work etc. Act (HASAWA) 1974 and the Electricity at Work Regulations (EWR) 1989. For work on electrical systems below 1,000 volts ac they should be able to work within the guidelines set out in BS 7671 'Requirements for electrical installations, IEE Wiring Regulations, 17th edition'.

Other work should be carried out according to the guidelines set out in the relevant industry standard. Those who wish to undertake electrical testing work would normally be expected to have more knowledge and to be able to demonstrate competence through the successful completion of a suitable training course.

More complex electrical tasks such as motor repair or maintenance of radio frequency heating equipment should only be carried out by someone who has been trained to do them. Work on higher voltage systems must be carried out by specialist electrical engineers trained for this purpose. Work on live electrical systems must be controlled and requires specialist competence and systems of work to ensure safety.

Use of safe systems of work

LIVE ELECTRICAL WORK

The Electricity at Work Regulations (EWR) 1989 sets out requirements for live electrical work.

"No person shall be engaged in any work activity on or so near any live conductor that danger may arise, unless it is unreasonable in all the circumstances for it to be dead."

Figure 6-31: Work on live conductors. *Source: EWR 1989 Regulation 14.*

This duty means that if danger could be present, work where possible, should be carried out with the electrical system dead. If it is necessary to work on live conductors, very strict controls must be in place and a safe system of work adhered to.

These will include:

- A full justification of why there is no reasonably practicable alternative to live working.
- A live electrical permit-to-work which will be valid for the stated task only.
- At least two competent persons must be present during the work and the more senior of these will sign off the permit when the work is complete and after all equipment has been restored to a fully safe condition.
- Restriction of work area to these competent people.
- Protection of the work area from other hazards, such as vehicles.
- Protection of workers from non-essential live conductors, by isolation or screening.
- Provision of information on the system and task.
- Use of suitable, insulated test equipment and tools.
- Adequate lighting and clear space to work.
- First-aid service immediately available.
- Competent supervision.

ISOLATION

The Electricity at Work Regulations (EWR) 1989 sets out requirements for isolation.

"'Isolation' means the disconnection and separation of the electrical equipment from every source of electrical energy in such a way that this disconnection and separation is secure."

Figure 6-32: Isolation. *Source: EWR 1989 Regulation 12.*

Health and Safety Executive (HSE) booklet 'Electricity at Work - Safe Working Practices (HSG85)' provides information on isolation procedures when working on both Low Voltage (LV) and High Voltage (HV) systems.

The requirement of the Electricity at Work Regulations (EWR) 1989 means that any isolation method used must be adequate and secure. This means that turning equipment off at a general on off switch or other mechanism is not adequate. Isolation therefore requires disconnection at the primary isolation mechanism for the equipment or circuit.

In order to ensure a high level of security if work on the circuit or equipment takes the person away from constant site of the isolator mechanism, a lock may be added. Isolation procedures, often referred to as 'lockout/tagout', in conjunction with a 'permit-to-work' often form part of a 'safe system of work'. Various competences are required to ensure full compliance with these procedures, with specialist training and supervision required.

Figure 6-33: Multi-lock system. *Source: RMS.*

If multi-lock systems are used *(see figure ref 6-33)* there must be a contingency plan to deal with the likelihood that someone will lose a key or even leave at the end of a shift without removing their personal pad lock.

LOCATING BURIED SERVICES

Excavation operations should not begin until all available service location drawings have been identified and thoroughly examined. Record plans and location drawings should not be considered as totally accurate but serve only as an indication of the likelihood of the presence of services, their location and depth.

It is possible for the position of an electricity supply cable to alter if previous works have been carried out in the location due to the flexibility of the cable and movement of surrounding features since original installation of the cable.

In addition, plans often show a proposed position for the services that does not translate to the ground, such that services are placed in position only approximately where the plan says.

Before groundwork is due to commence it is common and good practice to check for presence of any of the services or hazards by using a detection device. A common detection device used is the cable avoidance tool (CAT), more commonly known as a CAT scanner.

It is important that 'service location devices' such as a CAT scanner are used by competent, trained operatives to assist in the identification and marking of the actual location and position of buried services.

When identified it is essential that physical markings be placed on the ground to show where these services are located.

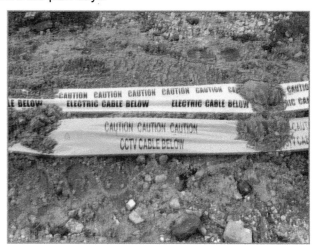

Figure 6-34: Marking of services.   *Source: RMS.*

PROTECTION AGAINST OVERHEAD CABLES

Contact with live overhead lines kills people and causes serious injuries every year.

It is important, where possible, to eliminate the danger by:

- Avoidance - carrying out as much work as is possible remote from the lines.
- Diversion - diverting all overhead lines clear of the work area.
- Isolation - make lines dead while the work is in progress.
- Insulation.

If the danger cannot be eliminated, the risk must be managed by controlling access to, and work beneath, overhead power lines.

For lower voltage cables it may be possible to temporarily isolate the supply and fit insulation to prevent contact with the live conductor when power is restored.

The following precautions may also be needed to manage the risk:

- Isolate the supply.
- Erect 'goal-post' barriers to define clearance distances.
- Clearly mark danger zones with signs and/or bunting.
- Ensure safe access under lines.
- Use banksman or marshals where appropriate.
- Restrict the use of metal equipment such as ladders and scaffolds.

See also 'Element 6.3 - Control measures for working near overhead power lines'.

Inspection and maintenance strategies

THE LEGAL DUTY FOR INSPECTION AND MAINTENANCE

The Electricity at Work Regulations (EWR) 1989, Regulation 4(2) sets out requirements for the owner to maintain electrical systems.

*"As may be necessary to prevent danger, **maintain** all systems so as to prevent, so far as is reasonably practicable, such danger."*

Figure 6-35: Maintenance of electrical systems.   *Source: EWR 1989 Regulation 4(2).*

Danger is defined as the risk of injury from electric shock, electric burn, fire of electrical origin, electric arcing or explosion initiated or caused by electricity.

Guidance form the HSE document 'Maintaining portable and transportable electrical equipment' (HSG107) indicates that maintenance is a general term that in practice can include visual inspection, repair, testing and replacement. Maintenance will determine whether equipment is fully serviceable or needing repair.

It further suggests that an effective maintenance strategy should adopt a three-stage approach:

1) Checks by the user.
2) Formal visual inspections by a person appointed to do this.
3) Combined inspection and tests (more commonly known as PAT) by a competent person or by a contractor.

The Memorandum of Guidance on the EWR 1989 defines a system as any equipment that is, or may be, connected to a common source of electrical energy. The requirement therefore applies to the permanent installation in a building, including wiring, fixed equipment, such as a bench mounted circular saw, and portable equipment such as sanders or drills.

In order to identify what systems will need maintenance, they should be listed. This same listing can be used as a checklist, recording that the appropriate checks have been carried out. It may also include details of the type of equipment, as well as the checks and tests to be carried out.

USER CHECKS

A procedure should be established by which the user brings faults to the attention of a supervisor and/or a competent person who might rectify the fault.

The user of portable electrical equipment should, after basic training, look critically at equipment and its source of power and make *user checks* for defects. If any defects are found, the equipment should be marked and quarantined and not be used again before examination by a competent person.

Checks by the user should be aimed at identifying the following:

- Damaged cable sheaths.
- Damaged plugs. Cracked casing or bent pins.
- Taped or other inadequate cable joints.
- Outer cable insulation not secured into plugs or equipment.
- Faulty or ineffective switches.
- Burn marks or discolouration.
- Damaged casing.
- Loose parts or screws.
- Wet or contaminated equipment.
- Loose or damaged sockets or switches.

FORMAL INSPECTION AND TESTS

Visual inspection

The maintenance system should always include *formal visual inspection* of all portable electrical equipment and electrical tests.

The frequency depends on the type of equipment and where it is used. The inspection can be carried out by a member of staff who has been trained in what to look for and has basic electrical knowledge. They should know enough to avoid danger to themselves or others.

Visual inspections are likely to need to look for the same types of defects as user checks, but should also include the following.

Opening plugs of portable equipment to check for:

- Use of correctly rated fuse.
- Effective cord grip.
- Secure and correct cable terminations.
- No bare wire is visible other than at the terminals.

Inspection of fixed installations for:

- Damaged or loose conduit, trunking or cabling.
- Missing broken or inadequately secured covers.
- Loose or faulty joints.
- Loose earth connections.
- Moisture, corrosion or contamination.
- Burn marks or discolouration.
- Open or inadequately secured panel doors.
- Ease of access to switches and isolators.
- Presence of temporary wiring.

User checks and a programme of formal visual inspections will find the majority of faults.

Testing

Faults such as loss of earth or broken wires inside an installation or cable cannot be found by visual inspection, so some apparatus needs to have a *combined inspection and test*.

This is particularly important for all earthed equipment and leads and plugs connected to hand held or hand operated equipment. The power supply system should be tested regularly in accordance with Institute of Electrical Engineers (IEE) requirements; tests may include earth continuity and impedance tests and tests of insulation material.

FREQUENCY OF INSPECTION AND TESTING

Question:	*"I have been told that I have to have my desk lamp tested every six months. Is this correct?"*
Answer:	*"No. The law requires it to be maintained. It does not require any elaborate or rigorous system of frequent electrical testing."*

Figure 6-36: Testing frequency.   *Source: HSE Note INDG 160L.*

Deciding the frequency

Many approaches to establishing frequency suggest that they should be carried out regularly. As can be seen above, the word 'regularly' is not specified in terms of fixed time intervals for all systems; a management judgment must be made to specify an appropriate timetable.

In effect, the frequency will depend on the condition the system is used in; for example, a test of office portable equipment may be sufficient if conducted every three years, whereas equipment used on a construction site may need to be tested every three months.

The system as a whole rather than just portable equipment must also be tested periodically and again this will depend on the conditions of use and may vary from ten years to six months.

Factors to be considered when deciding the frequency include:

- Type of equipment.
- Whether it is hand held.
- Manufacturer's recommendations.
- Its initial integrity and soundness.
- Age.
- Working environment.
- Likelihood of mechanical damage.

- Frequency of use.
- Duration of use.
- Foreseeable use.
- Who uses the equipment.
- Modifications or repairs.
- Past experience.

RECORDS OF INSPECTION AND TESTING

In order to identify what systems and equipment will need inspection and testing they should be listed.

This same listing can be used as a checklist recording that the appropriate checks, inspections and tests have been carried out. It would be usual to include in records details of the type of the equipment, its location and its age.

It is helpful to keep centralised records of the results of inspection and testing within an organisation. Such records can then be used for setting the frequency for further appliance testing, to verify whether unlabelled equipment had been tested or had merely lost its label and to provide a record of past faults on all appliances that had been reported. This approach may help to demonstrate that compliance with legislation.

Figure 6-37: PAT labels.   *Source: RMS.*

A record of equipment and its status should be available to those that are responsible for using the equipment as well as those that are conducting the inspection or test. In addition, it is common practice to add a label to the equipment to indicate that an inspection and/or test has taken place and its status following this. Some labels only show the date that the inspection/test took place and others show the date of next inspection/test as well.

The HSE Guidance 'Maintaining portable and transportable electrical equipment' (HSG107) states that while not required by law, duty holders with large amounts of equipment may find it useful to label equipment to indicate that the equipment has been tested satisfactorily, i.e. has been passed as safe, and when it was tested.

It further states that if a label is applied by the tester then there should not be a next test due date on it as the person carrying out the testing should not assess when the next test is due, this decision should be made by the duty holder based on a risk assessment.

Equipment used on construction sites may need to be tested more frequently than equipment used in other activities, for example, in an office or light engineering environment. The factors to consider when making the risk assessment and deciding the frequency of inspection/test are set out earlier in this section.

On construction sites, employees may bring to work their own electrically powered equipment, including tools to do their work and equipment for welfare reasons, for example, radios and kettles. All such equipment should be recorded, inspected and tested by a competent person before use and at regular intervals, as if it were company property.

ADVANTAGES AND LIMITATIONS OF PORTABLE APPLIANCE TESTING

The purpose of portable appliance testing (PAT) is to periodically confirm the critical aspects of the electrical integrity of portable appliances. The advantage of portable appliance testing is that it can identify faults that other methods may not, for example, loss of earth integrity (perhaps due to a broken earth wire in a flexible cable) or deterioration of insulation integrity.

However, portable appliance testing requires a greater degree of competence (in terms of knowledge, training and experience) than visual inspection alone. This is because appropriate electrical knowledge is needed to undertake the tests and interpret the test results. It also requires the use of equipment capable of making the type of electrical tests required.

A further limitation with portable appliance testing is that people may have an over-reliance on the apparent assurance that the test indicates. They may be tempted to see it as a permanent assurance that the equipment is safe. This can lead to users not making their own pre-use checks of the appliance. It is important to recognise that it is only a test, and therefore assurance, at a point in time. It does not assure that someone has not, for example, altered the fuse and put one in with an incorrect rating or that the cable grip has not come loose.

It must also be recognised that there is little benefit in having a perfect portable appliance if it is plugged into a defective socket which may be without proper insulation, with a switch that does not work properly, with the polarity reversed or with a high resistance earth connection.

Emergency procedures following an electrical incident

Anyone working around electrical systems should be aware of what needs to be carried out for a casualty of electrical shock.

If someone is lying unconscious and in contact with conductors the following actions should be taken in an order depending on the circumstances:

- Assess the situation.
- Summon help, including qualified medical support.
- If possible shut off the power.
- Do not touch the casualty - there may be enough voltage across the body of the casualty to shock the would-be rescuer. The problem with this rule is that the source of power may not be known, or easily found in time to save the casualty from shock.
- Remove the power. If possible prove the system is discharged and dead. If this is not possible take the following action.
- Remove the casualty from the power. It may be possible to dislodge the casualty from the circuit with a dry wooden board or piece of non-metallic material or using a jacket as a loop around the person, holding both sleeves and pulling away.
- Reassess the situation and any remaining danger to yourself and the casualty.
- Once the casualty has been disconnected from the source of electric power, the immediate medical concerns for the casualty should be respiration and circulation (breathing and pulse). If the rescuer is trained in cardio pulmonary resuscitation (CPR), they should follow the appropriate steps of checking breathing (including the airway) and pulse, then applying CPR as necessary to keep the casualty's body from de-oxygenating.
- If the casualty is conscious, lay them in the recovery position and keep them warm to reduce the chances of physiological shock until qualified medical personnel arrive on the scene.
- Keep the casualty under observation for secondary effects. Cool burns with water.

Figure 6-38: First-aid sign. *Source: RMS.*

Further considerations:

- Do not go near the casualty until the electricity supply is proven to be off. This is especially important with overhead high voltage lines: keep yourself and others at least 18 metres away until the electricity supply company personnel advise otherwise.
- Do not delay - after 3 minutes without blood circulation irreversible damage can be done to the casualty.
- Do not wait for an accident to happen - train in emergency procedures and first-aid, plan procedures for an emergency (calling for help, making calls to the emergency services, meeting ambulances and leading them to the casualty) and hold emergency drills.
- Establish if the incident has to be reported under the Reporting of Injuries, Diseases and Dangerous Occurrences Regulations (RIDDOR) 2013.

6.3 - Control measures for working near overhead power lines

Control measures

Every year people are seriously hurt by coming into contact with overhead power lines, so it is important to identify the overhead cables and implement adequate control measures. Any lines found on a construction site should always be treated as live until they are proved to be otherwise.

Control measures might include diversion of the power lines, temporary isolation of supply, safe access points, restricted vehicle movements, barriers and fencing.

AVOIDANCE WHERE POSSIBLE

It may be possible to have the overhead power lines diverted away from the site while work is carried out. Access routes to sites should be sited a safe distance away from overhead cables; if this is not possible then the adequate control measures should be adopted.

PRE-PLANNING AND CONSULTATION WITH SERVICE PROVIDER

Planning and consultation with service providers is essential and forms part of the safe system of work, as it may be necessary to isolate the supply in the event of an incident. Access routes should be established in consultation and these should be away from overhead cables. They should be clearly identified, signed and marked. Where this is not possible, then clear passing places with clear goal posts erected at both ends should be established, clearly signed, including clearance height and notice to driver to lower jibs. Lighting may be required if work is to take place after sunset.

Isolation/diversion of supply

The supply may need to be isolated at some point in the event of heavy equipment movements on or around the site. Where isolation is not practical then arrangements will need to be made with the utility suppliers, to divert the supply away from the site in order to maintain continuous supply to local consumers.

Therefore, it is essential that this has been adequately planned and a procedure has been adopted and approved with the electricity supplier.

GROUND LEVEL BARRIERS, GOAL POSTS AND CORRECT CLEARANCE DISTANCES

If work is to be carried out near overhead lines then barriers should be used, along with warning signs. The recommended distance for the position of the barriers is 6 metres (horizontally) from the nearest line. Some construction vehicles have jib's or telescopic arms that extend long distances, therefore, the measurement should be taken with the reach of the jib (maximum outreach) measured (horizontally) from the position of the ground barrier. For very high voltages these distances may be increased significantly. Bunting may also be required to show drivers of these vehicles the position of the lines. The bunting should be placed at a height of 3 to 6 metres. The barriers should be sturdy enough so that they cannot be moved easily and should be coloured coded with red and white stripes.

Types of barrier commonly used include:

- 200 litre drums filled with rubble or concrete.
- Railway sleepers.
- A raised earth bank to 1 metre and marked by posts to prevent vehicle entry.
- A tension wire fence with flags attached (this should be earthed in consultation with the electricity supplier).

Figure 6-39: Working near overhead power lines.   *Source: HSE, HSG150.*

Access and egress routes beneath overhead cables should be clearly marked with clearance distances using a vertical pole each side of the opening and a height limiting barrier above and between. This work practice is commonly referred to as cross under 'goal posts'.

The safe clearance distance from the overhead line depends on the level of voltage of the line as it possible for electricity to arc between the line and any conducting material in contact with an earth. This means the correct clearance may have to be determined by consultation with the electrical service provider responsible for the overhead line.

RESTRICTION OF EQUIPMENT/VEHICLE REACH

There may be a requirement to restrict certain equipment, for example, rough terrain fork-lift trucks or cranes from working under power lines, due to the possibility of jibs or forks coming into contact with lines or near enough to form an arc from the power lines.

Similarly, the reach of telescopic cranes may be restricted by the application of electronic or mechanical restraints.

Figure 6-40: Overhead cable protection on traffic route.   *Source: HSE, HSG144.*

Exam practice

1. **Explain** how the following two protective measures reduce the risk of electric shock **AND**, in **EACH** case, give an example of their use in construction activities.

    (a)   Reduced low voltage. (4)

    (b)   Double insulation. (4)

2. A fire has started on a construction site immediately adjacent to a bench mounted electric circular saw.

    (a)   **Outline** how the saw's electrical power system may have caused the fire. **(4)**

    (b)   **Outline** the possible effects of an electric shock to the saw operator. **(4)**

3. A road is being resurfaced in an area that has overhead power lines crossing it. The work involves the use of tipper vehicles, excavators and a road planning machine that has an extended jib.

    Outline control measures to reduce the risk from contact with the overhead power lines. **(8)**

4. (a)   **Outline** the control measures that should be used by someone using a hand-held electric drill on a construction site to reduce the risk of electric shock. **(4)**

    (b)   Other than electricity, **identify FOUR** hazards associated with the use of hand-held electric drills on construction sites. **(4)**

5. (a)   **Explain** why a fuse fitted to hand-held electrical power tools only provides limited electric shock protection to the user of the tool. **(2)**

(b)   **Identify** the advantages and limitations of using a residual current device to provide users of hand held electrical power tools from electric shock. **(4)**

(c)   **Outline** the advantages of double insulation for hand-held electrical power tools. **(2)**

Please refer to the back of the assessment section for answers.

Fire safety

Learning outcomes

On completion of this element, candidates should be able to demonstrate understanding of the content through the application of knowledge to familiar and unfamiliar situations. In particular they should be able to:

7.1 Describe the principles of fire initiation, classification and spread and the additional fire risks caused by construction activities in an existing workplace.

7.2 Outline the principles of fire risk assessment.

7.3 Outline the principles of fire prevention and the prevention of fire spread in construction workplaces.

7.4 Identify the appropriate fire detection, fire alarm systems and firefighting equipment for construction activities.

7.5 Outline the requirements for an adequate and properly maintained means of escape in the construction workplace.

7.6 Outline the factors which should be considered when implementing a successful evacuation of a construction workplace in the event of a fire.

Content

7.1 - Fire initiation, classification and spread 171
  Basic principles of fire 171
  Classification of fires 173
  Principles of heat transmission 173
  Reasons why fires spread 174
  Common causes and consequences of fire during construction activities 175
7.2 - Fire risk assessment 177
  Requirement and matters to be addressed in carrying out the assessment 177
  Factors to be considered in carrying out the risk assessment 177
  Additional risk assessment factors related to construction 179
7.3 - Fire prevention and prevention of fire spread 181
  Control measures to minimise the risk of fire in a construction workplace 181
  Storage of small quantities of highly flammable/flammable liquids 186
  Structural measures to prevent spread of fire and smoke 188
  Use of suitable electrical equipment in flammable atmospheres 189
7.4 - Fire detection, fire alarm and firefighting equipment 190
  Common fire detection and alarm systems 190
  Portable firefighting equipment 191
  Extinguishing media 192
  Access for fire and rescue services and vehicles 194
7.5 - Means of escape 194
  General requirements for means of escape 194
7.6 - Evacuation of a construction workplace 196
  Emergency evacuation procedures 196
Exam practice 198

Sources of reference

Reference information provided, in particular web links, is correct at time of publication, but may have changed.

Dangerous Substances and Explosive Atmospheres Regulations (DSEAR) 2002 - ACOP and guidance, L138 (second edition 2013), HSE Books, ISBN 978-0-7176-6616-4 http://www.hse.gov.uk/pubns/priced/l138.pdf

Fire safety in construction, HSG168 (second edition 2010), HSE Books, ISBN 978-0-7176-6345-3 http://www.hse.gov.uk/pubns/priced/hsg168.pdf

Fire Safety Risk Assessment series, Communities and Local Government Publications, https://www.gov.uk/workplace-fire-safety-your-responsibilities/fire-safety-advice-documents:

Fire Safety Risk Assessment - Offices and shops, ISBN-13 978-1-851128-15-0

Fire Safety Risk Assessment - Factories and warehouses, ISBN-13 978-1-851128-16-7

Fire Safety Risk Assessment - Sleeping accommodation, ISBN-13 978-1-851128-17-4

Fire Safety Risk Assessment - Residential care premises, ISBN-13 978-1-851128-18-1

Fire Safety Risk Assessment - Educational premises, ISBN-13 978-1-851128-19-8

Fire Safety Risk Assessment - Small and medium places of assembly, ISBN-13 978-1-851128-20-4

Fire Safety Risk Assessment - Large places of assembly, ISBN-13 978-1-851128-21-1

Fire Safety Risk Assessment - Theatres, cinemas and similar premises, ISBN-13 978-1-851128-22-8

Fire Safety Risk Assessment - Open air events and venues, ISBN-13 978-1-851128-23-5

Fire Safety Risk Assessment - Healthcare premises, ISBN-13 978-1-851128-24-2

Fire Safety Risk Assessment - Animal premises and stables, ISBN-13 978-1-851128-84-6

Fire Safety Risk Assessment - Transport premises and facilities, ISBN-13 978-1-851128-25-9

Safe use and handling of flammable liquids, HSG140 (first edition), HSE Books, ISBN 978-0-7176-0967-3 http://www.hse.gov.uk/pubns/priced/hsg140.pdf

The storage of flammable liquids in containers, HSG51 (second edition), HSE Books, ISBN 978-0-7176-1471-4 http://www.hse.gov.uk/pubns/priced/hsg51.pdf

Relevant statutory provisions

Construction (Design and Management) Regulations (CDM) 2015

Dangerous Substances and Explosives Atmospheres Regulations (DSEAR) 2002

Fire Safety (Employees' Capabilities) (England) Regulations (FSECE) 2010

Fire Safety (Employees' Capabilities) (Wales) Regulations (FSECW) 2012

Fire (Scotland) Act (FSA) 2005

Fire Safety (Scotland) Regulations (FSSR) 2006

Health and Safety (Safety Signs and Signals) Regulations (SSSR) 1996

Management of Health and Safety at Work Regulations (MHSWR) 1999

Regulatory Reform (Fire Safety) Order (RRFSO) 2005

7.1 - Fire initiation, classification and spread

Basic principles of fire

THE FIRE TRIANGLE

In order for combustion to take place the three essential elements of a fire have to be brought together - fuel, oxygen and source of ignition (heat) - this is called the fire triangle.

In order to prevent fires these elements, particularly the fuel and ignition sources, are kept apart. When they are brought together in the right proportions combustion takes place.

It should be noted that it is only the vapour from a fuel that burns. A solid or liquid must be heated to a temperature where the vapour given off can ignite before combustion takes place.

This principle is important when considering combustible dusts as this combustion process happens so quickly it becomes an explosion.

Figure 7-1: Fire triangle.   Source: RMS/Corel.

This explosion can be caused by a source of ignition, for example, a spark; a small dust explosion can often disturb more dust to fuel a bigger explosion. The other important aspect of this combustion principle is that if one or more of these elements of the fire is removed the fire will be extinguished. This can be carried out by:

Cooling	The fire to remove the heat - by applying water to the fire.
Starving	The fire of fuel - by moving material from the area of a fire or closing off an area of combustible material from the fire, for example, isolating a gas valve to extinguish a gas fire.
Smothering	The fire by limiting its oxygen supply - by closing a lid on a metal bin that contained a fire, covering a fire with a fire blanket or applying an extinguishing medium such as foam.

SOURCES OF IGNITION

Any source of heat is a possible ignition source.

Examples could be:

- Discarded smokers' materials (not such a big problem now that smoking is prohibited in the workplace).
- Naked flames.
- Fixed or portable heaters - particularly those that use liquid fuel.
- Hot processes for example, welding, cutting and grinding.
- Burning of vegetation or rubbish on site.
- Lighting.
- Cooking.
- Electrical equipment - overloading electrical circuits.
- Machinery - sparks, overheating of drive belts due to over tightening.
- Static electricity - most commonly from lightning strikes although sparks from static charges are very dangerous in flammable and explosive atmospheres.

Figure 7-2: Illicit smoking.   Source: FSTC Ltd.

Figure 7-3: Festoon lighting: an incorrect fixing creates a potential source of ignition. Source: HSE, HSG168.

SOURCES OF FUEL

Anything that burns is a fuel for a fire:

- Flammable liquids, for example, petrol storage areas.
- Flammable gases, for example, liquefied petroleum gas (LPG) heater cylinders.
- Flammable chemicals, for example, paints and solvents.
- Wood, for example, pallets, packing material and dust from carpentry processes.
- Plastics, rubber and foam, for example, liners and sealant.
- Paper and card, for example, packing and office stationery.
- Insulating materials, for example, polystyrene foam in walls and partition components.
- Waste materials, chemicals, waste packing, and general waste.

The structure of the building should also be considered. The building itself could be made from wood or other flammable material or may contain flammable materials as part of the decoration, for example, wallpaper, etc.

SOURCES OF OXYGEN

The main source of oxygen for a fire is in the air around us. In an enclosed building this is provided by the ventilation system in use. This generally falls into one of two categories; either natural airflow through doors, windows and other openings; or mechanical air conditioning systems and air handling systems. In many buildings there will be a combination of systems, which will be capable of introducing/extracting air to and from the building. Leaks from cylinders or piped oxygen supplies, combined with poor ventilation, can lead to an oxygen enriched atmosphere. Materials that ordinarily will burn only slowly will burn very vigorously in an oxygen-enriched atmosphere. Others such as greases and oils may burst into flames in this kind of atmosphere.

As well as the precautions outlined above for flammable gases, the following points should be remembered:

- Never use oxygen instead of compressed air.
- Never use oxygen to improve air quality in a working area or confined space.
- Never use grease or oil on equipment containing oxygen.

OXIDISING MATERIALS

Combustion involves the oxidation of a combustible (burnable) material. When a combustible material burns, a chemical reaction occurs in which the combustible material combines with oxygen and gives off heat, gases, and generally light. The usual source of oxygen for combustion is air. However, oxidising materials can supply combustible materials with a source of oxygen and support a fire even when air is not present. Although most oxidising materials do not burn themselves, they can produce very flammable or explosive mixtures when combined with combustible materials. The involvement of an oxidising material can speed up the development of a fire and make combustion more intense. Oxidising materials can cause materials that do not readily burn in air to burn rapidly in their presence.

In addition, they can cause combustible materials to burn at ambient temperature without the presence of an obvious source of ignition, such as a spark or flame. Although oxidising materials may not be widely present on construction sites, construction activities may take place in locations where oxidising materials are present.

What happens when an oxidising material comes into contact with a combustible material mainly depends on the chemical stability of the oxidising material, the less stable an oxidising material is, the greater the chance that it will react in a dangerous way. Oxidising materials come in the form of gases, liquids and solids.

Examples of gases include oxygen and ozone; liquids include nitric acid and chromic acid, and solids include chromate and potassium permanganate. The UN has established a non-legally binding international agreement called 'Globally Harmonized System of Classification and Labelling of Chemicals (GHS)'. It has been widely accepted globally and is being established in national legislation of the countries that are adopting it. Within GHS is a classification of materials principally based on the physical hazards they present, including oxidising materials. Materials that come under the class called oxidising gases fall under a single hazard category, whilst those classed as oxidising liquids and oxidising solids have 3 classifications.

Oxidising gases - Annex 1 of GHS			
	Category 1		
Pictogram			
Signal word	Danger		
Hazard statement	May cause or intensify fire; oxidiser		

Oxidising liquids and solids - Annex 1 of GHS			
	Category 1	Category 2	Category 3
Pictogram			
Signal word	Danger	Danger	Warning
Hazard statement	May cause fire or explosion; strong oxidiser	May intensify fire; oxidiser	May cause or intensify fire; oxidiser

Classification of fires

A basic understanding of the classes of fire needs to be achieved because many fire extinguishers state the classes of fire on which they may be used.

Class A	Fires involving solids - wood, paper or plastics (usually material of an organic nature).
Class B	Fires involving liquids or liquefiable solids - petrol, oil, paint, fat or wax.
Class C	Fires involving gases - liquefied petroleum gas, natural gas, acetylene, methane, etc.
Class D	Fires caused by burning metals that combust easily on contact with air, such as magnesium and lithium. Such specialised fires require a specialised metal powder fire extinguisher to deal with them, and will be required in scientific labs or where manufacturing processes involve the risk of metal fires. For example, aluminium dust or swarf (pieces of waste metal from machining process) can catch fire, so any process involving cutting, drilling or milling aluminium holds potential risk.
Electrical fires	Though this is not a class of fire electricity is often a source of ignition and the presence of electricity is a very serious consideration where water is used as the extinguishing medium.
Class F	Fires involving cooking oils and fats usually found in commercial kitchens such as restaurants and fast food outlets.

Figure 7-4: Classification of fires.   *Source: RMS.*

Principles of heat transmission

There are four methods by which heat may be transmitted:

1) Convection

The movement of hotter gases up through the air (hot air rises). Convection can quickly move hot gases to another part of a building where they raise the temperature of combustible materials to a point that combustion takes place, for example, hot gases rising up a staircase through an open door.

Control measure: protection of openings by fire doors and the creation of fire-resistant compartments in buildings.

2) Conduction

The movement of heat through a material (usually solid). Some materials, such as metal can absorb heat readily and transmit it to other rooms by conduction, where it can set fire to combustible items that are in contact with the heated material, for example, metal beam or pipe transmitting heat through a solid wall.

Control measure: insulation of the surface of a beam or pipe with heat resistant materials.

3) Radiation

Transfer of heat as invisible waves through the air (the air or gas is not heated, but solids and liquids in contact with the heat are). Radiation transfers heat in the air in the same way that an electric heater heats a room. Any material close to a fire will absorb the radiated heat until the material starts to smoulder and then burn. For example, a fire in a waste skip stored too near to a building may provide enough radiant heat to transfer the fire to the building.

Control measure: separation distances or fire-resistant barriers.

4) Direct burning

Combustible materials in direct contact with a naked flame, for example, curtains or carpet tiles may be consumed by combustion and enable fire to be transferred along them to other parts of a building.

Control measure: the use of fire retardant materials.

Reasons why fires spread

FAILURE OF EARLY DETECTION

Early detection of fire spread can be delayed by:

- No detection system or patrols.
- No automatic alarm system in place.
- People not knowing or confusing the sound of an alarm.
- People not raising the alarm on discovery of a fire.
- Fire starting in an unoccupied area, remaining undetected for some time.
- Fire starting out of normal work hours, when employees are not there.
- Building material waste may be being burnt as a normal routine and smoke and other signs of fire may not be seen as unusual and ignored.
- Numerous hot working tasks conducted - therefore, smells of burning ignored.
- Frequent occurrence of small, local fires caused by hot work, and not seen as significant.

ABSENCE OF COMPARTMENTS IN BUILDING STRUCTURE

Fire spread within a building can result from an absence of compartments:

- An open plan layout.
- False ceilings.
- The structure may be under construction or alteration incomplete and have reduced separation between levels and/or sections on a level.

COMPARTMENTS UNDERMINED

Fire spread within a building can result from compartments being undermined:

- Fire doors wedged open.
- Poor maintenance of door structure.
- Holes may be designed to pass through compartments and are waiting fitment of services and subsequent sealing.
- Holes cut for ducts or doorways or to provide temporary access to locate/remove equipment.
- Compartments may be progressively reduced in buildings under alteration, thus increasing the risk of fire spread.

Figure 7-5: Compartment undermined-holes cut.   *Source: RMS.*

MATERIALS INAPPROPRIATELY STORED

Inappropriate storage of materials can cause fire spread:

- Flammable liquids not controlled - too much or in unsuitable containers.
- Boxes in corridors/access routes or in stairways.
- Off cuts of wood and sawdust left in the areas where work has taken place.
- Packing materials used in the process, such as shredded paper, polystyrene, bubble wrap etc.
- Pallets and waste materials inappropriately stored or discarded, for example, near to buildings where they increase the risk of arson.

Figure 7-6: No fire door fitted. *Source: HSE, HSG168.*

Figure 7-7: Materials inappropriately stored.   *Source: RMS.*

Common causes and consequences of fire during construction activities

CAUSES

Causes of fire may be split into the following four main groups.

1) Careless actions and accidents

Careless actions and accidents as causes of fires involve people working or acting without sufficient thought for the risk of causing a fire. For example, hot work may be conducted inappropriately, such as welding, cutting and grinding in areas where combustible materials are located; a lighted cigarette end or match may be discarded without thought; bonfires may be left to burn unattended or left to smoulder or an electrician may make poor electrical connections that could produce heat.

2) Misusing equipment

Misusing equipment relates to overloading electrical circuits and/or using fuses of too high a rating, failure to follow servicing instructions, failure to repair faulty machinery/equipment promptly or use beyond its capacity causing overheating.

3) Defective machinery or equipment

Defective machinery or equipment as a cause relates to machinery and equipment that is used while in a defective condition that could cause a fire. Electrical insulation failure may occur when affected by heat, damp, chemicals or mechanical damage. This, and other electrical faults, could cause electrical short circuits that could be a source of ignition due to local overheating, sparks or arcs.

In addition, machinery moving parts may develop faults that cause them to get hot. For example, parts of a bearing may wear out causing increased friction in the area of the bearing, leading to the bearing and rotating parts getting very hot.

4) Deliberate ignition (arson)

Deliberate ignition is the crime of maliciously and intentionally, or recklessly, starting a fire or causing an explosion. Deliberate ignition may be carried out for a number of reasons, for example, insurance fraud, concealment of another crime, for political gain by activists, for malicious reasons by an aggrieved person or for reasons of vandalism.

Figure 7-8: Careless action - hot work. *Source: RMS.*

Figure 7-9: Misusing equipment - foil fuse, no earth. *Source: RMS.*

Figure 7-10: Defective electrical equipment. *Source: RMS.*

Figure 7-11: Potential for deliberate ignition. *Source: RMS.*

CONSEQUENCES

Consequences may be split into four main groups.

1) Human harm

Each year some 320 people die due to fires in the UK and around 10,000 non-fatal casualties are caused. Though most of these do not occur in the workplace, fire has the potential for major loss of life in the workplace due to direct contact with heat and flame or from the effects of smoke and toxic gases. The HSE reported that for the period 2013/14 that there was one work-related fatality reported, 36 major/specified injuries and 148 over 7 day absence injuries caused by fires across all industries. In the construction industry over this period there were no deaths caused by work-related fires, however, there were five major/specified injuries and 13 over 7 day absence injuries. Exposure to the radiant heat and flames of a fire can cause death or a range of other effects. The degree of exposure to heat or flames will influence their effect on the body. The heat of a fire and contact with flames can give rise to the risk of heat stroke or burns. Major exposure to heat and flames could quickly lead to shock, coma or death.

The most common cause of death from a fire is due to being overcome by gas or smoke. Both the hot gases and smoke involved in fires represent separate hazards to a person involved in a fire. The hot gases and smoke can present a direct effect on the lungs causing restriction in breathing and burns. In addition, toxic gases may be liberated as part of a fire, for example, carbon monoxide, which if breathed in sufficient quantities can lead to asphyxiation. Other toxic products of combustion can include hydrogen cyanide and chlorine.

2) Economic effects

The Department of Communities and Local Government reported that in 2013/14 there were 3,000 fires in retail distribution premises, 2,500 in industrial premises and 2,200 in restaurants, bars and similar premises. When fires do occur in the workplace the business is usually so badly affected it does not resume business again.

The occurrence of a fire during construction activities can have a disastrous effect on the organisation commissioning the construction work. Business plans and objectives may fail to be achieved and services not provided. The effects may be particularly pronounced in situations where the construction activity is taking place alongside the organisation's normal activities. These normal business activities may suffer greatly because of the fire. The Centre for Economics and Business Research suggests that the British economy has lost £1 billion in GDP and 1,000 jobs have been lost because of preventable fires in warehouses in the last five years. Furthermore, the consequential effects of each fire include an average of 21 local businesses impacted by road closures and air and water contamination.

3) Legal effects

There is a legal requirement under the Regulatory Reform (Fire Safety) Order (RRFSO) 2005 in England and Wales and the Fire (Scotland) Act (FSA) 2005/Fire Safety (Scotland) Regulations (FSSR) 2006 in Scotland to prevent fire, protect employees and other relevant persons from the effects of fire and to mitigate the effect of fire on anyone in the vicinity of premises on fire. Failure to comply with legislation could result in prosecutions and, if found guilty, fines.

4) Environmental harm

Large uncontrolled fires create pollutants, such as smoke, that enter the atmosphere. The fire itself may cause damage to storage areas with the subsequent leakage of chemicals onto land or into water courses and the run-off from fire hoses may ultimately enter the water system. *See figures 7-12 and 7-13* which show some of the damage caused by the Buncefield oil storage depot disaster in December 2005. The plume of smoke was so large it could be seen from space.

Figure 7-12: Buncefield - run-off from fire hoses. *Source: BBC News.*

Figure 7-13: Buncefield oil storage depot disaster. *Source: Royal Chiltern Air.*

7.2 - Fire risk assessment

Requirement and matters to be addressed in carrying out the assessment

The purpose of a fire risk assessment (FRA) is to identify where fire may start in the workplace, the people who would be put at risk, and to reduce the risk where possible.

Specific legal duties to conduct risk assessments are set out in the Regulatory Reform (Fire Safety) Order (RRFSO) 2005 and the Fire Safety (Scotland) Regulations (FSSR) 2006, which require the 'responsible person' (employer, person in control or owner) to make a suitable and sufficient assessment of:

- The risks to the health and safety of his employees to which they are exposed whilst they are at work.
- The risks to the health and safety of persons not in his employment (relevant persons) arising out of or in connection with the conduct by him of his undertaking.

Similarly, the self-employed must make a suitable and sufficient assessment of:

- The risks to their **own** health and safety to which they are exposed whilst at work.
- The risks to the health and safety of **persons not in his employment** (relevant persons), arising out of or in connection with the conduct by them of their undertaking.

This will require fire risk assessments to be conducted at the project planning stage of construction to determine what the risks are related to both the construction activities and the final constructed item. The choice of materials and building/structure design can have a major influence on the risk of fire during and after construction. All phases of construction must be considered in the risk assessment process. The scope of the assessment should include consideration of the effects of construction work on existing premises as well as temporary site accommodation, which may be used for office, welfare or sleeping purposes. It is important that risk assessments are maintained in the light of changes planned and those that take place. The process may require co-operation with clients whose premises may be affected by the construction activities,

Factors to be considered in carrying out the risk assessment

Depending upon the work to be carried out there will be different things to consider, for example, for new builds compared to the refurbishment of an existing building.

For a new build, consideration will need to be given to its location and proximity to other buildings, the type of construction materials and methods to be used. During construction and before final fire protection is in place the building will be more vulnerable to fire, for example, a timber framed structure is more vulnerable to fire before the external finishes are in place. Existing buildings should meet fire protection standards required by the Building Regulations (BR) 2011.

However, before a refurbishment project can be undertaken consideration will need to be given to the age and construction of the premises. For example, an older building is likely to have a relatively heavy fire load due to the materials used in its construction, including lath and plaster ceilings and walls, wooden panelling and floors.

There may also have been changes to the fabric of the building that could have significant consequences in a fire. The assessments must, at least, identify the measures needed to satisfy the 'General Fire Precautions' of the RRFSO 2005 or the FSSR 2006. The legislation requires fire and other emergency provisions to be in place; as such, risk assessments must be conducted to determine fire risks and the provisions necessary for the protection of people and the environment.

The measures would include:

- Reduction of the risk of fire.
- Prevention of fire spread.
- Adequate means of escape from fire.
- Maintenance measures to ensure means of escape available at all times.
- Means to fight fire.
- Means to detect and warn of fire.
- Fire actions/instructions and training.
- Actions to mitigate the effects of a fire.

Where the employer employs five or more employees they must record the significant findings of the assessment and any group of his employees identified by it as being especially at risk.

Assessments must be reviewed by the 'responsible person' if there is reason to suspect that it is no longer valid or there has been a significant change in the matters to which it relates.

Step 1 - Identify fire hazards

- **Identify sources of ignition** - smokers' materials, naked flames, heaters, hot processes, cooking, machinery, boilers, faulty or misused electrical equipment, lighting equipment, hot surfaces, blocked vents, friction, static electricity, metal impact and arson.
- **Identify sources of fuel** - flammable liquids, flammable chemicals, wood, paper and card, plastics, foam, flammable gases, furniture, textiles, packaging materials, waste materials including shavings, off cuts and dust.
- **Identify sources of oxygen** - natural ventilation, doors, windows, forced ventilation systems, air conditioning, oxidising materials, oxygen cylinders or piped oxygen systems.

Step 2 - Identify people at risk

- Consider people in the premises - staff, visitors, contractors, public, old, young, disabled, and their level of discipline and training. Contractors in sleeping accommodation on site would be a particular group to identify.
- Consider how fire, heat or smoke could spread to areas that people occupy, for example, by convection, conduction, radiation or direct burning.
- Identify where the people are that may be at risk, for example, people carrying out noisy tasks, placed high at the top of a building or crane, conducting work in confined spaces, nearby workers or the public.
- Identify people who are especially at risk, for example, new sub-contractors, visitors or people with language difficulties.
- Consider how people will be warned of fire and determine whether people could be trapped by fire.
- Consider members of the fire and rescue service that might be at risk when fighting the fire.

Step 3 - Evaluate, remove, or reduce and protect from risk

The way the site is managed will affect the precautions that will need to be put in place. With a new build the person in control may be the principal contractor, whereas for refurbishment work part of the site may remain occupied during the work. This may involve the need to work with managing agents or building owners. In multiple occupancy buildings, all those with some control must co-operate to reduce the risk to an acceptable level.

Risk reduction by prevention

- **Reduce sources of ignition** - remove unnecessary sources of heat or replace with safer alternatives, ensure electrical fuses are of the correct rating, ensure safe and correct use of electrical equipment, enforcing a 'hot work' permit system, safe smoking policy, arson reduction measures.
- **Minimise potential fuel for a fire** - remove or reduce amount of flammable materials, replace materials with safer alternatives, ensure safe handling, storage and use of materials, safe separation distances between flammable materials, use of fire-resisting storage, repair or replace damaged or unsuitable furniture, control and removal of flammable waste, care of external storage due to arson, good housekeeping.
- **Reduce sources of oxygen** - close all doors and windows not required for ventilation particularly out of working hours, shutting down non-essential ventilation systems, not storing oxidising materials near heat sources or flammable materials, controlling the use of oxygen cylinders and ensuring ventilation to areas where they are used. During new build and refurbishment activities close doors, windows and other openings not required for ventilation, particularly out of working hours.

Risk reduction by protection

Consider existing fire safety measures, risk reduction by protection (controls), in the workplace and consider possible improvements.

- Reducing unsatisfactory structural features.
  - Remove, cover or treat large areas of combustible wall and ceiling linings, improve fire resistance of workplace, install fire breaks into open voids.
- Fire detection and warning.
  - Can fire be detected quickly enough to allow people to escape?
  - Can means of warning be recognised and understood?
  - Do staff know how to operate the system?
  - Will workers know what to do if the alarm operates?
  - Are fire notices posted around workplace?
- Means of escape.
  - How long will it take for people to escape once they are aware of a fire?
  - Is this time reasonable?
  - Are there enough exits?
  - Are exits in the right places?
  - Is there suitable means of escape for all people, including disabled?
  - Could a fire happen that would affect all escape routes?
  - Are escape routes easily identifiable?
  - Are exit routes free from obstructions and blockages?
  - Are exit routes suitably lit at all times?
  - Have workers been trained in the use of the escape routes?
- Means of fighting fire.
  - Is the firefighting equipment suitable for the risk?

- Is it suitably located?
- Is it signed where necessary?
- Have people been trained to use equipment where necessary?
- Maintenance and testing.
  - Check all fire doors, escape routes, lighting and signs.
  - Check all firefighting equipment.
  - Check all fire detectors and alarms.
  - Check any other equipment provided to help means of escape arrangements.
  - Are there relevant instructions to staff regarding maintenance and testing?
  - Are those who carry out maintenance and testing competent?
- Fire procedures and training.
  - Is there an emergency plan?
  - Does the emergency plan take account of all reasonably foreseeable circumstances?
  - Are all workers familiar with the plan, trained in its use, and involved in testing it?
  - Is the emergency plan made available to staff?
  - Are fire procedures clearly indicated throughout the workplace?
  - Have all people likely to be present, been considered?

Step 4 - Record, plan, inform, instruct and train

Where the employer employs five or more employees they must record the significant findings (actions already taken, plus actions that will be taken) of the assessment and any group of employees identified by it as being especially at risk. A record must also be kept of measures that have been or will be taken by the responsible person.

Emergency plans

Following completion of the fire risk assessment, an emergency plan should be devised.

The plan should include the following:

- Action on discovery of fire.
- Action on hearing alarm.
- Details of the fire warning system.
- Details of the evacuation process.
- Means of escape - travel distances.
- Location of assembly points.
- Identification of escape routes - signs, emergency lighting.
- Details of firefighting equipment.
- Specific duties of workers.
- Safe evacuation of people who need assistance to escape.
- Safe working practices in high risk areas.
- Procedures for calling the fire and rescue service.
- Training needs and arrangements for providing training.

Step 5 - Review and monitor

The assessment and the fire safety measures must be reviewed regularly. In addition, a review should be carried out:

- At each significant stage of construction to determine what effect the previous stage may have on the fire risk assessment of the next phase.
- When failure of fire precautions occurs, for example, fire-detection and alarm systems.
- Changes to workplace are proposed, for example, increased storage of flammable materials or alterations to the building, including the internal layout.
- Changes to work process/activity are proposed, for example, introducing a new night shift.
- Changes to number or type of people present are proposed, for example, public are invited on site.
- A near miss or a fire occurs.

See also 'NGC1 - Element 4 - Health and safety management systems 3 - planning', for more information on risk assessment technique.

Additional risk assessment factors related to construction

TEMPORARY WORKPLACES AND CHANGES TO WORKPLACES

Many serious fires occur in existing buildings during maintenance and construction work. Due to the increased fire risks during these periods of time, additional fire precautions may be needed.

Dependent upon the nature of the work to be carried out and the size and use of the workplace, it may be necessary to carry out a new fire risk assessment to include all the new hazards that will be created during the construction work.

Fire risk assessments must be conducted for all workplaces, even for temporary workplaces. It may be possible to utilise a generic fire risk assessment approach if the construction activities are simple consistent and short term. However, it is important to ensure the generic risk assessment is appropriate to each temporary workplace as small changes in location of the workplace may make a significant difference. A temporary construction workplace in the grounds of a school may be significantly different to one in the grounds of communication equipment located in the countryside. Changes made to existing workplaces during construction must be considered as part of the risk assessment. The changes may affect others occupying the workplace as well as construction workers and increase the risk of fire.

Figure 7-14: Misleading fire exit signage, exit no longer available.
Source: HSE, HSG168.

In some cases the increased risk will be due to the increase of sources of ignition or additional materials. In other cases it will be due to the effect on the controls in place at the premises. Some work may require the isolation of smoke detectors or an alarm system. Normally well controlled escape routes may become cluttered by equipment, materials or workers.

Attention should be paid to:

- Accumulation of flammable waste and building materials.
- The obstruction or loss of exits and exit routes.
- Fire doors being propped open, wedged open or removed.
- Openings created in fire-resisting structures.
- Isolation of fire detection, or fixed firefighting systems.
- Introduction of additional electrical equipment, or other sources of ignition.
- Use of hot work process.
- Introduction of flammable products, for example, adhesives or flammable gases.
- The addition of new people to the premises that may be unfamiliar with fire arrangements, for example, alarm, routes, roll calls, assembly points.
- People working in unusual locations, for example, the roof, basement or duct areas.
- People working outside normal working hours.

NEED FOR CONTINUAL REVIEW AS WORK PROGRESSES

In all workplaces there is a need to actively review and revise the fire risk assessment. This may lead to changes to the fire safety measures that apply and the fire/emergency plans. This aspect of fire safety is absolutely vital in construction sites or any other workplace where layout changes are constantly taking place.

Dependent upon the state of the build, fire risks should be reviewed frequently, possibly weekly or daily depending on work progress. Checks and assessment should be made to ensure that the risk control measures for means of escape are still appropriate and that the following fire safety measures are not being compromised, leading to increased risk:

- Escape routes.
- Access to fire alarms.
- Audibility of fire alarm systems.
- Access and availability of firefighting equipment.
- Suitability of fire safety signage.
- Need for and suitability of escape lighting.
- New workers and the need for 'fire induction'.
- Fire protection/fire-resistant structures within the building.
- Introduction of new fire hazards, for example, hot works.
- Correct storage/use of flammable materials.
- Site security/arson prevention.

If, as a result of any construction work that needs to be carried out, fire safety standards may be reduced the effects should be identified, assessed and additional compensating factors introduced. For example, if detector heads need to be covered to prevent false alarms a fire watch system of patrols may be introduced to compensate. As can be seen, fire safety is a constantly changing factor that must be integral to the everyday management of site safety.

CONSIDERATION OF SHARED WORKPLACES

Under the Management of Health and Safety at Work Regulations (MHSWR) 1999, Regulation 11 - 'Co-operation and coordination', employers who work together in a common workplace have a duty to co-operate to discharge their duties under relevant statutory provisions. They must also take all reasonable steps to inform their respective employees of risks to their health or safety that may arise out of their work. Specific arrangements must be made to ensure compliance with fire legislation, including the assessment of risk.

Regulation 10 of MHSWR 1999 sets out that clear instruction must be provided concerning any preventative or protective control measures; this would include those relating to serious and imminent danger and fire assessments. Details of any competent persons nominated to discharge specific duties in accordance with the regulations must also be communicated as should risks arising from contact with other employers activities.

SITE SPECIFIC EMERGENCY PLANS

The site emergency plan is one of the control measures used to manage fire risk and should be evaluated at the time of conducting the fire risk assessment, to determine if it is suitable and sufficient to provide effective control of the risk. Just as risk assessments should be site specific, it is important that a site specific emergency plan that includes fire risks is drawn up. Generic emergency plans that are designed to suit all sites may remain insufficient in detail to be effective.

A copy of the emergency plans should be available at the point of entry to the site. The plan should be updated from time to time to reflect any changes made to the site during each stage of the build or demolition phase to reflect changes in access and storage. Site plans should contain the name and details of how to contact the responsible person in the event of an emergency. Consideration should be given to ensuring there is a responsible person available (24 hours, 7 days) until the construction work is completed and handed back to the client. The content of emergency plans will vary, but typically will contain information on what to do in the event of a fire, including raising the alarm, evacuation and assembly. It will usually also include the location and names of first-aiders, site entry restrictions, location of flammable materials etc., location of any streams or buried services.

7.3 - Fire prevention and prevention of fire spread

Control measures to minimise the risk of fire in a construction workplace

USE AND STORAGE OF FLAMMABLE AND COMBUSTIBLE MATERIALS

Where possible employers should seek to *eliminate* the use of flammable materials in the workplace, for example, replacing adhesives that have a flammable content with those that are water based. Where this is not possible the amount used should be *reduced* and kept to the minimum.

Quantities of material stored in the workplace must be in suitable containers and controlled to the minimum for immediate work needs. Flammable materials not in use should be removed to a purpose designed store in a well-ventilated area, preferably outside the building but in a secure area. Lids should be kept on containers at all times when they are not in immediate use.

Any waste containers, contaminated tools or materials should be treated in the same way and removed to a store in fresh air, until dealt with. Containers and contaminated materials need to be disposed of in a controlled manner so that they do not present a risk of fire.

Care has to be taken to control the delivery and therefore the storage of flammable and combustible materials to site. There is a temptation to have large quantities all delivered at the same time, but where possible deliveries should be staggered to reflect the rate of use in order to minimise the amount stored on site.

CONTROL OF IGNITION SOURCES

Hot work

Hot work has been responsible for causing many fires and includes welding, cutting, grinding, brazing and soldering processes. One of the most tragic fires due to hot work was Dusseldorf Airport Fire in 1996. The fire was started by welding on an open roadway and resulted in damage in excess of £200 million, several hundred injuries and 17 deaths.

It is imperative that good safe working practices are utilised. Combustible materials must be removed from the area or covered over. Consideration must be given to the effects of heat on the surrounding structure, and where sparks, flames, hot residue or heat will travel to.

It is often necessary to have a fire watcher to spot any fires that may be started. Fire extinguishers need to be immediately available and operatives must know how to use them. The work area must be checked thoroughly for some time after the completion of work to ensure there are no smouldering fires. Strong consideration should be given to the use of hot work permits.

Welding

Welding activities represent a significant ignition source from the 'naked flame' of an oxy-acetylene torch or electric arc and from the hot materials created by the process, for example, recently welded material that remains hot for some time or from sparks created in the process.

In addition, the equipment can represent an explosion risk if it is used incorrectly or not fitted with proper protective devices.

The following would be good practices for welding and would reduce sources of ignition from the process:

- Only use competent trained workers. Regulators should be of a recognised standard. Colour code hoses:
  - Blue - oxygen.
  - Red - acetylene.
  - Orange - propane.
- Fit non-return valves at blowpipe/torch inlet on both gas lines.
- Fit flashback arrestors incorporating cut-off valves and flame arrestors fitted to outlet of both gas regulators.
- Use crimped hose connections not jubilee clips.
- Do not let oil or grease contaminate oxygen supply due to explosion hazard.
- Check equipment visually before use, and check new connections with soapy water for leaks.
- Secure cylinders in upright position.
- Keep hose lengths to a minimum.
- Follow a permit-to-work system.
- Do not store standby gases that are not connected to welding apparatus in the workplace.

Figure 7-15: Welding equipment.   *Source: RMS.*

Smoking

It is now against the law to smoke inside any public buildings (includes the workplace). Prohibition of smoking may lead to illicit smoking and extra vigilance may be needed. Where smoking is allowed, provide easily accessible, non-combustible receptacles for cigarette ends and other smoking material and empty daily. Smoking should cease half an hour before close down.

Arson

Arson is the single greatest cause of fire (the arson detection rate is only 8 percent, compared to 24 percent for other offences) and as such simple, but effective, ways to deter the arsonist involve giving attention to security, both external and internal, which should encompass the following:

External security

- Control of people having access to the building/site.
- Use of patrol guards.
- Lighting the premises at night - linked to closed circuit television (CCTV).
- Safety of keys.
- Structural protection.
- Siting of rubbish bins/skips at least 8m from buildings.

Internal security

- Good housekeeping and clear access routes.
- Inspections and audits.
- Visitor supervision.
- Control of sub-contractors.
- Control door access by keypad or electronic locks.

Figure 7-16: Control arson by external security.   *Source: RMS.*

Figure 7-17: Control arson by housekeeping.   *Source: RMS.*

SYSTEMS OF WORK

Systems of work combine people, equipment, materials and the environment to produce the safest possible climate in which to work. In order to produce a safe system of work, it is essential to make an assessment of the area to determine where the hazards and risks arise and how best to control them.

The requirement to carry out a fire risk assessment should address the following:

■ Identify potential fire hazards.
■ Decide who may be in danger, and note their locations.
■ Evaluate the risks and carry out any necessary improvement measures.
■ Record findings and action taken.
■ Keep assessment under review.

In addition to the fire risk assessment carried out, other measures may include implementing the following strategies.

1) A safe place

A safe place begins with ensuring that the fabric of the building is designed or planned in a way that will prevent ignition, suppress fire spread and allow for safe, speedy unobstructed evacuation with signs to direct people.

Factors to consider will include compartmentalisation, fire-resistant materials, proper and suitable means of storage, means of detection, means of raising the alarm good housekeeping and regular monitoring and review.

2) Safe person

A safe person begins with raising awareness to individuals of any risk of loss resulting from outbreak of fire. Information can be provided that will identify where to raise the alarm, what the alarm sounds like, how to evacuate and where to muster, responsibility for signing in and out of the site register, fire drill procedures, trained authorised fire appointed persons, use and storage of flammable materials, good housekeeping and use of equipment producing heat or ignition (including hot processes, for example, welding).

3) Safe materials

Safe materials begin with providing information and ensuring safe segregation and storage for materials and sources of ignition/heat. In addition, providing information on the correct way to handle materials and substances, including a substances register that will detail methods of tackling a fire involving hazardous substances, is necessary.

4) Safe equipment

Safe equipment begins with user information and maintenance to ensure good working and efficient order. Information should also provide the user with a safe method for use and the limitations of and risks from the equipment. Supervision may be necessary to ensure correct use and prevent misuse that may lead to short circuiting or overheating that could result in fire. Where work involves hot processes by nature (welding, grinding, casting, etc.) then permit-to-work procedures may be necessary in order to tightly control the operations.

Other equipment required in relation to fire hazards and control may include smoke or heat detection equipment, alarm sounders/bells, alarm call-points and appropriate fire extinguishing apparatus. It should be noted that in the event of a fire alarm, all the passenger lifts should not be used. Under normal circumstances the lift will return to the ground floor and remain in that position with the doors locked in the open position. All equipment should be regularly tested to ensure its conformity and be accompanied with a suitable certificate of validity.

Safe systems must also include consideration of who is at risk, including those persons with special needs such as the young, elderly, infirm or disabled. There may be a requirement to prevent smoking in the workplace or employ appointed persons to take control of the situation and coordinate emergency responses in the event of an alarm. If the building relies solely on internal artificial lighting, then the requirement to install emergency back-up lighting will be needed. All systems must be regularly monitored in order to reflect changes to the environment and put remedies in place to ensure full preparedness in the event of a fire.

PERMIT-TO-WORK PROCEDURES

A permit-to-work is an official, documented safe system of work that is used for controlling high risk activities. Implementation is required prior to work beginning to ensure that all precautions are taken and securely in place to prevent danger to the workforce.

When managed correctly, a permit-to-work prevents any mistakes or deviations through poor verbal communication by stating the specific requirements of the project. For fire control, a permit-to-work is typically used where there is a requirement to use flammable materials or when hot work or processes are being carried out.

The authorised person shall issue the permit-to-work and will sign the document to declare that all isolations are made and remain in place throughout the duration of the project. In addition to this, the authorised person will make checks to ensure that all controls to be implemented by the acceptor are in place before work begins

The acceptor of the permit-to-work shall assume responsibility for carrying out the works. The acceptor shall sign the document to declare that the terms and conditions of the permit-to-work are understood and will be complied with fully at all times by the entire work team.

Compliance with a permit-to-work system includes ensuring the required safeguards are implemented and that the work will be restricted to the equipment only stated within the document.

Items included in a permit-to-work are:

- Permit issue number.
- Authorised person identification.
- Locations of firefighting equipment.
- Locations of flammable materials.
- Warning information sign locations.
- Emergency muster points.
- Details of the work to be carried out.

- Signature of authoriser.
- Signature of acceptor.
- Signature for works clearance/extension/handover.
- Signature for cancellation.
- Other precautions (risk assessments, method statements, PPE).

HOT WORK PERMITS

Hot work permits are formal management documents that control and implement a safe system of work whenever methods of work that utilise heat or flame are used. If the risk of fire is low, it may not be necessary to implement a hot work permit; however they should always be considered.

The hot work permit should be issued by an authorised person who ensures that the requirements stated in them are complied with before the permit is issued, and during duration of the work. Hot work permits should be issued for a specific time, for a specific place, for a specific task, and are issued to a designated competent person.

Figure 7-18: Hot work.　　　Source: Speedy Hire Plc.

STORAGE, TRANSPORT AND USE OF LIQUEFIED PETROLEUM AND OTHER GASES IN CYLINDERS

Liquefied petroleum gas (LPG) is a term that relates to gas stored in a liquefied state under pressure; common examples are propane and butane. LPG and other gas cylinders should be stored in line with the principles detailed below:

Storage

- Storage area should preferably be in clear open area outside.
- Stored in a secure compound - 2m high fence.
- Safe distance from toxic, corrosive, combustible materials, flammable liquids or general waste.
- Stored safe distance from any building.
- If stored inside building, kept away from exit routes, consideration should be given to fire-resisting storage.
- Well ventilated area - 2.5% of total floor and wall area as vents, high and low.
- Oxygen cylinders at least 3m away from flammable gas cylinders.
- Acetylene may be stored with LPG if quantity of LPG less than 50kg.

Figure 7-19: Secure LPG storage.　　　Source: HSE, HSG168.

- Access to stores should be controlled to prevent LPG etc. being stored unsafely in the general workplace.
- More than one exit (unlocked) may need to be available from any secure storage compound where distance to exit is greater than 12m.
- Lock storage compound when not in use.
- Protection from sunlight.
- Flameproof lighting.
- Empty containers stored separate from full.
- Fire extinguishers located nearby - consider powder and water types.

Transport

- Upright position.
- Secured to prevent falling over.
- Protection in event of accident, for example, position on vehicle.
- Transport in open vehicle preferably.
- Avoid overnight parking while loaded.
- Park in secure areas.
- 'Trem card' and warning signs.
- Driver training.
- Firefighting equipment.

Use

General use

■ Cylinder connected for use may be stored in the general workplace; any spare cylinders must be secured in a purpose built store until required for use.
■ Fixed position to prevent falling over, or on wheeled trolley - chained.
■ Well ventilated area.
■ Away from combustibles.
■ Kept upright unless used on equipment specifically designed for horizontal use, for example, gas powered lift truck.
■ Handled carefully - do not drop.
■ Allow to settle after transport and before use.
■ Consider manual handling and injury prevention.
■ Turn off cylinder before connecting, disconnecting equipment.
■ Check equipment before use.
■ Any smell of gas during use, turn off cylinder and investigate.
■ Use correct gas regulator for equipment/task.
■ Use equipment in line with manufacturers' instructions.

Use in huts

■ Only allow cylinders in a hut if it is part of a heater (cabinet heater).
■ Pipe into site huts from cylinder located outside where possible.
■ If cylinder is outside the hut use the shortest connecting hose as possible.
■ Hut to be adequately ventilated high and low.
■ Heaters fitted with flame failure devices.
■ Turn off heater and cylinder after use and overnight.
■ Be aware of danger of leaks inside huts, especially overnight as a severe risk of fire or explosion may occur.
■ Keep heaters away from clothing and other combustibles.

Figure 7-20: Gas cylinders for huts, located outside.   *Source: RMS.*

GOOD HOUSEKEEPING

Housekeeping means the general tidiness and order of the building. At first sight, this may seem a strange matter to discuss when considering fire safety, but as housekeeping affects so many different aspects of this subject, it cannot be ignored.

Housekeeping and its effect on fire safety

Fires need fuel. A build-up of redundant combustible materials, rubbish and stacks of waste materials provide that fuel.

All combustible materials cannot be eliminated, but they can be controlled.

Any unnecessary build-up of rubbish and waste should be avoided.

If a fire starts in a neatly stacked pile of timber pallets, around which there is a clear space, the fire may be spotted and extinguished before it can spread.

However, if the same pile were strewn around in an untidy heap, along with adjacent rubbish, the likelihood is that fire would spread over a larger area and involve other combustible materials.

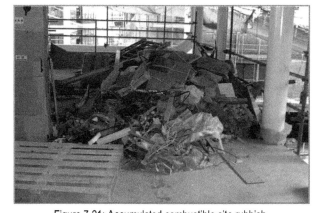

Figure 7-21: Accumulated combustible site rubbish.
Source: HSE, HSG168.

Poor housekeeping can also lead to:

■ Blocked fire exits.
■ Obstructed escape routes.
■ Difficult access to fire alarm call-points/extinguishers/hose reels.
■ Obstruction of vital signs and notices.
■ A reduction in the effectiveness of automatic fire detectors and sprinklers.

Checklists

Fire prevention is a matter of good routine and the following checklists are provided as a guide to what should be checked:

List A - Routine checks

Daily at the start of business - including:

- Doors which may be used for escape purposes - unlocked and escape routes unobstructed.
- Free access to hydrants, extinguishers and fire alarm call-points.
- No deposits on electric motors.

List B - Routine checks

Daily at close-down - including:

- Inspection of whole area of responsibility - to detect any incipient smouldering fires.
- Fire doors and shutters closed.
- All plant and equipment safely shutdown.
- Waste bins emptied.
- No accumulation of combustible process waste, packaging materials or dust deposits.
- Safe disposal of waste.
- Premises left secure from unauthorised access.

List C - Periodic inspection

During working hours - weekly/monthly/quarterly as decided:

- Goods neatly stored so as not to impede firefighting.
- Clear spaces around stacks of stored materials.
- Gangways kept unobstructed.
- No non-essential storage in production areas.
- Materials clear of light fittings.
- Company smoking rules known and enforced.

Storage of small quantities of highly flammable/flammable liquids

TERMS USED WITH FLAMMABLE LIQUIDS

Flash point

'Flash point' is defined as the lowest temperature at which, in a specific test apparatus, sufficient vapour is produced from a liquid sample for momentary or flash ignition to occur on the application of an ignition source.

The flash point of a substance is the critical characteristic when deciding flammability. It must not be confused with ignition temperature, which can be considerably lower.

Flammable

Flammability (or inflammability) is the ease with which the vapours of a substance will ignite, causing fire or combustion. Substances with vapours that will ignite at temperatures commonly encountered are considered flammable.

The term flammable has various national definitions that give a temperature requirement relating to flammability.

The United Nations (UN) Globally Harmonised System of Classification and Labelling of Chemicals (GHS) has established an international definition of the term.

This has also been reflected in the UN Recommendations on the Transport of Dangerous Goods (UNRTDG) as it relates to packaging for transport.

The GHS has established a definition that 'a flammable liquid is a liquid having a flash point of not more than 93°C'. It further defines that a flammable liquid is classified in one of four categories.

Category	Flash point	Initial boiling point	Symbol	Signal word	Hazard statement
1	<23°C	≤35°C	Flame	Danger	Extremely flammable
2	<23°C	>35°C	Flame	Danger	Highly flammable
3	≥23°C ≤60°C	-	Flame	Warning	Flammable
4	≥60°C ≤93°C	-	No symbol	Warning	Combustible liquid

Figure 7-22: Flammable liquids classification.   *Source: UN, Globally Harmonised System of Classification and Labelling of Chemicals.*

These definitions and classifications have been adopted globally and are supported by the internationally agreed labelling under the UN Globally Harmonised System of Classification and Labelling of Chemicals (GHS).

Label elements for flammable liquids			
Classification	Category 1	Category 2	Category 3
GHS Pictograms			
Signal word	Danger	Danger	Warning
Hazard statement	H224: Extremely flammable liquid and vapour	H225: Highly flammable liquid and vapour	H226: Flammable liquid and vapour

Figure 7-23: Flammable liquids classification and labelling.   *Source: EU, Classification, Labelling and Packing (CLP) Regulations.*

The definitions, categorisation and labelling are being introduced by many countries progressively and have often required transitional arrangements to move to the new criteria. In time, the wider use of the GHS will make uniform the classification and other criteria for all workplace activities involving chemicals.

The flash points of some common solvents are:

- Ethanol   +12°C.
- Toluene   +4°C.
- Methyl ethyl ketone   - 9°C.
- Acetone   -19°C.

STORAGE OF SMALL QUANTITIES

The objective in controlling the risk from these materials is to remove all unnecessary quantities from the workplace to a recognised storage area outside the building. This may be carried out as part of a close down routine at the end of the day. It is accepted that quantities of this material may need to be available in a workplace during normal working. This should not exceed 50 litres in any work area unless a full scale purpose constructed store is used.

In other cases local small scale storage of up to **50 litres of highly flammable** or up to **250 litres of flammable** liquids may be kept within the workplace provided it is controlled and placed in a suitable store container. Highly flammable or flammable liquids removed from storage must be in suitable containers to prevent spills and loss of vapours.

Figure 7-24: Poor storage of flammable liquids.   *Source: RMS.*   Figure 7-25: Storage of flammable materials.   *Source: RMS.*

Storage in the workplace

General points to prevent fires involving flammable liquids stored in the workplace include:

- In a suitable sealed container.
- In a suitable cabinet, bin or other store container.
- In a designated area of the workplace.
- Away from ignition sources, working or process areas.
- Capable of containing any spillage.
- In a 30 minute fire-resistant structure.
- Provided with hazard warning signs to illustrate the flammability of the contents.
- Prohibition signs for smoking and naked flame.
- Not contain other substances or items.

Storage in the open air

General points to prevent fires involving flammable liquids stored in the open air include:

- Formal storage area on a concrete pad, with a sump for spills.
- Bunded all around to take content of largest drum plus an allowance of 10%.
- Away from other buildings.
- Secure fence and gate 2m high.
- Marked by signs warning of flammability.
- Signs prohibiting smoking or other naked flames.
- Protection from sunlight.
- If lighting is provided within store it must be flameproof.
- Provision for spill containment materials.
- Fire extinguishers located nearby - consider powder type.
- Full and empty containers separated.
- Clear identification of contents.

Figure 7-26: Outdoor storage of flammable liquids.   *Source: HSE, HSG51.*

Structural measures to prevent spread of fire and smoke

PROPERTIES OF COMMON BUILDING MATERIALS

Brickwork/blockwork

Both brickwork and blockwork perform well in fires. Dependent upon the materials, workmanship, thickness, and the load carried, fire resistance of 30 minutes to two hours may be achieved.

Steelwork

Steel and other metals are extensively used in modern building structures. Generally they can be affected by fire at relatively low temperatures unless they are protected from the effects of the fire by some form of fire retardant materials. This may be carried out by encasing in concrete, fire retardant boards or spray coatings.

Timber

Timber performs very well in fires as long as it is of sufficient size that, as its outer coat burns away, there is still sufficient strength to do its task. Generally timber does not fail rapidly in a fire, unlike steel.

Glass

Glass generally performs poorly in a fire unless it is fire-resistant glass. At high temperatures glass will melt and sag, which is why the traditional fire-resistant glass has wire within it.

STRUCTURAL MEASURES TO PREVENT SPREAD

Measures to prevent spread of fire and smoke include:

- Fire-resisting structures.
- Compartmentalisation to confine the fire to a predetermined size.
- Fire stopping of ducts, flues and holes in fire-resistant structures.
- Fire-resisting doors.
- Smoke seals and intumescent (a material which expands and insulates the surface, when heat is applied) materials on doors.
- Early and rapid detection of a fire by use of 'intelligent' fire alarm systems.
- Sprinklers in large compartments, in particular 'rapid response' systems to limit the size of the fire.
- Control of smoke and toxic fumes by ventilation systems, so that clear air is maintained at head height level, to enable persons to escape.

Figure 7-27: Magnetic door holder linked to alarm.   *Source: RMS.*

Figure 7-28: Door stop with automatic release.   *Source: RMS.*

PROTECTION OF OPENINGS AND VOIDS

Consideration should be given to the protection of openings and voids by the use of fire barriers such as fire shutters, cavity barriers and fire curtains. It is important that when construction or maintenance work takes place it is managed to minimise the effect on the structure being worked on to keep fire precautions intact as much as possible. This will involve planning for the prompt re-instatement of protection of openings and voids as soon after their breach to do work as is possible. The temptation to leave all breaches to the end of work and then re-instate them should be avoided - the longer that breaches are left open the higher the risk from fires.

Use of suitable electrical equipment in flammable atmospheres

The Dangerous Substances and Explosive Atmospheres Regulations (DSEAR) 2002 apply to most workplaces where a potentially explosive atmosphere may occur. DSEAR 2002 requires employers to eliminate or control the risks from potentially explosive atmospheres.

CLASSIFICATION OF AREAS WHERE EXPLOSIVE ATMOSPHERES MAY OCCUR

Employers must classify areas where hazardous explosive atmospheres may occur into zones. The classification given to a particular zone, and its size and location, depends on the likelihood of an explosive atmosphere occurring and its persistence if it does occur. Schedule 2 of DSEAR 2002 contains descriptions of the various classifications of zones for gases and vapours and for dusts.

There are three zones for gases and vapours:

Zone 0	Flammable atmosphere highly likely to be present - may be present for long periods or even continuously.
Zone 1	Flammable atmosphere possible but unlikely to be present for long periods.
Zone 2	Flammable atmosphere unlikely to be present except for short periods of time - typically as a result of a process fault condition.

Similarly, there are three zones for dusts:

Zone 20	Dust cloud likely to be present continuously or for long periods.
Zone 21	Dust cloud likely to be present occasionally in normal operation.
Zone 22	Dust cloud unlikely to occur in normal operation, but if it does, will only exist for a short period.

SELECTION OF EQUIPMENT AND PROTECTIVE SYSTEMS

Areas classified into zones must be protected from sources of ignition. Electrical equipment for use in hazardous explosive atmospheres needs to be designed and constructed in such a way that it will not provide a source of ignition. Equipment intended to be used in zoned areas should be selected to meet the requirements of the Equipment and Protective Systems Intended for Use in Potentially Explosive Atmospheres Regulations (EPS) 1996. Zone zero and zone 20 are the zones with the highest likelihood of an explosive atmosphere occurring and persisting; electrical equipment for this zone needs to be very well protected against providing a source of ignition.

There are a number of ways in which electrical equipment can be designed to prevent ignition of explosive atmospheres, each achieves this in different ways. The types of protection include intrinsically safe (cannot produce a spark with sufficient energy to cause ignition), flameproof (ingress of explosive atmosphere is controlled and any ignition is contained in the equipment) and type 'E' equipment (do not produce sparks or hot surfaces).

7.4 - Fire detection, fire alarm and firefighting equipment

Common fire detection and alarm systems

FIRE DETECTION

Heat detection

Sensors operate by the melting of a metal (fusion detectors) or expansion of a solid, liquid or gas (thermal expansion detectors).

Radiation detection

Photoelectric cells detect the emission of infra-red/ultra-violet radiation from the fire.

Smoke detection

Using ionising radiations, light scatter (smoke scatters beams of light), obscuration (smoke entering a detector prevents light from reaching a photoelectric cell).

Figure 7-29: Smoke detector.   *Source: RMS.*

Flammable gas detection

Measures the amount of flammable gas in the atmosphere and compares the value with a reference value.

ALARM SYSTEMS

The purpose of a fire alarm is to give an early warning of a fire in a building for two reasons:

1)   To increase the fire safety of occupants by encouraging them to escape to a place of safety.
2)   To increase the possibility of early extinction of the fire thus reducing the loss of or damage to the property.

There are a number of methods of operation for fire alarm systems including:

Voice	Simplest and most effective type, but effectiveness very limited because it is dependent upon the size of the workplace and background noise levels.
Hand operated	Rotary gong, hand bell or triangle and sounder, but effectiveness limited by the scale of the building.
Call-points with sounders	Standard system, operation of one call-point sounds alarm throughout workplace.
Automatic system	System as above, with added fire detection to initiate the alarm.

Single-stage alarm

The alarm sounds throughout the whole of the building and calls for total evacuation.

Two-stage alarm

In certain large/high rise buildings it may be better to evacuate the areas of high risk first, usually those closest to the fire or immediately above it. In this case, an evacuation signal is given in the affected area, together with an alert signal in other areas. If this type of system is required, early consultation with the fire and rescue service is essential.

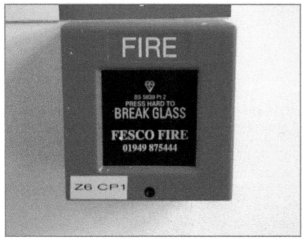

Figure 7-30: Easy operation alarm call-point.   *Source: RMS.*

Figure 7-31: Alarm point identified and well located.   *Source: RMS.*

Staff alarms

In some premises, an immediate total evacuation may not be desirable, for example, nightclubs, shops, theatres, cinemas. A controlled evacuation by the staff may be preferred, to prevent distress and panic to the occupants. If such a system is used, the alarm must be restricted to the staff and only used where there are sufficient members of staff and they have been fully trained in the action of what to do in case of fire.

Alarms must make a distinctive sound, audible in all parts of the workplace (sound levels should be 65dB (A) or 5dB (A) above any other noise - whichever is the greater). The meaning of the alarm sound must be understood by all. They may be manually or automatically operated.

Portable firefighting equipment

SITING

Portable fire extinguishers should always be sited:

- On the line of escape routes.
- Near, but not too near, to danger points.
- Near to room exits inside or outside according to occupancy and/or risk.
- In multi-storey buildings, at the same position on each floor, for example, top of stair flights or at corners in corridors.
- Where possible in groups forming fire points.
- So that no person needs to travel an excessive distance to reach an extinguisher. Travelling more than 30 metres (by direct measurement) or 45 metres (actual) taking into account fixtures, stock and other obstructions to reach an extinguisher may be considered to be excessive. In high fire hazard areas 45 metres may be considered excessive and fire extinguishers may need to be located nearer to workers.
- Placed on a purpose designed floor stand or hung on a wall at a convenient height. If hung on a wall, this would usually be with the carrying handle about one metre from the floor to facilitate ease of handling/removal from the wall bracket.
- Away from excesses of heat, cold dirt or dust.

MAINTENANCE AND INSPECTION

Any firefighting equipment provided must be properly maintained and subject to examination and test at intervals such that it remains effective.

Maintenance

This means service of the fire extinguisher by a competent person. It involves thorough examination of the extinguisher (internal/external) and this is usually carried out annually.

Inspection

A monthly check should be carried out to ensure that extinguishers are in their proper place and have not been discharged, lost pressure or suffered obvious damage. It may be necessary to increase the frequency of checks made for fire extinguishers on a construction site to a weekly basis, due to the less structured or controlled work environment that they are sited in. This could mean that there is a higher risk of them being damaged or used without notification.

FIREFIGHTING EQUIPMENT TRAINING REQUIREMENTS

The 'responsible person' must take measures for firefighting as necessary. They should nominate competent persons to implement these measures and provide training and equipment accordingly. It would be good practice to make sure that those that may need to take a lead in operating fire extinguishers can do this competently and for most people this would mean practising how to use them in a situation that reproduces the circumstances of a fire.

Training should include:

- Understanding of the principles of combustion and classification of fires.
- Identification of the various types of fire extinguisher available to them.
- Principles of use and limitations of extinguishers.
- Considerations for personal safety and the safety of others.
- How to identify if the extinguisher is appropriate to the fire and ready to use.
- How to attack fires with the appropriate extinguisher(s).
- Any specific considerations related to the environment the extinguishers are kept or used in.

Training has to clarify the general and specific rules for use of extinguishers:

General - aim at the seat of the fire and move the extinguisher across the fire to extinguish it - this is particularly appropriate for Class A fires.

Specific - if using a foam extinguisher for Class B fires the foam is allowed to drop onto the fire by aiming just above it. If this is for a flammable liquid fire contained in an open tank it is possible to get good results by this process or aiming it to the back of the tank and allowing the foam to float over the liquid. For other specific limitations or approaches to the use of individual types of extinguishing media, see the next section.

Extinguishing media

WATER (PORTABLE EXTINGUISHER - COLOUR CODE - RED)

Water should only be used on Class A fires - those involving solids like paper and wood. Water works by cooling the burning material to below its ignition temperature, therefore removing the heat part of the fire triangle, and so the fire goes out. Water is the most common form of extinguishing media and can be used on the majority of fires involving solid materials. It must not be used on liquid fires or in the vicinity of live electrical equipment.

Figure 7-32: Fire point sign.
Source: BCW Office Products.

Figure 7-33: Water extinguisher colour coded red by label and sign.
Source: RMS.

Figure 7-34: Fire point sign.
Source: Warning Signs Direct.

Figure 7-35: Cream colour coded extinguisher.
Source: Low Cost Fire.

FOAM (PORTABLE EXTINGUISHER - COLOUR CODE - CREAM)

Foam is especially useful for extinguishing Class B fires - those involving burning liquids and solids which melt and turn to liquids as they burn. Foam works in several ways to extinguish the fire, the main way being to smother the burning liquid, i.e. to stop the oxygen reaching the combustion zone. Foam can also be used to prevent flammable vapours escaping from spilled volatile liquids and also on Class A fires. It is worth noting that the modern spray foams are more efficient than water on a Class A fire. *It must not be used in the vicinity of live electrical equipment, unless electrically rated.*

DRY POWDER (PORTABLE EXTINGUISHER - COLOUR CODE - BLUE)

Designed for Class A, B and C fires but may only subdue Class A fires for a short while. One of the main ways in which powder works to extinguish a fire is the smothering effect, whereby it forms a thin film of powder on the burning liquid, thus excluding air. The extinguishing media is also excellent for the rapid knock down (flame suppression) of flammable liquid spills. Powders generally provide extinction faster than foam, but there is a greater risk of re-ignition. If used indoors, a powder can cause problems for the operator due to the inhalation of the powder and obscuration of vision. This type of extinguishing media may be used on live electrical equipment.

Figure 7-36: Fire point sign.
Source: Warning Signs Direct.

Figure 7-37: Blue colour coded extinguisher. *Source: The Sharpedge.*

Figure 7-38: Fire point sign.
Source: BCW Office Products.

Figure 7-39: Black colour coded extinguisher. *Source: Blazetec Fire Protection.*

CARBON DIOXIDE (CO₂) (PORTABLE EXTINGUISHER - COLOUR CODE - BLACK)

Carbon dioxide (CO_2) is safe and excellent for use on live electrical equipment. It may also be used for small Class B fires in their early stages of development, indoors or outdoors with little air movement. CO_2 replaces the oxygen in the atmosphere surrounding the fuel and the fire is extinguished. CO_2 is an asphyxiant and should not be used in confined spaces. As it does not remove the heat there is the possibility of re-ignition. CO_2 extinguishers are very noisy due to the rapid expansion of gas on release; this can surprise people when they operate a portable extinguisher. This expansion causes severe cooling around the discharge horn and can freeze the skin if the operator's hand is in contact with the horn. As most carbon dioxide portable extinguishers last only a few seconds, only small fires should be tackled with this type of extinguisher.

EXTINGUISHING MEDIA FOR SPECIFIC CLASSES OF FIRE

Class C fires

Except in very small occurrences, a Class C fire involving gas should not normally be extinguished. If a gas fire is to be extinguished, then isolation of the gas supply must also take place.

Class D fires

Class D metal fires are a specialist type of fire and they cannot be extinguished by the use of ordinary extinguishing media. In fact, it may be dangerous to attempt to fight a metal fire with ordinary extinguishing media as an explosion of the metal may take place or toxic fumes may be produced. Metal fires can be extinguished by smothering them with dry sand. However, the sand must be absolutely dry or an explosion may occur. Other extinguishing media used are pyromet, graphite, talc or salt. All of these extinguishing media basically operate by the smothering principle.

Figure 7-40: Fire point sign. *Source: Midland Fire Ltd.*

Figure 7-41: Yellow colour coded extinguisher. *Source: Midland Fire Ltd.*

Class F fires (Wet chemical) (Portable extinguisher - Colour code - Yellow)

New style wet chemical extinguishing media have been designed to specifically deal with Class F cooking oil fires. This type of extinguishing media congeals on top of the oil and excludes the oxygen. It may also be used on Class A fires depending upon the manufacturer's instructions.

SUMMARY MATRIX - FIRE EXTINGUISHING MEDIA

	Method	*Class 'A'*	*Class 'B'*	*Class 'C'*	*Class 'D'*	*Electric*	*Class 'F'*
Water	Cools	Yes	No	No	No	No	No
Spray foam	Smothers	Yes	Yes	No	No	No	No
Wet chemical	Chemical	Some Manufacturers	No	No	No	No	Yes
Dry powder	Smothers and Chemical	Limited	Yes	Yes and Isolate	Special Powders	Yes - Low Voltage	No
Vapourising liquids	Chemical and Smothers	Special Uses					
Carbon dioxide	Smothers	No	Yes - Small Fires	No	No	Yes	No

Figure 7-42: Summary matrix - fire extinguishing media.

Source: RMS.

Access for fire and rescue services and vehicles

As firefighting is generally carried out within buildings it makes good sense to ensure that the fire and rescue services can access a building as quickly as possible in the event of a fire. The responsible person should ensure that facilities, equipment and devices provided are maintained in an efficient state, in efficient working order and in good repair.

VEHICLE ACCESS

The fire and rescue services need to get their appliances as close as possible to buildings to prevent time being wasted with running out unnecessary hose. Minimum access requirements for pumping appliances and high reach appliances will vary dependent upon the height, floor area of the building and if a fire main is fitted.

Access will be required for a minimum to 15% of the perimeter or within 45m of every point of the footprint of the building, up to a maximum of 100% of the perimeter, dependent upon the above factors.

This may differ in practice between one building and another depending on what requirement was imposed on the building when it was built and the level of maintenance.

ACCESS FOR FIREFIGHTING

In low rise buildings additional access requirements are not normally required as use of the normal means of escape and access to the building by the use of ladders, in conjunction with the vehicle access requirements shown previously, are normally sufficient. In other buildings, additional facilities, including firefighting lifts, firefighting stairs and lobbies (usually called a firefighting shaft), are needed.

The addition of these measures would allow the fire and rescue services to quickly access the fire floor or to access the floor below a fire, from which an operating base can be set up. In general, buildings with floor levels over 18m, or basements more than ten metres below a fire, allow rescue service vehicle access.

7.5 - Means of escape

General requirements for means of escape

The Regulatory Reform (Fire Safety) Order (RRFSO) 2005 requires the responsible person to *"make and give effect to such arrangements as are appropriate, having regard to the size of his undertaking and the nature of its activities, for the effective planning, organisation, control, monitoring and review of the preventive and protective measures."* The RRFSO 2005 also sets out the type of requirements necessary with regard to emergency routes and exits. An adequate means of escape is essential for all premises. The following general factors should be taken into consideration when planning means of escape.

TRAVEL DISTANCES

Travel distance is a significant component of a successful means of escape plan. Travel distances are judged on the basis of distance to a place of safety in the open air and away from the building; the distance needs to be kept to the minimum. The distance includes travel around obstructions in the workplace and may be greatly affected by any work in progress on a construction site. If someone is outside on a scaffold it is unlikely to be considered as a place of safety and the distance would usually be taken as that to reach the ground away from the building (for example, at an assembly point).

The route must be sufficiently wide and of a sufficiently short distance to allow speedy and safe evacuation. There should normally be alternative routes leading in different directions. Everyone should be able to escape unaided (if able bodied). The distance between work stations and the nearest fire exit should be minimised.

Table 1 Maximum travel distances

	Fire hazard		
	Lower	Normal	Higher
Enclosed structures:			
Alternative	60 m	45 m	25 m
Dead-end	18 m	18 m	12 m
Semi-open structures:			
Alternative	200 m	100 m	60 m
Dead-end	25 m	18 m	12 m

Notes:

Semi-open structures are completed or partially constructed structures in which there are substantial openings in the roof or external walls, which would allow smoke and heat from any fire to readily disperse, and which are not at risk of exposure from radiation or direct impingement from a fire on the site.

Figure 7-43: Fire escape - hazard of falling on exit due to height from ground. *Source: RMS.*

Figure 7-44: Maximum travel distances. *Source: HSE, HSG168.*

STAIRS

Staircases form an integral part of the means of escape from fire in most buildings. If they are to be part of the escape route, the following points must be ensured:

- Fire-resistant structure.
- Fitted with fire doors.
- Doors must not be wedged open.
- Wide enough to take the required number of people.
- Must lead direct to fresh air, or to two totally separate routes of escape.
- Non slip/trip and in good condition.
- No combustible storage within staircase.

External escape stairs and ladders

External temporary escape stairs may be required, if an internal protected stairway is not available.

Stairways can be constructed from scaffolding. The external wall against which the stairway is erected should be fire-resistant without openings onto the stairway with 30 minutes fire resistance for 9m vertically below the stairway and 1.8m either side or above, as measured from the stair treads. All doors, apart from the uppermost one leading onto the external stairway, should have 30 minutes' fire resistance and be self-closing. Any other openings, including windows, which are not of fire-resisting construction, should be suitably protected, for example, with plasterboard, proprietary mineral fibre-reinforced cement panels or steel sheets.

Figure 7-45: Protected temporary fire escape. *Source: HSE, HSG168.*

PASSAGEWAYS

If passageways are to be part of the escape route, the following points must be ensured:

- The route should lead directly to the open air via a protected route (where necessary).
- Route to be kept unobstructed.

DOORS

If doors are to be part of the escape route, the following points must be ensured:

- Exit doors are to open outwards easily (unless small numbers of people involved).
- Provide fire doors along the escape route.
- Fire doors along with fire-resistant structures serve two purposes:
  - Prevent the spread of fire.
  - Ensure that there is means of escape for persons using the building.
- They should not be wedged open.
- Lead to open air - safety.

EMERGENCY LIGHTING

Emergency lighting should be considered if escape is likely to be required in dark conditions. This could mean late afternoon in winter time, not just at night time.

EXIT AND DIRECTIONAL SIGNS

Fire escape signs are provided to guide escape from wherever people are in a building, via a place of relative safety (the escape route) to the place of ultimate safety (the assembly area). Fire escape signs are not needed on the main route into or out of a building (the one used by people for normal arrival and exit), but alternative escape routes and complicated escape routes do need to be signed. It must not be assumed that everyone will know all safe routes through the building or that once people are out of the building they will know how to get to the assembly point. Signs directing to the assembly point will also be needed. *See also 'NGC1 - Element 4 - Health and safety management systems 3 - planning' - Safety signs.*

Figure 7-46: Fire escape sign. *Source: RMS.*

ASSEMBLY POINTS

The assembly point is a place of safety where people wait whilst any incident is investigated, and where confirmation can be made that everyone has evacuated the premises.

The main factors to consider are:

- Safe distance from buildings.
- Sited in a safe position.
- Not sited so that workers will be in the way of the fire and rescue service.
- Must be able to walk away from assembly point and back to a public road.
- Clearly signed.
- More than one provided to suit numbers and groups of people.
- Communications should be provided between assembly points.
- Measures provided to decide if evacuation successful.
- Person must be in charge of assembly point and identified.
- Person to meet/brief the fire and rescue service.

Figure 7-47: Assembly point.   Source: RMS.

NEED FOR CONTINUAL REVIEW AS CONSTRUCTION ACTIVITY PROGRESSES

In all workplaces there is a need to actively review and revise the fire safety measures that relate to means of escape. This aspect of fire safety is absolutely vital in construction sites as the layout may change as construction activities progress. Dependent upon the state of the build, fire means of escape may need to be reviewed on a weekly or even daily basis. Checks and assessment should be made to ensure that the means of escape are still appropriate and that they have not being compromised:

- Travel distances remain within limits.
- Egress via stairs or passageways is achievable without restriction.
- Doors have not been filled in, moved or become unusable.
- Exit and directional signs still relate to the actual escape route.
- Emergency lighting has not become obscured by processes that could contaminate the surface or screened by new structures.
- Assembly points remain accessible and in place, for example, not built over.

7.6 - Evacuation of a construction workplace

Emergency evacuation procedures

Article 15 of the RRFSO 2005 sets out requirements for the responsible person to establish emergency evacuation procedures.

"Establish and, where necessary, give effect to appropriate procedures, including safety drills, to be followed in the event of serious and imminent danger to relevant persons."

Figure 7-48: Article 15 of RRFSO 2005.   Source: The Regulatory Reform (Fire Safety) Order (RRFSO) 2005.

Furthermore, it sets out a requirement to nominate a sufficient number of competent persons to implement evacuation procedures. The danger that may threaten people if an emergency occurs at work depends on many different factors; consequently it is not possible to construct one model procedure for action in the event of fire and emergency for all premises. Evacuation procedures need to reflect the type of emergency, the people affected and the premises involved. Many of the different issues to consider for different emergencies have common factors, for example, evacuation in an efficient/effective manner, an agreed assembly location (which may be different for different emergencies) and checks to ensure people are safe. These factors are considered below with regard to fire emergencies.

ROLE AND APPOINTMENT OF FIRE MARSHALS

In all premises a person should be nominated to be responsible for coordinating the fire evacuation plan. This may be the same person that organises fire instruction and training and drills and coordinates the evacuation at the time of the fire. They may appoint persons such as fire marshals to assist them in fulfilling the role. This involves the appointment of certain staff to act as fire marshals to assist with evacuation. The way in which they assist will vary between organisations; for example, some will check areas of the building in the event of a fire to ensure no person is still inside and others will lead the evacuation to show where to go. The fire marshals' appointment should be made known to workers and they should be clearly identifiable at the time of emergency so that those that are asked to evacuate understand the authority of the person requiring them to do so. The appointment of fire marshals contributes to an employer's compliance with the requirement to establish competent persons to assist with health and safety.

FIRE INSTRUCTION NOTICES

At conspicuous positions in all parts of the location, and adjacent to all fire alarm actuating points (for example, break glass operated call-points), printed notices should be exhibited stating, in concise terms, the essentials of the action to be taken upon discovering a fire and on hearing the fire alarm. It is usual to also state what someone must do when they discover a fire.

Fire action

The action in the event of a fire and upon discovery needs to be immediate, and a simple fire action plan should be put into effect. A good plan of action would include the following points.

On discovering a fire

- Sound the fire alarm (to warn others).
- Call the fire service.
- Go to the assembly point.

On hearing the alarm

- Leave the building by the nearest exit.
- Close doors behind you.
- Go to the assembly point.
- Get out of the building and stay out.

On evacuation

- Do not take risks.
- Do not stop for personal belongings.
- Do not use lifts.
- Do not return to the building unless authorised to do so.
- Report to assembly point.
- Consider the wording on notices that are posted and ensure that workers are instructed and trained to do what is asked of them.

Figure 7-49: Fire instruction notice. *Source: RMS.*

FIRE TRAINING

Typical issues to be included in a fire training programme relating to emergency action are:

- Fire prevention.
- Recognition of fire alarms and the actions to be taken.
- Understanding the emergency signs.
- Location of fire escape routes and assembly points.
- Requirements for safe evacuation (for example, non-use of lifts, do not run etc.).
- Location and operation of call-points and other means of raising the alarm.
- How the fire service is called.
- Location, use and limitations of firefighting equipment.
- Consideration of people with special needs.
- Identity and role of fire marshals.

FIRE DRILLS

A fire drill is intended to ensure, by means of training and rehearsal, that in the event of fire:

- The people who may be in danger act in a calm, orderly and efficient manner.
- Those designated with specific duties carry them out in an organised and effective manner.
- The means of escape are used in accordance with a predetermined and practised plan.
- An opportunity for management leadership.

The fire drill enables all people involved in the evacuation to practice and learn under as near realistic circumstances as possible. This can identify what works well in the evacuation procedure and what does not.

Practice in the form of a drill helps people to respond quickly to the alarm and, because they have done it before, to make their way efficiently to the assembly point. At least once a year a practice fire drill should normally be carried out simulating conditions in which one or more of the escape routes from the building are obstructed. This will assist in developing an awareness of the alternative exits that can be taken and assist in ensuring people understand the unpredictability of fires.

ROLL CALL

The traditional method of undertaking a roll call is by use of a checklist of names. Very few workplaces can now operate this system as they do not have such a static workforce as this system requires. Where they can operate they will provide a speedy and efficient means of identifying who has arrived at the assembly point and who has not. Where strict security control to a construction site is used, with signing in and out, this may make this process more viable. This requires people on site to report to their allocated assembly point and for someone (for example, a fire marshal) to confirm that they have arrived safely and determine if anyone is missing. If it is not known exactly who is in a building a system of fire marshals who can make a check of the building at the time of their own evacuation (without endangering their own safety) may be employed. This can assist with the process and may identify people that have not evacuated. However, this system may not be able to provide an absolute confirmation that everyone has evacuated as there may be limited opportunity for the fire marshal to check the whole of the area allocated to them. Any doubt or confirmed missing persons should be reported to the person nominated to report to the fire service, who in turn will provide a report to the fire service as soon as they arrive.

PROVISIONS FOR THE INFIRM AND DISABLED

When planning a fire evacuation system employers need to consider who may be in the workplace, their abilities and capabilities. Any disability for example, hearing, vision, mental or mobility impairment must be catered for. Some of the arrangements may be to provide the person with a nominated assistant(s) to support their speedy escape, for example, with the use of a specially designed evacuation chair to enable them to make their way out of a building down emergency exit stairs.

Part of the provision is to make sure they are capable of knowing that an emergency exists. This may mean providing them with special alarm arrangements that cater for their disability, for example, a visual and or vibrating alert for the hearing impaired.

Figure 7-50: Fire refuge sign for disabled people.
Source: Safety Selector.

In some cases, disabled people may need to use a refuge area, a relatively safe waiting area for short periods. A refuge area is separated from the fire by a fire-resisting structure and has access via a safe route to a fire exit. It provides a temporary space for disabled people to wait for others who will help them to evacuate. Some buildings may be equipped with an evacuation lift, which has been specifically designed within a fire-resisting enclosure and having a separate power supply.

BUILDING PLANS TO INCLUDE RECORD OF EMERGENCY ESCAPE

Building plans should be drawn up to aid the emergency services. These will help identify the quickest and shortest route through the building, but can also be used to aid search and rescue. Plans should clearly identify call-points, the siting of firefighting equipment/sprinklers (if fitted), fire doors, travel distances, escape routes, refuge areas for the disabled, assembly points.

Exam practice

1. Arson is the single greatest cause of fire.

   (a) **Identify** factors that make some construction sites vulnerable to arson attacks. **(4)**

   (b) **Outline** control measures that can be taken to reduce the risk of arson on a construction site. **(4)**

2. Liquefied petroleum gas (LPG) is often stored on construction sites. **Identify** control measures for the safe storage of LPG on construction sites. **(8)**

3. Fire is a significant hazard on refurbishment projects that involve hot works.

   (a) **Identify THREE** activities that can be considered as 'hot works'. **(3)**

   (b) **Outline** the precautions that may be taken to reduce the risk of a fire occurring during 'hot works'. **(5)**

4. **Outline** the factors that would need to be covered in the induction training of workers to enable their response to a fire emergency on a construction site. **(8)**

5. **Outline** the factors to be considered when assessing fire risks and the effects on the current fire risk reduction measures of a major refurbishment project on one floor of an occupied multi-floor office block. **(8)**

Please refer to the back of the assessment section for answers.

Chemical and biological health - hazards and risk control

Learning outcomes

On completion of this element, candidates should be able to demonstrate understanding of the content through the application of knowledge to familiar and unfamiliar situations. In particular they should be able to:

8.1 Outline the forms of, and classification of, and the health risks from exposure to, hazardous substances.

8.2 Explain the factors to be considered when undertaking an assessment of the health risks from substances encountered in construction workplaces.

8.3 Explain the use and limitations of Workplace Exposure Limits including the purpose of long term and short term exposure limits.

8.4 Outline control measures that should be used to reduce the risk of ill-health from exposure to hazardous substances.

8.5 Outline the hazards, risks and controls associated with specific agents.

8.6 Outline the basic requirements related to the safe handling and storage of waste on construction sites.

Content

8.1 - Health risks from hazardous substances 201
  Forms of chemical agent 201
  Forms of biological agents 201
  Main classification of substances hazardous to health 202
  Difference between acute and chronic health effects..207
8.2 - Assessment of health risks 208
  Routes of entry of hazardous substances into the body 208
  Factors to be taken into account when assessing health risks 211
  Sources of information..212
  Role and limitations of hazardous substance monitoring 215
  Basic monitoring equipment 216
8.3 - Workplace exposure limits...218
  Purpose of workplace exposure limits 218
  Long-term and short-term exposure limits..219
  Significance of time weighted averages 219
  Limitations of exposure limits...220
  Application of relevant limits 220
  Reducing exposure levels...221
8.4 - Control measures...222
  Duty to prevent exposure or adequately control it..222
  Ensuring the workplace exposure limit is not exceeded..223
  Principles of good practice as regards control of exposure...223
  Common measures used to implement the principles of good practice.................................227
  Control of substances with specific effects...236
8.5 - Specific agents..237
  Health risks and controls associated with other specific agents 237
  Generation and control of dust on a construction site 244
  Health risks and controls associated with asbestos 244
  Duty to manage asbestos 245
8.6 - Safe handling and storage of waste 251
  Basic environmental issues relating to waste disposal and effluent.....................................251
Exam practice 253

Sources of reference

Reference information provided, in particular web links, is correct at time of publication, but may have changed.

Asbestos essentials task sheets, HSE, http://www.hse.gov.uk/asbestos/essentials/index.htm

Asbestos: The Survey Guide, HSG264 (second edition), HSE Books, ISBN 978-0-7176-6502-0 http://www.hse.gov.uk/pubns/priced/hsg264.pdf

A step by step guide to COSHH assessment, HSG97 (second edition 2004), HSE Books, ISBN 978-0-7176-2785-1 http://www.hse.gov.uk/pubns/priced/hsg97.pdf

Controlling airborne contaminants at work - A guide to local exhaust ventilation, HSG258 (second edition 2011), HSE Books, ISBN 978-0-7176-6415-3 http://www.hse.gov.uk/pubns/priced/hsg258.pdf

Control of Substances Hazardous to Health Regulations 2002 (as amended) - ACOP and guidance, L5 (sixth edition 2013), HSE Books, ISBN 978-0-7176-6582-2 http://www.hse.gov.uk/pubns/priced/l5.pdf

EC Regulation No 1272/2008 Classification Labelling and Packaging of Substances and Mixtures (CLP) http://www.hse.gov.uk/chemical-classification/legal/clp-regulation.htm

EH40/2005 Workplace exposure limits (second edition 2011), HSE Books, ISBN 978-0-7176-6446-7 http://www.hse.gov.uk/pubns/priced/eh40.pdf

Globally Harmonized System of Classification and Labelling of Chemicals (GHS) (revision 5 2013), United Nations ISBN 978-92-1-117067-2

http://www.unece.org/fileadmin/DAM/trans/danger/publi/ghs/ghs_rev05/English/ST-SG-AC10-30-Rev5e.pdf

Managing and working with asbestos - Control of Asbestos Regulations 2012 - ACOP and guidance, L143 (second edition 2013), HSE Books, ISBN 978-0-7176-6618-8 http://www.hse.gov.uk/pubns/priced/l143.pdf

Managing asbestos in buildings - A brief guide, INDG223 (rev5 2012), HSE, http://www.hse.gov.uk/pubns/indg223.pdf

Personal Protective Equipment at Work Regulations 1992 (as amended) - Guidance on Regulations, L25 (second edition 2005), HSE Books, ISBN 978-0-7176-6139-3 http://www.hse.gov.uk/pubns/priced/l25.pdf

Respiratory protective equipment at work - A practical guide, HSG53 (fourth edition 2013), HSE Books, ISBN 978-0-7176-6454-2 http://www.hse.gov.uk/Pubns/priced/hsg53.pdf

Relevant statutory provisions

Control of Asbestos Regulations (CAR) 2012

Control of Substances Hazardous to Health Regulations (COSHH) 2002 (as amended)

Personal Protective Equipment at Work Regulations (PPER) 1992

8.1 - Health risks from hazardous substances

Forms of chemical agent

The form taken by a hazardous substance is a contributory factor to its potential for harm. The form affects how easily a substance gains entry to the body, how it is absorbed into the body and how it reaches a susceptible site. Chemical agents take many forms, the most common being the primary forms or states - solids, liquids, gases, and the derivative forms - dusts, fibres, fumes, smoke, mists and vapours.

SOLIDS

Solids are materials that are solid at normal temperature and pressure. The atoms, molecules or ions that make up a solid may be arranged in an orderly repeating pattern or irregularly. Materials whose constituents are arranged in a regular pattern are known as crystals. Crystals that are large enough to see and handle are known as crystallites. Other materials are called polycrystalline, which simply means they are composed of many crystallites of varying size and orientation.

Almost all common metals, silicon and many ceramics are polycrystalline. Unlike a liquid, a solid object does not flow to take on the shape of its container, nor does it expand to fill the entire volume available to it like a gas. The risk from hazardous solids increases with reduction in particle size, particularly when it becomes a dust that can become airborne.

LIQUIDS

Liquids are substances that are liquid at normal temperature and pressure. Liquids have a definite volume but no fixed shape. Similar to a gas, a liquid is able to flow and take the shape of a container. Some liquids, such as water, resist compression, while others can be compressed. Unlike a gas, a liquid does not disperse to fill every space of a container and maintains a fairly constant density. The density of a liquid is usually close to that of a solid and much higher than that of a gas.

GASES

Gases are formless fluids usually produced by chemical processes involving combustion or by the interaction of chemical substances. A gas will normally seek to fill the space completely into which it is liberated, for example, chlorine gas, carbon monoxide and methane.

DUSTS

Dusts are solid airborne particles, often created by operations such as grinding, crushing, milling, sanding or demolition, for example, silica, asbestos, cotton fibres, flour and cement.

FIBRES

Dust may be created that is made up of tiny fibres, for example, mineral wool and asbestos.

FUMES

Fumes are solid particles formed by condensation from the gaseous state, for example, lead fume and welding fume.

SMOKE

Smoke is particles that result from incomplete combustion. They are a combination of gases and very small particles that can be in either solid or liquid state.

MISTS

Mists are finely dispersed liquid droplets suspended in air. Mists are mainly created by spraying, foaming, pickling and electro-plating, for example, mists from a water pressure washer, paint spray, pesticide or oil.

VAPOUR

Vapour is the gaseous form of a material normally encountered in a liquid or solid state at normal room temperature and pressure. Typical examples of vapours are those released from solvents, for example, trichloroethylene, which releases vapours when the container holding it is opened.

Forms of biological agents

FUNGI

Fungi are a variety of organisms that act in a parasitic manner, feeding on organic matter. Most are either harmless or positively beneficial to health; however a number cause harm to humans and may be fatal. An example of a fungi organism is the mould from rotten hay called aspergilla, which causes aspergillosis ('farmer's lung'). Farmer's lung is an allergic reaction to the mould.

This occurs deep in the lungs in the alveoli region (where the exchange of oxygen and carbon dioxide takes place). It leads to shortness of breath, which gets progressively worse at each exposure. The resulting attack is similar to asthma. Aspergilla can also cause short-term effects of irritation to the eyes and nose and also causes coughing.

Figure ref 8-1 shows Aspergillus with its characteristic chains of spores emerging from the head. Moulds from the same family can cause ringworm and athlete's foot.

BACTERIA

Bacteria are single cell organisms. Most bacteria are harmless to humans and many are beneficial. The bacteria that can cause disease are called pathogens.

Examples of harmful bacteria are leptospira (causing Weil's disease), bacillus anthracis (causing anthrax), and legionella pneumophila (causing legionnaires disease).

VIRUSES

Viruses are the smallest known type of biological agent. They invade the cells of other organisms, which they take over and make copies of themselves, and while not all cause disease many of them do.

Figure 8-1: Mould - Aspergillus.   *Source: National Geographic.*

Examples of viruses are hepatitis, which can cause liver damage, and the Human Immunodeficiency Virus (HIV), which causes acquired immune deficiency syndrome (AIDS).

Figure 8-2: Bacteria - legionella pneumophila. *Source: European hospital.*

Figure 8-3: Virus - hepatitis C.   *Source: National public radio.*

Main classification of substances hazardous to health

The European Union Regulation on Classification, Labelling and Packaging of Substances and Mixtures (CLP Regulation) introduced the UN 'Globally Harmonized System of Classification and Labelling of Chemicals (GHS)' into the UK.

The CLP Regulation lists classification and labelling of substances that conforms to the UN GHS and makes them legally binding within the European Union. The CLP Regulation follows the GHS and classifies chemicals based on their effect on human health.

Criteria for classifying chemicals have been established in the GHS and adopted in the CLP Regulations for the following health hazard classes:

- Acute toxicity.
- Skin corrosion/irritation.
- Serious eye damage/eye irritation.
- Respiratory or skin sensitisation.
- Germ cell mutagenicity.
- Carcinogenicity.
- Reproductive toxicity.
- Specific target organ toxicity - single exposure.
- Specific target organ toxicity - repeated exposure.
- Aspiration hazard.

A substance may be classified under more than one classification, although those with specific target organ toxicity only apply if other classifications do not. The various hazard classifications for substances harmful to health are defined in Annex 1, Part 3, of the CLP Regulations. The pictograms associated with the classifications are set out in tables in the annex.

The following information on hazard classifications and their associated pictograms are drawn from Annex 1, Part 3, of the CLP Regulations.

The information is presented in a simplified format, for full details of the classifications the annex should be consulted. Text provided in brackets in a quotation is not part of the quotation from the CLP Regulations, but has been added so that it can be more easily understood.

Acute toxicity

"Acute toxicity means those adverse effects occurring following oral or dermal administration of a single dose of a substance, or multiple doses given within 24 hours, or an inhalation exposure of 4 hours."

The classification is divided into five categories related to the level of toxicity of the chemical. The subdivisions arise from the quantity of the substance that would prove lethal to 50% of the population exposed to that substance through the main routes of entry to the body - oral, dermal and inhalation.

A sample of the exposure routes (oral) is shown to illustrate the doses and pictograms related to the hazard and category.

Acute oral toxicity	Category 1	Category 2	Category 3	Category 4
Oral dose	≤ 5 mg/kg	>5 <50 mg/kg	>50 <300 mg/kg	>300 <2,000 mg/kg
Pictogram				
Signal word	Danger	Danger	Danger	Warning
Hazard statement	Fatal if swallowed	Fatal if swallowed	Toxic if swallowed	Harmful if swallowed

The classification of categories and labelling for acute skin and inhalation toxicity are the same as for oral exposure, except for slightly different hazard statements. An example of a substance with acute oral toxicity is arsenic, which is a systemic poison. Another example is methanol, which is known to cause lethal intoxications in humans (mostly via ingestion) in relatively low doses and is a category 3 substance for acute oral toxicity.

Skin corrosion/irritation

"Skin corrosion means the production of irreversible damage to the skin; namely, visible necrosis (dead skin cells) through the epidermis (outermost skin cells) and into the dermis (the middle layer of skin cells), following the application of a test substance for 4 hours. Corrosive reactions are typified by ulcers, bleeding, bloody scabs, and, by the end of observation at 14 days, by discolouration due to blanching of the skin, complete areas of alopecia, and scars."

The corrosion effect for this hazard category is divided into three categories related to duration of exposure necessary to create an observable effect after a period of time. Skin irritation is a lessor form of harm within this classification.

"Skin irritation is the production of reversible damage to the skin following the application of a test substance for up to four hours."

Examples of substances classified under the skin corrosion/irritation category are sulphuric (battery) acid and sodium hydroxide (caustic soda).

Skin corrosion/irritation	Category 1A	Category 1B	Category 1C	Category 2
Exposure Observation	≤ 3 minutes ≤ 1 hour	>3 minutes ≤ 1 hour ≤ 14 days	>1 hour ≤ 4 hours ≤ 14 days	
Pictogram				
Signal word	Danger	Danger	Danger	Warning
Hazard statement	Causes severe skin burns and eye damage	Causes severe skin burns and eye damage	Causes severe skin burns and eye damage	Causes skin irritation

Serious eye damage/eye irritation

"Serious eye damage means the production of tissue damage in the eye, or serious physical decay of vision, following application of a test substance to the anterior (outer) surface of the eye, which is not fully reversible within 21 days of application."

"Eye irritation is the production of changes in the eye following the application of a test substance to the anterior surface of the eye, which are fully reversible within 21 days of application."

Serious eye damage/eye irritation generally relates to effects on the cornea, iris or conjunctiva:

Serious eye injury/eye irritation	Category 1	Category 2		
Effect on eye	Irreversible	Reversible		
Pictogram				
Signal word	Danger	Warning		
Hazard statement	Causes severe eye damage	Causes severe eye irritation		

The difference between category 1 and 2 for eye injury is whether the harm to the eye is fully reversible within the observation period.

Respiratory or skin sensitisation

"Respiratory sensitiser means a substance that will lead to hypersensitivity of the airways following inhalation of the substance."

"Skin sensitiser means a substance that will lead to an allergic response following skin contact."

Sensitisation takes place in two stages. The first is the recognition stage where, following contact with the airways or skin, the substance is recognised by the body as a pathogen (something that can cause harm to health). The second stage is the antibody generation and allergic response to further exposure to the substance.

Each class of sensitiser has a single category, Category 1. Category 1 for respiratory sensitisers is established by direct evidence that exposure will lead to specific hypersensitivity, for example, asthma, rhinitis, conjunctivitis or alveolitis (inflammation of the alveoli). Flour dust and isocyanates are examples of respiratory sensitisers.

Category 1 substances that are skin sensitisers are ones where there is strong documented evidence of causing allergic contact dermatitis.

Nickel and epoxy resins are examples of skin sensitisers.

Sensitisers	Respiratory sensitisation Category 1	Skin sensitisation Category 1
Pictogram		
Signal word	Danger	Warning
Hazard statement	May cause allergy or asthma symptoms or breathing difficulty if inhaled	May cause an allergic skin reaction

Germ cell mutagenicity

"A mutation means a permanent change in the amount or structure of the genetic material in a cell. The term 'mutation' applies both to heritable genetic changes ... and to the underlying DNA modifications when known."

The different categories of mutagenicity reflect the degree of knowledge about the chemical and the indications that it may cause mutagenicity.

Category 1 substances are known or are presumed, because of related evidence, to induce heritable mutations, whereas Category 2 substances are ones where there is concern that they may induce heritable mutations.

The differences between category 1A and 1B mainly relate to how the evidence is gathered to come to a conclusion on the effects of the chemical being assessed for categorisation.

If a specific route of exposure is proven to be the only route causing harm, this route must be stated in the hazard statement.

Germ cell mutagenicity	Category 1A	Category 1B	Category 2	
Pictogram				
Signal word	Danger	Danger	Warning	
Hazard statement	May cause genetic defects	May cause genetic defects	Suspected of causing genetic defects	

Carcinogenicity

"Carcinogen means a substance or a mixture of substances which induce cancer or increases its incidence. Substances which have induced benign and malignant tumours in well-performed experimental studies on animals are considered also to be presumed or suspected human carcinogens unless there is strong evidence that the mechanism of tumour formation is not relevant to humans."

Carcinogenicity	Category 1A	Category 1B	Category 2	
Pictogram				
Signal word	Danger	Danger	Warning	
Hazard statement	May cause cancer	May cause cancer	Suspected of causing cancer	

As with the different categories of mutagenicity, the categories for carcinogenicity reflect the degree of knowledge about the chemical and the indications that it may cause cancer.

Category 1 substances are known or are presumed, because of related evidence, to induce cancer, whereas Category 2 substances are ones where there is concern that they may induce cancer.

The differences between category 1A and 1B mainly relate to how the evidence is gathered to come to a conclusion on the effects of the chemical being assessed for categorisation.

If a specific route of exposure is proven to be the only route causing harm, this route must be stated in the hazard statement.

Benzyl chloride is an example of a carcinogenic substance. Another example is benzene, which affects bone marrow, causing leukaemia.

Reproductive toxicity

"Reproductive toxicity includes effects on sexual function and fertility in adult males and females, as well as developmental toxicity in the offspring."

The classification covers two main headings:

1) Adverse effects on sexual function and fertility - including alterations to the reproductive system, effects on the onset of puberty or the reproductive cycle, sexual behaviour, fertility and pregnancy outcomes.
2) Adverse effects on development of the offspring - including interference with the development of the foetus or child, before or after birth, resulting from exposure of either parent prior to conception or during development of the offspring.

The genetically based inheritable effects in offspring come under the classification 'germ cell mutagenicity'. The adverse effects of chemicals on or via lactation are also included in reproductive toxicity, but for classification purposes are treated separately.

This is because it is desirable to be able to classify chemicals specifically for an adverse effect on lactation so that a specific hazard warning about this effect can be provided for lactating mothers.

Reproductive toxicity	Category 1A Known effect	Category 1B Presumed effect	Category 2 Suspected effect	Additional category for effects on or via lactation
Pictogram				No pictogram
Signal word	Danger	Danger	Warning	No signal word
Hazard statement	May damage fertility or the unborn child	May damage fertility or the unborn child	Suspected of damaging fertility or the unborn child	May cause harm to breast-fed children

The classification principally provides a warning for pregnant women and men and women of reproductive capacity. Category 1 substances are known or are presumed, because of related evidence, to be a human reproductive toxicant, whereas Category 2 substances are ones where there is concern that they may be a human reproductive toxicant.

Category 1A relates to substances that have a known reproductive effect and Category 1B relates to those with a presumed reproductive effect. If a specific route of exposure is proven to be the only route causing harm, this route must be stated in the hazard statement.

An example of a substance classified as reproductive toxic is 2-ethoxyethanol (a solvent used in commercial and industrial cleaning operations), which has been implicated in impairing fertility. In addition, the effect of lead on the development of the brain of an unborn foetus has long been established.

Specific target organ toxicity - single exposure

This classification is for substances that produce specific, non-lethal target organ toxicity arising from a single exposure. The effects may be reversible or non-reversible, immediate or delayed, but are not covered in other classifications. Specific target organ toxicity can occur by any route and therefore includes oral, dermal and inhalation routes.

Specific target organ toxicity	Category 1	Category 2	Category 3 Respiratory tract irritation	Category 3 Narcotic effects
Pictogram				
Signal word	Danger	Warning	Warning	Warning
Hazard statement	Causes damage to organs	May cause damage to organs	May cause respiratory irritation	May cause drowsiness or dizziness

Category 1 substances are known to have produced significant toxicity in humans. Category 2 substances are presumed, because of related evidence, to produce significant toxicity in humans, whereas Category 3 substances cause transient target organ effects that affect the respiratory tract or have a narcotic effect.

Respiratory tract effects include localised redness, accumulation of fluids, unpleasant sensation and/or pain that impair respiration function.

Symptoms include coughing, pain, choking and breathing difficulties. Narcotic effects involve depression of the central nervous system, including drowsiness, loss of reflexes, lack of coordination, vertigo and reduced alertness.

The symptoms may include severe headache, nausea, dizziness, sleepiness, irritability, fatigue, impaired memory function, perception, coordination or reaction time. Some solvents causing narcosis or central nervous system failure may take effect after a single exposure. If a specific organ is affected it should be stated in the hazard statement.

Specific target organ toxicity - repeated exposure

As with the similar classification for single exposure, this classification is for substances that produce specific, non-lethal target organ toxicity, but arising from repeated exposure.

The effects may be reversible or non-reversible, immediate or delayed, but are not covered in other classifications. Specific target organ toxicity can occur by any route and therefore includes oral, dermal and inhalation routes.

Specific target organ toxicity	Category 1 Known effect	Category 2 Presumed effect		
Pictogram				
Signal word	Danger	Warning		
Hazard statement	Causes damage to organs through prolonged or repeated exposure	May cause damage to organs through prolonged or repeated exposure		

Category 1 substances are known to have produced significant toxicity in humans. Category 2 substances are presumed, because of related evidence, to produce significant toxicity in humans.

If a specific route of exposure is proven to be the only route causing harm, this route must be stated in the hazard statement.

Similarly, if specific organs are known to be affected these organs must be stated.

Aspiration hazard

"Aspiration means the entry of a liquid or solid substance directly through the oral or nasal cavity, or indirectly from vomiting, into the trachea and lower respiratory system."

Aspiration toxicity includes severe acute effects such as chemical pneumonia, varying degrees of pulmonary injury or death following aspiration.

Aspiration hazard	Category 1			
Pictogram				
Signal word	Danger			
Hazard statement	May be fatal if swallowed and enters airways			

There is only one category in this classification, Category 1, which relates to substances that are known or are regarded to have caused aspiration toxicity in humans. Substances in Category 1 include some hydrocarbons, turpentine and pine oil.

Difference between acute and chronic health effects

The effect of a substance on the body depends not only on the substance, but also on the dose, and the susceptibility of the individual. No substance can be considered non-toxic; there are only differences in degree of effect.

ACUTE EFFECT

An acute effect is an immediate or rapidly produced, adverse effect, following a single or short term exposure to an offending agent, which is usually reversible (the obvious exception being death).

Examples of acute effects are those from exposure to solvents, which affect the central nervous system causing dizziness and lack of coordination or carbon monoxide, which affects the level of oxygen in the blood causing fainting.

CHRONIC EFFECT

A chronic effect is an adverse health effect produced as a result of prolonged or repeated exposure to an agent. The gradual or latent effect develops over time and is often irreversible.

The effect may go unrecognised for a number of years. Examples of chronic effects are lead or mercury poisoning, cancer and asthma.

Other common terms used in the context of occupational health are:

Toxicology	The study of the body's responses to substances. In order to interpret toxicological data and information, the meaning of the following terms should be understood.
Toxicity	The ability of a chemical substance to produce injury once it reaches a susceptible site in or on the body. A poisonous substance (for example, organic lead), which causes harm to biological systems and interferes with the normal functions of the body. The effects may be acute or chronic, local or systemic.
Dose	The level of environmental contamination multiplied by the length of time (duration) of exposure to the contaminant.
Local effect	Usually confined to the initial point of contact. Possible sites affected include the skin, mucous membranes or the eyes, nose or throat. Examples are burns to the skin by corrosive substances (acids and alkalis), for example, cement, or dermatitis caused by solvents.
Systemic effect	Occurs in parts of the body other than at the point of initial contact. Frequently the circulatory system provides a means to distribute the substance round the body to a target organ/system.
Target organs	An organ within the human body on which a specified toxic material exerts its effects, for example, lungs, liver, brain, skin, bladder or eyes.
Target systems	Central nervous system, circulatory system, and reproductive system.

Examples of substances that have a systemic effect and their target organs/systems are:

Alcohol	Central nervous system, liver.
Lead	Bone marrow and brain damage.
Mercury	Central nervous system.

It must be noted that many chemicals in use today can have both an acute and chronic effect. A simple everyday example is lead.

Symptoms of acute lead toxicity include upset stomach (gastrointestinal problems), dullness, restlessness, irritability, poor attention span, headaches, kidney damage, hypertension and hallucinations.

Health effects of chronic exposure to lead are blood disorder effects, such as anaemia, or neurological disturbances, including headache, irritability, lethargy, convulsions, muscle weakness, tremors and paralysis.

Chronic lead exposure also causes cardiovascular and renal toxicity. In children, lead exposure may lead to cognitive deficits, such as a decrease in intelligence quotient (IQ). Chronic exposure to lead can cause adverse effects on both male and female reproductive functions.

8.2 - Assessment of health risks

Routes of entry of hazardous substances into the body

INHALATION

The most significant industrial entry route is inhalation. It has been estimated that at least 90% of industrial poisons are absorbed through the lungs.

Harmful substances can directly attack the lung tissue causing a local effect or pass through to the blood system, to be carried round the body and affect target organs, such as the liver. The effects of substances that enter the body through inhalation may be local or systemic.

Local effect

A local effect is where the hazardous substance has an effect where it first contacts the body. For example, Silicosis, caused by inhalation of silica dust, where dust causes scarring of the lung, causing inelastic fibrous tissue to develop and reducing lung capacity.

Systemic effect

A systemic effect is where the hazardous substance has an effect on a different site from where it first contacts the body. For example, anoxia, caused by inhalation of carbon monoxide - the carbon monoxide replaces oxygen in the bloodstream affecting the nervous system.

INGESTION

The ingestion route normally presents the least problem as it is unlikely that any significant quantity of harmful liquid or solid will be swallowed without deliberate intent.

However, accidents will occur where small amounts of contaminant are transferred from the fingers to the mouth if eating, drinking or smoking is allowed in chemical areas or where a substance has been decanted into a container normally used for drinking.

The sense of taste will often be a defence if chemicals are taken in through this route, causing the person to spit it out.

If the substance is taken in, vomiting and/or excretion may mean the substance does not cause a systemic problem, though a direct effect, for example, ingestion of an acid, may destroy cells in the mouth, oesophagus or stomach. The skin turns red and in some cases may be itchy.

Small blisters may occur and the condition may take the form of dry and cracked skin.

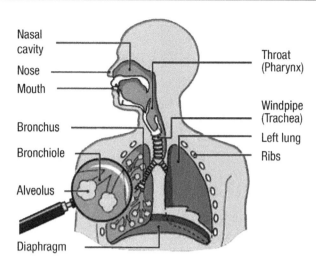

Figure 8-4: Respiratory system. *Source: BBC.*

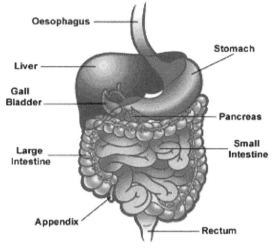

Figure 8-5: Digestive system. *Source: STEM.*

Figure 8-6: Skin layer. *Source: SHP.*

Contact dermatitis (irritant contact dermatitis)

If a person's skin is frequently in contact with some substances or is exposed for a long duration, such persistent contact can lead to irritation and then dermatitis. There are many chemicals used in the construction industry that may irritate the skin leading to this condition; including cement, soaps, detergents, epoxy resins and hardeners, acrylic sealants, bitumen and solvents used in paints or glues.

Removal from contact with the substance usually allows normal cell repair. A similar level of repeat exposure results in the same response. This class of dermatitis is called contact dermatitis.

Sensitisation dermatitis (allergic contact dermatitis)

A second form of dermatitis is called sensitisation dermatitis. In cases of sensitisation dermatitis a person exposed to the substance develops dermatitis in the usual way. When removed from exposure to the substance the dermatitis usually repairs, but the body gets ready for later exposures by preparing the body's defence mechanisms. A subsequent small exposure is enough to cause a major response by the immune system.

The person will have become sensitised and will no longer be able to tolerate small exposures to the substance without a reaction occurring. Though the range of substances an individual may become sensitised to varies, some substances have the tendency to cause sensitisation in a large number of people. For example, cement may contain two well known sensitisers chromate and cobalt. Epoxy resins of the type used in the construction industry also have a tendency to cause sensitisation.

Dermatitis can be prevented by:

- Pre-employment screening for sensitive individuals.
- Careful attention to skin hygiene principles.
- Clean working conditions and properly planned work systems.
- Use of protective equipment.
- Prompt attention to cuts, abrasions and spillages onto the skin.
- Avoid the overuse of hand cleaners containing abrasives such as ground pumice stone.
- Correct selection and use of skin barrier cream, used to repel water, oil or solvents from exposed hands.

INJECTION

Injection is a forceful breach of the skin, perhaps as a result of injury, which can carry harmful substances through the skin barrier. For example, handling broken glass, that cuts the skin and transfers a biological or chemical agent into the blood. On construction sites there are quite a few items that present a hazard of penetration, such as nails in broken up falsework that might be trodden on and penetrate the foot presenting a risk of infection from tetanus.

In addition, some land or buildings being worked on may have been used by intravenous drug users and their needles may present a risk of injection of a virus, such as hepatitis. The forced injection of an agent into the body provides an easy route past the skin, which usually acts as the body's defence mechanism and protects people from the effects of many agents that do not have the ability to penetrate.

When identifying possible routes of entry, it must be remembered that many substances have multiple possibilities. For example, trichloroethylene, which is a known carcinogen, will absorb through the skin and is denoted 'sk' in EH40 to indicate this. However, when in use, it also gives off very harmful vapours that may be inhaled and, because it is liquid, there is the possibility of accidental ingestion.

BODY RESPONSE TO AGENTS AND PROTECTIVE MECHANISMS

The body's response against the invasion of substances likely to cause damage can be divided into external or superficial defences and internal or cellular defences.

Superficial defence mechanisms

Respiratory (inhalation):

Nose	On inhalation many substances and minor organisms are successfully trapped by nasal hairs, for example, the larger wood dust particles. Gases such as carbon monoxide are inhaled through the nose and easily defeat the defence mechanisms, the most superficial of which is smell. Carbon monoxide is highly poisonous to humans and has no smell.
	Vehicle exhausts and petrol driven power tools are a common source of carbon monoxide on construction sites.
Respiratory tract	The next line of defence against inhalation or substances harmful to health begin here, where a series of reflexes activate the coughing and sneezing mechanisms to forcibly expel the triggering substances. Silica and cement dust generated during construction activities may be trapped in the respiratory tract and ejected by coughing and sneezing.
Ciliary escalator	The passages of the respiratory system are also lined with mucus and well supplied with fine hair cells which sweep rhythmically towards the outside and pass along large particles. The respiratory system narrows as it enters the lungs where the ciliary escalator assumes more and more importance as the effective defence. Smaller particles of agents, such as some silica particles, are dealt with at this stage. The smallest particles, such as organic solvent vapours and asbestos, reach the alveoli and are either deposited or exhaled. Legionella bacteria that are inhaled can also defeat the ciliary escalator and reach the alveoli. Hardwood dusts (oak, mahogany, etc.), which are carcinogenic, if inhaled during cutting or machining operations, are usually trapped by the mucus in the escalator.

Gastrointestinal (ingestion):

Mouth	The mouth is used for the ingestion of substances in general. Saliva in the mouth provides a useful defence against hazardous substances that are not excessively acid or alkaline or present in large quantities.
Gastrointestinal tract	Acid in the stomach also provides a useful defence similar to saliva. Vomiting and diarrhoea are additional reflex mechanisms which act to remove substances or quantities that the body is not equipped to deal with.

Skin (absorption):

Skin	The body's largest organ provides a useful barrier against the absorption of many foreign organisms and chemicals (but not against all of them). Its effect is, however, limited by its physical characteristics. The outer part of the skin is covered in an oily layer and substances have to overcome this before they can damage the skin or enter the body.
	The outer part of the epidermis is made up of dead skin cells. These are readily sacrificed to substances without harm to the newer cells underneath. Repeated or prolonged exposure could defeat this. When attacked by substances, the skin may blister in order to protect the layers beneath. Openings in the skin such as sweat pores, hair follicles and cuts can allow entry and the skin itself may be permeable to some chemicals, for example, trichloroethylene.

Cellular mechanisms

The cells of the body possess their own defence systems.

Scavenging action	A type of white blood cell called macrophages attack invading particles in order to destroy them and remove them from the body. This process is known as phagocytosis.
Secretion of defensive substances	This is carried out by some specialised cells. Adrenaline is a hormone produced by the adrenal glands during high stress or exciting situations. This powerful hormone is part of the human body's acute stress response system, also called the 'fight or flight' response. It works by stimulating the heart rate, contracting blood vessels, and dilating air passages, all of which work to increase blood flow to the muscles and oxygen to the lungs. Histamine is a chemical that is released when the body is exposed to an allergen. Allergens may include airborne allergens (such as pollen and dust mites), certain foods (such as peanuts and shellfish) or insect venom. Histamine is released in an effort to protect the body from an allergen; however, sometimes an overload of histamine can result in life-threatening symptoms.
Prevention of excessive blood loss	Reduced circulation through blood clotting and coagulation prevents excessive bleeding and slows or prevents the entry of bacteria. Heparin is an anticoagulant (blood thinner) that prevents the formation of blood clots and is produced naturally in the lungs and liver.
Repair of damaged tissues	This is a necessary defence mechanism which includes removal of dead cells, increased availability of defender cells and replacement of tissue strength, for example, scar tissue caused by silica.
The lymphatic system	The lumphatic system acts as a 'form of drainage system' throughout the body for the removal of foreign substances. Lymphatic glands or nodes at specific points in the system act as selective filters, preventing infection from entering the blood system. In many cases, a localised inflammation occurs in the node at this time.

Other measures to complement the body's protection mechanisms

Practical measures include:

- Maintain good personal hygiene.
- Do not allow cosmetics to be applied in the workplace.
- Do not allow eating or drinking in the workplace.
- Provide proper containers/storage for food and drink.
- Provide and ensure the use of appropriate personal protective equipment.
- Taking care when removing contaminated protective clothing.

Factors to be taken into account when assessing health risks

In order to assess the health risks it is necessary to know the following:

- The *form the substance is in*, for example, solid, liquid, dust or gas. The form of the substance directly influences the way that the substance will enter the body. Solid objects, such as concrete or metal, cannot enter the body in their solid state. But if the concrete is cut with a disc cutter, dust is generated, which if not controlled may be inhaled. If the steel contains chromium, when it is machined or welded, particles which become airborne in the form of dust or fume can be inhaled and prove toxic.
- The *classification of the hazard*, for example, toxic, corrosive or sensitiser. If the substance is toxic, small quantities inhaled, ingested or absorbed through the skin may have a catastrophic effect on the well-being of the individual who is exposed. Sensitisers may cause allergic dermatitis when the employee comes into contact with the substance, or respiratory sensitisers may cause breathing difficulties when inhaled.
- *How much of the substance* will be present and its concentration. Ammonia occurs naturally in the environment and humans are regularly exposed to low levels of ammonia in air, soil and water. Ammonia exists naturally in the air at levels between one and five parts in a billion parts of air (ppb). Ingesting liquid ammonia at 35ppm, for example, from the use of a typical household cleaner, may cause burns to the mouth and throat. Exposure to higher concentrations of liquid ammonia in the eyes causes severe chemical eye burns and can lead to blindness.
- The *routes of entry into the body*, for example, inhalation, ingestion or skin absorption. Some substances cause harm immediately on contact with the skin, for example, acids. Other substances may be present as a gas, mist or fume and be in the air. Humans have to breathe so airborne substances are likely to be inhaled as a route of entry into the body.
- Whether the substance has an *acute or chronic effect* or both. Acute effects can often warn the person that they have come into contact with a hazardous substance and a reaction occurs almost instantly. This allows the person to take avoidance measures. Lower-level concentrations of substances, however, may not cause significant harm initially, but the damage builds up over time. Substances such as organic

solvents can cause skin or eye irritation quickly (acute) and have longer-term exposure consequences (chronic), where damage to the liver and kidneys can occur.

- The extent to which the **body's defences** will deal with the substance. The body's defence systems try to prevent harm but also help the body to heal itself when it gets injured or sick. However, hazards arising from bacteria, viruses, chemicals, dusts, vapours, noise, extreme temperatures or work processes can break down (weaken) the body's defence systems. In some instances, the body's defence mechanisms can be defeated and illness or death can result.
- The **first signs of damage or ill-health**. The body has nerve receptors located all over its surface, so often the first sign of damage will be the sensation of pain. Visual signs of damage may be blood from a cut or break in the skin. When a harmful substance has been ingested or inhaled the first signs are often vomiting or diarrhoea or restrictions in breathing.
- The **vulnerability of the people involved** in the process, for example, young persons, pregnant workers, anyone who has existing health problems, such as skin problems or bronchitis. Anyone with a pre-existing medical condition or with underdeveloped defence systems will be at higher risk than employees who are fit and well.
- The effectiveness of **existing control measures**. Preventing exposure to hazardous substances is the most effective way of controlling health risks. Where exposure cannot be prevented, measures should be taken to eliminate or reduce the risk of harm. The effectiveness with which control measures have been applied will greatly affect the degree of exposure of the employee.

Considering these factors will help the assessor decide whether the risks to health are tolerable or acceptable or further controls are needed.

Sources of information

PRODUCT LABELS

Hazardous chemicals have to be labelled so that workers are informed about their effects when they are exposed to them. The label should draw attention to the inherent hazards to those handling or using the chemical and provide information on precautions to prevent harm.

European regulation on classification, labelling and packaging of chemical substances

The European Union (EU) Regulation on Classification, Labelling and Packaging of Chemical Substances and Mixtures (CLP) introduced throughout the EU a system for classifying and labelling chemicals based on the United Nations' Globally Harmonised System (GHS). The CLP regulation is concerned with the hazards of chemical substances and mixtures and how to inform others about them. Its purpose is to protect people and the environment from the effects of those chemicals by requiring suppliers to classify and provide information about the hazards of the chemicals and to package them safely.

It is the responsibility of manufacturers to establish what the hazards of substances and mixtures are before they are placed on the market, and to classify them in line with the identified hazards. When a substance or a mixture is hazardous, it has to be labelled in accordance with CLP so that workers are informed about its effects if it is used. Note that 'mixture' is the same as the term 'preparation', which has been used previously. All substances available for use in the workplace should be labelled in accordance with CLP, including the use of the appropriate CLP hazard pictogram. Information on the use of symbols to indicate the harm related to various dangerous substance hazard classifications is provided earlier in this element **(see also - 'Main Classification of Substances Hazardous to Health')**. The following table provides a general indication of the meaning of the pictogram, for more specific use and meaning the CLP regulation and its annexes should be consulted.

The CLP regulation requires hazardous substances to carry a hazard label in a specified format, which is made up of specific symbols (known as 'pictograms'), warnings and precautions. These pictograms and the wording that supports them are defined in the CLP regulation, which requires chemical suppliers to use them where hazardous properties have been identified.

CLP pictogram	Description
	This pictogram indicates that the substance may cause acute toxic health effects. Some substances marked with this symbol may have fatal effects.
	This pictogram indicates that the substance may cause severe skin corrosion and serious eye damage.

	This pictogram indicates that the substance may cause less serious health effects, such as skin irritation/sensitisation or harmful toxic effects.
	This pictogram indicates that the substance may cause more serious longer term health effects, such as carcinogenicity and respiratory sensitisation.

Figure 8-7: CLP pictograms.   Source: CLP Regulation.

Article 17 of the CLP regulation requires that hazard labels include the following elements:

- Name, address and telephone number of the supplier(s).
- The nominal quantity of the substance or mixture in the package where this is being made available to the general public, unless this quantity is specified elsewhere on the package.
- Product identifiers.
- Hazard pictograms, where applicable.
- The relevant signal word, where applicable.
- Hazard statements, where applicable.
- Appropriate precautionary statements, where applicable.
- A section for supplemental information, where applicable.

A hazard *pictogram* is a graphical composition that includes a symbol plus other graphic elements, such as a border, background pattern or colour that is intended to convey specific information on the hazard concerned. The pictogram forms an integral part of the label and gives an immediate idea of the types of hazards that the substance or mixture may cause.

A *signal word* indicates the relative level of severity of hazardous substances to alert the potential reader of the significance of the hazard. More severe hazards are identified by the signal word 'danger', while less severe hazards are identified by the signal word 'warning'.

A *hazard statement* is a phrase assigned to a hazard class and category that describes the nature and severity of the hazard.

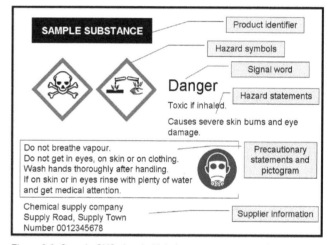

Figure 8-8: Sample GHS chemical labels.   Source: RMS.

A *precautionary statement* is a phrase and/or pictogram that describe recommended measure(s) to prevent or minimise adverse effects resulting from exposure to a hazardous substance or mixture due to its use.

	Hazard statements		Precautionary statements
H240	Heating may cause an explosion	P102	Keep out of reach of children
H320	Causes eye irritation	P271	Use only outdoors or in well-ventilated area
H401	Toxic to aquatic life	P410	Protect from sunlight

Figure 8-9: Hazard and precautionary statements table.   Source: CLP.

Where a dangerous chemical is supplied in a package, the package must be labelled, if it is large enough. Packaging must be safe and able to withstand the conditions it is exposed to during supply.

EH40 WORKPLACE EXPOSURE LIMITS

EH40, which is prepared and published annually by the Health and Safety Executive (HSE), contains the lists of Workplace Exposure Limits (WEL) for use with the Control of Substances Hazardous to Health Regulations (COSHH) 2002 (amended), a description of the limit setting process, technical definitions and explanatory notes. EH40 is mostly guidance, but does contain sections of special legal status. Some sections have been approved by the Health and Safety Executive (HSE) and are statutory requirements that must be complied with.

MANUFACTURERS' HEALTH AND SAFETY DATA SHEETS

Section 6 of the Health and Safety at Work etc Act (HASAWA) 1974 requires manufacturers, importers and suppliers to provide information on substances for use at work; this is usually provided in the form of a data sheet. REACH (Registration, Evaluation, Authorisation and restriction of Chemicals) is the system for controlling chemicals in Europe. It became law in the UK on the 1st June 2007. Article 31 of REACH specifically requires the supplier to provide the recipient of the chemical with a safety data sheet (SDS). It also requires that suppliers ensure that any revisions to SDSs for hazardous chemicals are prepared and are provided to those who have been previously supplied with the chemical.

Safety data sheets established in accordance with REACH require the following sixteen headings to be included:

1) Identification of the substance/mixture and of the company/undertaking, including the product identifier shown on the label, its recommended use and contact information for the supplier, including for emergencies.

2) Hazards identification, including signal words, hazard statements and precautionary statements – the pictogram of hazard symbols may be provided.

3) Composition/information on ingredients.

4) First-aid measures for initial care must be described in a way that can be understood by an untrained responder. Whether medical attention or special treatment is required, including the urgency with which it may be needed and symptoms of any effects.

5) Firefighting measures, including suitable media, hazards of combustion and advice to firefighters.

6) Accidental release measures for non-emergency responders and emergency responders, including spills containment and cleaning up.

7) Handling and storage, including any incompatibilities and the effects of things like weather.

8) Exposure controls/personal protection, including workplace exposure limit values and requirements for such things as local exhaust ventilation and specific personal protective equipment (PPE).

9) Physical and chemical properties, such as odour, flash point, vapour pressure.

10) Stability and reactivity, including conditions to avoid, for example, heat or incompatible materials.

11) Toxicological information, including the health hazards, for example, carcinogenicity, route of entry, symptoms and the effects, including delayed and immediate effects from short and long-term exposure.

12) Ecological information, in order to evaluate the environmental impact of dealing with spills and arrangements for waste.

13) Disposal considerations, including methods and properties that may affect landfill or incineration.

14) Transport information, including UN number and transport hazards.

15) Regulatory information, including relevant national information on the regulatory status of the chemical where it is being supplied.

16) Other information, including the date the SDS was prepared, changes from previous versions and advice on training appropriate for workers to ensure protection of human health.

Annex II of REACH requires that:

The information in the safety data sheet must be written in a clear and concise manner. The safety data sheet must be prepared by a competent person who shall take into account the specific needs and knowledge of the user audience, as far as they are known. The language used in the safety data sheet must be simple, clear and precise, avoiding jargon, acronyms and abbreviations. Statements such as 'may be dangerous', 'no health effects', 'safe under most conditions of use' or 'harmless' or any other statements indicating that the substance or mixture is not hazardous or any other statements that are inconsistent with the classification of that substance or mixture must not be used.

SDS information does not have to be provided for:

■   The offer or sale of dangerous substances or mixtures to the general public provided sufficient information is provided to enable users to take the necessary measures as regards safety, protection of human health and the environment.

■   Unless a SDS is requested by a downstream user or distributor.

■   If the substances/mixtures are supplied in the UK and not classified as dangerous.

■   For certain products intended for the final user, for example, medicinal products or cosmetics.

LIMITATIONS OF INFORMATION IN ASSESSING RISKS TO HEALTH

Information provided by manufacturers and contained within the HSE Guidance Note EH40 may be very technical and require a specialist to explain its relevance to a given activity. Some substances have good toxicological information, usually gained from past experience of harm; many others have a limited amount of useful toxicological information available to guide us as to the harm it may produce.

This can lead to a reliance on data that is only our best understanding at the time and this may have to be revised as our knowledge on the substance changes. This is reflected in the use of WELs. Individual susceptibility of workers differs by, for example, age, gender or ethnic origin, and this can limit the value of information sourced from manufacturers and guidance documents related to workplace exposure limits.

Exposure history varies over the working life of an individual and current exposure may not indicate that the individual may suffer due to a cumulative effect from the earlier exposures. For example, an individual may have been or be engaged in a number of processes within a variety of workplaces or personal pastimes. These limitations are reflected in the use of workplace exposure limits, where the limits are considered to be a maximum and control measures may be applied to control assessed risks to well below this limit.

Role and limitations of hazardous substance monitoring

ROLE OF HAZARDOUS SUBSTANCE MONITORING

The role of hazardous substance monitoring is to determine the level of likely exposure of workers to substances in order to establish the likely effects on the worker.

Hazardous substance monitoring can help to identify and assess health risks in the workplace. It can be used to determine the level of compliance with national or other worker exposure limits. Monitoring can provide information on patterns of exposure and levels of risk that managers can use and provide to workers. It can also indicate the need for health surveillance of groups and individual workers.

Monitoring can establish if current controls are adequate to limit exposure and assist in choosing appropriate control measures to remain within the limits, including personal protective equipment (PPE). Monitoring is required to ensure that worker exposure has not exceeded a control limit and to identify deterioration in control measures that may result in harm if exposure is not adequately controlled.

LIMITATIONS OF HAZARDOUS SUBSTANCE MONITORING

As described previously, the health effects of exposure to toxic substances can be acute or chronic. It is therefore necessary to use appropriate methods of measurement to distinguish these effects.

It is also important to understand the limitation of any hazardous substance monitoring method used, for example, the risk of cross-contamination of similar substances and the fact that general workplace monitoring may not represent specific worker exposure. Hazardous substance monitoring of the presence of a chemical in the air may not represent the worker's complete exposure as, for example, there may be additional exposure to the chemical by skin contact or orally through poor hygiene arrangements.

One of the main limitations of hazardous substance monitoring is the competence of the person conducting it. It relies on that person conducting monitoring at the time that represents real exposure of workers and using methods that will give reliable measurements. When carrying out monitoring related to dusts, it is important to discern the amount of dust that can penetrate the airway and cause harm. If the person conducting the monitoring does not understand the difference between 'total inhalable dust' and 'respirable dust' there is a risk that unsuitable measurements may be taken.

'Total inhalable dust' is the amount of airborne material that enters the nose and mouth during breathing and is available for deposition in the body. 'Respirable dust' is the amount of airborne material that penetrates to the gas exchange region of the lung'.

GENERAL APPROACH TO HAZARDOUS SUBSTANCE MONITORING

When embarking upon a monitoring campaign to assess the hazardous risk to the workforce, several factors need to be considered, the substance(s), who might be affected, the sample period and the method of sampling.

The substance

Considering the substance involves a review of the materials, processes and operating procedures being used within a process, coupled with discussions with management, workers and health and safety practitioners. A brief 'walk-through' survey can also be useful as a guide to the extent of monitoring that may be necessary.

Safety data sheets are also of use. When the background work has been completed it can then be decided what is to be measured.

Who might be affected

Who might be affected depends on the size and diversity of the group that the hazardous substance monitoring relates to. From the group of workers being considered, the sample of workers to be monitored should be selected; this must be representative of the group and the work undertaken. Selecting the workers with the highest exposure can be a reasonable starting point. If the group is large then random sampling may have to be used, but care has to be exercised to ensure a representative sample is taken. The group should also be informed of the reason for the monitoring to ensure their full co-operation.

Sample period

Where monitoring is not continuous, the sample period selected should reflect the workers' exposure patterns. Factors to consider include the total exposure period and whether exposure is at the same level continuously.

If so, a sample taken at any convenient time would be suitable. However, if exposure is occasional, the sample period must reflect this occasional exposure. The duration of the sample period will also be influenced by whether the hazard presented by the substance is acute or chronic. Substances that present an acute hazard are usually sampled over a shorter sample period that reflects the short-term worker exposure limits set by international or national authorities, whereas substances that represent a chronic hazard may be sampled over a longer period to better reflect the long-term worker exposure limits. The sample period may also be influenced by the type of equipment available, including whether it provides a continuous, long-term or a short-term measurement.

Method of monitoring

The particular measurement method will be based on the hazard presented by the substance, any limits in detection ability and what resources are available to measure the presence of the substance accurately. A typical approach is outlined in *figure ref 8-10.*

Measurements to determine	Suitable types of measurement
Chronic hazard	Continuous personal dose measurement
	Continuous measurements of average background levels
	Short term readings of containment levels at selected positions and times
Acute hazard	Continuous personal monitoring with rapid response
	Continuous background monitoring with rapid response
	Short term readings of background contaminant levels at selected positions and times
Environmental control status	Continuous background monitoring
	Short term readings of background contaminant levels at selected positions and times
Whether area is safe to enter	Direct reading instruments

Figure 8-10: Sampling strategy.   Source: RMS.

Basic monitoring equipment

SHORT TERM SAMPLERS

Stain tube detectors (multi-gas/vapour)

A stain tube detector is a simple device for the measurement of contamination on a grab (short term) sampling basis. It incorporates a glass detector tube, filled with inert material. The material is impregnated with a chemical reagent which changes colour ('stains') in proportion to the quantity of contaminant as a known quantity of air is drawn through the tube.

There are several different manufacturers of detector tubes, including Dräger and Gastec. It is important that the literature provided with the pumps and tubes is followed. These provide a quick and easy way to detect the presence of a particular airborne contaminant. However they possess inherent inaccuracies and tube manufacturers claim a relative standard deviation of 20% or less (i.e. 1ppm in 5ppm).

Types of tube construction

Types of tube construction include:

■ The most common is the simple stain length tube, but it may contain filter layers, drying layers, or oxidation layers.
■ Double tube or tube containing separate ampoules, avoids incompatibility or reaction during storage.
■ Comparison tube.
■ Narrow tube to achieve better resolution at low concentrations.

This list shows the main types of tubes; however, there are more variations and the manufacturer's operating instructions must be read and fully understood before tubes are used.

Pumps

There are four types of pump:

1) Bellows pump.
2) Piston pump.
3) Ball pump.
4) Battery operated pump.

Pumps and tubes made by different manufacturers may not be compatible and they should not be mixed when taking measurements.

How to use stain tube detectors

The general approach to using stain tube detectors is:

■ Choose tube to measure material of interest and expected range.
■ Check tubes are in date.

- Check leak tightness of pump.
- Read instructions to ensure there are no limitations due to temperature, pressure, humidity or interfering substances.
- Break off tips of tube, prepare tube if necessary and insert correctly into pump. Arrows normally indicate the direction of air flow.
- Draw the requisite number of strokes, to cause the given quantity of air to pass through the tube.
- Immediately, unless operating instructions say otherwise, evaluate the amount of contaminant by examining the stain and comparing it against the graduations on the tube. If there is any doubt when reading the tube, always err on the safe side (higher end of the scale of discolouration).
- Remove tube and discard according to instructions.
- Purge pump to remove any contaminants from inside the pump.

Figure 8-11: Gas detector pump. *Source: Dräger.*

Figure 8-12: Dräger short-term detection tubes (before and after). *Source: Dräger.*

Advantages of short term samplers

The advantages of short-term samplers are:

- Quick and easy to use.
- Instant reading without further analysis.
- Does not require much expertise to use.
- Relatively inexpensive.

Disadvantages of short term samplers

The disadvantages of short-term samplers are:

- Tubes can be cross sensitive to other contaminants.
- Accuracy varies - some are only useful as an indication of the presence of contaminants.
- Is only a grab sample (taken at a single location point and may not represent the workplace as a whole).
- Relies on operator to accurately count pump strokes (manual versions).
- Only suitable for gases and vapours (not dusts).
- The tubes must be used within a short time period to prevent decay of the reagent and loss of reliability.
- The tubes are fragile and break easily.
- Used/expired tubes must be disposed of as chemical waste in accordance with legal requirements.

Direct reading dust sampler

A simple method of measuring dust is by direct observation of the effect of the dust on a strong beam of light, for example, using a dust lamp (Tyndall effect). High levels of small particles of dust show up under this strong beam of light. Other ways are by means of a direct-reading instrument. This establishes the level of dust by, for example, scattering of light. Some also collect the dust sample.

Advantages of direct reading dust samplers

The advantages of direct dust samplers are:

- Instant reading.
- Continuous monitoring.
- Can record electronically.
- Can be linked to an alarm.
- Suitable for clean-room environments.

Disadvantages of direct reading dust samplers

The disadvantages of direct dust samplers are:

- Some direct-reading instruments can be expensive.
- Does not differentiate between dusts of different types.
- Most effective on dusts of a spherical nature.

LONG-TERM SAMPLERS

Personal samplers

Passive personal samplers

Passive samplers are so described as they have no mechanism to draw in a sample of the contaminant, but instead rely on passive means to sample. As such they take a time to perform this function, for example, acting as an absorber taking in contaminant vapours over a period of a working day. Some passive samplers, like gas badges, are generally fitted to the lapel and change colour to indicate contamination.

Active personal samplers

Filtration devices are used for dusts, mists and fumes. A known volume of air is pumped through a sampling head and the contaminant filtered out. By comparing the quantity of air with the amount of contaminant a measurement is made.

Sampling head in consistent position (eg mid point on shoulder seam)

Battery operated sampling pump

Figure 8-13: Personal sampling equipment. *Source: ROSPA OS and H.*

The filter is either weighed or an actual count of particles is carried out to establish the amount, as with asbestos. The type of dust can be determined by further laboratory analysis. Active samplers are also used for static sampling.

Static sampling

These devices are stationed in the working area. They sample continuously over the length of a shift, or longer period if necessary. Active static samplers use mains or battery-operated pumps to draw a known quantity of air through the sampler. They are similar in principle to personal samplers, but the equipment is tailored to suit static use. Very small quantities of contaminant may be detected using static samplers and the techniques they use include absorption, bubblers, and filtration.

Advantages of long-term samplers

The advantages of long-term samplers are:

■ Will monitor the workplace over a long period of time.
■ Will accurately identify 8 hour time weighted average.

Disadvantages of long-term samplers

The disadvantages of long-term samplers are:

■ Will not generally identify a specific type of contaminant.
■ Will not identify multiple exposure i.e. more than one contaminant.
■ Does not identify personal exposure.
■ Unless very sophisticated, will not read peaks and troughs.

SMOKE TUBES

Smoke tubes are simple devices that generate a 'smoke' by means of a chemical reaction. A tube similar in type to those used in stain tube detectors is selected, its ends broken (which starts the chemical reaction) and it is inserted into a small hand bellows. By gently pumping the bellows smoke is emitted. By watching the smoke air flow can be studied. This can be used to survey extraction and ventilation arrangements to determine their extent of influence.

8.3 - Workplace exposure limits

Purpose of workplace exposure limits

The purpose of workplace exposure limits (WELs) is to assist in the assessment of risk and control of exposure of workers to a variety of substances that can have harmful effects on health. Failure to control exposure to such substances can lead to many forms of ill-health. Therefore, it is important to know in advance what risks may arise from substances, what are acceptable workplace exposure limits and how to protect people at work.

The establishing of WELs at national level provides an opportunity to assess evidence of likely harm from substances and decide what is an acceptable maximum level of exposure that workers can be exposed to each working day for their worklife.

The setting and publishing of WELs provides employers with information on the substances and on the levels of exposure that they must not exceed. This means that all employers are expected to work to nationally agreed maximum exposure limits and will direct that good practices to prevent exposure are applied.

The Health and Safety Executive set WELs for a range of hazardous substances and these are published in a document called EH40, which is updated periodically. They are published to establish clear limits that employers work to when controlling exposure of workers to substances that may harm their health. The absence of a substance from EH40 does not mean that it will not cause adverse effects on health. Limits tend to be set where there is sufficient evidence to establish the limit, in some cases this evidence may still be in the process of being established.

Long-term and short-term exposure limits

The health effects of exposure to chemicals vary considerably depending on the nature of the chemical and the pattern of exposure. Some effects require prolonged or accumulated exposure, whereas others may arise from very short or a single exposure to a particular chemical.

LONG-TERM EXPOSURE LIMITS

Long-term exposure limits (LTEL) are concerned with the total exposure of the worker to a concentration of the chemical, averaged over a reference period that represents a work period, usually 8 hours. They are therefore a time-weighted average (TWA) worker exposure. This is appropriate for protecting against the effects of long-term exposure to a substance that may have chronic health effects. If workers are exposed for longer periods than 8 hours, because they work longer work periods, the long-term exposure limits have to be adjusted to reflect this.

Examples of substances that have long-term workplace exposure limits established by the HSE in Guidance Note EH40 are shown in *figure ref 8-14*.

Substance	8-hour time-weighted average workplace exposure limit
Portland cement	Inhalable dust 10 mg/m^3 - Respirable dust 4 mg/m^3
Benzene	1ppm or 3.25 mg/m^3
Formaldehyde	2ppm or 2.5 mg/m^3

Figure 8-14: Examples of substances with long-term workplace exposure limits. *Source: HSE, EH40.*

SHORT-TERM EXPOSURE LIMITS

Short-term exposure limits (STEL) are primarily aimed at avoiding the acute health effects of exposure to chemicals, for example, eye irritation, or at least reducing the risk of their occurrence. Short-term exposure limits are set to control the total exposure of workers to a concentration of the substance averaged over a short reference period, usually 15 minutes.

For those chemicals that do not have a short-term exposure limit, it is usually recommended that a figure of three times the long-term limit be used as a guide for controlling short-term peaks in exposure.

Examples of substances that have short-term workplace exposure limits established by the HSE in Guidance Note EH40 are shown in *figure ref 8-15*. Note that some of these also have long-term exposure limits.

Substance	Time-weighted average workplace exposure limit	
	Short-term (15 minutes)	Long-term (8 hours)
Chlorine	0.5ppm or 1.5 mg/m^3	None
Phenol	4ppm or 16 mg/m^3	2ppm or 7.8 mg/m^3
Phosgene	0.06ppm or 0.25 mg/m^3	0.02ppm or 0.08 mg/m^3
Trichloroethylene	150ppm or 820 mg/m^3	100 mg/m3 or 550 mg/m^3

Figure 8-15: Examples of substances with short-term workplace exposure limits. *Source: HSE, EH40.*

It can be seen, for example, that trichloroethylene has both a long-term and short-term WEL to accommodate its acute effect (narcosis) and its chronic effect (possible cancer). It is also expressed as parts per million (ppm) to protect from its harmful vapours and, because processes that use trichloroethylene can create mists, it is also regulated limits set in milligrams per cubic metre (mg/m^3).

Significance of time weighted averages

When considering the health effects of a hazardous substance, it is important to know what amount a worker has been exposed to over a period of time, (the dose), as this will influence the amount of the substance taken into the worker's body and any effects which may result from exposure. In workplace situations, the concentration of a substance in the air a worker breathes may vary significantly over the reference period, depending on the activity being carried out.

For example, the process of mixing powder in a container may give a high concentration of the substance in the air the worker breathes while the powder is added, but while the mixing is taking place the concentration in the air may reduce as water is added to the powder.

If a measurement was taken while filling the container with powder this would give the highest concentration, if a measurement was taken during mixing this would give the lowest concentration. Neither measurement would represent the dose received by the worker over time as one would be too high and the other too low.

For this reason, the high and low concentration measurements taken are averaged over a reference time period. This is carried out by determining the amount of time that each of the concentrations is valid and averaging the combined concentrations/times over the reference period.

This is the average of the concentrations of substance in the air the worker breathes over the reference period and is called a time weighted average.

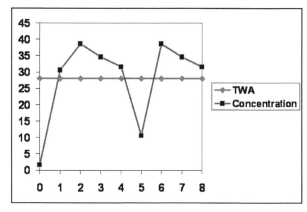

Figure 8-16: Time weighted average compared with actual concentration. *Source: RMS.*

Workplace exposure limits are set in such a way to control the dose that a worker's body may receive by establishing a time weighted average concentration of a substance that a worker may be exposed to over a reference period, for example, 8 hours or 15 minutes.

Because workplace exposure limits are set as time weighted averages, a worker exposed to the workplace exposure limit may be exposed to concentrations of a hazardous substance that are higher than the specified time weighted average for some of the time.

This is acceptable provided the average concentration is not exceeded. As some work activities conducted in the period may create a concentration that is particularly low, this will offset those when it is high. This effect is particularly important to consider where workers have a variety of tasks and take breaks away from the workplace where exposure is usually negligible.

Limitations of exposure limits

There are many reasons why control of exposure should not be based solely on exposure limits, including the following factors that could influence their use:

- **Compound routes of entry**. Many substances, for example, trichloroethylene, have the ability to absorb through the skin. Workplace exposure limits only account for routes of entry by inhalation.
- **Individual susceptibility**. The majority of the work to establish workplace exposure limits has been based on the average male physiology from the countries in which studies were conducted. The workplace exposure limits relate to average males and it is possible for individuals to have a higher than average susceptibility to some substances. In addition, there may be a difference in susceptibility of females to some substances. Some work has been carried out where specific health-related effects have been noted amongst females, for example, exposure to lead compounds.
- **Origin of exposure limit data**. Work carried out to date has mainly been based upon exposure to individuals in the developed countries, for example, Europe and the USA.
- **Variations in control**. Local exhaust ventilation systems may not always work consistently because of lack of maintenance, overwhelming levels of contamination, etc. Changes in the environmental conditions, for example, increased humidity or air pressure, may increase the harmful potential of the substance. This may lead to workplace exposure limits being exceeded inadvertently.
- **Errors in monitoring**. Measuring microscopic amounts of contamination requires very accurate and sensitive equipment. Devices have a range of accuracies, and lack of maintenance and misuse can lead to inaccuracies in monitoring due to equipment becoming contaminated.
- **Synergistic effects**. The workplace exposure limits that are available relate to single substances; the effects of multiple substances in the workplace need to be considered.

Application of relevant limits

The Control of Substances Hazardous to Health Regulations (COSHH) 2002 (amended) requires that exposure to hazardous substances should be prevented, where it is reasonably practicable, by changing the process.

Where this cannot be carried out, exposure should be reduced by other methods. Other methods include control of worker exposure levels by limiting the concentration of the substance in the atmosphere or inhaled by the worker and reducing the time workers are exposed to the substance. WELs are limits set under COSHH 2002, published in EH40, and are legally binding limits. It is a specific requirement of COSHH 2002 that WELs must not be exceeded. They are designed to protect the health of workers by establishing a maximum concentration of an airborne substance that a worker may be exposed to, averaged over a reference time period. The two reference periods that are used are 8-hours and 15-minutes.

The 8-hour WEL is known as a LTEL (long-term exposure limit) and is used to help protect against chronic ill-health effects. 15-minute STELs (short-term exposure limits) are set to protect against acute ill-health effects such as eye irritation, which may happen in minutes of exposure or where there is the risk of high level peak exposures over short time intervals during the working day. Airborne substances can be solid (dust), liquid (mist/aerosol), gas, vapours or fumes. Solids and liquids can be measured by weight (milligrams - mg), for example, a workplace exposure limit for cement dust may be expressed as 10 mg/m^3. Gas, vapours and fumes are weightless. Therefore, the WEL is expressed as a concentration in the atmosphere, for example, a workplace exposure limit for trichloroethylene may be expressed as 100 parts per million (ppm). WELs may be set relating to long-term exposure, short-term exposure or to establish a maximum allowable concentration for all circumstances, sometimes called a ceiling limit. WEL's therefore establish limits to guide action and establish effective control of worker exposure to substances by requiring employers to put prevention and control measures in place to ensure workplace exposure limits are not exceeded.

When employers are identifying hazards and establishing risk controls it is important to consider WELs set in EH40. When workplace exposure measurements are made as part of an employer's assessment process they should be compared with WELs set in EH40. This will help to establish the presence of a workplace hazard, the level of risk and will indicate the need to establish prevention and control measures. The comparison of workplace exposure measurements to WELs will also show how effective the prevention and control measures will need to be if the workplace exposure limits are to be met.

As prevention and control measures are put in place, new workplace exposure measurements should be made and compared with the WELs. This will determine the level of progress towards meeting the WELs and might indicate success or further work is required. Workplace exposure measurements should be made at intervals and after changes have been made in the workplace. The results of the measurements should be compared with WELs to enable health risks to be monitored and action taken if the performance of prevention and control measures declines.

It should be remembered that because workplace exposure limits are set as time weighted average concentrations of a substance in the air, a worker may be exposed to concentrations of a substance that are higher than the WEL for a period of time while they are working. This is acceptable, provided that the average concentration over the reference period for the WEL is not exceeded. Where WELs, measured over the reference period, are exceeded immediate action should be taken to reduce the level of workplace exposure to the substance.

Reducing exposure levels

As stated in the previous section, COSHH 2002 (amended) requires that exposure to hazardous substances should be prevented where it is reasonably practicable. Where this cannot be carried out by, for example, changing the process, substituting it for something that presents lower health risks or enclosing the process, exposure should be adequately controlled. These controls must ensure that any WEL set for the susbstance is not exceeded.

The limits set by WELs should be considered to be a maximum allowable limit and it is undesirable to see them as a normal working level if measures can easily be put in place to reduce them significantly below the WEL. If the levels of exposure are to be maintained below the WEL, with confidence, it will be necessary to work below them sufficiently to account for changes in work situation. This is particularly important with those WELs that are set for substances that are carcinogens or sensitisers. By working 'at the limit' employers do not allow for sensitive people who may be affected by relatively low exposures. Nor do they account for variations or inaccuracies in monitoring, sudden surges of contaminant or partial failures of control measures.

Regulation 7 (7) of COSHH 2002 sets out the criteria that controls must conform to in order to be considered adequate. It emphasises the requirement that carcinogens and sensitisers must be controlled to a level as low as is reasonably practicable.

"(7) ....where there is exposure to a substance hazardous to health, control of that exposure shall only be treated as adequate if:

(a) The principles of good practice for the control of exposure to substances hazardous to health set out in Schedule 2A are applied.

(b) Any workplace exposure limit approved for that substance is not exceeded.

(c) For a substance:

(i) Which carries the risk phrase R45, R46 or R49 (i.e. carcinogens), or for a substance or process that is listed in Schedule 1.

(ii) Which carries the risk phrase R42 or R42/43 (i.e. respiratory sensitisers), or which is listed in section C of HSE publication 'Asthmagen? Critical assessments of the evidence for agents implicated in occupational asthma' as updated from time to time, or any other substance which the risk assessment has shown to be a potential cause of occupational asthma, exposure is reduced to as low a level as is reasonably practicable."

Figure 8-17: Regulation 7 (7) of COSHH 2002.   Source: The Control of Substances Hazardous to Health Regulations (COSHH) 2002 (amended).

Work practices and control strategies for carcinogens and respiratory sensitiers should be continually reviewed to ensure the lowest levels of exposure are achieved, as far as is reasonably practicable.

8.4 - Control measures

Duty to prevent exposure or adequately control it

PREVENTION OF EXPOSURE

Legislation, including COSHH 2002, and good practice establish a clear need to prevent exposure where it is reasonably practicable.

If exposure is prevented then no harm to workers can be done. This is the most effective control measure and, although it may involve substantial investment, change is usually the best long-term solution to health risks presented by substances.

> *"Every employer shall ensure that the exposure of his employees to substances hazardous to health is either prevented or, where this is not reasonably practicable, adequately controlled."*

Figure 8-18: Regulation 7 (1) of COSHH 2002.   *Source: The Control of Substances Hazardous to Health Regulations (COSHH) 2002 (amended).*

Prevention of exposure to hazardous substances might be achieved by:

- Changing the method of work so that the operation giving rise to the exposure is no longer present.
- Modifying a process to eliminate the production of a hazardous by-product or waste product.
- Substituting, wherever reasonably practicable, a non-hazardous substance that presents no risk to health where a hazardous substance is currently used.

ADEQUATE CONTROL OF EXPOSURE

In many workplaces, it will not be possible or reasonably practicable to prevent exposure to substances hazardous to health completely. If exposure cannot be prevented, preferably by avoiding the use of a hazardous substance, then employers must adequately control exposure. This is a requirement of Regulation 7 (7) of COSHH 2002.

To achieve this employers must consider and apply, where appropriate for the circumstances of the work:

- The measures set out in Regulation 7(3) in the priority order given.
- The specific measures in Regulation 7(4).
- The principles of good practice for the control of exposure to substances hazardous to health set out in Schedule 2A.
- Any approved WEL for the substance, including the prevention of it being exceeded.
- The need to reduce exposure to as low as is reasonably practicable for substances listed, including carcinogens and sensitisers.

In order to meet the requirements of Regulation 7(3) the employer must apply protection measures appropriate to the activity and consistent with the priority order specified in the regulation:

- Provision of a high level of inherent health and safety by careful design, selection and use of appropriate work processes, systems and engineering controls, and use of suitable work equipment and materials. Where it is necessary to use a hazardous substance, an employer should consider whether it is possible to reduce exposure by using an alternative less hazardous substance, a different form of the same substance, for example, by using a substance in pellet rather than powder form, or a different process. Systems and processes may be used that reduce to the minimum required the amount of hazardous substance used or produced, or equipment may totally enclose the process.
- Controlling exposure at source, for example, by including adequate ventilation systems and appropriate organisational measures such as reducing to a minimum the number of workers exposed and the level and duration of their exposure.
- Using personal protective equipment in addition to the previous measures where those measures alone cannot achieve adequate control.

To meet the requirements of Regulation 7(4) the employer's protection measures must include:

- Arrangements for the safe handling, storage and transport of substances hazardous to health, and of waste containing such substances, at the workplace.
- The adoption of suitable maintenance procedures.
- Reducing, to the minimum required for the work concerned:
  - The number of employees subject to exposure.
  - The level and duration of exposure.
  - The quantity of substances hazardous to health present at the workplace.
- The control of the working environment, including appropriate general ventilation.
- Appropriate hygiene measures including adequate washing facilities.

Details on the eight principles of good practice for the control of exposure to substances hazardous to health set out in Schedule 2A of COSHH 2002 can be found later in this element in the section *'Principles of good practice as regards control of exposure'*.

Ensuring the workplace exposure limit is not exceeded

The HSE has established WELs for a number of substances that have been determined to be hazardous to health. These are intended to prevent excessive exposure to specified substances by requiring employers to ensure exposure is maintained below a set limit. Regulation 7(7) of COSHH 2002 specifically requires that workplace exposure limits established in EH40 are not exceeded. As part of achieving this, employers must apply the principles of good practice specified in scheduled 2A of COSHH 2002.

The principles of good control practice require the degree to which exposure is reduced below the WEL to be proportionate to the health risk. If employers apply the principles of good practice for the control of substances hazardous to health correctly, exposure should be below any relevant WEL.

Where the health effects arising from exposure are more serious, such as cancer or asthma, then employers are required to have a high standard of control of exposure. In this case, the extent to which employers should reduce exposure below the WEL depends on the degree of risk presented by the substance, weighed against the cost and effort involved in taking measures to reduce the risk. Employers should therefore ensure exposure is reduced to a level that is as low as is reasonably practicable. This would mean improving control of exposure until the cost of further reduction becomes grossly disproportionate when weighed against the benefit gained.

If an individual develops occupational asthma due to exposure to a substance, their exposure must be controlled to prevent triggering further attacks. This will usually require levels of exposure for that individual to be well below any WEL set for the substance.

A WEL is the maximum concentration of an airborne substance averaged over a reference period to which employees may be exposed by inhalation. This relationship between level (concentration) and duration of exposure is an important feature of workplace exposure limits. Where the concentration of a substance in the air of a workplace fluctuates it is possible for an employer to establish an average concentration over a defined period. In this way, the high concentration levels may be compensated for by the lower concentration levels.

This time weighted average allows employers to exceed concentrations stated in WELs for short periods, providing the periods of low concentration ensure the time weighted average concentration does not exceed the WEL. The workplace exposure limits set in EH40 are helpful as they specify the period of time that the concentration levels are averaged over, 8 hours or 15 minutes depending on the characteristics of the substance. To prevent WELs being exceeded, employers may have to carry out a programme of workplace exposure monitoring to determine the time-weighted average concentration of substances in the workplace.

Workplace monitoring is a requirement of Regulation 10 of COSHH 2002, where a risk assessment confirms it is appropriate.

Principles of good practice as regards control of exposure

Regulation 7 (7) of the Control of Substances Hazardous to Health Regulations (COSHH) 2002 (amended) requires employers to apply the principles of good practice detailed in schedule 2A of the Regulations in order to control exposure to hazardous substances in situations where exposure cannot be prevented. The eight principles of good practice set out in schedule 2A are:

1) Design and operate processes and activities to minimise emission, release and spread of substances hazardous to health.

2) Take into account all relevant routes of exposure - inhalation, skin absorption and ingestion - when developing control measures.

3) Control exposure by measures that are proportionate to the health risk.

4) Choose the most effective and reliable control options which minimise the escape and spread of substances hazardous to health.

5) Where adequate control of exposure cannot be achieved by other means, provide, in combination with other control measures, suitable personal protective equipment.

6) Check and review regularly all elements of control measures for their continuing effectiveness.

7) Inform and train all employees on the hazards and risks from the substances with which they work and the use of control measures developed to minimise the risks.

8) Ensure that the introduction of control measures does not increase the overall risk to health and safety.

Each of the principles of good practice is outlined in the following headings.

MINIMISING EMISSION, RELEASE AND SPREAD OF HAZARDOUS SUBSTANCES

It is important, where possible to minimise emission, release and spread of hazardous substances by effective design and operation of processes and task activities. A useful approach to control exposure to hazardous substances is to reduce the actual quantity of the substance which can become airborne. For example, prevention of large volumes of airborne vapours by use of a paint brush rather than an aerosol or paint-spraying equipment.

Emissions of vapours from hazardous substances can be minimised by process controls that limit the temperature of the substance so that fewer vapours are given off, and processes that usually create dust may be controlled by keeping the process wet. All processes and equipment should be checked and maintained to ensure that containment of hazardous substances is effective, for example, seals on joints may need to be replaced or kept tight.

Minimising release and spread can involve removing the contaminant at source so that its range of contamination is minimised. Removal is usually achieved by mechanical air handling in the form of ventilation.

Local exhaust ventilation or dilution ventilation are the options available, with the type chosen depending on the amount and toxicity of the contaminant. Local exhaust ventilation is located closer to the source of the contaminant and is more effective than dilution ventilation.

In the case of disposal of acids, the risk of acid burns or corrosion will be removed by neutralisation with a suitable alkali.

Changes in work patterns can ensure that fewer employees are exposed. It might be possible that some work takes place at night or weekend when fewer people are present.

Change of work patterns to reduce length of time of exposure forms the basis of workplace exposure limits, i.e. long-term exposure limits (8 hours time weighted average value) and short-term exposure limits (15 minutes weighted average value). This is particularly relevant when considering shift patterns, where 12 hour shifts are common and the individual operators' work arrangements may need to be rotated, within a shift, to ensure 8 hours time weighted averages are not exceeded.

Remove contaminant at source so that its range of contamination is minimised. Removal is usually achieved by mechanical air handling. Local exhaust ventilation or dilution ventilation are the options available depending on the amount and toxicity of the contaminant.

TAKING INTO ACCOUNT ROUTES OF EXPOSURE AND CONTROL OPTIONS

It is important to take into account all relevant routes of exposure, along with the effectiveness and reliability of control options. Exposure can occur through, inhalation; to or through the skin; or by ingestion.

When selecting control options consideration will therefore need to be given to the:

- Way the substances are used and how exposure occurs.
- Degree of exposure.
- Health effects that the substances can cause.

When all sources and routes of exposure have been identified these should be ranked in order of importance. In many case it will be found that not all routes of exposure will occur. For example, for people potentially exposed to crystalline silica, when cutting stone or concrete, the only relevant route of entry is by inhalation, whereas, for those handling a low volatility substance, such as diesel, the primary route of entry will be through the skin. In this way, control can be directed at the main sources and routes of exposure.

Inhalation

Where inhalation is the most relevant route, the main focus for control will be the control of sources of emission to air. Typical controls include total enclosure of the process or local exhaust ventilation (LEV) to capture any emission into the workplace before it can cause harm to the worker. Care is needed to identify any fugitive emissions, particularly where very toxic substances may need to be controlled, and it may be necessary to consider other controls to protect the workers, such as the provision of breathing apparatus in addition to LEV.

Ingestion

Where the most relevant route is ingestion, the main control will be the prohibition of eating, drinking, smoking and use of cosmetics in workplaces where substances are used that cause harm by ingestion. Welfare arrangements will need to be provided in separate clean areas and workers must be instructed to remove any contaminated clothing or PPE and to wash before entering such areas.

Skin contact

Where the most relevant route is contact with the skin, care will need to be taken to identify such substances. Some substances such as acids and alkalis will cause skin cellular damage if they come into contact with the skin, other substances may pass through the skin and cause injury within the body. Controls include clean working regimes and the use of suitable PPE to protect the skin and eyes from contact with substances when in use. Where these risks of contamination exist, it is important to train workers in safe removal of inadvertent spillages and safe removal of any contaminated clothing or PPE. It may be appropriate to locate drench showers in the work area for use by workers if there is a possibility of significant contamination when carrying out their work.

CONTROL EXPOSURE BY MEASURES PROPORTIONATE TO THE HEALTH RISK

The more severe the potential health effect, and the greater the likelihood of it occurring, the stricter the measures required to control exposure.

Control measures have to take into account the nature and severity of the hazard, the magnitude, frequency and duration of exposure and the number and type of people exposed. They should be proportionate to the risk.

If the risk is low and not likely to cause long-term harm, the control measures may be simple procedural issues such as replacing the lid tightly on tins and containers or a regime of regular cleaning. However, if the consequences are likely to be diseases such as dermatitis, asthma or cancer then more robust and reliable measures must be implemented.

CHOOSING THE MOST EFFECTIVE AND RELIABLE CONTROL OPTIONS

It is important to choose the most effective and reliable control options for the circumstances and direct these at the main sources and causes of exposure. Some control options are inherently more reliable and effective than others. For example, the protection afforded by PPE is dependent upon good fit and attention to detail. In contrast, a very reliable form of control is changing the process so that less of the hazardous substance is emitted or released.

A set of integrated control measures that are effective and reliable enough to control exposure adequately has to be developed. It is important that the 'hierarchical' approach to reliability and effectiveness is not viewed so rigidly that some control options are seen as 'good', while others are seen as ineffective. Some control measures are more reliable than others are.

There is a general hierarchy of controls available:

- **Elimination of the substance -** This is the most effective though least realistic option. If elimination can be achieved it means that no exposure can take place and there is no residual risk to manage.
- **Reduction of exposure -** By substituting a less harmful substance or reducing the number of people exposed and/or the frequency and duration of exposure. This method protects all employees but there will be residual risk to deal with.
- **Isolation of the substance -** Secure storage facilities with limited access.
- **Controls -** Engineering controls such as local exhaust ventilation. These have to be carefully monitored to ensure, for example, that the captor hood is correctly positioned.
- **Personal protective equipment -** Or other devices worn by individuals such as exposure monitors. The main disadvantage of this method is that it only protects the user. Furthermore, it will only protect the user if the equipment/device is worn correctly, if at all.

The important consideration is that there is a hierarchy of reliability of control options and this is often linked to their effectiveness. Always consider elimination first. If this is not possible, a reliable form of control is to change the process so that it releases less substance. Controls applied to the process might be as effective, but will require maintenance and are unlikely to be as reliable. There is a range of control options available.

Each will have its own characteristics as to when it is appropriate to be applied, how much it can reduce exposure, and how reliable it is likely to be. In many cases, an effective set of control measures will turn out to be a mix of options, some more reliable than others. Control options, such as change of process or applied controls, are likely to be more effective and reliable than PPE, and be cheaper in the long term, but it may take longer to plan and organise them. It is important not to rely solely on PPE as the only control option and believe exposure is adequately, effectively and reliably controlled.

Employers should also consider the consequences of failure of the control measure when making their selection. If failure of the control measure would lead to exposure of workers to a high risk of harm, and if failure of the control measure to control harm was likely, it would be preferable to use a control that was more reliable. Decisions to use PPE as a control measure should consider its likely level of success in preventing harm. When working with high risk substances, it would be preferable to use controls that are more reliable than PPE.

The person responsible for designing the control measures needs appropriate knowledge, skills and experience. The competencies required will depend on the scope and complexity of the exposure problems to be addressed and solved.

USE OF PERSONAL PROTECTIVE EQUIPMENT IN CONJUNCTION WITH OTHER MEASURES

When adequate control of exposure cannot be achieved by other means, a combination of control measures and PPE may be applied. This will provide more effective protection of workers in the circumstances that the control measures provide limited protection or protection is required where their reliability may mean they fail.

An example of this is where the control measure provided is local exhaust ventilation (LEV). In this situation, the LEV will provide a degree of effective removal of the contaminant, but to increase the effectiveness of protection the worker may also wear respiratory protective equipment (RPE), such as a respirator.

The use of personal protective equipment is considered in more detail later in this element and also in 'NGC1 - Element 4 - Health and safety management systems - Check'.

CHECKS AND REVIEW OF CONTROL MEASURES TO CONFIRM EFFECTIVENESS

All control measures require regular checks and review to ensure their continued effectiveness and efficiency. There are a number of reasons why this approach should be adopted.

- Legal obligations.
- To comply with WELs.
- Provision of information to employees.
- To indicate the need for health surveillance.
- For insurance purposes.
- To develop in-house exposure standards.

Exactly what checks should be carried out depends on such factors as:

- The control measures in use.
- The reliability of the controls.
- The consequences of failure of the control measure.

PROVISION OF INFORMATION AND TRAINING

For control measures to be effective, people need to know how to use them. Furthermore, employees should be consulted during the development of control measures. Employees who have been actively involved in the design of controls are more likely to appreciate the need for their use and, therefore, more likely to use them correctly. Regulation 12 of COSHH 2002 sets out requirements for information, instruction and training, **see figure ref 8-19**.

"(1) Every employer who undertakes work which is liable to expose an employee to a substance hazardous to health shall provide that employee with suitable and sufficient information, instruction and training.

(2) Without prejudice to the generality of paragraph (1), the information, instruction and training provided under that paragraph shall include:

(a) Details of the substances hazardous to health to which the employee is liable to be exposed including:

(i) The names of those substances and the risk which they present to health.

(ii) Any relevant occupational exposure standard, maximum exposure limit or similar occupational exposure limit.

(iii) Access to any relevant safety data sheet.

(iv) Other legislative provisions which concern the hazardous properties of those substances.

(b) The significant findings of the risk assessment.

(c) The appropriate precautions and actions to be taken by the employee in order to safeguard himself and other employees at the workplace.

(d) The results of any monitoring of exposure in accordance with Regulation 10 and, in particular, in the case of a substance hazardous to health for which a maximum exposure limit has been approved, the employee or his representatives shall be informed forthwith, if the results of such monitoring show that the maximum exposure limit has been exceeded.

(e) The collective results of any health surveillance undertaken in accordance with Regulation 11 in a form calculated to prevent those results from being identified as relating to a particular person.

(f) Where employees are working with a Group 4 biological agent or material that may contain such an agent, the provision of written instructions and, if appropriate, the display of notices which outline the procedures for handling such an agent or material.

(3) The information, instruction and training required by paragraph (1) shall be:

(a) Adapted to take account of significant changes in the type of work carried out or methods of work used by the employer.

(b) Provided in a manner appropriate to the level, type and duration of exposure identified by the risk assessment.

(4) Every employer shall ensure that any person (whether or not his employee) who carries out work in connection with the employer's duties under these Regulations has suitable and sufficient information, instruction and training.

(5) Where containers and pipes for substances hazardous to health used at work are not marked in accordance with any relevant legislation listed in Schedule 7, the employer shall, without prejudice to any derogations provided for in that legislation, ensure that the contents of those containers and pipes, together with the nature of those contents and any associated hazards, are clearly identifiable."

Figure 8-19: Regulation 12 of COSHH 2002.   *Source: The Control of Substances Hazardous to Health Regulations (COSHH) 2002 (amended).*

The instruction and training must ensure that people at work on the premises do not put themselves or others at risk through exposure to substances hazardous to health.

In particular, the information and training must be sufficient and suitable for workers to know:

- How and when to use the control measures.
- The defined methods of work.
- How to use the PPE, and especially RPE. For example, the correct method of removing and refitting gloves and masks and determining how long protective gloves should be worn before any liquid contamination is liable to permeate them.
- The cleaning, storage and disposal procedures they should follow, why they are required and when they are to be carried out, for example, cleaning contaminated PPE with water or a vacuum fitted with a high-efficiency particulate arrester (HEPA) filter, and not with an airline, or the risks of using contaminated PPE.
- The procedures to be followed in an emergency.

Training should include elements of theory as well as practice. Training in the use and application of control measures and PPE should take account of recommendations and instructions supplied by the manufacturer.

CONTROL MEASURES NOT TO INCREASE OVERALL RISK TO HEALTH AND SAFETY

People designing control measures have to consider the possibility that the new measures might introduce new risks. For example, personal protective equipment can affect mobility and interfere with the senses. The introduction of local exhaust ventilation means that it will have to be maintained and, therefore, will introduce the hazards attendant to maintenance operations and the use of enclosures might increase the chances of an explosion.

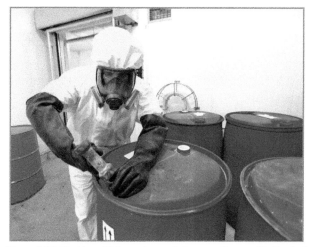

Figure 8-20: Working with hazardous substances. *Source: Shutterstock.*

Common measures used to implement the principles of good practice

ELIMINATION

This represents an extreme form of control and is appropriately used where high risk is present from such things as carcinogens (cancer forming substances). It is usually achieved through the prohibition of use of these substances. Care must be taken to ensure that all stock is safely disposed of and that controls are in place to prevent their re-entry, even as a sample or for research. If this level of control is not achievable then another must be selected.

REDUCTION

By substitution

The substitution of a less toxic substance in place of a more highly toxic one, for example, toluene for benzene, glass fibre for asbestos, or water-based adhesives for solvent-based adhesives is a frequently used technique.

It is also possible to substitute the form of the substance in that a substance that requires mixing from dry products, such as cement, may be ordered pre-prepared, thus avoiding the additional contact with the substance in the mixing process and in the dry state where dust may be liberated. In the same way, dust generated in a demolition process may be watered down so that it becomes liquid slurry.

Quantity

A useful approach is to reduce the actual quantity of the substance presenting the hazard. This may be achieved by limiting the amount used or stored. For example, with acids, it may be possible to use a more dilute form than is presently being used. In the case of disposal, it is possible to reduce the quantity by neutralisation (a chemical reaction that forms a salt).

PROCESS CHANGES

The role of the occupational hygienist is to identify peaks in exposure to operators during their normal working day, for example, when charging or discharging process equipment - at this time higher than normal background levels of contamination may occur in the general work area.

Figure 8-21: Reduced exposure - bulk supply. *Source: RMS.*

Whenever process changes occur through plant failure or maintenance, consideration needs to be given to exposure to those affected at these times. It may be necessary to reassess the process/maintenance arrangements to ensure adequacy of health controls.

REDUCED TIME EXPOSURE AND SIGNIFICANCE OF TIME WEIGHTED AVERAGES

The level of harm to a worker's health is dependent on the concentration of a substance that they are exposed to over time. In situations where the concentration of the substance cannot be reduced easily, reduction in the time workers are exposed to the substance will reduce the harm to their health. Individual worker time exposure reduction can be achieved by introducing worker rotation during the work period. For example, rotation of four workers over an 8-hour work period so that each worker spends an equal portion of time doing the same task that exposes them to a substance would reduce individual worker exposure by 75%.

ENCLOSURE OF HAZARDS

The strategy of enclosure of hazards is based on the containment of a dangerous substance to prevent its free movement in the working environment. It may take a number of forms, for example, enclosure of activities, pipelines, closed conveyors, laboratory fume cupboards. In construction situations, this control measure is used in asbestos removal, where the work being carried out is enclosed in plastic sheeting in order to contain the asbestos hazard and prevent its release into the surrounding areas. In a similar way, enclosure of hazards may be used for a building cleaning processes that uses glass beads that are fired by air pressure or for spray protection being applied to a structure.

In its simplest form, enclosure of hazards can mean putting lids on substances that have volatile vapours, such as tins of solvent-based products. In this way, the strategy is to enclose the hazard so that vapours are not given off. In this case, this is best carried out when the substance is not in use; this does not just mean at the end of the day but at intervals when the substance is not actually in use. This is a very simple and effective control of exposure to hazards.

SEGREGATION OF PROCESS AND PEOPLE

Segregation of process and people is a useful method of controlling the risks from dangerous substances and can involve physical separation of people and segregation of people by worker characteristics.

Segregation by physical separation

Physical separation of people can be a relatively simple method, such as keeping the number of workers working with dangerous substances to a minimum and distancing (segregating) them from the general workforce. If the hazards cannot be enclosed close to their source it may be preferable that the workforce be segregated from the hazards in the process by providing physical separation in the form of a refuge, for example, a control room of a chemical process or the cab of construction equipment.

Segregation by worker characteristics

The protection of young workers in certain work activities is important. A good example is working with lead, where young workers are usually excluded from lead processes. In this case the Control of Lead at Work Regulations (CLAW) 2002 excludes the employment of young persons in lead processes. There also remains the possibility of gender linked vulnerability to certain toxic substances such as lead; segregation affords a high level of control in these circumstances. In addition, workers that have shown a susceptibility to substances may be segregated to ensure they are not exposed to them, for example, respiratory sensitisers like flour dust or some wood dusts.

LOCAL EXHAUST VENTILATION

Hazards that can be controlled by the effective use of local exhaust ventilation (LEV) include:

- Dust and fibres that could cause coughing, sneezing and various other respiratory diseases.
- Chemicals that might cause sensitisation or other toxic effects.
- Allergens that could aggravate asthmatic conditions.
- Micro-organisms that can cause diseases.
- Asphyxiants that can lead to breathing difficulties, unconsciousness and, ultimately, death.

Local exhaust ventilation is more frequently being used to control construction dust. Many items of construction equipment that create dust have on-tool extraction to provide local exhaust ventilation.

Figure 8-22: Wall chasing using on-tool extraction.   *Source: HSE.*

Figure 8-23: Extraction unit.   *Source: HSE.*

General applications and principles

Various LEV systems are in use in the workplace and the main types are called receptors and captors. Receptors are designed to use low velocity extraction and are best suited to gases, vapours and lightweight dusts travelling at low velocity from the source. Captors are designed to use high velocity extraction and are best suited to remove metal fume from welding operations or waste dust from high speed grinding or cutting equipment. *See figure ref 8-25,* which shows the fixed extractor hood, flexible hose ducting and rigid duct. Many construction tools that creat dust are designed to use captor LEV systems.

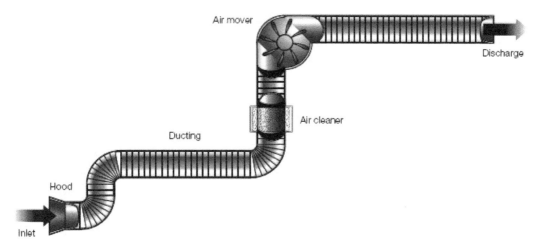

Figure 8-24: Common elements of a simple LEV system. *Source: HSE, INDG408.*

Components of a basic system

The components of a basic LEV system are:

- **Hood(s)** to collect airborne contaminants at, or near, where they are created (the source).
- **Ducts** to carry the airborne contaminants away from the process. *See figure ref 8-29* which shows the length of ducting with curves not corners.
- **Air cleaner** to filter and clean the extracted air.
- **Fan** must be the right size and type to deliver sufficient 'suck' to the hood. *See figure ref 8-26* as it clearly shows the size of a fan and motor required for industrial scale LEV.
- **Discharge** the safe release of cleaned, extracted air into the atmosphere.

Figure 8-25: Captor system on circular saw. *Source: RMS.*

Figure 8-26: LEV fan and motor. *Source: RMS.*

Figure 8-27: Flexible hose and captor hood. *Source: RMS.*

Figure 8-28: Portable self-contained unit. *Source: RMS.*

Factors that reduce a LEV system's effectiveness

The efficiency of LEV systems can be affected by many factors including the following:

- Damaged ducting.
- Unauthorised alterations.
- Incorrect hood location. **See figure ref 8-27** which shows how a captor hood can be repositioned to suit the work activity by the use of a flexible hose.
- Too many bends or sharp bends in ducts.
- Blocked or defective filters.
- Leaving too many ports open.
- Process changes leading to overwhelming amounts of contamination.
- Fan strength or incorrect adjustment of fan.
- Excessive amounts of contamination.

The cost of heating/cooling air introduced to the workplace to replace that removed by the LEV system may encourage some employers to reduce extraction rates. When arranging installation of LEV it is vital that the pre-ventialtion and post-ventilation contamination levels are specified and the required reduction should be part of the commissioning contract.

Figure 8-29: Length of ducting with curves. *Source: RMS.*

Figure 8-30: Shows a number of ports at the end of one duct - not all ports being used. *Source: RMS.*

Requirements for thorough examination and inspection

LEV systems should be thoroughly examined at suitable specified intervals to ensure that they are continuing to perform as originally intended. COSHH 2002 Regulation 9(2) and schedule 4 set out requirements for inspection of LEV systems. A thorough examination and test must take place once every 14 months (more frequently for those processes listed in schedule 4). Records must be kept available for at least 5 years from the date on which it was made.

Regular inspection of LEV systems should be carried out in addition to the thorough examination. This should identify that the features for effectiveness are in place, for example, blanking covers for inlets not being used, and that no obvious defects exist.

The majority of ventilation systems, although effective in protecting workers' health from airborne contaminants, can create other hazards. One of the main hazards that need to be considered when designing LEV systems is that of noise. Even if it has been considered as a design feature when establishing LEV systems, it should be monitored on a periodic basis.

USE AND LIMITATIONS OF DILUTION VENTILATION

Dilution ventilation is a system designed to induce a general flow of clean air into a work area. A particularly simple approach to providing dilution ventilation is to open a window and door and allow natural air flow to dilute the workplace air. This is not a reliable means of dealing with toxic contaminants and may be over relied on in the construction industry. On its own it may prove inadequate, but supported by respiratory protection equipment it may be acceptable for some substances. Dilution ventilation may be achieved by driving air into a work area, causing air flow around the work area, dilution of contaminants in the work area and then out of the work area through general leakage or through ventilation ducts to the open air.

A variation on this is where air may be forcibly removed from the work area, but not associated with a particular contaminant source, and air is allowed in through ventilation ducts to dilute the air in the work area. Sometimes a combination of these two approaches is used; an example may be general air conditioning provided into an office environment. Because dilution ventilation does not target any specific source and it relies on dispersal and dilution instead of specific removal, it can only be used with nuisance contaminants that are themselves fairly mobile in air. Dilution ventilation systems will only deal with general contamination and will not prevent contaminants entering a person's breathing zone. Local exhaust ventilation is the preferred means of controlling a person's exposure to substances.

Dilution ventilation may only be used as the sole means of control in circumstances where there is:

- Non-toxic contaminant or vapour (not dusts).
- Contaminant which is uniformly produced in small, known quantities.
- No discrete point of release.
- No other practical means of reducing levels.

The limitations of dilution ventilation are:

- It is not suitable for substances of high toxicity.
- Large sudden releases of a contaminant are not coped with well.
- It tends to move dust around rather than remove it.
- Areas in the location may exist where natural airflow does not create air movement.
- Stagnant air or non-moving air is likely to hold high concentrations of the contaminant.

RESPIRATORY PROTECTIVE EQUIPMENT

Regulation 7(3)(c) and principle (e) of the principles of prevention in COSHH 2002 require the employer to provide employees with suitable PPE where it is neccessary, for example, respiratory protective equipment (RPE). This would be in addition to other control measures if the control measures fail to achieve adequate control of exposure.

Purpose, application and effectiveness of RPE

Damage to health and death can be caused by breathing in hazardous substances, such as dusts, fumes, vapours, gases or even micro-organisms. If direct prevention or control of exposure is not possible then RPE may be needed; this should always be seen as a measure of last resort in the hierarchy of control measures.

RPE includes a very wide range of devices from simple respirators offering basic protection against low levels of nuisance dusts to self-contained breathing apparatus. The effectiveness of respiratory protection depends on using the proper equipment for the specific task.

Before selecting respiratory protection equipment, the following issues should be considered:

- Operations and work sites where there is any kind of contamination.
- Jobs where a lack of oxygen is a problem.
- Specific contaminants that are present at the work site.
- Harmful properties of the contaminants.
- Form of the contaminant material: dust, mist, spray, gas, vapour, fume, or some combination of these.
- Concentrations of each contaminant.

Types of respiratory protection equipment

There are two main categories of respiratory protection:

1) Respirators.
2) Breathing apparatus.

Respirators

Respirators filter the air breathed but do not provide additional oxygen.

There are a number of types of respirator that provide a variety of degrees of protection from dealing with nuisance dusts to high efficiency respirators for solvents or asbestos.

Some respirators may be nominated as providing non-specific protection from contaminants whereas others will be designed to protect from a very specific contaminant such as solvent vapours.

Figure 8-31: Paper filter respirator. *Source: Shutterstock.*

There are five main types of respirators:

1) Filtering face piece.
2) Half mask respirator.
3) Full face respirator.
4) Powered air purifying respirator.
5) Powered visor respirator.

Advantages

The advantages of a respirator are:

- Unrestricted movement.
- Often lightweight and comfortable.
- Can be worn for long periods.

Limitations

The limitations of a respirator are:

- Purifies the air by drawing it through a filter to remove contaminants. Therefore, can only be used when there is sufficient oxygen in the atmosphere.
- Requires careful selection by a competent person.
- Requires regular maintenance.
- Knowing when a filter or cartridge is at the end of its useful life.
- Requires correct storage facilities.
- Can give a 'closed in'/claustrophobic feeling.
- Relies on user for correct fit/use etc.
- Incompatible with other forms of personal protective equipment (PPE).
- Performance can be affected by beards and long hair.
- Interferes with other senses, for example, sense of smell.

Figure 8-32: 3M filtering face-piece respirator. *Source: RMS.*

Breathing apparatus

Breathing apparatus provides a separate source of supply of air (including oxygen) to that which surrounds the person. Because of the self-contained nature of breathing apparatus it may be used to provide a high degree of protection from a variety of toxic contaminants and may be used in situations where the actual contaminant is not known or there is more than one contaminant.

There are three types of breathing apparatus:

1) Fresh air hose apparatus - clean air from uncontaminated source.
2) Compressed air line apparatus from compressed air source.
3) Self-contained breathing apparatus - from cylinder.

Figure 8-33: Full face canister respirator. *Source: Shutterstock.*

Figure 8-34: Breathing apparatus. *Source: Haxton Safety.*

Advantages

The advantages of breathing apparatus are:

- Supplies clean air from an uncontaminated source. Therefore, can be worn in oxygen deficient atmospheres.
- Has high assigned protection factor (APF), this term is explained further on the next page. Therefore may be used in an atmosphere with high levels of toxic substance.
- Can be worn for long periods if connected to a permanent supply of air.

Limitations

The limitations of breathing apparatus are:

- Can be heavy and cumbersome which restricts movement.
- Requires careful selection by competent person.
- Requires special training.
- Requires arrangements to monitor/supervise user and for emergencies.
- Can give a 'closed in'/claustrophobic feeling.

- Relies on user for correct fit/use etc.
- Incompatible with other forms of PPE.
- Performance can be affected by, for example, long hair.
- Interferes with other senses, for example, sense of smell.
- Requires correct storage facilities.

Selection, use and maintenance

There are a number of issues to consider in the selection of RPE, not least the advantages and limitations shown in the previous list. A general approach must not only take account of the needs derived from the work to be carried out and the contaminant to be protected from, but must include suitability for the person. This includes issues such as face fit and the ability of the person to use the equipment for a sustained period, if this is required. One of the important factors is to ensure that the equipment will provide the level of protection required.

This is indicated by the APF given to the equipment by the manufacturers - the higher the factor the more protection provided. With a little knowledge it is possible to work out what APF is needed using the following formula:

APF = <u>Concentration of contaminant in the workplace</u>

Concentration of contaminant in the face-piece

It is important to understand that this factor is only an indication of what the equipment will provide. Actual protection may be different due to fit and the task being conducted.

Every employee must use any PPE provided in accordance with the training and instructions that they have received. It is important that the worker using the RPE conduct a face fit test to ensure the equipment is providing the protection needed. Where RPE (other than disposable RPE) is provided, the employer must ensure that thorough examination and where appropriate testing, of that equipment is carried out at suitable intervals.

OTHER PROTECTIVE EQUIPMENT AND CLOTHING

Hand/arm protection including gloves

There are numerous types of glove and gauntlet available that offer protection from hazards:

■ Chemical hazards such as acids, alkalis etc.
■ Thermal hazards such as hot surfaces.
■ Mechanical hazards in the form of splinters and sharp edges.

The materials used in the manufacture of these products are an essential feature to consider when making the selection. There are several types of rubber (latex, nitrile, PVC, butyl) all giving different levels of protection against aqueous chemicals; leather affords protection against heat , splinters and cuts; space age technology in the form of Kevlar (a tough, lightweight material) protects against cuts from knife blades and is used in the sleeves of jackets for those using chainsaws.

Figure 8-35: Gloves.   *Source: Speedy Hire plc.*

Figure 8-36: Protective clothing - gloves.   *Source: Haxton Safety.*

Protective clothing

There are numerous types of clothing available that offer protection from hazards:

■ Protective outer clothing - normally PVC, often high-visibility to alert traffic.
■ Protective inner clothing - overalls, aprons.

Head protection

Head protection includes safety helmets or scalp protectors (bump caps). Scalp protectors only give limited protection and are unsuitable for use in confined spaces. Safety helmets generally have a useful life of three years; however, this may be shortened by prolonged exposure to ultraviolet (UV) light. It is a common requirement on construction sites to wear head protection where there is risk of injury from falling objects.

Eye protection

When selecting suitable eye protection, some of the factors to be considered are:

■ Type and nature of hazard (impact, chemical, ultra violet (UV) light, etc.).
■ Type/standard/quality of protection.

- Comfort and user acceptability issues.
- Compatibility.
- Maintenance and training requirements.
- Cost.

Figure 8-37: Eye and ear protection.   *Source: Speedy Hire plc.*

Figure 8-38: Arc welding visor - UV reactive.   *Source: RMS.*

Types	Advantages	Limitations
Spectacles	<ul><li>Lightweight, easy to wear.</li><li>Can incorporate prescription lenses.</li><li>Do not 'mist up'.</li></ul>	<ul><li>Do not give all round protection.</li><li>Relies on the wearer for use.</li></ul>
Goggles	<ul><li>Give all round protection.</li><li>Can be worn over prescription lenses.</li><li>Capable of high impact protection.</li><li>Can protect against other hazards, for example, dust, molten metal.</li></ul>	<ul><li>Tendency to 'mist up'.</li><li>Uncomfortable when worn for long periods.</li><li>Can affect peripheral vision.</li></ul>
Face shields (visors)	<ul><li>Gives full face protection against splashes.</li><li>Can incorporate a fan which creates air movement for comfort and protection against low level contaminants.</li><li>Can be integrated into other PPE, for example, head protection.</li></ul>	<ul><li>Require care in use, otherwise can become dirty and scratched.</li><li>Can affect peripheral vision.</li><li>Unless the visor is provided with extra sealing gusset around the visor, substances may go underneath the visor to the face.</li></ul>

Footwear - safety boots/shoes

The importance of foot protection is illustrated by the fact that around 21,000 foot and ankle injuries are reported annually.

Inadequate protection and a lack of discipline on the part of the wearer commonly cause these.

There are many types of safety footwear on the market, many of them offering different types of protection.

It is vital that the nature of the hazard is considered when selecting appropriate footwear.

Here are some common examples:

- Falling objects   - steel toe-caps.
- Sharp objects   - steel in-soles.
- Flammable atmospheres   - anti-static footwear.
- Spread of contamination - washable boots.
- Electricity   - rubber soles.
- Wet environments   - impermeable wellingtons.
- Slippery surfaces   - non-slip soles.
- Cold environments   - thermally insulated soles.

Figure 8-39: Personal protective equipment.   *Source: RMS.*

Ear protection

See also 'Element 9 - Physical and psychological health - hazards and risk control', for details of ear protection.

PERSONAL HYGIENE AND PROTECTION REGIMES

Personal hygiene and good housekeeping have an important role in the protection of the health and safety of people at work. Laid down procedures and standards are necessary for preventing the spread of contamination. The provision of adequate washing/showering facilities is important to remove contamination from the body. The provision of laundry facilities for overalls and PPE reduces the effect of contamination. Barrier creams and suitable hand protection are important considerations for chemical and biological risks.

Where personal hygiene is critical, for example, when stripping asbestos, a 'three room system' is employed. Workers enter the 'clean end' and put work clothes on, leaving by means of the 'dirty end'. When work has been completed they return by means of the 'dirty end', carry out personal hygiene and leave by means of the 'clean end'.

Vaccination

Where construction workers work in the vicinity activities like water treatment/sewage and medical treatment there is a higher than average risk from some biological hazards. Where segregation is not possible consideration may have to be given to those involved being immunised against common high risks, for example, hepatitis B. Whilst vaccination can be an effective way of preventing ill-health as a result of exposure to biological agents, it is important that employers are aware of problems that can arise. In the first instance, vaccination is intrusive. Employers need the permission of employees before adopting this method - this may not always be forthcoming. Secondly, it is possible that some people will suffer adverse effects from the vaccination. Finally, not all diseases are treatable by vaccination and, for those that are, vaccination might not be available.

HEALTH SURVEILLANCE AND BIOLOGICAL MONITORING

Health surveillance

'Health surveillance' is concerned with collecting and using information about a worker's health related to their work and systematically watching out for work-related ill-health in workers exposed to certain health risks. Health surveillance of workers may be useful for:

- Assessment of the health of workers in relation to risks caused by exposure to chemicals.
- Early diagnosis of work-related diseases and injuries caused by exposure to hazardous chemicals.
- Assessment of the worker's ability to wear or use required respiratory or other PPE.

Health surveillance may be appropriate where exposure to hazardous substances is such that an identifiable disease or adverse health effect may be linked to the exposure. There must be a reasonable likelihood that the disease or effect may occur under the particular conditions of work prevailing and valid techniques must exist to detect such conditions and effects.

The Management of Health and Safety at Work Regulations (MHSWR) 1999, Regulation 6, deals with health surveillance and gives employers a duty to provide it where it is appropriate. Further details on health surveillance are contained in other Regulations, for example, COSHH 2002. *(Details can be found in the Approved Code of Practice Schedule 6; Extracts from the ACOP follow).*

Substances for which health surveillance is appropriate		Processes
Vinyl Chloride Monomer (VCM).		In manufacturing, production, reclamation, storage, discharge, transport, use or polymerization.
Nitro or amino derivatives of phenol and of benzene or its homologues.		In the manufacture of nitro or amino derivatives of phenol and of benzene or its homologues and the making of explosives with the use of any of these substances.
Orthotolidine and its salts.	Dianisidine and its salts. Dichlorbenzidene and its salts.	In manufacture, formation or use of these substances.
Auramine.	Magenta.	In manufacture.
Carbon Disulphide. Disulpher Dichloride. Benzene, including benzol.	Carbon Tetrachloride. Tricholoroethylene.	Process in which these substances are used, or given off as a vapour, in the manufacture of indiarubber or of articles or goods made wholly or partially of indiarubber.
Pitch.		In manufacture of blocks of fuel consisting of coal, coal dust, coke or slurry with pitch as a binding substance.

Figure 8-40: Schedule 6 medical surveillance.   *Source: COSHH ACoP.*

Though construction workers are not engaged in the manufacture of these substances they may work in locations where manufacture takes place. Other than the cases stated in Schedule 6 of COSHH 2002 (amended), surveillance may be appropriate where exposure to hazardous substances is such that an identifiable disease or adverse health effect may be linked to the exposure. There must be a reasonable likelihood that the disease or effect may occur under the particular conditions of work prevailing and that valid techniques exist to detect such conditions and effects.

Health surveillance may include medical surveillance conducted by an approved medical practitioner and, where appropriate, examination and investigations that may be necessary to detect exposure levels and early biological effects and responses.

The types of checks that can be included in a health surveillance programme are:

- Clinical examinations.
- Diagnostic tests such as by X-ray or scan.
- Function measurements, for example, a lung function test.
- Biological tests of the blood.
- Skin checks for signs of rashes.
- Eye and hearing tests.
- Self-checks once the symptoms have been explained.

It may also include simple techniques for the early detection of effects on health, for example, a health assessment by questionnaire.

When a valid and generally accepted method of biological monitoring of workers' health exists for the early detection of the effects on health of exposure to specific occupational risks, it may be used to identify workers who need a detailed medical examination, subject to the individual worker's consent.

It is good practice for the employer to keep records of health surveillance, including biological monitoring, in respect of each worker for an appropriate duration related to the health risk. COSHH 2002 (amended) requires employer to keep records of surveillance in respect of each worker for at least 40 years. This requirement still applies where companies cease to trade, in which case the records must be offered to the HSE.

Biological monitoring guidance values

Biological monitoring may be particularly useful in circumstances where:

- There is likely to be significant skin absorption and/or gastrointestinal tract uptake following ingestion.
- Control of exposure depends on respiratory protective equipment.
- There is a reasonably well-defined relationship between biological monitoring and effect.
- It gives information on accumulated dose and target organ burden which is related to toxicity.

Biological Monitoring Values (BMGVs) are set where they are likely to be of practical value, suitable monitoring methods exist and there are sufficient data available. BMGVs are non-statutory and any biological monitoring undertaken in association with a guidance value needs to be conducted on a voluntary basis (i.e. with the fully informed consent of all concerned).

Where a BMGV is exceeded it does not necessarily mean that any corresponding airborne standard has been exceeded nor that ill-health will occur. It is intended that where they are exceeded this will give an indication that investigation into current control measures and work practices is necessary. Similarly, a low BMGV should not suggest that there is no need to reduce workplace exposure further.

Table 2 EH40/2005 lists BMGVs; a few examples of common substances can be seen in *figure ref 8-41.*

Substance	Biological monitoring guidance value	Sampling time
Butan-2-one	70µmol butan-2-one/L in urine	Post shift
Carbon monoxide	30ppm carbon monoxide in end-tidal breath	Post shift
Lindane (Organo chlorine pesticide)	35nmol/L (10µg/L of Lindane in whole blood (equivalent to 70nmol/Lidane in plasma)	Random
Xylene, o-, m-, p- or mixed isomers	650 mmol methyl hippuric acid/mol creainine in urine	Post shift

Figure 8-41: Biological Monitoring Values (BMGVs).   *Source: EH40/2005 Workplace exposure limits.*

Control of substances with specific effects

CARCINOGENS

Carcinogens are substances that have been identified as having the ability to cause cancer. Examples of these include arsenic, hardwood dusts and used engine oils.

GENETIC DAMAGE

Substances known as mutagens have been identified that cause changes to DNA, increasing the number of genetic mutations above natural background levels. These changes can lead to cancer in the individual affected or be passed to their offspring as genetic material, for example, thalidomide and plutonium oxide.

Due to the serious and irreversible nature of cancer and genetic changes, an employer's first objective must be to prevent exposure to carcinogens and mutagens. These substances should not be used or processes carried out with them, if a safer alternative less hazardous substance can be used instead.

Where this is not feasible suitable control measures should include:

- Totally enclosed systems.
- Where total enclosure is not possible, exposure to these substances must be kept to as low a level as possible through the use of appropriate plant and process control measures such as handling systems and local exhaust ventilation (these measures should not produce other risks in the workplace).
- Storage of carcinogens/mutagens must be kept to the minimum needed for the process, in closed, labelled containers with warning and hazard signs, including waste products until safe disposal.
- Areas where carcinogens/mutagens are present must be identified and segregated to prevent spread to other areas.
- The number of people exposed and the duration of exposure must be kept to the minimum necessary to do the work.
- Personal protective equipment is considered a secondary protection measure used in combination with other control measures.
- Measures should be in place for monitoring of workplace exposure and health surveillance for work involving carcinogens and mutagens.

OCCUPATIONAL ASTHMA

Occupational asthma is caused by substances in the workplace that trigger a state of specific airway hyper-responsiveness in an individual, resulting in breathlessness, chest tightness or wheezing. These substances are known as asthmagens or respiratory sensitisers. Exposure to these substances should be prevented, and where that is not possible, kept as low as reasonably practicable.

Control measures used should take account of long-term time-weighted averages and short-term peak exposures to the substance. If an individual develops occupational asthma, their exposure must be controlled to prevent any further attacks. Workers who work with asthmagens must have regular health surveillance to detect any changes in respiratory function.

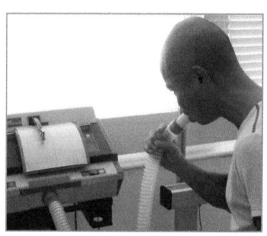

Figure 8-42: Person taking lung function test.
Source: www.elitecycling.co.uk.

8.5 - Specific agents

Health risks and controls associated with other specific agents

BLOOD BORNE VIRUSES

Blood borne viruses (BBVs) are mainly found in blood or bodily fluids and can transfer from one person to another in these fluids. The main BBVs of concern in the workplace are Human Immunodeficiency Virus (HIV), Hepatitis B and Hepatitis C.

HIV

The earliest symptoms of HIV can resemble flu and they generally clear up within a month or two. These symptoms may include fever, headache, fatigue, and swelling in the lymph nodes, particularly those in the neck and groin. However, not everyone who acquires HIV will experience these symptoms. Similarly, for several years, perhaps as long as a decade, a person with HIV might not have any symptoms at all. HIV progresses differently for each person affected. The course of the disease is determined by the specific infections or complications a person with HIV develops. HIV complications can affect different parts of the body.

Some are *localised to the mouth (white patches in the mouth or pharynx), others in the brain (dementia, difficulty in processing information, brain tumours)* and others result in total body changes like losing body weight (loss of muscle as well as fat). Skin conditions in the form of sores or lesions are also common.

HIV is transmitted through contact with body fluids, in particular blood, semen, vaginal secretions and breast milk. It is not transmitted through casual contact. The main method of transfer at work is through laceration or puncture of the skin or contamination of the eyes.

Hepatitis is an inflammation of the liver usually caused by a virus, although some forms of the disease can be caused by the effects of drugs, toxins, disease or alcohol abuse. There are three types of hepatitis: A, B and C.

Each of these types is caused by a different virus. Vaccines are available to prevent infection by the hepatitis A and B viruses, but no vaccines are currently available to prevent hepatitis C infection, and current treatments for it are not effective in all cases.

Symptoms of hepatitis A

Hepatitis A is a type of viral liver infection that is widespread in parts of the world such as Africa and India. Initial symptoms of hepatitis A are similar to flu and include experiencing a low-grade fever with body temperatures usually no higher than 39.5°C (103.1°F). In addition, there may be joint pain and feeling/being sick.

This may then be followed by symptoms related to the liver becoming infected, such as:

- Yellowing of the skin and eyes (jaundice).
- Passing very dark-coloured urine and pale faeces (stools).
- Abdominal pain.
- Itchy skin.

Symptoms usually clear up within two months, although occasionally last up to six months. Older adults tend to have more severe symptoms. In most cases, the liver will make a full recovery.

Symptoms of hepatitis B

Most people remain healthy without any symptoms while they fight off the virus that causes hepatitis B. Some individuals will not even know they have been infected. However, until the virus has been cleared from their body, they can pass it onto others. If there are any symptoms, they will develop on average 60-90 days after exposure to the virus.

Common symptoms of hepatitis B include:

- Flu-like symptoms, such as tiredness, general aches and pains, headaches and a high temperature of or above 38°C (100.4°F).
- Loss of appetite and weight loss.
- Feeling sick or being sick.
- Diarrhoea.
- Pain in the upper right-hand side.
- Yellowing of the skin and eyes (jaundice).

Symptoms will usually pass within one to three months.

Hepatitis B is said to be chronic when the infection lasts for longer than six months. The symptoms are usually much milder and tend to come and go. In many cases, people with chronic hepatitis B infection will not experience any noticeable symptoms.

Symptoms of chronic hepatitis B may include:

- Feeling tired all the time (fatigue).
- Loss of appetite.
- Feeling sick.
- Abdominal pain.
- Muscle and joint pains.
- Itchy skin.

Symptoms of hepatitis C

The earliest symptoms of infection by hepatitis C may start about six to seven weeks after exposure to the virus. This is considered the acute phase of the virus. Symptoms may include loss of appetite, fever, nausea, fatigue, vomiting, joint pain, jaundice, dark urine or abdominal pain. However, it is not unusual to be infected with hepatitis C and never experience any of these symptoms.

Some people are able to completely recover from hepatitis C after the acute phase. Others will develop the chronic form of the disease. Chronic cases of hepatitis C range from mild to severe and it is possible to have chronic hepatitis C with a mild degree of liver damage yet experience no serious health problems. Occasionally severe infection with hepatitis C may result in liver failure or cirrhosis (scarring) of the liver. Liver failure may occur more rapidly if an individual has HIV in addition to hepatitis C. Most people do not know if they are infected and may live for many years without symptoms. A proportion of people take 20 to 30 years to develop severe liver disease, some recover completely with treatment, and others recover without any treatment at all. A small proportion of infected people develop liver cancer.

Hepatitis B and C are easily transmitted through contaminated blood. Hepatitis B is mainly transmitted through contact with body fluids, such as blood, semen, vaginal fluid and breast milk. Hepatitis C is mainly transmitted through blood, with a low risk of transmission through semen and vaginal fluid.

Workers who come into contact with bodily fluids from other humans are at risk from BBVs, particularly if their work also involves sharp or abrasive implements or substances that may break the skin.

Healthcare workers are at an obvious risk. Less obvious, perhaps, are those who work for cleansing or recreation/parks departments and staff who conduct bodily searches or searches of personal effects. Staff who works in these circumstances may come into contact with used needles.

Risk factors for BBVs

The level of risk related to BBVs will depend on:

- Frequency and scale of contact with bodily fluids.
- The type of fluid or material they come into contact with.
- The activity the person must conduct in relation to the infectious material.
- The nature of the infection contained in the material.

Risks controls for BBVs

Where a risk of exposure to BBVs has been identified, simple, inexpensive measures to prevent or control risks can be taken:

- Ensure good personal hygiene practices are observed, in particular hygienic hand-washing.
- Use procedures such as avoiding the use of sharps such as needles, blades, glass, etc.
- Also consider using equipment with built-in safety devices.
- Use personal protective equipment such as gloves, eye protection, face masks, etc.
- Ensure contaminated waste is disposed of in a safe manner, for example, sharps disposal bin.
- Use disposable equipment where there is a risk of BBV contamination, otherwise decontamination procedures must be strictly complied with.
- Ensure workers are aware of immediate steps to be followed upon contamination with blood or other body fluids, for example, needle stick injuries procedure.
- Vaccination where appropriate.
- Decontamination and disinfection procedures.

ORGANIC SOLVENTS

Organic solvents include highly volatile/flammable cleaning agents such as acetone, organo chlorides such as trichloroethylene (used for commercial degreasing) or carbon tetrachloride used in dry cleaning processes. In the construction industry they may be encountered as residual contents of storage tanks or may be used as convenient cleaning substances to remove adhesives. Trichloroethylene is capable of absorption through the skin, it is a narcotic and classified 'harmful'. If the vapours are inhaled, it can cause drowsiness very quickly, depressing the central nervous system and leading to liver failure and death if exposure is for prolonged periods.

Controls for organic solvents include consideration of the use of an alternative process that does not use organic solvents. If substitution is not feasible then the process should be totally enclosed, which will enable solvent vapours to be collected and recovered. If it is not reasonably practicable to enclose the process, for example, an open-topped tank containing solvents for degreasing, care should be taken to operate the tank in accordance with current good working practice. This would usually involve ensuring the maximum solvent level was not exceeded and temperature control of the solvent was closely monitored and kept to a minimum.

Tanks used for degreasing would usually be fitted with condensers and local exhaust ventilation in order to control the vapours given off by the process. The surface area available for evaporation of the solvent should be kept to a minimum, large tanks may be provide with floating balls that cover the surface or covers for when it is not in use.

Smaller containers should be provided with a lid or similar method to limit vapour release. It is important that processes are conducted in controlled conditions that enable good general ventilation and sufficient fresh air for the workers exposed.

Regular monitoring of vapour levels and the use of respirators, protective gloves and clothing will also need to be considered carefully. Where flammable solvents are used, ensuring minimum quantities are in use in the workplace and the control of ignition sources will be additional factors to consider when establishing controls.

CARBON DIOXIDE

Carbon dioxide (CO_2) is a simple asphyxiant that can displace oxygen in the air that we breathe, resulting in insufficient oxygen reaching the brain. CO_2 at levels of 1.5% can cause hyperventilation and headaches, whilst at levels of 10% and above it can lead to collapse and death.

Carbon dioxide may be encountered during construction activities in fixed firefighting installations in buildings and as a by-product of the work being conducted in the premises being worked on, for example, in brewing processes and the manufacture of carbonated soft drinks.

In addition, it may be encountered in confined spaces, such as trenches, particularly in chalky soil where carbon dioxide is evolved naturally from the chalk deposits. The gas is heavier than air and tends to gather in low areas. Areas where CO_2 is likely to occur should be monitored whilst workers are exposed. Fixed and portable carbon dioxide detectors with alarm functions are inexpensive and readily available.

Figure 8-43: CO_2 detector for fixed applications. *Source: Safelinks Ltd.*

Figure 8-44: CO_2 portable detector. *Source: Safelinks Ltd.*

NITROGEN

Nitrogen (N_2) is a simple asphyxiant gas. When nitrogen is released into a confined area it displaces a proportion of oxygen in the air and can, like carbon dioxide, lead to reduced amounts of oxygen reaching the brain, causing dysfunction, collapse and death. This may happen with very few warning symptoms or signs, since the human carotid body (a small cluster of receptors that measure oxygen and carbon dioxide levels in the blood) does not detect low-oxygen (hypoxia) levels very quickly. Two or three deep breaths of nitrogen are sufficient to cause the average person to cease breathing.

Direct skin contact with liquid nitrogen causes severe frostbite (cryogenic burns) within moments to seconds, although not instantly on contact, depending on the form of liquid nitrogen (liquid or mist) and surface area of the nitrogen-soaked material.

Nitrogen may be encountered in construction activities relating to premises that have manufactured or used the chemical, for example, it is commonly used to purge air in chemical plant. In addition, it is used as part of the proof testing processes that are used to test the integrity of tanks and vessels after construction or installation, for example, fuel storage tanks or chemical storage vessels.

Controls include education of workers regarding the risks, control over vessel entry, monitoring the atmosphere where it is likely to be present and training in the use of emergency respirators where bulk supplies are used continuously. In addition, first-aiders qualified to resuscitate those collapsed from nitrogen inhalation and appropriate equipment should be available. The provision of air or pure oxygen will not resuscitate on its own, the victim must be treated with a mixture of oxygen and carbon dioxide to trigger the breathing response.

ISOCYANATES

The principal health risks from isocyanates are that they are sensitising agents, in particular they sensitise the lungs and skin. Toluene di-isocyanate (TDI) and methylene bisphenyl di-isocyanate (MDI) are highly toxic in very small amounts (parts per billion) and inhalation will result in a severe respiratory reaction. TDI and MDI are heavier than water and may gather in the bottom of tanks or other enclosed vessels filled with water. Isocyanates rapidly decompose in contact with water above 50°C with explosive potential if the material is contained before mixing.

Isocyanates may be encountered in construction activities related to the manufacture of resins and urethane foams, where common compounds are toluene di-isocyanate (TDI) and methylene bisphenyl di-isocyanate (MDI). TDI is an extremely volatile vapour and is evolved during the manufacture of foams. In addition, they are used in some glues and specialised paints that use the isocyanate as a hardener and in some expanding foams that may be used as a filler for gaps in building structures. Thermal decomposition of polyurethane materials may lead to the evolution of free isocyanate. Construction tasks that may involve exposure to isocyanates due to the heating of polyurethanes include soldering wire coated with polyurethane plastic, 'hotwire' cutting of polyurethane foam, welding pipes lagged with polyurethane foam and burning off polyurethane paint. Depending on the type of isocyanate used, controls will range from the use of respirators, through to local exhaust ventilation and breathing apparatus and full body secondary protection. If handling isocyanates, care will need to be taken to prevent skin contact by using handling/mixing aids and wearing gloves. The presence of isocyanates should be identified before engaging in hot work that might evolve isocyanates. Covered storage should be provided and procedures need to be in place to ensure early detection and handling of damaged containers.

LEAD

Lead is a poisonous metal that can damage nerve connections in the body (especially in young children) and cause blood and brain disorders. Lead poisoning typically results from ingestion of food or water contaminated with lead, but may also occur after accidental ingestion of contaminated soil, dust, or lead based paint.

Similarly, lead poisoning can also develop from exposure to inhaled lead dust. Long-term exposure to lead or its salts (especially soluble salts or the strong oxidant PbO_2) can cause kidney damage, and colic-like abdominal pains. The main target for lead toxicity is the nervous system. Long-term exposure can result in decreased mental performance and weakness in fingers, wrists, or ankles, increases in blood pressure and can cause anaemia. In the case of pregnant women, high levels of exposure to lead may cause miscarriage and it reduces fertility in males. Lead may be encountered in construction work on premises that use or used lead in their processes. It is widely used in the manufacture of lead-acid batteries, bullets and shots, weights, solders, pewters and crystal glass. Exposure to lead that has been left over from previous processes may occur during site remediation activities. Demolition of premises that conducted work using lead could lead to high levels of exposure, as could the disturbing of lead paint through its removal or cutting sections of a structure coated with lead paint. In addition, lead may be encountered as part of construction materials used for roofing.

Controls include prohibition of eating, drinking and smoking in workplaces, provision of washing and separate washing facilities. The presence of lead deposits or paint should be identified during a pre-remediation or pre-demolition survey and measures taken to limit exposure of workers by the use of the above controls, accompanied by the use of personal protective equipment. Work clothing should be kept separate from other clothing and laundered by a specialised industrial laundry. It may be necessary to remove lead dust deposits as part of the construction activities. Because leaded dust is so small, it cannot be seen by the naked eye.

Special cleaning methods are needed to make sure all harmful dust is removed. All visible and invisible particles need to be removed. Lead dust is hard to remove with an ordinary vacuum cleaner, particularly in poorly maintained buildings with rough and ageing surfaces. An ordinary vacuum will send lead dust through the work area because holes in the filter are not small enough to filter the dust out. A HEPA (High Efficiency Particulate Air) vacuum is equipped with a special filter that removes lead dust particles from the vacuums exhaust air stream that would otherwise be sent throughout the workplace.

CARBON MONOXIDE

Carbon monoxide (CO) is a colourless and odourless chemical asphyxiant produced as a by-product of incomplete combustion of carbon fuels, for example, gas water heaters, compressors, pumps, dumper trucks or generators. It is a particular risk when operated in poorly ventilated confined areas where workers are forced to inhale it. Carbon monoxide has a great affinity (200 times that of oxygen) with the haemoglobin in red blood cells, which means it will inhibit oxygen uptake by red blood cells, resulting in chemical asphyxiation, leading to collapse and death.

Acute effects

The earliest symptoms, especially from low-level exposures, are often non-specific and readily confused with other illnesses, typically flu-like viral syndromes, depression, chronic fatigue syndrome, and migraine or other headaches. This often makes the diagnosis of carbon monoxide poisoning difficult. If suspected, the diagnosis can be confirmed by measurement of blood carboxyhaemoglobin. Common problems encountered are difficulty with higher intellectual functions and short-term memory, dementia, irritability, gait disturbance, speech disturbances, Parkinson-like syndromes, cortical blindness and depression.

Chronic effects

Long-term, repeat exposures present a greater risk to persons with coronary heart disease and in pregnant women. Chronic exposure may increase the incidence of cardiovascular symptoms in some workers, such as motor vehicle examiners, firefighters and welders. Patients often complain of persistent headaches, light-headedness, depression, confusion and nausea. Upon removal from exposure, the symptoms usually resolve themselves. Control measure include ensuring that any work carried out in relation to gas appliances in premises is undertaken by a Gas Safe Registered engineer, competent in that area of work. The HSE strongly recommends the use of audible carbon monoxide alarms as a useful back-up precaution, but they must not be regarded as a substitute for proper installation and maintenance of gas appliances by a Gas Safe Registered engineer. Always make sure there is enough fresh air when using any gas appliance or internal combustion engine, for example, diesel plant, generators, pumps, petrol driven tools, and where any gas welding is carried.

CEMENT

Cement is used extensively in the construction industry as part of the mix for mortar and concrete.

It is mildly corrosive and can cause harm in the following ways:

- Skin contact - causing contact dermatitis. If it is trapped inside a worker's boot or glove then it can cause severe chemical burns.
- Eye contact - causing irritation and inflammation.
- Inhalation - causing irritation of the nose and throat. Possible long term respiratory problems.

Figure ref 8-45 shows severe burns a worker sustained from kneeling in wet cement for three hours; the worker's right leg had to be amputated.

Figure 8-45: Cement burns. *Source: SHP.*

Where possible, exposure should be eliminated by pouring and vibrating the cement into position. Gloves, protective overalls, boots and masks should be worn and any contaminated clothing should be removed and not reused until thoroughly cleaned. Good hygiene standards should be maintained, for example, washing the skin and hands thoroughly after contact with cement.

LEGIONELLA/LEGIONNAIRES' DISEASE

Legionellosis is a potentially fatal disease and is a type of pneumonia caused by legionella pneumophila, a bacterium. Legionnaires' disease is the most severe form of this disease. Other forms of the illness that are not so severe are Lochgoilhead fever and Pontiac fever. Legionella pneumophila is widely present in water and frequently present in water-cooling systems and domestic hot water systems. Large workplace buildings are therefore susceptible to infected water systems, especially hotels and hospitals.

The organism is ubiquitous in water and frequently present in water cooling systems and domestic hot water systems. Large workplace buildings are therefore susceptible to infected water systems, especially hotels and hospitals.

The organism is widespread in the environment, but needs certain conditions to multiply, for example, the presence of sludge, scale, algae, rust and organic material plus a temperature of 20-50°C. Transmission is via inhalation of the organism in contaminated aerosols. Smoking, age and alcohol may increase susceptibility.

Symptoms are aching muscles, headaches and fever followed by a cough. Confusion, emotional disturbance and delirium may follow the acute phase. In some cases, death may occur. The fatality rate for those that contract Legionnaires' disease has ranged between 5% and 30% during outbreaks; for example, those occurring in the UK are reported to be about 12%. The death rate for older people and the infirm who contract the disease is often as high as 50%.

The greatest risk areas are from showers used for bathing, air conditioning sprays, water cooling towers, fountains and recirculating water cooling systems. The hazard can be controlled by proper design of water systems i.e. locating hot and cold water supply pipework separate from each other, avoiding the use of water storage tanks, use of plastic tanks instead of metal to avoid rust deposits and hot water being heated to 55-60°C. Regular use of biocides is necessary for cleaning open water systems, such as cooling towers. Showers should be designed to drain water completely after use, to avoid stagnant water retention.

LEPTOSPIRA

The leptospira (spiral-shaped) bacteria enter the body through broken skin or mucous membrane, causing leptospirosis (Weil's disease). Rodents represent the most important reservoir of infections, especially rats (also gerbils, voles, and field mice). Other sources of infection are dogs, hedgehogs, foxes, pigs, and cattle.

These animals are not necessarily ill, but carry leptospires in their kidneys and excrete it in their urine. Infection can be transmitted directly via direct contact with blood, tissues, organs or urine of one of the host animals or indirectly by contaminated environment. Symptoms vary but include flu-like illness, conjunctivitis, liver damage (including jaundice), kidney failure and meningitis. If untreated infection may be fatal. Early diagnosis, by blood analysis, is essential to prevent fatal symptoms developing.

Construction workers are most at risk from leptospira bacteria when they work where rats prevail, including water and sewage work, demolition or refurbishment of old unoccupied buildings, and those working on sites adjoining rivers and other watercourses. The bacteria's survival depends on protection from direct sunlight, so it survives well in water courses and ditches protected by vegetation. Typical control measures include good personal hygiene (for example, hand-washing), PPE (gloves), covering cuts and grazes, preventing animal (rat) infestations and issuing a worker with an 'At Risk' card to show a doctor if they develop flu-like symptoms after being exposed to contaminated water.

Figure 8-46: Treatment for leptospira. *Source: Bio-Rad.*

Figure 8-47: Leptospira magnified many times shown on SEM shows spiral shape. *Source: Wikipedia.*

SILICA

Silica exists naturally as crystalline minerals. A common variety is quartz (tridymite, cristobalite). Industrially silica is used in the morphous (after heating) form, for example, fumed silica, silica gel. In construction activities it may be encountered in stone work or work with quartz based tiles.

Inhalation of silica can result in silicosis, a fibrosis of the lung. *Silicosis* (also known as Grinder's disease and Potter's rot) is a form of occupational lung disease caused by inhalation of crystalline silica dust, and is marked by inflammation and scarring in forms of nodular lesions in the upper lobes of the lungs. Silicosis (especially the acute form) is characterised by shortness of breath, fever, and cyanosis (bluish skin). It may often be misdiagnosed as pulmonary oedema (fluid in the lungs), pneumonia, or tuberculosis.

Typical control measures include preventing the dust from being inhaled by using alternative work methods, using dust suppression or dust collection (LEV). Employees should wear RPE and be subject to health surveillance (lung function testing, etc.).

FIBRES

Fibres include man-made mineral fibres, for example, extruded glass fibres, glass wools and ceramic fibres. They also include other fibres, like synthetic organic fibres made from gypsum and calcium carbonate. These fibres are commonly used within the construction industry as insulation materials, used in roofs, walls and voids. Exposure to these fibres must be controlled by the use of personal protective equipment, for example, suitable respiratory protective equipment, eye protection, gloves and long sleeved overalls.

HEPATITIS

See 'Blood borne viruses' earlier.

TETANUS

Tetanus is a life-threatening disease caused by toxins produced by the bacterium Clostridium tetani, which often enters and grows at the site of a cut or wound while working with soil or even from a bite from an animal.

There is greater risk of developing tetanus if the wound is deep or if it gets dirty with soil or manure, but even small wounds such as a prick from a thorn can allow enough bacteria to get into the body to cause tetanus.

Muscles in the jaw first become stiff, and then rigidly fixed (lockjaw). This can progress to other parts of the skeletal muscles causing the body to shape into a characteristic form called opisthotonos (behind tension) of the spine.

Figure 8-48: Tension of the spine.　　*Source: Painting by Charles Bell.*

Prevention includes skin protection, such as gauntlet gloves and tough material leggings and boots. Medical attention is required for any contaminated deep cuts. Exposed workers can be vaccinated against tetanus; this should be carried out every 10 years or at the time of injury.

HYDROGEN SULPHIDE

Hydrogen sulphide (H_2S) is a colourless, highly flammable gas that is heavier than air. Hydrogen sulphide is very poisonous. It has the characteristic odour of rotten eggs, which can be detected at very low concentrations, typically 0.0005 parts per million (ppm). This is well below the threshold to causes harm; H_2S has an 8 hour exposure limit of 5ppm. The toxicity of H_2S is comparable with that of hydrogen cyanide, but H_2S can be detected in minute quantities compared with hydrogen cyanide. On inhalation H_2S forms a complex bond with essential maintenance cells preventing cellular repair and respiration. The human body produces small amounts of H_2S and has a tolerance to very small concentrations; low levels of H_2S may be tolerated indefinitely.

Early symptoms of low toxic exposure include eye irritation, a sore throat and cough, nausea, shortness of breath, and fluid in the lungs. Exposure in excess of 300 ppm leads to increased fluid in the lungs and ultimately death.

Hydrogen sulphide is produced by anaerobic (without oxygen) bacterial digestion of organic matter. The gas is present in gas released from land fill sites, excavations in soils rich in organic material, sewers and some well waters. Large quantities of H_2S are produced in oil refineries where it is used to produce the element sulphur, which is primarily used in fertilisers and the production of sulphuric acid.

Precautions include the early detection of the gas at low levels. Many personal safety gas detectors, such as those used by petrochemical and sewage workers, are set to alarm at 5 to 10 ppm and to go into high alarm at 15 ppm. Additional measures are the use of respiratory protection and the absence of ignition sources where the material is handled or may be found naturally.

Generation and control of dust on a construction site

CEMENT DUST

Cement dust is generated when handling the dry product in bags and when opening the bags in preparation for mixing. In addition, it may be generated during scabbling processes and when using cut off saws for cutting concrete, for example, curb stones or paving slabs.

Control of cement dust should be achieved by working in a way that avoids dusty methods of work. For example, scabbling, which is often carried out to ensure an adequate bond between successive concrete pours and the amount of scabbling can be reduced by larger pours. The need to cut or break hardened concrete can be reduced by designing work so as to allow for tolerances, by not relying on perfect fit or cutting away to make things fit, by leaving positive gaps and specifying expanding grout, mastic or resilient materials as joint fillers.

Work should be carried out in such a way that minimises the amount of dust produced. Bags of cement should be opened with care and mixed carefully. Dry dusty materials like cement should be handled in a well-ventilated area.

Workers must be provided with and wear clothing to protect their skin from cement and cement mixtures, for example:

- Gloves.
- Overalls with long sleeves and full-length trousers.
- Waterproof boots.

Clothing should be worn so as to avoid 'traps' for fresh mortar or concrete to fall in, i.e. with sleeves over the gloves and trouser legs over the boots - not tucked inside. If 'trapping' does happen, steps should be taken immediately to clean the contaminated skin and protective clothing with copious amounts of clean water.

Suitable respiratory protective equipment should be used if work in dusty conditions cannot be avoided. Suitable eye protection must be worn when conditions give rise to a risk of eye injury (for example, opening cement sacks, during mixing where splashing might occur).

WOOD DUST

Exposure to wood dust has long been associated with a variety of adverse health effects, including dermatitis, allergic respiratory effects, mucosal and non-allergic respiratory effects, and cancer. Contact with the irritant compounds in wood sap can cause dermatitis and other allergic reactions.

The respiratory effects of wood dust exposure include asthma, hypersensitivity pneumonitis (inflammation of the air sacks in the lungs), and chronic bronchitis.

The main construction activities likely to produce high dust levels are:

- Machining operations, particularly sawing, routing and turning.
- Sanding, by machine and by hand.
- Using compressed air lines to blow dust off wood products that have been worked on before spraying.

Controls will include the use of local exhaust ventilation, the use of respiratory protective equipment and the removal of dust deposits from flat surfaces at all levels especially at height. Compressed air should not be used to displace dust; instead a suitable vacuum system should be available for all cleaning tasks.

Health risks and controls associated with asbestos

HEALTH RISKS

Asbestos is a general term used to describe a range of mineral fibres (commonly referred to by colour i.e. white, chrysotile; brown, amosite and blue, crocidolite).

Asbestos was mainly used as an insulating and fire-resisting material. Asbestos fibres are a particular form of fibrous dust that readily become airborne when disturbed and may enter the lungs, where they cause fibrosis (scarring and thickening) of the lung tissue (asbestosis) or pleura (diffuse pleural thickening). The pleura is a two-layered membrane that surrounds the lungs and lines the inside of the ribcage. Asbestosis typically takes more than 10 years to develop.

Research suggests that 50 per cent of asbestos sufferers will also develop cancer of the lung or bronchus.

Figure 8-49: Asbestos label. *Source: Scaftag.*

Asbestosis is often classified separately from pneumoconiosis even though asbestos is a dust - but it is a special form of fibrous dust. Like silicosis, asbestosis is a serious condition which is incurable and can result in death at an early age. The primary symptom of asbestosis is generally the slow onset of shortness of breath on exertion. In severe, advanced cases, this may lead to respiratory failure. Coughing is not usually a typical symptom, unless the patient has other, concomitant respiratory tract diseases. Symptoms of mesothelioma may not appear until 20 to 50 years after exposure to asbestos. Shortness of breath, cough, and pain in the chest due to an accumulation of fluid in the pleural space are often symptoms of pleural mesothelioma.

The HSE reported that there were 464 deaths in 2012 where asbestosis is described as likely to have contributed to the cause of death and there were 900 new cases of disablement benefit for asbestosis in 2013.

The HSE reported that the annual number of mesothelioma deaths had increased since 1968, where annual recorded deaths were 153, reaching 2535 deaths in 2013/14. This exceeded the expected number of deaths amongst males which was predicted to increase to a peak of 2,500 in the year 2016. 2145 new cases of mesothelioma were assessed for Industrial Injuries Benefit in 2013. In the majority of cases mesothelioma is rapidly fatal following diagnosis.

The HSE identified that the ten male occupations found to have the highest risk of asbestos related diseases were carpenters, plumbers, electricians, labourers in other construction trades, metal plate workers, pipe fitters, construction operatives, managers in construction, construction trades and energy plant operatives.

CONTROLS

The Control of Asbestos Regulations (CAR) 2012 place emphasis on assessment of exposure; exposure prevention, reduction and control; adequate information, instruction and training for employees; monitoring and health surveillance. CAR 2012 also applies to incidental exposure to asbestos.

General controls required by CAR 2012 related to asbestos include:

■ The presence of asbestos must be identified and must be labelled.
■ An assessment must be carried out of work which exposes employees to asbestos.
■ Training is mandatory for those that may be exposed to asbestos fibres at work, including maintenance workers, cable installers or others that may come into contact with or disturb asbestos.
■ A written plan of work is required for work with asbestos.

The CAR 2012, Regulation 3, requires that employers who work with asbestos must be licensed unless the circumstances are that:

(a) The exposure of employees to asbestos is sporadic and of low intensity.

(b) It is clear from the risk assessment that the exposure of any employee to asbestos will not exceed the control limit.

(c) The work involves:

  (i) Short, non-continuous maintenance activities.

  (ii) Removal of materials in which the asbestos fibres are firmly linked in a matrix.

  (iii) Encapsulation or sealing of asbestos-containing materials which are in good condition.

  (iv) Air monitoring and control, and the collection and analysis of samples to ascertain whether a specific material contains asbestos.

Other controls required by CAR 2012 related to asbestos include:

■ Work with asbestos other than that listed previously must be notified to the employer's enforcing authority.
■ Exposure must be prevented or reduced by controls.
■ Controls must be used and maintained.
■ The employer is responsible for the cleaning of personal protective equipment and clothing.

CAR 2012 introduced a category of work called Notifiable Non-Licensed Work (NNLW). This required the appropriate enforcing authority to be notified if this category of work was to be carried out. Records of work carried out must be kept and workers must have a periodic medical examination.

Duty to manage asbestos

The duty to manage asbestos is covered by Regulation 4 of the CAR 2012. In many cases, the duty holder is the person or organisation that has clear responsibility for the maintenance or repair of non-domestic premises through an explicit agreement such as a tenancy agreement or contract. Where there are domestic premises such as flats the duty holder will be responsible for common areas such as corridors or walkways.

The duty holder has the responsibility to:

■ Take reasonable steps to find out if there are materials containing asbestos in non-domestic premises and if so, amount, location and condition.
■ Presume materials contain asbestos unless there is strong evidence that they do not.
■ Record the location and condition of the asbestos containing materials or materials which are presumed to contain asbestos.
■ Assess the risk of anyone being exposed to fibres from the materials identified.
■ Prepare a plan that sets out in detail how the risks from these materials will be managed.
■ Take the necessary steps to put the plan into action.

- Periodically review and monitor the plan.
- Provide information on the location and condition of the materials to anyone who is liable to work on or disturb them.

There is also a requirement on anyone to co-operate as far as is necessary to allow the duty holder to comply with the requirements shown previously. If asbestos containing materials are in good condition they may be left in place and their condition monitored and managed.

ASBESTOS IDENTIFICATION

There are three main types of asbestos, which is a naturally occurring mineral. It can be amphibole asbestos which includes crocidolite (blue) and amosite (brown) asbestos, or serpentine asbestos which is chrysotile (white) asbestos. All three of these main types have been used in Great Britain at some time.

Types of survey

Management survey

This is the standard survey used to identify the presence and extent of any asbestos containing materials (ACMs) in the building which could be damaged or disturbed during normal occupancy, including foreseeable maintenance and installation, and to assess their condition.

A management survey might involve minor intrusive work and some disturbance which will vary between premises and depend on what is reasonably practicable for individual properties.

Management surveys can involve a combination of sampling to confirm asbestos is present or presuming asbestos to be present.

Refurbishment and demolition surveys

A refurbishment and demolition survey will be needed before any work of this type is carried out. This survey will be used to locate and describe all ACMs in the area where the work will take place or in the whole building if demolition is planned.

This type of survey is fully intrusive and involves destructive inspection to gain access to all areas, including those that may be difficult to reach. A refurbishment and demolition survey may also be required in other circumstances, for example, when more intrusive maintenance and repair work will be carried out or for plant removal or dismantling.

Who can undertake them

An independent expert/specialist organisation must:

- Have adequate training and be experienced in survey work.
- Able to demonstrate independence, impartiality and integrity.
- Have an adequate quality management system.
- Carry out any asbestos survey work in accordance with recommended HSE guidance HSG264 'Asbestos: The Survey Guide'.

HSG264 states that organisations offering an asbestos survey service should be able to demonstrate their competence by holding United Kingdom Accreditation Service (UKAS) accreditation to ISO/IEC 17020 and individuals to ISO/IEC 17024.

Competence for assessment

The HSE document 'Managing and work with asbestos', the approved code of practice and guidance to the Control of Asbestos Regulations (CAR) 2012 clarifies competence requirements for those that carry out asbestos risk assessments.

The ACOP to Regulation 6 of CAR 2012, relating to assessment of work which exposes employees to asbestos, states:

> *"Whoever carries out the assessment should:*
>
> *Have adequate knowledge, training and expertise in understanding the risks from asbestos and be able to make informed and appropriate decisions about the risks and precautions needed.*
>
> *Know how the work activity may disturb asbestos.*
>
> *Be familiar with and understand the requirements of the Regulations ACOP.*
>
> *Have the ability and the authority to collate all the necessary and relevant information.*
>
> *Be able to assess other non-asbestos risks on site.*
>
> *Be able to estimate the expected level of exposure to decide whether or not the control limit is likely to be exceeded."*

Figure 8-50: Competence to carry out asbestos risk assessments.   *Source: HSE ACOP to CAR 2012.*

Where it can be located

Asbestos has a number of valuable properties; these include physical strength, resistance to chemicals, non-combustibility and good thermal and electrical insulation.

Asbestos is commonly mixed with other materials and is typically used in the following applications:

- As yarn or cloth - for protective clothing, etc.
- Insulation boards - for protection of buildings against fire.
- Asbestos cement products - for construction of buildings and pipes.
- Asbestos resins - for clutch faces and brake linings.
- Various other applications - in gaskets, filters, floor tiles and decorative plasterwork in old buildings.
- Asbestos spraying for thermal and acoustic insulation of buildings and plant, and for fire-resistance in structural steelwork, is no longer carried out, although it is encountered as a problem when being removed.

Asbestos has been used in many parts of buildings, examples of uses and locations where asbestos can be found include:

Asbestos products	What it was used for
Sprayed asbestos (limpet)	Fire protection in ducts and to structural steel work, fire breaks in ceiling voids etc.
Lagging	Thermal insulation of pipes and boilers
Asbestos insulating boards (AIB)	Fire protection, thermal insulation, wall partitions, ducts, soffits, ceiling and wall panels
Asbestos cement products, flat or corrugated sheets	Roofing and wall cladding, gutters, rainwater pipes, water tanks
Certain textured coatings	Decorative plasters, paints
Bitumen or vinyl materials	Roofing felt, floor and ceiling tiles

Figure 8-51: Examples of uses and locations where asbestos can be found.   *Source: RMS.*

Sprayed coatings, lagging and insulating board are more likely to contain blue or brown asbestos. In general, materials that contain a high percentage of asbestos are more easily damaged. Asbestos insulation and lagging can contain up to 85% asbestos and are most likely to give off fibres. Work with AIB can result in equally high fibre release if power tools are used. Asbestos cement is of lower risk, since it contains only 10-15% asbestos. The asbestos is tightly bound into the cement and the material will only give off fibres if it is badly damaged or broken, or is worked on, for example, if it is drilled, abraded or cut.

HIGH RISK MATERIALS

Figure 8-52: Asbestos pipe lagging.   *Source: HSE.*

Figure 8-53: Asbestos insulating board (AIB).   *Source: HSE.*

Figure 8-54: Textured decorative coating.   *Source: HSE.*

Figure 8-55: Window with AIB panel.   *Source: HSE.*

NORMALLY LOWER RISK MATERIALS

Figure 8-56: Asbestos cement roof sheeting.   *Source: HSE.*

Figure 8-57: Floor tiles containing asbestos.   *Source: HSE.*

As long as the ACM is in good condition, and is not being or going to be disturbed or damaged, there is negligible risk. But if it is disturbed or damaged, it can become a danger to health, because people may breathe in any asbestos fibres released into the air.

Workers who may be particularly at risk of being exposed to asbestos when carrying out building maintenance and repair jobs include:

- Construction and demolition contractors, roofers, electricians, painters.
- Decorators, joiners, plumbers, gas fitters, plasterers, shop fitters, heating and ventilation engineers, and surveyors.
- Anyone dealing with electronics, for example, phone and information technology (IT) engineers, and alarm installers.
- General maintenance engineers and others who work on the fabric of a building.

If asbestos is present that can be readily disturbed, is in poor condition and not managed properly, all people in the building could be put at risk.

PROCEDURE FOR THE DISCOVERY OF ASBESTOS DURING CONSTRUCTION ACTIVITY

Employers must have prepared procedures which can be put into effect in the case an incident or emergency that could put people at risk should occur. Information and instruction should be made available to emergency services attending the incident so that they can adequately protect themselves.

REQUIREMENTS IF PERSONS ARE ACCIDENTALLY EXPOSED TO ASBESTOS MATERIALS

Regulation 15 of the Control of Asbestos Regulations (CAR) 2012 requires employers to have arrangements in place to deal with accidents, incidents and emergencies. These procedures must include means of raising the alarm and means of evacuation. People not wearing PPE must leave the work area. If people have been contaminated then arrangements must include means of decontaminating. The contaminated area must be cleaned thoroughly by people wearing PPE. Contaminated PPE should be treated as contaminated waste. Supervisors and managers must make sure that the work has been carried out.

REQUIREMENTS FOR REMOVAL

Non-licensed work

Most asbestos work must be undertaken by a licensed contractor but any decision on whether particular work is licensable is based on the risk.

To be exempt from needing a licence the work must be:

- Sporadic and low intensity.
- Carried out in such a way that the exposure of workers to asbestos will not exceed the legal control limit of 0.1 asbestos fibres per cubic centimetre of air (0.1 f/cm^3).
- A short non-continuous maintenance task.
- A removal task, where the ACMs are in reasonable condition and are not being deliberately broken up.
- A task where the ACMs are in good condition and are being sealed or encapsulated.
- An air monitoring and control task to check fibre concentrations in the air, or it's the collection and analysis of asbestos samples to confirm the presence of asbestos in a material.

Notifiable non-licensed work

From April 2012, some non-licensed work, where the risk of fibre release is greater, is subject to three additional requirements:

1) Notification of work.
2) Medical examinations.
3) Record keeping.

This work is known as notifiable non-licensed work (NNLW). To decide if the work is NNLW, employers will need to consider the type of work that will be carried out, the type of material to be worked on and its condition:

- Decide what type of work will be carried out.
- Consider the asbestos type.
- Consider the material's condition.

Licensed work

Certain types of work with ACMs can only be carried out by those who have been issued with a licence by HSE. This is work which meets the definition of 'licensable work with asbestos' in Regulation 2(1).

That is work:

- Where worker exposure to asbestos is not sporadic and of low intensity.
- Where the risk assessment cannot clearly demonstrate that the control limit (0.1 f/cm^3 airborne fibres averaged over a four-hour period) will not be exceeded.
- On asbestos coating (surface coatings which contain asbestos for fire protection, heat insulation or sound insulation but not including textured decorative coatings).
- On asbestos insulation or AIB where the risk assessment demonstrates that the work is not sporadic and of low intensity, the control limit will be exceeded and it is not short duration work.

Short duration means the total time spent by all workers working with these materials does not exceed two hours in a seven-day period, including time spent setting up, cleaning and clearing up, and no one person works for more than one hour in a seven-day period.

If licensable work is to be carried out then the appropriate enforcing authority must be notified of details of the proposed work. Employers must carry out a risk assessment of the work. This assessment must be kept at the place where work is being carried out.

For licensable work, the plan of work *(see following section)* should be site specific and contain the following information:

- The scope of work as identified in the risk assessment.
- Details of hygiene facilities, transit route, vacuum cleaners, air monitoring, protective clothing, respiratory protection equipment (RPE), and communication between the inside and outside of the enclosure.
- Use of barriers and signs, location of enclosures and airlocks, location of skips, negative pressure units, cleaning and clearance certification, emergency procedures.

Notification and plan of work

If carrying out licensable work, it must be notified to the appropriate enforcing authority 14 days in writing before work commences (the authority may allow a shorter period in an emergency if there is a serious risk to health).

For any work involving asbestos, the employer must draw up a written plan of work. The plan of work must include the following information:

- Nature and duration of the work.
- Number of persons involved.
- Address and location of the work.
- Methods used to prevent or reduce exposure.
- Type of equipment used to protect those carrying out the work and those present or near the worksite.

Work must not take place unless a copy of the plan is readily available on site.

RESPIRATORY EQUIPMENT

If, despite other control measures an employee's exposure is likely to exceed the control limit or exceed 0.6f/cm^3 peak level measured over ten minutes, the employer must provide suitable RPE.

RPE must be matched to:

- The exposure concentrations (expected or measured).
- The job.
- The wearer.
- Factors related to the working environment.

Suitable RPE means:

- It provides adequate protection (i.e. reduces the wearer's exposure to asbestos fibres as low as is reasonably practicable, and anyway to below the control limits) during the job in hand and in the specified working environment (for example, confined spaces).
- It provides clean air and the flow rate during the whole wear period at least conforms to the minimum recommended by the manufacturer.
- The face piece fits the wearer correctly.
- It is properly maintained.
- The chosen equipment does not introduce additional hazards that may put the wearer's health and safety at risk.

PROTECTIVE CLOTHING

Protective clothing must be adequate and suitable. Cuffs, ankles and hoods should be elasticated and provide a tight fit at the face and neck.

Pockets or other attachments which could trap dust should be avoided. Where disposable overalls are used they should be Type 5 (under BS EN ISO 13982-1).

TRAINING

Asbestos awareness training should be given to all employees who could foreseeably be exposed to asbestos. In particular, training should be given to employees whose work is likely to disturb the fabric of the building.

The training should include the following topics:

- The properties of asbestos and its effects on health.
- The types, uses and likely occurrence of asbestos.
- Emergency procedures.
- How to avoid the risks from asbestos.

AIR MONITORING

Air testing is required for a number of reasons, such as to certify clearance after asbestos has been removed (a regulatory requirement in most cases), to ensure that leaks do not occur during asbestos treatment or removal and to provide reassurance that nobody has been placed at risk.

Personal air monitoring is also necessary to ensure that RPE is providing the appropriate level of protection. Records must be kept for 5 years or, where employees are under health surveillance, for 40 years.

MEDICAL SURVEILLANCE

Regulation 22 of the Control of Asbestos Regulations (CAR) 2012 requires all employers to ensure that all employees who are exposed to asbestos are under adequate health surveillance.

For licensable work with asbestos every employer must ensure that:

(a) A health record is maintained for all employees who are exposed to asbestos.
(b) The health record, or a copy of it, is kept available in a suitable form for at least 40 years from the date of the last entry made in it.
(c) Each employee who is exposed to asbestos is under adequate medical surveillance by a relevant doctor.

The medical surveillance required by a relevant doctor must include a medical examination not more than 2 years before the beginning of exposure to asbestos and periodic medical examinations at intervals of at least once every 2 years or such shorter time as the relevant doctor may require while exposure to asbestos continues. The medical examinations must include a specific examination of the chest.

For work with asbestos, which is not licensable work, and is not exempted by Regulation 3(2) of CAR 2012, the above requirements in (a) to (c) apply and a medical examination must take place not more than 3 years before the beginning of exposure to asbestos and a periodic medical examination are required at intervals of at least once every 3 years, or such shorter time as the relevant doctor may require while exposure to asbestos continues.

The employee health record to be maintained is not a medical confidential as it contains job exposure information and dates of previous medical examinations.

REQUIREMENTS FOR DISPOSAL

Licensed carrier

Health and Safety Executive (HSE) requirements on the licensed contractor has means that each company must have in place an up to date standard operating procedure manual, which should contain all of the details relating to the safe removal and disposal of asbestos.

This manual must also be sent to the local HSE inspector and constantly updated to reflect changes in guidance and legislation. Waste carriers licence involves a simple application and anyone looking to transport waste asbestos will need to be a Registered Waste Carrier.

Notification

Employers must notify the appropriate enforcing authority 14 days before carrying out any licensable work. This can be done on form FOD ASB5.

Licensed disposal site

Any facility looking to accept waste asbestos has to apply to the Environment Agency for a site licence. This will set out the range and volumes of wastes that can be accepted on the site, the site control and management systems, engineering and infrastructure, manning and qualification requirements and reporting and monitoring regimes.

8.6 - Safe handling and storage of waste

Basic environmental issues relating to waste disposal and effluent

Environmental pollution is a major issue today with the industrialised countries of the world concerned about the long-term effects on Earth's resources and on plant, animal and human life. Major concerns on health are often blamed on pollution and there are many pressure groups that focus on environmental issues, particularly pollution. Neighbours of construction sites are affected by air pollutants, including those generated as by-products of combustion, for example, from diesel and petrol compressors and associated noise nuisance from the use of heavy machinery and other activities such as piling. Plant failure and accidents can lead to abnormal releases following higher than expected temperatures and pressures leading to uncontrolled venting to the environment. Lack of control when filling tankers with waste effluent can lead to losses through overfilling or bad coupling, either of which could lead to a release to the environment.

GENERAL PRINCIPLES FOR SAFE HANDLING AND STORAGE OF WASTE

The handling and storage of waste chemicals and substances no longer required by an organisation, together with the risks to workers involved, should be included in the employer's assessment of risks. The chemicals should be handled, stored, treated or disposed of in a manner that eliminates or minimises the risk both to the health and safety of workers and to the environment, in accordance with legislation and good practice.

Principles of good practice will usually include the following:

(a) The method of identification of waste products. Waste products should be identified as waste, by their origins and also by their main components, where known. The main components should be determined from the history of the products. In cases of doubt about the degree of hazard, the waste should be classified as the highest hazard.

(b) The handling of contaminated containers. Empty containers which have not been cleansed of hazardous chemicals should be closed and stored to await disposal or reuse, and treated as if they contained those hazardous chemicals. Empty containers should retain the identification, marking and labelling of their previous contents.

(c) The identification, construction, nature, integrity and protection of waste containers. The waste containers should be designed or chosen to provide protection to workers against the hazards identified in (a) and (b) above, taking into account the methods of work and disposal to be followed.

(d) The effects on the working environment. The discharge of effluent, the disposal and transport of waste, and the emission of smoke and chemicals into the atmosphere should be undertaken in such a way as to prevent or minimise risks to workers and should be in accordance with legal and good practice requirements for the protection of the general public and the environment.

(e) The demarcation of disposal areas. Disposal areas and storage areas for waste products should be set aside. Sufficient space should be provided on site to prevent the presence of waste containers in the normal process and storage areas.

(f) The provision, maintenance and use of personal protective equipment and clothing. Personal protection should be provided against the hazards referred to in (a) and (b) above and in accordance with the method of work to be followed.

(g) The method of disposal or treatment. Where there are no on-site facilities to dispose of waste safely, hazardous waste products should be disposed of through a specialist contractor in accordance with legal and good practice requirements. Where an employer disposes of waste (for example, waste flammable solvents and residues) by burning, this should be in a plant or process designed to do this safely and following a clearly defined system of work.

Figure 8-58: GHS hazard label - environment. *Source: RMS.*

Figure 8-59: Environmental hazard. *Source: RMS.*

PERSONAL PROTECTIVE EQUIPMENT

The hazards that might be encountered during the collection, storage and disposal of waste are:

- Chemicals.
- Biological agents.
- Gases, vapours and fumes.
- Dusts.
- Oil, grease.

- Paint, solvents.
- Asbestos.
- Flammable, explosive substances.
- Radioactive materials.

When selecting suitable PPE it is essential that these issues are considered. This may mean the provision of a range of PPE, including RPE, protective clothing, gloves, boots and face/eye protection. The specific use of PPE should be identified through risk assessment and specified for different classes of waste. It may also be necessary to provide emergency showers in the area that waste is handled and stored to enable workers to wash off contamination that they may get on their body. The water from these showers should be collected in a waste system and treated to ensure environmental risks are minimised.

SEPARATE STORAGE OF INCOMPATIBLE WASTE STREAMS

In addition to general safe storage practices, segregated storage of incompatible materials is essential. As a minimum, wastes should be segregated according to similar hazards, such as flammability, corrosively, sensitivity to water or air, and toxicity.

Figure 8-60: Measures to control pollution. *Source: RMS.*

Figure 8-61: Measures to control pollution. *Source: RMS.*

When establishing a storage scheme, the main consideration should be the flammability characteristics of the material. If the material will contribute significantly to a fire (i.e. oxidisers) it should be isolated from the flammables. If a fire were to occur, the response to the fire with water that would produce fire water run-off would exacerbate the environmental situation.

Consider the toxicity of the material, with particular attention paid to regulated materials. In some cases, this may mean that certain wastes will be isolated within a storage area. For instance, a material that is an extreme poison, but is also flammable, should be locked away in the flammable storage area to protect it against accidental release.

There will always be some chemicals that will not fit singularly into one category or another, but with careful consideration of the hazards involved most of these cases can be handled in an appropriate manner. For the health and safety of all workers and to protect the integrity of the facilities, hazardous materials must be segregated.

PRINCIPLES OF PROTECTION AGAINST ACCIDENTAL RELEASE

Leaking and spillage can result from a number of sources: faulty valves or flanges to pipework; containers such as tins, drums or bags; loss from tanks (typically one tonne) of solids and liquids; road or rail freight containers; cargo vessels etc.

Typical techniques to contain spillage include: curbed areas for drum storage, tanker loading of liquids, bunded areas to contain sited tanks and drip trays at piped systems and drum decanting points. Portable tanks are available with two skins (a tank within a tank) to contain any leaks from the internal tank.

They are often used where there is a need for portability such as with storing fuels on construction sites. Similarly, cargo vessels may have double skinned tanks or hulls.

Accidental releases should be contained as much as possible, and materials to do this should be positioned in the areas where waste is handled or stored. This may include absorbent materials and barriers. In addition, where spills may occur, controls should be established to prevent waste going into drains that run into watercourses. This may include covering drains or ensuring that drains in the area of the waste have an interception system that captures and treats accidental releases.

Bunding

A bund, sometimes called a secondary containment system, often consists of an area contained by a rectangular wall built upon a concrete slab. The bund floor and walls should be treated to be impervious to any spillage or water that may be present. Storage tanks are located within this confined area. The bund must provide storage of at least 110% of the tank's maximum capacity. If more than one tank is stored, the bund system must be capable of storing 110% of the volume of the biggest of the tank's capacity, or 25% of the total capacity of all the tanks within the bund, whichever is the greater.

It is necessary to consider the potential escape of any spillage beyond the bund area in the event of the tank developing a hole (known as jetting).

The risk of this can be minimised by:

- Keeping the primary container as low as possible.
- Increasing the height of the bund wall.
- Leaving sufficient space between the tank and bund walls.
- Not sitting one tank above another.
- Providing screens or curtains.
- Ensure there is no direct uncontrolled outlet connecting the bund to any drain, sewer, watercourse, yard or unmade ground.

Ideally, pipework should not pass through the bund wall. If unavoidable, the pipe should be sealed into the bund with a material that is resistant to attack by the substance stored, to ensure the bund remains leak-proof.

The bund may also need protection from being struck by vehicles, and drains from the bund may need to go through an 'interceptor' so pollutants can be removed.

See also 'Element 2 - Construction site - hazards and risk control' for '2.2 - Appropriate general site control measures'.

Exam practice

1. Insulation board tiles that contain asbestos are to be removed from the ceiling of a storage area located within a high street department store.

   Outline measures that should be taken into consideration when planning the work to minimise the risks from asbestos. **(8)**

2. Exposure to cement dust can lead to adverse health effects if breathed in, for example, irritation of the nose and throat.

   (a) **Give** the meaning of the term 'workplace exposure limit'. **(2)**

   (b) **Outline** control measures that could be considered to control levels of cement dust in the workplace. **(6)**

3. **Identify FOUR** hazardous substances that are widely encountered in the construction industry **AND give** an associated health risk for **EACH**. **(8)**

4. **Identify** the information that should be included in a safety data sheet (SDS) for hazardous chemicals. **(8)**

5. (a) **Identify FOUR** forms of chemical agents that might be found in construction workplaces. **(4)**

   (b) **Outline** the differences between the acute and chronic effects from exposure to chemical agents. **(4)**

Please refer to the back of the assessment section for answers.

This page is intentionally blank

Physical and psychological health - hazards and risk control

Learning outcomes

On completion of this element, candidates should be able to demonstrate understanding of the content through the application of knowledge to familiar and unfamiliar situations. In particular they should be able to:

9.1 Outline the health effects associated with exposure to noise and appropriate control measures.

9.2 Outline the health effects associated with exposure to vibration and appropriate control measures.

9.3 Outline the health effects associated with ionising and non-ionising radiation and the appropriate control measures.

9.4 Outline the causes and effects of stress at work and appropriate control measures.

Content

9.1 - Noise 257
    Physical and psychological effects on hearing of exposure to noise 257
    The meaning of common sound measurement terms 257
    Assessment of noise exposure 258
    Basic noise control measures 262
    Personal hearing protection 263
    The role of monitoring and health surveillance 264
9.2 - Vibration 265
    The effects on the body of exposure to vibration 265
    The need for assessment of exposure, including limit and action values 266
    Basic vibration control measures 267
    Role of monitoring and health surveillance 268
9.3 - Radiation 269
    Differences between non-ionising and ionising radiation 269
    Types of non-ionising radiation 269
    Types of ionising radiation 270
    Typical occupational sources of non-ionising and ionising radiation 271
    The basic means of controlling exposures to ionising and non-ionising radiation 272
    The basic means of controlling exposures to radon 273
    Basic radiation protection strategies 273
    The role of monitoring and health surveillance 274
9.4 - Stress 275
    Introduction and meaning of 'work-related stress' 275
    Causes of stress 275
    Effects of stress 276
    Control measures 276
Exam practice 278

Sources of reference

Reference information provided, in particular web links, is correct at time of publication, but may have changed.

Controlling Noise at Work, The Control of Noise at Work Regulations, Guidance on Regulations (second edition 2005), L108, HSE Books, ISBN 978-0-7176-6164-4 www.hse.gov.uk/pubns/priced/l108.pdf

Hand-arm vibration, Control of Vibration at Work Regulations 2005, Guidance on Regulations, L140, HSE Books, ISBN 978-0-7176-6125-1 www.hse.gov.uk/pubns/priced/l140.pdf

Health and Safety Toolbox, online resource, HSE www.hse.gov.uk/toolbox/index.htm

HSE Stress Management Standards www.hse.gov.uk/stress/standards

Managing the causes of work-related stress: A step-by-step approach using the Management Standards, HSG218, second edition 2007, HSE Books, ISBN 978-0-7176-6273-9 ww.hse.gov.uk/pubns/priced/hsg218.pdf

Personal Protective Equipment at Work Regulations 1992 (as amended) - Guidance on Regulations, L25 (second edition 2005), HSE Books, ISBN 978-0-7176-6139-3 http://www.hse.gov.uk/pubns/priced/l25.pdf

Radon in the workplace http://www.hse.gov.uk/radiation/ionising/radon.htm

Safe Use of Work Equipment - ACOP and guidance, L22 (fourth edition 2014), HSE Books, ISBN 978-0-7176-6619-5 http://www.hse.gov.uk/pubns/priced/l22.pdf

Whole-body vibration; The Control of Vibration at Work Regulations 2005, Guidance on Regulations, L141, HSE Books, ISBN 978-0-7176-6126-8 www.hse.gov.uk/pubns/priced/l141.pdf

Relevant statutory provisions

Control of Artificial Optical Radiation at Work (CAOR) Regulations 2010

Control of Noise at Work Regulations (CNWR) 2005

Control of Vibration at Work Regulations (CVWR) 2005

Construction (Design and Management) Regulations (CDM) 2015

Ionising Radiations Regulations (IRR) 1999

Personal Protective Equipment at Work Regulations (PPER) 1992

Provision and Use of Work Equipment Regulations (PUWER) 1998

9.1 - Noise

Physical and psychological effects on hearing of exposure to noise

The ear senses **sound**, which is transmitted in the form of pressure waves travelling through a substance, for example, air, water, metals etc. Unwanted sound is generally known as **noise**.

The ear has 3 basic regions **see figure ref 9-1**:

1) The **outer** ear channels the sound pressure waves through to the eardrum.

2) In the **middle** ear, the vibrations of the eardrum are transmitted through three small bones (hammer, anvil and stirrup) to the inner ear.

3) The cochlea in the **inner** ear is filled with fluid and contains tiny hairs (nerves) which respond to the sound. Signals are then sent to the brain via the acoustic nerve.

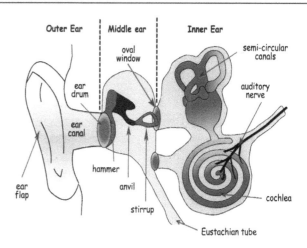

Figure 9-1: Inner ear diagram.   Source: www.echalk.co.uk.

PHYSICAL EFFECTS

Excessive noise over long periods of time can cause damage to the hairs (nerves) in the cochlea of the ear. This results in **noise induced hearing loss (deafness)**, which can be of a temporary or permanent nature. Also, a single high pressure event can damage the ear by dislocation of a bone or rupturing the ear drum. It has been shown that high levels of noise can cause, or increase the onset of, **tinnitus** ('ringing in the ears').

PSYCHOLOGICAL EFFECTS

Noise is often linked with adverse psychological effects such as stress, sleep disturbance or aggressive behaviour, and is frequently cited as the cause of friction between workers, particularly in a noisy office environment where there is a need for some individuals to concentrate on complex issues but they find this difficult or impossible because of background noise levels.

The meaning of common sound measurement terms

SOUND POWER AND PRESSURE

For noise to occur power must be available. It is the sound power of a source (measured in Watts) which causes the sound pressure (measured in Pascals) to occur at a specific point.

INTENSITY AND FREQUENCY

The amplitude of a sound wave represents the intensity of the sound pressure. When measuring the **amplitude** of sound there are two main parameters of interest **(as shown in figure ref 9-2)**. One is related to the energy in the sound pressure wave and is known as the 'root mean square' (RMS) value, and the other is the 'peak' level. We use the rms sound pressure for the majority of noise measurements, apart from some impulsive types of noise when the peak value is also measured.

Sound waves travel through air at the **'speed of sound'** which is approximately equal to 344 m/s.

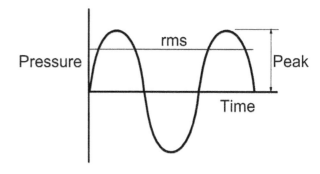

Figure 9-2: Rms and peak levels of a sound wave.   Source: RMS.

A sound can have a **'frequency'** or **'pitch'**, which is measured in cycles per second (Hz).

THE DECIBEL SCALE

The ear can detect pressures over a very wide range, from 20 µPa to 20 Pa (Pascals). To help deal with this wide range, the **deciBel (dB)** is used to measure noise. A decibel is a unit of sound pressure (intensity) measured on a logarithmic scale from a base level taken to be the threshold of hearing (0dB). Typical noise levels include:

Source	dB	Source	dB
Night club	110	Radio in average room	70
Smoke detector at 1 metre	105	Library	30
Machine shop	90	Threshold of hearing	0

Figure 9-3: Typical noise levels.   Source: RMS.

A problem with decibels is that they are based on a logarithmic scale and cannot be added together in the conventional way, for example:

- 2 dB + 2 dB = 5 dB (deciBel Arithmetic).
- 85 dB + 85 dB = 88 dB (deciBel Arithmetic).

Weighting scales - the terms dB(A) and dB(C)

The human ear can hear sound over a range of frequencies, from 20 Hz up to approximately 20,000 Hz (20 kHz). However, the ear does not hear the same at all frequencies; it naturally reduces (attenuates) low frequencies and very high frequencies to the range of speech. To take account of the response of the human ear sound level meters use weighting scales or filters. The most widely used sound level filter is the A scale. Using this filter, the sound level meter is thus less sensitive to very high and very low frequencies. Measurements made on this scale are expressed as dB(A) or referred to as 'A weighted'. The majority of measurements are made in terms of dB(A), although there are other weightings that are used in some circumstances. One of these is the C scale, which is used to assess the acoustic emissions of machines, in the selection of hearing protectors and analysis of environmental noise. The C scale is used to determine peak sound pressure levels and is particularly useful for impact or explosive noises. It has a broader spectrum than that of the A weighted scale and is more accurate at higher levels of noise. Measurements made on this scale are expressed as dB(C). There is also a (rarely used) B weighting scale, intermediate between A and C.

The range of frequencies that we encounter is often divided into **Octave Bands**. A noise can be measured in each octave band and these levels can be used when assessing the attenuation of hearing protectors, or when diagnosing noise problems.

Other noise units

In most situations the noise level varies with time. When measuring noise we need to determine the average, or 'equivalent continuous level', over a period of time. This is known as the **Leq**. Not all noise meters include a **Leq** function. Other noise units commonly encountered are shown in the following list:

L_{eq} — the average, or 'equivalent continuous level'.

$L_{EP,d}$ — daily personal exposure level, dB(A). This is equivalent to the L_{eq} over an 8-hour working day. The $L_{EP,d}$ is directly related to the risk of hearing damage.

L_{peak} — peak pressure - pascals or dB(C). This is the peak level of the sound pressure wave with no time constant applied. For noise at work measurements the peak level should be C weighted.

Assessment of noise exposure

THE NEED FOR ASSESSMENT OF EXPOSURE TO NOISE

Employers have a duty under the Control of Noise at Work Regulations (CNWR) 2005 to reduce the risk of hearing damage to their employees by controlling exposure to noise. There is a further requirement that the employer obtain an adequate noise assessment, which will enable compliance with duties to control noise exposure.

The assessment should establish which employees are at risk of hearing damage, and the level of risk. It will also identify sources of noise that particularly contribute to the noise level employees are exposed to for example, equipment and specific activities. This will enable analysis of the options to control the noise at source or by other means. This will also help the employer when providing suitable hearing protection, marking out ear protection zones and giving information, instruction and training to employees. Re-assessment should be carried out after action to control exposure, or after a reasonable time, to establish the effectiveness of the controls. If recorded, it will provide evidence of a structured risk assessment process.

RISK ASSESSMENT

When conducting the risk assessment, consideration should be given to the type, duration, effects of exposure, exposure limit/action values, effects on workers at particular risk, manufacturers' information, availability of replacement equipment or changes of process, the extension of exposure at the workplace (for example, in rest facilities) and information from health surveillance.

The employer should assess the level of noise the workers are exposed to by:

- Observation.
- Reference to information on expected levels for work conditions and equipment.
- If necessary by measurement of the level of noise to which their employees may be exposed.

It is not always necessary to carry out measurements of noise exposure as part of the assessment; an estimate of noise levels may be enough to decide that controls are required. The Health and Safety Executive (HSE) suggest estimation by observation may be sufficient to indicate there is a noise problem. This is where the assessor determines how easy it is for two people to hold a conversation at a distance from each other, by using the 'one and two metre rule'.

Two metre rule: If the conversation is difficult (need to raise the voice or repeat words) at a distance of two metres apart the noise level is likely to be above 85 dB.

One metre rule: If the conversation is difficult (need to raise the voice or repeat words) at a distance of one metre apart the noise level is likely to be above 90 dB.

Similarly, it may be possible to determine if there is a potential noise problem by considering expected levels of noise for work conditions and equipment. This may be done by considering noise data provided by the manufacturer or alternatively the HSE provides the table ***as shown in figure ref 9-4*** to help indicate expected noise levels.

If it is necessary to be more certain whether noise exposure levels exceed the action or limit values, measurements of actual noise levels may be preferred.

Process	*Work*	*Noise level*
Working with concrete: chipping, drilling, floor finishing, grinding etc.	Typical	85-90 dB
Labouring	General work	84 dB
	Shuttering	91 dB
	Shovelling hardcore	94 dB
	Concrete pour	97 dB
	Digging/scabbling	100 dB
Driving machines or vehicles	Typical	85-90 dB
Carpentry	Typical	92 dB
Angle grinding/cutting	Typical	90-100 dB
Piling	Machine operator	85 dB
	Piling worker	100 dB

Figure 9-4: Typical noise levels for a range of construction activities.   *Source: HSE.*

A detailed assessment should include consideration of:

- Level, type and duration of exposure, including any exposure to peak sound pressure.
- Effects of exposure to ***noise*** on employees or groups of employees whose health is at particular risk from such exposure.
- So far as is practicable, any effects on the health and safety of employees resulting from the interaction between noise and the use of toxic substances at ***work***, or between ***noise*** and vibration.
- Indirect effects on the health and safety of employees resulting from the interaction between noise and audible warning signals or other sounds that need to be audible in order to reduce risk at ***work***.
- Information provided by the manufacturers of ***work*** equipment.
- Availability of alternative equipment designed to reduce the emission of ***noise***.
- Any extension of exposure to noise at the workplace beyond normal ***working*** hours, including exposure in rest facilities supervised by the employer.
- Appropriate information obtained following health surveillance, including, where possible, published information.
- Availability of personal hearing protectors with adequate attenuation characteristics.

Employees or their representatives must be consulted and significant findings and measures taken or planned to comply with the regulations have to be recorded.

Noise is measured using a sound pressure level meter, which works in simple terms by converting pressure variations into an electric signal. This is achieved by capturing the sound with a microphone, pre-amplification of the resultant voltage signal and then processing the signal into the information required dependent on the type of meter (for example, 'A' weighting, integrating levels, fast or slow response).

The microphone is the most critical component within the meter as its sensitivity and accuracy will determine the accuracy of the final reading. Meters can be set to fast or slow response depending on the characteristics of the noise level.

Figure 9-5: Noise measurement.   *Source: HSE, L108.*

Where levels are rapidly fluctuating, rapid measurements are required and the meter should be set to fast time weighting. In most situations, the noise level that workers are exposed to varies over a period of time. When measuring noise we need to determine the average, or 'equivalent continuous level', over a period of time (time weighted average), this is often known as the L_{eq}.

Sound pressure level meters are used to measure the:

- Sound pressure level (L_p) - the intensity of sound at a given moment in time at a given position (i.e. the instantaneous level): an unweighted linear measurement in dB (L_{in}).
- Equivalent continuous sound level (L_{eq}) - an average measure of intensity of sound over a reference period, usually the period of time over which the measurement was taken, measured in dB(A). As the intensity and spacing of the noise levels usually vary with time, an integrating meter is used. An integrating meter automatically calculates the L_{eq} by summing or integrating the sound level over the measurement period.
- Daily personal exposure level, dB(A), LEP,d or $L_{Aep,8h}$ - this is equivalent to the L_{eq} over an 8-hour working day. The $L_{EP,d}$ or $L_{Aep,8h}$ is directly related to the risk of hearing damage.
- Peak pressure level, L_{peak} or $L_{C,peak}$ - this is the peak level of the sound pressure wave with no time constant applied. For noise at work measurements, the peak level should be C weighted.

Personal dosimeters are available for situations where the task of the worker involves movement around the workplace and exposure is likely to vary.

Sound pressure level meters should be calibrated using a portable acoustic calibrator and batteries checked before, during and after each measurement session. Laboratory calibration should be carried out annually or according to the manufacturer's instructions.

Workers or their representatives should be consulted and significant findings, measures taken or planned to control the risks should be recorded.

Re-assessment should be carried out after action is taken to control exposure, or after a reasonable time, to establish the effectiveness of the controls.

ACTION AND LIMIT VALUES

Noise in the workplace is a likely hazard related to machinery and work processes and is an example of a physical agent risk that should be controlled. As people respond differently to noise, the level at which noise will start to cause harm to the hearing of workers varies. Research has established that long periods of repeated exposure to workplace noise levels between 75dB(A) and 80dB(A) present a small risk of the average worker developing a hearing disability. As noise levels increase, the risk becomes greater. For example, exposure to noise levels of 90dB(A) - 95dB(A) presents a considerably greater risk of a worker developing hearing disability.

Standards concerning acceptable levels of noise, and therefore exposure limits, are usually based on an 8 hour work period, they may also provide exposure limits for shorter and longer working periods.

It should be remembered that exposure to noise below the acceptable noise level does not means a safe condition exists; it means that an eight hour exposure to the acceptable noise level is considered to represent an acceptable level of risk to workers hearing in the workplace.

Some workers may be affected by noise exposures below this level and therefore most national legislation will include a requirement to reduce exposure as far as is reasonably practicable and at least below the legally acceptable noise level.

The amount of damage caused by noise depends on the total amount of energy received by the worker's hearing over time. This means, as noise becomes more intense it causes damage to hearing in less time.

A 3dB(A) increase in noise level will produce twice the sound energy and cause the same damage in half the time.

Therefore, the acceptable duration of exposure at this noise level is halved. For example, if a worker is exposed to a noise level of 88dB(A) the acceptable duration would be 4 hours, half that of a worker exposed to 85dB(A), 8 hours.

Similarly, fifteen minutes of working in noise levels of 100dB(A) may cause the same damage as eight hours working in 85dB(A).

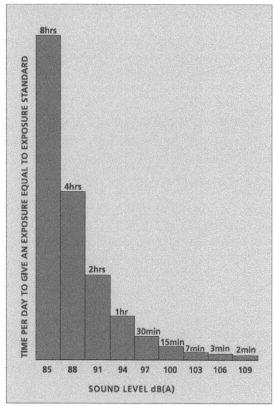

Figure 9-6: Exposure times.   *Source: Australia, SafeWork SA.*

Regulation 2 of the CNWR 2005 sets out the definition of 'daily average noise exposure' as the time weighted average of the noise to which a worker is exposed over an 8 hour working day, taking account of levels of noise and duration of exposure and including impulsive noises. Weekly noise exposure means the average of daily noise exposures over a week and normalised to five working days.

	Lower exposure action values	Upper exposure action values	Exposure limit values
Daily or weekly personal noise exposure (A-weighted).	80 dB	85 dB	87 dB
Peak sound pressure (C-weighted).	135 dB	137 dB	140 dB

Figure 9-7: Noise exposure values.   *Source: CNWR 2005.*

Under ***Regulation 4 of CNWR 2005*** if the exposure of the employee to noise in the workplace varies greatly the employer can choose to use weekly noise exposure instead of daily noise exposure in determining if values or limits are exceeded. The exposure can take into account personal hearing protection provided to the employee.

Lower exposure action values

Where an employee is likely to be exposed to noise at or above the lower exposure action values, the daily or weekly exposure of 80 dB(A) or a peak sound pressure level of 135 dB(C), the employer must make hearing protection available upon request and provide the employees and their representatives with suitable and sufficient information, instruction and training.

This must include:

■ Nature of risks from exposure to noise.
■ Organisational and technical measures taken in order to comply.
■ Exposure limit values and upper and lower exposure action values.
■ Significant findings of the risk assessment, including any measurements taken, with an explanation of those findings.
■ Availability and provision of personal hearing protectors and their correct use.
■ Why and how to detect and report signs of hearing damage.
■ Entitlement to health surveillance.
■ Safe working practices to minimise exposure to noise.
■ The collective results of any health surveillance in a form calculated to prevent those results from being identified as relating to a particular person.

Figure 9-8: Noise hazard sign.   *Source: RMS.*

Upper exposure action values

Where the noise exposure of an employee is likely to be at or above the upper exposure action values, the daily or weekly exposure of 85 dB(A) or a peak sound pressure level of 137 dB(C), the employer must:

■ Provide employees with hearing protection.
■ Ensure that the area is designated a hearing protection zone, fitted with mandatory hearing protection signs.

Figure 9-9: Mandatory hearing protection sign. *Source: Stocksigns.*

■ Ensure access to the area is restricted where practicable.
■ So far as reasonably practicable, ensure those employees entering the area wear hearing protection.

Exposure limit values

The employer must ensure that employees are not exposed to noise above an exposure limit value, the daily or weekly exposure of 87 dB(A) or a peak sound pressure level of 140 dB(C). If an exposure limit value is exceeded the employer must immediately:

■ Reduce exposure below the limit value.
■ Identify the reason for the limit value being exceeded.
■ Modify the organisational and technical measures to prevent a reoccurrence.

Basic noise control measures

Requirements for noise control set out in Regulation 6 of CNWR 2005 follow the general principles of prevention set out in the Management of Health and Safety at Work Regulations (MHSWR) 1999.

Employers must ensure that risk from the exposure of their employees to noise is either eliminated at source or, where this is not reasonably practicable, reduced to as low as is reasonably practicable. Consideration should be made to:

- Other ***working*** methods which reduce exposure to noise.
- Choice of appropriate ***work*** equipment emitting the least possible ***noise***, taking account of the ***work*** to be done.
- Design and layout of workplaces, ***work*** stations and rest facilities.
- Suitable and sufficient information and training for employees, such that ***work*** equipment may be used correctly, in order to minimise their exposure to ***noise***.
- Reduction of ***noise*** by technical means.
- Appropriate maintenance programmes for ***work*** equipment, the workplace and workplace systems.
- Limitation of the duration and intensity of exposure to ***noise***.
- Appropriate ***work*** schedules with adequate rest periods.

The employer has to take care that noise levels in rest facilities are suitable for their purpose. The employer must adapt measures provided to suit a group or individual employee whose health is likely to be of particular risk from exposure to noise at work. Employees or their representatives must be consulted on the measures used. Noise can be controlled at different points in the following 'chain':

- The source (for example, a noisy machine).
- The path (for example, through the air).
- The receiver (for example, the operator of a machine).

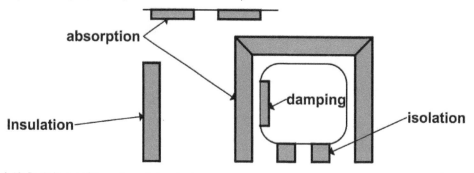

Figure 9-10: Basic layout of the main control methods.   Source: RMS.

The main methods of noise control are shown in the following list:

Isolation   Positioning an absorbent element (for example, rubber mount etc.) in the path of vibration can isolate a noise radiating area from a vibration input.

Absorption   When noise passes through porous materials (for example, foam, mineral, wool etc.) some of its energy is absorbed.

Insulation   Imposing a barrier (for example, a brick wall, lead sheet etc.) between the noise source and the receivers will provide noise insulation.

Damping   Mechanical vibration can be converted into heat by damping materials (for example, metal/plastic/metal panels).

Silencing   Pipes/boxes can be designed to reduce air/gas noise (for example, engine exhaust silencers, duct silencers, etc.).

Other specialist control methods (***not*** examinable):

- ***Force reduction*** - reduce impacts by using rubber pads or lower drop heights.
- ***Air exhaust and jet silencers*** - proprietary silencers can be used.
- ***Active*** - equal but opposite phase noise can cancel a problem noise.

In addition to controlling the amplitude of noise the ***exposure level*** can be reduced by minimising the amount of time an employee is exposed to noise, for example, by job rotation. Increasing the distance between noisy equipment and a work location can reduce the noise to which an employee is exposed.

Figure 9-11: Silenced diesel welder.   Source: Speedy Hire Plc.

© RMS

When buying new plant and equipment; employers should adopt a purchasing policy which results in the quietest machines being sourced.

Personal hearing protection

PURPOSE

The purpose of personal hearing protection is to protect the user from the adverse effects on hearing caused by exposure to high levels of noise. All hearing protection must be capable of reducing exposure to below the upper exposure action value as required by CNWR 2005 (85 dB averaged over 8 hours). All types of personal ear protection should carry a CE mark.

APPLICATION AND LIMITATIONS OF VARIOUS TYPES

Earmuffs:	*Application:*	*Limitations:*
■ Banded. ■ Helmet mounted. ■ Communication muffs.	■ Worn on the outside of the ear so less chance of infection. ■ Clearly visible therefore easy to monitor. ■ Can be integrated into other forms of personal protective equipment (PPE) for example, head protection.	■ Can be uncomfortable when worn for long periods. ■ Incompatibility with other forms of PPE. ■ Effectiveness may be compromised by for example, long hair, spectacles etc. ■ Requires correct storage facilities and regular maintenance.
Ear plugs:	*Application:*	*Limitations:*
■ Pre-moulded. ■ User formable. ■ Custom moulded. ■ Banded plugs.	■ Easy to use and store - but must be inserted correctly. ■ Available in many materials and designs, disposable. ■ Relatively lightweight and comfortable. Can be worn for long periods.	■ They are subject to hygiene problems unless care is taken to keep them clean. ■ Correct size may be required. Should be determined by a competent person. ■ Interferes with communication. ■ Worn inside the ear, difficult to monitor.

Figure 9-12: Application and limitations of various types.   *Source: RMS.*

Figure 9-13: Ear defenders.   *Source: RMS.*

Figure 9-14: Disposable ear plugs.   *Source: RMS.*

SELECTION

When selecting personal hearing protectors employers must take into consideration several factors, including:

- Noise attenuation (reduction) capability.
- Compatibility with other personal protective equipment.
- Suitability for the work environment.
- Readily available.
- Comfort and personal choice.
- Issue to visitors.
- Provision of information and training.
- Care and maintenance.

USE

All PPE should be used in accordance with employer's instructions, which should be based on manufacturer's instructions for use. PPE should only be used after adequate training has been given. Also, adequate supervision must be provided to ensure that training and instructions are being followed. Personal ear protection may not provide adequate protection due to any of the following reasons:

- Long hair, spectacles, earrings etc., may cause a poor seal to occur.

- Ear protectors are damaged, for example, cracked.
- Not fitted properly - due to lack of training.
- Not wearing ear protectors all of the time.
- Specification of protectors does not provide sufficient attenuation.

MAINTENANCE

Employers have a legal duty to ensure that any PPE is maintained in an efficient state, efficient working order and good repair. Simple maintenance can be carried out by the trained wearer, but more intricate repairs should only be done by specialist personnel. Maintenance in this context includes actions to keep personal hearing protection in use in good order. This will include the timely disposal of personal hearing protection that no longer affords adequate protection due to use.

ATTENUATION FACTORS

The attenuation (noise reduction) associated with personal hearing protectors must be supplied with the product. The information required is in terms of:

- SNR (Single Number Rating) values.
- HML (High, Medium and Low) values.
- Octave band values.

For example, a hearing protector might be designated with SNR 26, H=32, M=23, L=14. The estimated attenuation changes according to the noise spectrum of the environment in which the hearing protector is to be worn.

The SNR value is the result of a lengthy mathematical calculation; it gives a single-number rating of a hearing protector's attenuation for a specified percentage of the population. The SNR is significantly lower than the average attenuation across all of its test frequencies as the calculation contains correction factors to make it applicable to the broader population. While it is not the perfect measure of attenuation, SNR is a very useful standardised method for describing a hearing protector's attenuation in a single number. For example, if an environment has a weighted noise measurement of 100 dB(C) then by using an earplug with a SNR rating of 25 dB it will reduce the noise to 75 dB(A).

Using HML values, H is for high-frequency noise environments, M for mid-frequency and L for low-frequency. Note that the HML designation does not refer to noise level, rather the spectrum of the noise frequencies. To determine the predicted noise attenuation (PNA) it is necessary that a noise reading be taken in both A weighting and C weighting mode, at the worker's ear. If the difference between the A weighted reading and the C weighted reading is greater than 2 a formula using the medium and low values is used; if it is less than or equal to 2 a formula using the high and medium value is used. This method enables the effects of the frequency of the noise to be taken into account by using a sound level meter with A and C weighting.

If readings have been taken using an octave band sound level meter the octave band method can be used to produce a more accurate reflection of the effectiveness of hearing protectors. This can assist with ensuring a close match of a particular hearing protector with the noise created by a particular noise source. It involves quite complicated mathematics, so to assist employers the Health and Safety Executive (HSE) has produced a calculator, which can be found at http://www.hse.gov.uk/noise/calculator.htm. Calculators are also available for SNR and HML methods.

Whichever method is used to determine the predicted noise attenuation of hearing protection, the HSE recommends the reduction of the value by 4 dB to reflect what they see as 'real world factors'. This takes account of variances with fit or other user factors that may limit the effectiveness of the hearing protection.

The role of monitoring and health surveillance

Construction work includes the demolition, maintenance, repair, erection, construction of buildings/roads and any work of engineering construction. A great deal of this type of these activities can involve workers being exposed to high noise levels.

Construction workers are not only exposed to the noise from construction machinery, but may also the excessive noise levels generated by heavy traffic when work is being carried out on the side of a busy road. Because of the changing noise exposure levels that arise during construction activities it is important to monitor the noise and the effects of noise through health surveillance.

MONITORING

The role of noise monitoring is to ensure that noise designated areas and working conditions in those areas are kept under review.

The main functions of monitoring are to:

- Check that areas have been correctly designated for hearing protection.
- Identify any changes to noise levels so that appropriate control measures for restricting exposure can be proposed.

- Detect breakdowns in controls or systems, so as to indicate whether conditions are satisfactory for continuing work in that area.
- Ensure workers use the controls provided and report any defects.
- Ensure workers use hearing protection where its use is designated as mandatory.
- Provide information on those who may be at risk and in need of health surveillance.

HEALTH SURVEILLANCE

The role of health surveillance is to provide early detection of work-related ill-health. It will assist with the identification of noise hazards and the evaluation of noise control measures. By conducting health surveillance from the start of an employee's employment it is possible to detect early signs of hearing loss and provide early intervention to limit the continuing effects. Health surveillance can assist with confirming the success of noise controls at source and support the promotion of personal hearing protection.

Regulation 9 of the CNWR 2005 states that if a risk assessment indicates a risk to the health and safety of employees who are, or are liable to be, exposed to noise, and then they must be put under suitable health surveillance (including testing of their hearing). The employer must keep and maintain a suitable health record. The employer will, providing reasonable notice is given, allow the employee access to their health record.

Where, as a result of health surveillance, an employee is found to have identifiable hearing damage the employer shall ensure that the employee is examined by a doctor. If the doctor, or any specialist to whom the doctor considers it necessary to refer the employee, considers that the damage is likely to be the result of exposure to noise, the employer must:

- Ensure that a suitably qualified person informs the employee accordingly.
- Review the risk assessment.
- Review any measure taken to comply with the regulations.
- Consider assigning the employee to alternative work.
- Ensure continued health surveillance.
- Provide for a review of the health of any other employee who has been similarly exposed.

Employees must, when required by the employer and at the cost of the employer, present themselves during working hours for health surveillance procedures.

9.2 - Vibration

The effects on the body of exposure to vibration

Occupational exposure to vibration may arise in a number of ways, often reaching workers at intensity levels disturbing to comfort, efficiency and health and safety. Long-term, regular exposure to vibration is known to lead to permanent and debilitating health effects such as vibration white finger, loss of sensation, pain, and numbness in the hands, arms, spine and joints. These effects are collectively known as hand-arm or whole body vibration syndrome.

In the case of whole body vibration it is transmitted to the worker through a contacting or supporting structure that is itself vibrating, for example, the seat or floor of a vehicle (for example, dumper truck or road preparation/laying machine).

Figure 9-15: Use of circular saw - vibration.   *Source: RMS.*

By far the most common route of harm to the human body is through the hands, wrists and arms of the subject - so called segmental vibration, where there is actual contact with the vibrating source.

HAND-ARM VIBRATION

Prolonged intense vibration transmitted to the hands and arms by vibrating tools and equipment can lead to a condition known as ***Hand-arm Vibration Syndrome (HAVs).*** These are a range of conditions relating to long term damage to the circulatory system, nerves, soft tissues, bones and joints.

Probably the best known of these conditions is known as vibration white finger (VWF). Here the fingers go white and numb (known as ***Raynaud's phenomenon***), leading to sharp tingling pains in the affected area and an often painful deep red flush.

This seems to occur in response to a change in metabolic demand in the fingers induced, for example, by temperature change. It seems that the blood vessels are unable to dilate either at all or rapidly enough because of the thickened tissues that then become anoxic (lacking in oxygen).

Contributory factors

As with all work-related ill-health there are a number of factors which when combined result in the problem occurring. These include:

- Vibration frequency - most hand held tools generate random vibration over a wide range of frequencies ranging from 2-2000Hz; but the most serious health effects are in the 5 to 20 Hz range.
- Duration of exposure - this is the length of time the individual is exposed to the vibration.
- Contact force - this is the amount of grip or push used to guide or apply the tools or work piece. The tighter the grip the greater the vibration to the hand.
- Factors affecting circulation - including temperature and smoking.
- Individual susceptibility.

Examples of risk activities in construction

- The use of hand-held chain saws.
- The use of hand-held rotary tools in grinding, sanding or cutting.
- The use of hand-held percussive drills for drilling into concrete or similar materials.
- The use of vibrating compactors.
- The use of disc cutter/cut off saws and hand held saws or planners.
- The use of nail and other impact fixing guns.
- The use of scrabblers.
- The use of hand-held powered percussive drills or hammers.

The medical effects of sustained exposure to hand-arm vibration can be serious and permanent and are summarised in the following points:

- Vascular changes in the blood vessels of the fingers.
- Neurological changes in the peripheral nerves
- Muscle and tendon damage in the fingers, hands, wrists and forearms.
- Suspected bone and joint changes.
- Damage to the autonomic centres of the central nervous system in the brain influencing the endocrine, cardiac, vestibular and cochlear functions (not proven).

WHOLE BODY VIBRATION (WBV)

Whole-body vibration is vibration transmitted to the entire body via the seat or the feet, or both, often through driving or riding in vehicles (including fork-lift trucks, excavators, vehicles fitted percussion hammers and dumper trucks) or through standing on vibrating floors of equipment (including road preparation/laying equipment and concrete pumps).

Prolonged exposure can lead to considerable back pain and time off work and may result in permanent injury and having to give up work.

High-risk activities include driving construction site vehicles (for example, dumper trucks) and the prolonged use of compactors.

Figure 9-16: Dumper truck seat, vibration mountings. *Source: RMS.*

The need for assessment of exposure, including limit and action values

RISK ASSESSMENT

Regulation 5 of CVWR 2005 requires the employer to make a suitable and sufficient assessment of the risk created by work that is liable to expose employees to risk from vibration. The assessment must observe work practices, make reference to information regarding the magnitude of vibration from equipment and, if necessary, measurement of the magnitude of the vibration.

Consideration must also be given to the type, duration, effects of exposure, exposures limit/action values, effects on employees at particular risk, the effects of vibration on equipment and the ability to use it, manufacturers' information, availability of replacement equipment, and extension of exposure at the workplace (for example, rest facilities), temperature and information on health surveillance. The risk assessment should be recorded as soon as is practicable after it is made and be reviewed regularly.

EXPOSURE ACTION AND LIMIT VALUES

Regulation 4 of the CVWR 2005 states the personal daily exposure limits and daily exposure action values, normalised over an 8-hour reference period.

	Daily exposure action values	Daily exposure limit values
Hand arm vibration	$2.5m/s^2$	$5m/s^2$
Whole body vibration	$0.5m/s^2$	$1.15m/s^2$

Figure 9-17: Vibration exposure action and limit values.   *Source: CVWR 2005.*

Because the harm from vibration is considered to be related to the energy from the acceleration and the duration of exposure it is possible to be exposed to higher levels than the action and limit values provided they are for periods of time that are proportionately shorter than 8 hours. For example, exposure to a magnitude of $5m/s^2$ for 4 hours would be equivalent to $2.5m/s^2$ for 8 hours.

Exposure action values

Where an employee is likely to be exposed to vibration at or above an exposure action values, the employer must place the employee under suitable health surveillance and provide the employee and their representatives with suitable and sufficient information, instruction and training.

Exposure limit values

In general, the employer must ensure that employees are not exposed to vibration above an exposure limit value. If an exposure limit value is exceeded the employer must immediately:

- Reduce exposure below the limit value.
- Identify the reason for the limit value being exceeded.
- Modify the measures taken to prevent a reoccurrence.

Where exposure to vibration is usually below the exposure action value but varies markedly from time to time, the exposure limit value may be occasionally exceeded, providing that:

- Any exposure to vibration averaged over one week is less than the exposure limit value.
- There is evidence to show that the risk from the actual pattern of exposure is less than the corresponding risk from constant exposure at the exposure limit value.
- Risk is reduced to as low a level as is reasonably practicable, taking into account the special circumstances.
- Employees concerned are subject to increased health surveillance.

Basic vibration control measures

PREVENTIVE AND PRECAUTIONARY MEASURES

Regulation 6 of CVWR 2005 states that the employer must seek to eliminate the risk of vibration at source or, if not reasonably practicable, reduce it to as low a level as is reasonably practicable. Where it is not reasonably practicable to take preventive measures which eliminate the risk at source and the personal daily exposure action value is likely to be reached or exceeded, the employer must reduce exposure by implementing a programme of organisational and technical measures. These precautionary measures include the use of other methods of work, improved ergonomics, maintenance of equipment, design and layout, rest facilities, information, instruction and training, limitation by schedules and breaks and the provision of personal protective equipment to protect from cold and damp. Measures must be adapted to take account of any group or individual employee whose health may be of particular risk from exposure to vibration.

The following precautionary measures should be considered when protecting people who work with vibrating equipment.

CHOICE OF EQUIPMENT

It is important to consider vibration characteristics when purchasing new equipment or selecting equipment for a task. Some equipment will provide better control of vibration at source; others will have damping measures provided to limit vibration transmission to the user. Many manufacturers claim to use composite materials that, when moulded into hand-grips and fitted onto vibrating power tools, reduce vibration by up to 45%. Some equipment may provide beneficial design that can limit the effects of vibration, such as the routing of exhaust gases of portable petrol driven equipment through the operating handles, to keep the user's hands warm.

MAINTENANCE

Equipment should be maintained to its optimum performance level, thereby reducing vibration to a minimum (for example, the bearings of grinders).

LIMITING EXPOSURE

When controlling the effects of vibration by limiting worker exposure the following should be considered:

- Carry out a detailed assessment of hazardous tasks (for example, breaking asphalt with a road breaker). This should include duration and frequency of the task.
- The work schedule should be examined to reduce duration of vibration exposure and magnitude, either by alternating with non-vibration work or avoiding continuous vibration by, for example, scheduling ten minute

breaks every hour. Where equipment creates a high magnitude of vibration this must be clearly identified and its use by a single worker limited to short periods. Care should be taken to organise work schedules so that rest periods from this high risk work happen naturally in the process. Where they do not, it may be necessary to use reminders in the form of timed alarms or supervision.

■ Wearing gloves is recommended for safety and protection against the cold by the retention of heat. Gloves of this type will not absorb a significant fraction of the vibration energy which lies within the 30 - 300Hz range. Care needs to be taken to select appropriate gloves, as the absorbent material in some gloves for thermal insulation may introduce a resonance frequency which may increase the total energy input to the hands.

■ Warm clothing can help workers exposed to vibration to maintain a good body core temperature, which will assist circulation to the hands. It may be necessary for workers to be provided with a warm location for rest breaks or periods when cold is affecting their circulation. Workers with established HAVS should avoid exposure to cold and thus minimise the number of blanching attacks.

■ Workers with advanced HAVS, which health surveillance has determined as deteriorating, should be removed from further exposure. The medical priority of this action is to prevent fingertip ulceration (tissue necrosis).

Other precautionary measures

Other precautions for controlling the effects of vibration include:

■ The vibration characteristics of hand tools should be assessed and reference made to the BSI and ISO Guidelines.

■ Development of a purchasing policy to include consideration of vibration and, where necessary, vibration isolating devices.

■ Training of all exposed employees on the proper use of tools and the minimisation of exposure. The greater the coupling (hand and tool interface), the more energy enters the hand. Increasing grip force increases the coupling. There are working techniques for all tools and the expertise developed over time justifies an initial training period for new starters. Operators of vibrating equipment should be trained to recognise the early symptoms of HAVS and WBV and how to report them.

■ A continuous review should be conducted with regard to the redesigning tools, rescheduling work methods, or automating the process until such time as the risks associated with vibration are under control.

■ As with any management system, the controls in place for vibration should be subject to audit.

Regulation 8 of CVWR 2005 states that employers must provide information, instruction and training to all employees who are exposed to risk from vibration and their representatives. This includes any organisational and technical measures taken, exposure limits and values, risk assessment findings, why and how to detect injury, entitlement to and collective results of health surveillance and safe working practices.

Information, instruction and training shall be updated to take account of changes in the employer's work or methods. The employer shall ensure all persons, whether or not an employee, who carry out work in connection with the employer's duties have been provided with information, instruction and training.

Role of monitoring and health surveillance

MONITORING

The role of monitoring is to ensure where vibrating tools or equipment are used vibration exposure and control measures are kept under review.

The main functions of monitoring are to:

■ Check that equipment identified as high risk or of lower risk has been correctly designated.

■ Identify any changes to vibration exposure so that appropriate control measures for restricting exposure can be proposed.

■ Detect breakdowns in controls or systems, so as to indicate whether conditions are satisfactory for continuing work with the equipment.

■ Ensure workers use the controls provided and report any defects.

■ Ensure equipment is maintained.

■ Ensure equipment is used correctly for the purpose for which it was designed.

■ Ensure workers are protected from cold windy and wet conditions.

■ Ensure workers take regular rest breaks from vibration tasks.

■ To provide information on those who may be at risk and in need of health surveillance.

HEALTH SURVEILLANCE

The role of health surveillance is to provide early detection of work-related ill-health; it will assist with the identification of symptoms of the effects of vibration on health. By conducting health surveillance from the start of an employee's employment it is possible to detect early signs of the effects of vibration and provide early intervention to limit the continuing effects. Health surveillance can assist with confirming the success of vibration control measures.

Surveillance for HAVS usually involves the worker or an occupational health specialist examining the hands to identify early signs of tingling or blanching. For whole body vibration, it can be a simple reporting method or questionnaire relating to experience of lower back discomfort or pain.

Regulation 7 of CVWR 2005 states that health surveillance must be carried out if there is a risk to the health of employees liable to be exposed to vibration. This is in order to prevent or diagnose any health effect linked with exposure to vibration. A record of health shall be kept of any employee who undergoes health surveillance. The employer must, providing reasonable notice is given, provide the employee with access to their health records and provide copies to an enforcing officer on request.

If health surveillance identifies a disease or adverse health effect, considered by a doctor or other occupational health professional to be a result of exposure to vibration, the employer shall ensure that a qualified person informs the employee and provides information and advice. The employer must ensure they are kept informed of any significant findings from health surveillance, taking into account any medical confidentiality.

In addition the employer must also:

- Review risk assessments.
- Review the measures taken to comply.
- Consider assigning the employee to other work.
- Review the health of any other employee who has been similarly exposed and consider alternative work.

9.3 - Radiation

Differences between non-ionising and ionising radiation

Ionising radiation is that radiation, typically alpha and beta particles and gamma and x-rays, which has sufficient energy to produce ions by interacting with matter, whereas non-ionising radiation does not possess sufficient energy to cause the ionisation of matter.

Types of non-ionising radiation

Non-ionising radiation relates to the part of the electromagnetic spectrum covering two main regions, optical radiation (ultraviolet, visible and infrared) and electromagnetic fields (power frequencies, microwaves, and radio frequencies).

ULTRAVIOLET

Possible sources

There are many possible sources of Ultraviolet (UV) radiation to which people may be exposed at work:

- The sun.
- Electric arc welding.
- Insect killers.
- Sunbeds and sunlamps.
- Crack detection equipment.
- Tanning and curing equipment.
- Forgery detectors.
- Some lasers.
- Mercury vapour lamps.
- Tungsten halogen lamps.

Potential health effects

Much of the natural ultraviolet in the atmosphere is filtered out by the ozone layer. However, sufficient ultraviolet penetrates to cause sunburn and even blindness. Its effect is thermal and photochemical, producing burns and skin thickening, and eventually skin cancer.

Electric arcs and ultraviolet lamps can produce an effect on the lens and conjunctiva of the eyes, resulting in inflammation called photokeratitis (sometimes called 'arc-eye') and the formation of cataracts in the lens.

VISIBLE LIGHT (INCLUDING LASERS)

Possible sources

Any high intensity source of visible light can cause problems. Lasers are an obvious danger but so are light beams, powerful light bulbs and the sun. The danger is always due to direct or reflected radiation.

Potential health effects

Light in the visible frequency range can cause damage if it is present in sufficiently intense form. The eyes are particularly vulnerable but skin tissue may also be damaged. Indirect danger may also be created by employees being temporarily dazzled.

Figure 9-18: UV - from welding.   *Source: Speedy Hire Plc.*

INFRARED

Possible sources

Anything that glows is likely to be a source of infrared radiation, for example:

- Furnaces or fires.
- Molten metal or glass.
- Burning or welding.
- Heat lamps.
- Some lasers.
- The sun.

Potential health effects

Exposure results in a thermal effect such as skin burning and loss of body fluids (heat exhaustion and dehydration). The eyes can be damaged in the cornea and lens which may become opaque (cataract). Retinal damage may also occur if the radiation is focused.

RADIO FREQUENCY AND MICROWAVES

Possible sources

This type of radiation is produced by radio/television transmitters. It is used industrially for induction heating of metals and is often found in intruder detectors.

Figure 9-19: Radio mast. *Source: RMS.*

Potential health effects

Burns can be caused if persons using this type of equipment allow parts of the body that carry jewellery to enter the radio frequency field. Intense fields at the source of transmitters will damage the body and particular precautions need to be taken to isolate radio/television transmitters to protect maintenance workers. Microwaves can produce the same deep heating effect in live tissue as they can produce in cooking.

Types of ionising radiation

Ionising radiation occurs as either electromagnetic rays, for example, gamma rays or x-rays, or in particles, for example, alpha and beta particles. Radiation is emitted by a wide range of sources and appliances used throughout industry, medicine and research. It is also a naturally occurring part of the environment. All matter is composed of **atoms**. Different atomic structures give rise to unique **elements**. Examples of common elements, which form the basic structure of life, are hydrogen, oxygen and carbon.

Atoms form the building blocks of nature and cannot be further sub divided by chemical means. The centre of the atom is called the **nucleus**, which consists of **protons** and **neutrons**. Electrons take up orbit around the nucleus.

Protons - Have a unit of mass and carry a positive electrical charge.

Neutrons - These also have mass but no charge.

Electrons - Have a mass about 2,000 times less than that of protons and carry a negative charge.

In an electrically neutral atom the number of electrons equals the number of protons (the positive and negative charges cancel out each other). If the atom loses an electron then a positively charged atom is created. The process of losing or gaining electrons is called **ionisation**.

If the matter which is ionised is a human cell, the cell chemistry will change and this will lead to functional changes in the body tissue. Some cells can repair radiation damage, others cannot. The cell's sensitivity to radiation is directly proportional to its reproductive function; bone marrow, and reproductive organs are the most vulnerable; muscle and central nervous system tissue are affected to a lesser extent.

"Ionising radiation is that radiation which has sufficient energy to produce ions by interacting with matter."

Figure 9-20: Ionising radiation. *Source: RMS.*

Ionising radiation found in industry are alpha, beta and gamma, and X-rays. Whilst X-rays may occur in nature, generally they are created in the work place either with knowledge, for example, X-ray machines or sometimes without knowledge from high voltage equipment. The human body absorbs radiation readily from a wide variety of sources, mostly with adverse effects.

There are a number of different types of ionising radiation each with their different powers of penetration and effects on the body. Therefore, the type of radiation will determine the type and level of protection.

ALPHA PARTICLES

Alpha particles are comparatively large. Alpha particles travel short distances in dense materials, and can only just penetrate the skin. The principal risk is through ingestion or inhalation of a source for example, radon gas emits alpha particles. This might place the material close to vulnerable tissue such as the lungs; when this happens the high localised energy effect will destroy associated tissue of the organs affected.

BETA PARTICLES

Beta particles are much smaller and faster moving than alpha particles. They are smaller in mass than alpha particles, but have longer range, so they can damage and penetrate the skin. Whilst they have greater penetrating power than alpha particles, beta particles are less ionising and take longer to effect the same degree of damage.

GAMMA RAYS

These have great penetrating power. Gamma radiation passing through a normal atom will sometimes force the loss of an electron, leaving the atom positively charged; this is called an *ion*.

X-RAYS

X-rays are very similar in their effects to gamma rays. X-rays are produced by sudden acceleration or deceleration of a charged particle, usually when high-speed electrons strike a suitable target under controlled conditions. The electrical potential required to accelerate electrons to speeds where X-ray production will occur is a minimum of **15,000 volts**. X-rays and gamma rays have **high energy**, and **high penetration** power through fairly dense material. In low density substances, including air, they may travel long distances.

RADON

Radon is a naturally occurring radioactive gas that can seep out of the ground and enter buildings. It is also the most common source of exposure to radiation in Britain, easily exceeding exposure from nuclear power stations or hospital scans and X-rays. It is the second most common cause of lung cancer in the UK, tobacco smoking being the most common cause.

It occurs naturally from decaying uranium, and it is particularly abundant in regions with granite bedrock. Exposure is high in Cornwall, Devon and Somerset, because of these counties' underlying geology, and there are also 'hotspots' in Wales, the Cotswolds and the Pennines. However, the gas disperses outdoors so levels are generally very low.

Once inhaled into the lungs, the gas decays into other radioactive isotopes of lead, bismuth and polonium, including polonium 210. Those at potential risk of exposure include miners (uranium miners are exposed to the highest level). Other work activities include tunnelling, quarrying, cutting granite (kitchens, flooring) and oil and gas. Radon decay products emit alpha particles which, when breathed in, can cause harm to the sensitive cells of the lungs.

POTENTIAL HEALTH EFFECTS OF IONISING RADIATION

The effects on the body of exposure to ionising radiation will depend on the type of radiation, the frequency and duration of exposure. Acute effects will include nausea, vomiting, diarrhoea and burns (either superficial skin burns or deep, penetrating burns causing cell damage). Long-term (chronic) effects such as dermatitis, skin ulcers, cataracts and cancers can also be expected.

Typical occupational sources of non-ionising and ionising radiation

SOURCES OF NON-IONISING RADIATION

Ultraviolet

- The sun.
- Arc welding and cutting.
- Adhesive curing processes.
- Water treatment.
- Lights and torches. Ultraviolet is used to attract insects to an electric sterilising device located in areas where food preparation is carried out *(see figure ref 9-21)*.

Visible radiation

- Lasers, for example, in surveying or level alignment equipment.
- Other high intensity lights such as photocopiers and printers.

Figure 9-21: Pest control.   Source: RMS.

Infrared

- Furnaces or fires.
- Molten metal or glass.
- Burning or welding.
- Heat lamps.
- Some lasers.
- Toasters.

Radio frequency

- Overhead power lines.
- Plastic welding.
- High powered transmitters.

Microwave

- Telecommunications.
- Cooking equipment.

SOURCES OF IONISING RADIATION

The most familiar examples of ionising radiation in the workplace are in hospitals, dentist surgeries and veterinary surgeries where X-rays are used extensively. X-ray machines are used for security purposes at baggage handling points in airports. In addition, gamma rays are used in non-destructive testing of metals, for example, site radiography of welds in pipelines.

In other industries ionising radiation is used for measurement, for example, in the paper industry for the thickness of paper, and in the food processing industry for measuring the contents of sealed tins.

Public Health England (formerly known as the Health Protection Agency) and British Geological Survey have extensively surveyed the UK and the Government has defined the highest radon areas as radon affected areas.

Whilst all workplaces can be at risk from radon, workplaces at higher risk tend to be those located in affected areas. Underground workplaces such as mines and caves made available as tourist attractions are also at higher risk of increased radon levels, wherever their location might be.

The basic means of controlling exposures to ionising and non-ionising radiation

CONTROLS FOR NON-IONISING RADIATION

The Control of Artificial Optical Radiation at Work Regulations (CAOR) 2010 requires an employer to conduct a specific risk assessment and to eliminate or reduce risks. Optical radiation includes ultraviolet, visible light and infrared. Exposure limit levels are set for this form of radiation.

Information and training is to be provided to those that may be affected, which includes employees and others carrying out work on behalf of the employer. Medical examination and health surveillance is to be provided for those employees that receive over exposure.

Ultraviolet

Protection from natural sources of UV is relatively simple and includes the provision of outdoor workers with barrier creams, suitable lightweight UV rated clothing and head protection, and as appropriate eye protection. In addition, workers should be encouraged to take breaks in the shade where possible and consideration should be made to adjusting work schedules so outside tasks may be conducted at times of day that are less affected by UV.

Control of artificial sources of UV includes segregation of UV emitting processes and the use of warning signs. UV radiation emitted from industrial processes can be isolated by physical shielding such as partitions or plastic curtains. It should be borne in mind that some plastic materials differ in their UV absorption abilities and care should be taken in their selection.

Users of UV emitting equipment, such as welders, can protect themselves by the use of goggles and protective clothing - the latter to avoid 'sunburn'. Assistants in welding processes often fail to appreciate the extent of their own exposure, and require similar protection. Workers should check skin exposed to UV frequently to identify possible effects that might lead to skin cancer.

Visible light

The eye detects visible light. It has two protective control mechanisms of its own, the eyelids ('blinking' or closing the eyelids) and the iris (dilates). These are normally sufficient to provide general protection, as the eyelid has a reaction of 150 milliseconds. However, where this is not adequate because of the intensity of light or the sustained exposure of the eye to it other precautions should be considered, including confinement of high-intensity sources, matt finishes to nearby paint-work, and provision of optically-correct protective glasses for outdoor workers in snow, sand or near large bodies of water. Where the high intensity visible light is artificially created those not involved in the process must also be protected. Warning signs should be posted and access restricted to the process area.

Infrared

Controls to limit exposure include engineered measures, such as remote controls, screening, interlocks and clamps to hold material to enable the worker to be outside the exposure area. This can be supplemented by forms of personal protective equipment where exposure cannot be prevented, for example, face shields, goggles or other protective eyewear, coveralls and gloves. The management of enforced maximum working periods should be used where exposure cannot be reduced to an acceptable level; this can include a routine change of activity/job rotation. It is important to protect others not directly involved in the process by using screens, curtains and restricted access.

Radio frequency and microwaves

Radio frequency and microwave radiation can usually be shielded at point of generation, to protect the users. If size and function prohibits this, restrictions on entry and working near an energised microwave device will be needed. Metals, tools, flammable and explosive materials should not be left in the electromagnetic field generated by microwave equipment. Appropriate warning devices should be part of the controls for each such appliance.

CONTROLS FOR IONISING RADIATION

Reduced time

Reducing the duration of exposure through redesigning work patterns, giving consideration to shift working, job rotation etc. The dose received will also depend upon the time of the exposure. These factors must be taken into account when devising suitable operator controls.

Increased distance

Radiation intensity is subject to the inverse square law. Energy received (dose) is inversely proportional to the square of the distance from the source.

Shielding

The type of shielding required giving adequate protection will depend on the penetration power of the radiation involved. For example, it may vary from thin sheets of silver paper to protect from beta particles through to several centimetres of concrete and lead for protection against gamma or X-rays.

In addition to the previous specific controls, the following general principles must be observed:

- Radiation should only be introduced to the work place if there is a positive benefit.
- Safety information must be obtained from suppliers about the type(s) of radiation emitted or likely to be emitted by their equipment.
- Safety procedures must be reviewed regularly.
- Protective equipment provided must be suitable and appropriate, as required by relevant Regulations. It must be checked and maintained regularly.
- Emergency plans must cover the potential radiation emergency.
- Written authorisation by permit should be used to account for all purchase/use, storage, transport and disposal of radioactive substances.

The basic means of controlling exposures to radon

Control of radon exposure in new buildings can be done by installing a 'radon proof membrane' within the floor structure. In areas more seriously affected by radon it may be necessary to install a 'radon sump' to vent the gas into the atmosphere. A radon sump has a pipe connecting a space under a solid floor to the outside.

A small electric fan in the pipe continually sucks the radon from under the house and expels it harmlessly to the atmosphere. Modern sumps are often constructed from outside the building so there is no disruption inside. In existing buildings it is not usually possible to provide a radon proof barrier, so alternative measures are used to control the build-up of radon in the building and subsequent exposure to it.

Figure 9-22: Radon sump.   *Source: HSE.*

Such measures include a mixture of active and passive systems such as improved under floor and indoor ventilation in the area, positive pressure ventilation of occupied areas, installation of radon sumps and extraction pipework and sealing large gaps in floors and walls in contact with the ground.

Basic radiation protection strategies

Basic radiation protection strategies include the application of the principles of time, distance and shielding. Exposure should be limited to as few people as possible and those individuals should be monitored and exposure levels maintained within limits.

Regulation 8 of the Ionising Radiation Regulations (IRR) 1999 sets out requirements for the employer to control exposure to ionising radiation:

> *"Every radiation employer shall, in relation to any work with ionising radiation that he undertakes, take all necessary steps to restrict so far as is reasonably practicable the extent to which his employees and other persons are exposed to ionising radiation."*

Figure 9-23: Control of exposure to ionising radiation.   *Source: IRR 1999 Regulation 8.*

In the case of ionising radiation, where possible only sealed sources should be used and a system developed to minimise dose levels to individuals. This work must be under the control of a radiation protection advisor.

RADIATION PROTECTION ADVISERS (RPA)

With the exception of the operations specified in Schedule 1 of the IRR 1999, at least one radiation protection adviser (RPA) must be appointed in writing by employers using ionising radiation. The numbers of RPA appointed must be appropriate to the risk and the area where advice is needed is to be stated. Employers must consult the RPA on:

- The implementation of controlled and supervised areas.
- The prior examination of plans for installations and the acceptance into service of new or modified sources of ionising radiation in relation to any engineering controls, design features, safety features and warning devices provided to restrict exposure to ionising radiation.
- The regular calibration of equipment provided for monitoring levels of ionising radiation and the regular checking that such equipment is serviceable and correctly used.
- The periodic examination and testing of engineering controls, design features, safety features and warning devices and regular checking of systems of work provided to restrict exposure to ionising radiation.

Adequate information and facilities must be provided by the employer to the RPA in order to allow them to fulfil their functions.

RADIATION PROTECTION SUPERVISOR

A radiation employer is required to appoint one or more radiation protection supervisors for the purpose of securing compliance with the regulations in respect of work carried out in any area subject to 'local rules for work in controlled or supervised areas'. Their area of work needs to be defined and they must be trained so that they understand the requirements of legislation and local rules insofar as they affect their area of work. They also need to understand the reasons for the precautions that need to be taken in their area of work, and they should command the respect of those they supervise.

CLASSIFIED WORKERS

Persons entering a controlled area should either be classified or be entering in accordance with 'written arrangements' designed to ensure that doses will not exceed, in cases of persons over 18, levels which would otherwise require the persons to be classified. In the case of other persons the relevant dose limit is applicable.

The role of monitoring and health surveillance

Regulation 19 of the Ionising Radiation Regulations (IRR) 1999 requires every employer who designates an area as a controlled or supervised area to ensure that levels of ionising radiation are adequately monitored for each such area and that working conditions in those areas are kept under review.

The main role of monitoring is to:

- Check that areas have been correctly designated.
- Help determine radiation levels and contamination from particular operations, so that appropriate control measures for restricting exposure can be proposed.
- Detect breakdowns in controls or systems, so as to indicate whether conditions are satisfactory for continuing work in that area.
- Provide information on which to base estimates of personal dose for non-classified persons.

Regulation 24(2) of the Ionising Radiation Regulations (IRR) 1999 requires every employer to ensure that each of his employees affected by the regulations is under adequate health surveillance by an appointed doctor or employment medical adviser to determine their fitness for the work with ionising radiation. Fitness in this sense is not restricted to possible health effects from exposure to ionising radiation. Those conducting the health surveillance will need to take account of specific features of the work with ionising radiation, such as the fitness of the individual. This will include such things as:

- Their ability to wear any personal protective equipment (including respiratory protective equipment) required to restrict exposure.
- Whether they have a skin disease which could affect their ability to undertake work involving unsealed radioactive materials.
- Whether they have serious psychological disorders which could affect their ability to undertake work with radiation sources that involves a special level of responsibility for safety.

9.4 - Stress

Introduction and meaning of 'work-related stress'

Stress is the feeling of being under too much mental or emotional pressure. Pressure turns into stress when an individual feels unable to cope. People have different ways of reacting to stress, so a situation that feels stressful to one person may be motivating to someone else. Many of life's demands can cause stress, particularly work, relationships and financial problems. When an individual feels stressed, it can get in the way of sorting out these demands, and can affect everything else in their life.

The effect of stress-related conditions can be difficult to calculate, but it has been estimated that in the UK alone, the harmful effects of stress cost the economy around £4 billion a year, with almost 13 million working days lost and over half a million people reporting that they were suffering from work-related stress.

In the UK the Health and Safety Executive defines stress as:

> *"Stress is the adverse reaction people have to excessive pressures or other demands placed on them."*

Figure 9-24: Definition of stress. *Source: HSE.*

Causes of stress

Stress in workers can be caused by a range of issues that relate to the organisation they work in and issues that are external to the organisation but influence the worker while they are at work, for example, personal relationship problems at home.

The issues that relate to the organisation can be considered using the structure depicted in the Health and Safety Executive (HSE) Management Standards for stress at work. The standards define the positive characteristics or culture of an organisation where stress is being managed effectively, but if these characteristics are absent they can be a cause of stress.

DEMAND

This includes issues like workload and work patterns, stress may be due to an individual not being able to cope with the demands of the job and the work environment itself, for example, heavy physical work or demands caused by several revisions of a designer's specification on a construction project.

Work patterns that could lead to stress include shift working, excessive overtime and unsocial hours. Workers may be encouraged to work excessive hours to get the job done, for example, if the work is subject to a late penalties clause in the contract. Additional hours may be added to the day's work if workers need to travel long distances to and from the site. If the work pattern or job demands are such that the worker does not get adequate breaks this can also lead to stress. Typical workplace environmental stressors are:

- Noise.
- Extremes of temperature.
- Poor lighting.

CONTROL

If an individual has little control over the pace and manner they work this can create stress. In particular, work that has repetitive or monotonous features that the worker has no ability to control or adjust may lead to stress.

SUPPORT

If a worker perceives a lack of encouragement or resources provided by the organisation, line management or co-workers a feeling of remoteness can be created. The failure to provide support was highlighted in the landmark case, **Lancaster v Birmingham City Council (1999),** where liability was admitted when an employee had taken three periods of sick leave and had then been medically retired. She had been moved from her job as draughtswoman to work as a neighbourhood housing officer.

In addition to dealing with members of the public who were often intimidating and abusive, she was not given sufficient administrative support, and had a high workload, partly as a result of an unfilled vacancy. She said she was expected to do the job without ever having been given proper training. In July 1999 she was awarded more than £67,000 in compensation.

WORK RELATIONSHIPS

As long ago as 1994, Staffordshire University Business School published the results of a survey indicating that 1 in 2 UK employees have been bullied at work during their working life.

The Manufacturing, Science and Finance Union (MSF) have identified workplace bullying as:

> *"Persistent, offensive, abusive, intimidating, malicious or insulting behaviour, abuse of power or unfair penal sanctions which make the recipient feel upset, threatened, humiliated, or vulnerable, which undermines their self-confidence and which may cause them to suffer stress. Harassment, in general terms, is unwanted conduct affecting the dignity of men and women in the workplace. It may be related to age, sex, race, disability, religion, sexual orientation, nationality or any personal characteristic of the individual, and may be persistent or*

> an isolated incident. The key is that the actions or comments are viewed as demeaning and unacceptable to the recipient."

Figure 9-25: Bullying. Source: CIPD.

If relationships with co-workers, customers or suppliers are poor, this can put the worker under pressure, which may lead to stress. This is particularly so if the relationship involves such issues as harassment, discrimination or bullying. If the relationship part of the work includes the fear of violence, this can put the worker under significant pressure when conducting their job, particularly if they feel they can do nothing to manage the risk. Poor work relationships can lead to poor communications, and vica versa, which can cause the worker to feel isolated or unprepared for the work they are doing. In the same way, if workers are not consulted or involved in processes that might affect them and their work, like risk assessment, they may feel under additional pressure because they do not understand or accept the outcomes from the process.

ROLE

If workers do not understand their role in the organisation, or have conflicting roles, this can increase the potential for stress. In particular, undertaking new or difficult work without first achieving the appropriate skills to complete it successfully or safely could put the individual under pressure.

CHANGE

If the management of organisational change is not conducted or communicated well, individuals can be confused or feel threatened by the change and this could lead to stress. Changes that cause the worker to feel their job or salary may be insecure due to re-organisation or redundancy can particularly have this effect. The absence of consultation of workers when change is considered can add to concerns about the change and lead to stress.

Effects of stress

Being exposed to stressful situations brings about changes in behaviour and also physical well-being.

Physical effects
- Increased heart rate and sweating.
- Headache.
- Dizziness.
- Blurred vision.
- Aching neck and shoulders.
- Skin rashes.
- Lowered resistance to infection.

Behavioural effects
- Increased anxiety.
- Irritability.
- Increased alcohol intake.
- Increased smoking.
- Erratic sleep patterns.
- Poor concentration.
- Feeling of inability to cope with everyday tasks.

This can result in
- Lack of motivation.
- Lack of commitment.
- Poor timekeeping.
- Increase in mistakes.

- Increase in sickness absence.
- Poor decision making.
- Poor planning.

Stress is reflected in relationships at work as
- Tension between colleagues/supervisors.
- Poor service to clients.

- Deterioration in industrial relations.
- Increase in disciplinary problems.

Control measures

The Health and Safety Executive (HSE) Management Standards for stress at work set out the positive characteristics or culture of an organisation where stress is being managed effectively. Stress, like other risks should be subject to a risk assessment in order to identify the causes of pressure that can lead to stress and to evaluate the current controls.

The HSE Management Standards are based on the six main stress factors of demands, control, change, relationships, role and support. Each standard defines a desired state (best practice) to be achieved in order to minimise the risk of stress in the workplace.

DEMAND

The standard is - 'employees indicate they can cope with the demands of the job and there are systems in place locally to respond to any individual concerns'. Control measures to meet this include:
- Balancing the demands of the work to the agreed hours of work, consider shift working, the amount of additional hours worked and unsocial hours.
- Provision of regular and suitable breaks from work and rest periods.
- Matching worker skills and abilities to the job demands.
- Designing jobs so they are within the capability of workers.
- Minimising the work environment risks, such as noise and temperature.

CONTROL

The standard is - 'employees indicate that they are able to have a say about the way they do their work and there are systems in place locally to respond to any individual concerns'. Control measures to meet this include:

■ Providing, where possible, workers with control over their pace and manner of work, consider reducing the effects of repetitive and monotonous work by job rotation.
■ Encouraging workers to use their skills and initiative to do the work.
■ Encouraging workers to develop to enable them to do more challenging or new work.
■ Providing workers with opportunity to influence when breaks are taken.
■ Consulting workers regarding work patterns.

SUPPORT

The standard is - 'employees indicate that they receive adequate information and support from their colleagues and superiors and there are systems in place locally to respond to any individual concerns'. Control measures to meet this include:

■ Establishing policies and procedures that provide support, particularly where workers may feel other factors are putting them under pressure.
■ Provide systems that enable and encourage managers to identify where workers need support, consider where workers deal with the public in demanding environments, where new workers are introduced and times of high demand.
■ Provide systems that enable and encourage managers to provide support to workers, consider particularly those working remotely by virtue of their location or time of working and new workers.
■ Encourage co-workers to support each other.
■ Ensure workers understand what resources and support is available and how they access it.
■ Provide regular constructive feedback to workers.

WORK RELATIONSHIPS

Improving work relationships and attempting to modify people's attitudes and behaviour is a difficult and time-consuming process. Effective strategies include regular communication with staff, provision of accurate and honest information on the effect of organisational changes on them, adopting partnership approaches to problems, provision of support. The onus is on employers to promote a culture that respects the dignity of others - if it is left to employees to do this it will not happen.

The standard is - 'employees feel able to indicate that they are not subjected to unacceptable behaviours, for example, bullying at work and there are systems in place locally to respond to any individual concerns'. Control measures to meet this include:

■ Promote positive behaviour that avoids conflict and leads to fairness; consider co-workers, customers and suppliers.
■ Establish policies and procedures that resolve unacceptable behaviour that leads to conflict.
■ Encourage managers to deal with unacceptable behaviour, such as harassment, discrimination or bullying.
■ Encourage workers to report unacceptable behaviour.
■ Establish systems that ensure communication with managers and workers, consider timeliness of communication to those that work isolated by location or time.
■ Establish systems that ensure involvement and consultation, such as regarding the process of conducting risk assessments.

ROLE

The standard is - 'employees indicate that they understand their role and responsibilities and there are systems in place locally to respond to any individual concerns'. Control measures to meet this include:

■ Ensure workers have the knowledge, skill and experience to conduct their role or are being supported appropriately; consider workers undertaking new or difficult work.
■ Ensure role requirements are compatible, for example, that the need to manage costs does not conflict with health and safety.
■ Ensure role requirements are clear.
■ Ensure workers and their managers understand the roles and responsibilities.
■ Provide systems to enable workers to raise concerns about role uncertainty or conflict, particularly consider the work life balance for those workers that provide care for others outside their work.

CHANGE

The standard is - 'employees indicate that the organisation engages them frequently when undergoing organisational change and there are systems in place locally to respond to any individual concerns'. Control measures to meet this include:

■ Provide workers with timely information to help them understand the change, reasons for it and timing of effects.

- Ensure worker consultation on proposed changes.
- Provide workers with information on likely impacts of change on their jobs.
- Provide training and support through the period of change.

In addition to the six specific factors that relate to the HSE management standards for stress at work there are a number of general control measures that should form part of a stress management strategy. These include:

- Introducing a stress policy and procedures to demonstrate to managers, workers, worker representatives and enforcing agencies that the organisation recognises stress as a serious issue worthy of a commitment to manage the risk.
- Providing training and support for workers and all levels of management in the form of stress awareness and stress management training, as appropriate.
- Addressing the issue of work-life balance, which may include consideration of job-share, part-time work, voluntary reduced hours, home-working, flexitime etc.
- Promoting general health and well-being awareness initiatives within the organisation, such as diet, exercise and fitness programmes.
- Providing access to occupational health practitioners, counselling support or assistance programmes for those that may be affected by stress.

Stress is summarised in *figure 9-26*.

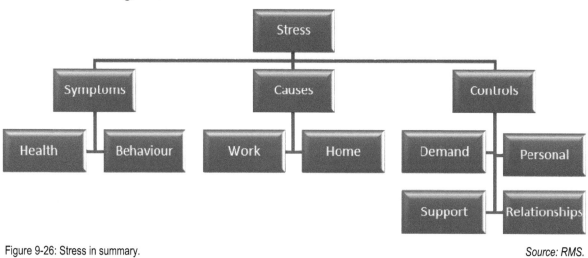

Figure 9-26: Stress in summary.   Source: RMS.

Exam practice

1. A noise survey carried out on a building site identified that noise exposure action values given in the Control of Noise at Work Regulations 2005 were being exceeded.

    (a) **Identify** the lower **AND** upper noise exposure action values defined in the Control of Noise at Work Regulations 2005. **(2)**

    (b) **Outline** the control measures an employer is required to take by the Control of Noise at Work Regulations 2005 when employees are exposed to noise at or above the upper noise exposure action value. **(6)**

2. **Outline** the work-related issues that might increase the levels of occupational stress amongst workers on a construction site. **(8)**

3. As part of major football stadium refurbishment, seat anchors are to be installed by workers using hand-held powered percussive equipment that produce high levels of vibration.

    (a) **Identify** possible health effects due to exposure to vibration. **(4)**

    (b) **Outline** control measures that could be used to reduce the risk of health effects due to vibration in this refurbishment work. **(4)**

4. (a) **Identify TWO** types of ionising radiation that workers in construction activities might encounter. **(4)**

    (b) **Identify TWO** types of non-ionising radiation that workers in construction activities might encounter. **(4)**

        Outline the range of health effects of exposure to non-ionising radiation. **(4)**

Please refer to the back of the assessment section for answers.

Working at height - hazards and risk control

Learning outcomes

On completion of this element, candidates should be able to demonstrate understanding of the content through the application of knowledge to familiar and unfamiliar situations. In particular they should be able to:

10.1   Explain the hazards of working at height and outline the precautions necessary to control them.

10.2   Explain safe working practices for access equipment and roof work.

10.3   Outline control measures necessary to protect other persons not involved in the work at height.

10.4   Outline control measures to reduce risk when working over or near to water.

Content

10.1 - Working at height hazards and risks...281
   Work activities involving a risk of injury from falling from height 281
   Basic hazards and factors affecting the risk from working at height 281
   Methods of avoiding working at height 284
   Main precautions necessary to prevent falls and falling materials 285
   Emergency rescue..286
   Measures to minimise distance and consequences of a fall 286
   Requirements for head protection 288
   Inspection requirements for work equipment...288
10.2 - Safe working practices for access equipment and roof work 289
   Scaffolding 289
   Mobile elevating work platforms 299
   Ladders...300
   Other techniques for working at height...304
   Fall arrest equipment 306
   Roof work..308
10.3 - Protection of others...310
10.4 - Working over or near water 311
   Prevention of drowning 311
   Additional control measures 312
Exam practice 313

Sources of reference

Reference information provided, in particular web links, is correct at time of publication, but may have changed.

Inspection and reports, HSE Construction Information Sheet no 47 (rev1) Series Code, CIS47REV1
http://www.hse.gov.uk/pubns/cis47.pdf

Health and Safety in Construction, HSG150, HSE Books, ISBN 978-0-7176-6182-2
http://www.hse.gov.uk/pubns/priced/hsg150.pdf

Health and safety in roof work, HSG33, HSE Books, ISBN 978-0-7176-6527-3
http://www.hse.gov.uk/pubns/priced/hsg33.pdf

Managing Health and Safety in Construction, Construction (Design and Management) Regulations 2015, Guidance on Regulations, L153, HSE Books, ISBN: 978-0-7176-6626-3

http://www.hse.gov.uk/pubns/priced/L153.pdf

Personal Protective Equipment at Work (Guidance), L25, HSE Books, ISBN: 978-0-7176-6139-3
http://www.hse.gov.uk/pubns/priced/l25.pdf

Protecting the public: Your next move, HSG151, HSE Books, ISBN 978-0-7176-6294-4
http://www.hse.gov.uk/pubns/priced/hsg151.pdf

Safe use of work equipment, ACOP L22, HSE Books, ISBN 978-0-7176-6295-1
http://www.hse.gov.uk/pubns/priced/l22.pdf

Working at Height: A brief guide, INDG401, HSE Books, http://www.hse.gov.uk/pubns/indg401.pdf

Relevant statutory provisions

Construction (Design and Management) Regulations (CDM) 2015
Personal Protective Equipment at Work Regulations (PPER) 1992
Provision and Use of Work Equipment Regulations (PUWER) 1998
Work at Height Regulations (WAH) 2005

10.1 - Working at height hazards and risks

Work activities involving a risk of injury from falling from height

The HSE reported in 2014/15 that construction accounted for 35 of the 142 fatal injuries to workers and falls from height are the most common cause. The HSE reported 41 fatal injuries as a result of falls from height in 2014/5 and almost half of fatal falls took place in construction.

Between 2012/13 and 2014/15 around 65,000 construction workers in the UK sustained an injury at work and around 25% of these resulted in absence from work of over 7-days. In 2014/15 figures show over 5,400 reported non-fatal injuries to employees in the construction sector. Reported non-fatal injuries are categorized as either specified (for example fractures, amputations, serious burns) or as resulting in over 7-days off work. Over 50% of all reported 'specified' injuries in the construction sector are due to either falls from a height or slip, trip or fall on the same level.

Much of the work carried out on a construction site is done above ground at height, commonly more than two metres. Typical activities that involve working at height are:

- Steel erecting.
- Fixing of cladding, roof work.
- Painting and decorating.
- Demolition and dismantling.
- Falls from ladders.

- Bricklaying.
- Scaffold erection.
- Electrical installation and maintenance.
- Bridge construction repairs.

Basic hazards and factors affecting the risk from working at height

Work at height is classified as anything above floor level. The nature and range of the hazards from work at height will depend on the location and work activity involved with the work at height.

There are four main types of hazard associated with work at height:

1) Falls of persons.
2) Falling objects.
3) Contact with or crushed against structures.
4) Access to normally inaccessible hazards, for example, overhead power cables.

Whether a fall is liable to cause injury may depend on:

- The height of the fall.
- Dangers associated with falling onto or into material below.
- Dangers associated with passing traffic.
- Whether there is rough or uneven ground.
- The type of structure and its security.

The risks of falls from height are substantial, however long or short the work activity. Risks related to work activities at height are increased by the presence of fragile roofs, roof lights, voids, deteriorating materials and the weather. Some jobs rarely involve the average worker needing to work above ground level, such as welding and machinery maintenance. This means that employees of this type with little or no experience of work at height find themselves exposed to the dangers of working above ground level when carrying out their usual job in a construction setting. The main factors affecting the risk of work at height include:

- Effectiveness of design.
- Vertical distance that employees may fall.
- Fragile roofs, roof lights and deterioration of materials.
- Unprotected edges.
- Stability and condition of access equipment.
- Weather conditions.
- Falling materials.

EFFECTIVENESS OF DESIGN

Perhaps the biggest factor affecting the risk from working at height is the design of structures and equipment where access to height is required in order to work. For example, older buildings may not have parapet walls on their roof and structures were often designed without thought of access requirements beyond the construction period. Good design that prevents the need to approach edges or built in fall prevention measures will significantly affect the risk. If means of access is not built in to the design it means that access has to be provided by other methods and will involve risks related to erection and dismantling of means of access to height as well as working with temporary access arrangements.

The failure of design to anticipate the need for access may introduce overhanging canopies that prevent access equipment being positioned close to the building or structure, leading to more complex arrangements for access equipment and increased time exposed to work at height while arrangements are put in place or removed.

VERTICAL DISTANCE

Though some construction work involves work activities to be carried out at a significant height (vertical distance), for example, on a roof or scaffold, it should not be assumed that work at less significant heights is without risk. Major injuries can occur if a fall results whilst carrying out tasks at height of less than 2 metres, for example, fitting false ceilings or installing utilities inside buildings. This remains a significant risk and many injuries result each year. Legislation, the Work at Height Regulations (WAH) 2005 (as amended in 2007), reflects this risk and requires controls to be in place to manage the risk of falling, whatever the height. This legislation applies to workplaces in general, and therefore includes construction activities. Under these regulations the interpretation of 'work at height' includes any place of work at, above, or below ground level that a person could fall a distance liable to cause personal injury; including places for obtaining access or egress, except by staircase in a permanent workplace.

Where people are working at heights of greater than 2 metres the impact experienced having fallen this vertical distance to a lower level is significant and above this height it is very likely to result in major injury or a fatality. This should not give the impression that people are not injured by falls from heights less than 2 metres. This remains a significant risk and many series injuries occur from falls of less than this vertical distance.

WAH 2005 Regulation 6 states that work at height must only be carried out when it is not reasonably practicable to carry out the work otherwise. If work at height does take place, suitable and sufficient measures must be taken to prevent a fall of any distance, to minimise the distance and the consequences of any fall liable to cause injury. Employers must also make a risk assessment, as required by regulation 3 of the Management of Health and Safety at Work Regulations (MHSWR) 1999.

ROOFS

Working at height and on roofs carries a high risk of accidents, unless proper procedures and precautions are taken. The danger of people or materials falling affects the safety of those working at height and those working beneath. Particular danger arises from two types of roof - fragile roofs and sloping roofs.

Fragile roofs

Any roof that has not been specifically designed to carry a load, other than that which may be imposed on the roof by weather, should be considered a fragile roof. Fragile roofs can present a hidden hazard, as it is not always obvious that there is potential problem. Sheets used in roofing material may deteriorate over time leaving the remaining material in a particularly fragile state.

Materials such as asbestos, cement, glass or plastic are likely to be unable to bear the weight of a person. Asbestos sheet deteriorates over time leaving the remaining material in a particularly fragile state. Though the sheet looks intact it will only have a small fraction of its original strength. In a similar way plastic roof material, such as may be used in roof lights, will be affected by exposure to sunlight, leaving it brittle. It should not be assumed that it is safe to walk on newly installed roof material. Though the material may have some strength it may not be enough to bear the weight of a worker. All fragile roofs and/or access routes to them should be marked with an appropriate warning sign.

The WAH 2005 Regulation 9 states that every employer shall ensure that suitable and sufficient steps are taken to prevent any person at work falling through any fragile surface; and that no work may pass across or near, or work on, from or near, fragile surfaces when it is reasonably practicable to carry out work without doing so. If work has to be from a fragile roof then suitable and sufficient means of support must be provided that can sustain foreseeable loads. No person at work should be allowed to pass or work near a fragile surface unless suitable and sufficient guard rails and other means of fall protection is in place. Signs must be situated at a prominent place at or near to work involving fragile surfaces or persons must be made aware of the fragile roof by other means.

Sloping roofs

Sloping roofs are those with a pitch greater than 10 degrees. Falls from the edge of sloping roofs can cause serious injury even when the eaves are relatively low. The hazard of sloping roofs is less obvious when the pitch is small causing people to underestimate the possibility of employees sliding off the edge. The material and therefore the surface of the roof have a significant influence on the hazard, for example, a smooth sheet metal surface can present a significant hazard even when the pitch is small.

The chances of an accident are increased when working on roofs that are wet or covered in moss growth and in extreme weather conditions such as high winds. The other significant influencing issue is the footwear used by the worker, smooth flat soled footwear may seem suitable in dry conditions but may not provide sufficient grip and deal with surface water in wet conditions. A build-up of dry particles or grit on a roof can present a surface that leads to a high risk of slipping as the particles become free to move and form a mobile layer between the roof and the worker's foot.

Roof-lights

Plastic domed roof lights or lead framed glass roof lights will deteriorate with age, exposure to sunlight (UV) and acid rain. Heavy bodily contact with them may cause them to shatter or collapse. Corrugated plastic lights designed to match the roof profile of metal or asbestos sheeting will have similar failure characteristics, but with the added problem that they may be covered with mould or moss growth obscuring them completely from the other sturdier parts of the roof. Obscured roof lights present a significant fall through risk to employees on the roof structure. Inspection of the roof from inside the building is essential to enable them to be identified and located before any roof work is considered.

VOIDS

Voids in ground works, for example, cellars, drains or old mine shafts could remain undetected which could lead to major hazards. A site survey should be completed prior to commencing any work to identify these hazards. Excavations, incomplete scaffolding/boards or guard rails, ladders should be inspected/checked on a daily basis for damage or unauthorised alterations to reduce any potential hazards. A variety of voids will be created during the construction phase of a multi storey building; these include holes in floors for services, spaces for stairwells and lifts. It is important at the planning stage to make provision for fall protection to include guard rails for stairwells and lift shafts, and hand rails on stairs; fixing covers over other holes in floors; providing adequate levels of lighting; and ensuring a good standard of housekeeping and a high level of supervision and control.

DETERIORATION OF MATERIALS

The condition of the materials of a structure on which people are working can deteriorate with time. The rate of deterioration will accelerate if the structure is exposed to adverse weather conditions (including extremes of temperature) or attack by chemicals, animals, insects etc. In particular, asbestos cement, fibreglass and plastic deteriorate with age and become more fragile. Similarly, steel sheets may rust or due to corrosion of supports may not be supported properly.

It may not always be obvious that deterioration has occurred and this should be a factor to be considered at the pre-work assessment. Unsound materials present a hazard when people walk on them causing them to break, or by the material that has deteriorated breaking and the pieces falling on employees below.

UNPROTECTED EDGES

Roofs, scaffolds, unfinished steel work and access platforms may sometimes have open sides. This increases the likelihood of someone or something falling, particularly if people have to approach them, work at them or pass by them repeatedly. It is very easy in these circumstances to lose perception of the hazard and forget that it is there. Errors, such as stepping back over an edge, overreaching, or being pushed over the edge whilst manoeuvring materials can easily lead to fatal falls.

UNSTABLE/POORLY MAINTAINED ACCESS EQUIPMENT

An employer, having committed to providing access to height by the provision of work equipment, needs to understand that employees using it are at risk from basic hazards relating to its stability and maintenance. Working with mobile elevated work platforms (MEWPs), ladders and scaffolds have their own specific stability and maintenance issues, the hazard of falling from height whilst using them being the common theme. Each is influenced by the problem of the stability of the ground conditions they are placed on and the height they are used at compared to their stability base. *See also - Mobile Elevating Work Platforms - later in this element.*

The effective working of the hydraulics of a MEWP is critical and failure to maintain this could lead to a sudden and catastrophic failure of the MEWP whilst it is extended. Scaffolds need periodic maintenance to ensure load-bearing parts are still secured and those critical items such as brakes on mobile scaffolds are in place and effective. Failure to maintain them can quickly undermine the strength, integrity and stability of the scaffold leading to collapse or overturning.

All equipment, access equipment being no exception, can fail if not properly maintained. Cracks may occur in the sides of ladders and loose rungs can lead to failure. They may warp or rot if left exposed to the elements. Defects in ladders may be hidden if they are painted or covered in plaster.

WEATHER

Adverse weather can have a significant effect on the safety of those working at height. Rain, snow and ice increase the risk of slips and falling from a roof. When handling large objects, such as roof panels, then high wind can be a serious problem and may cause the person to be blown off the roof. Extremely cold temperatures can increase the likelihood of brittle failure of materials and therefore increase the likelihood of failure of roof supports, scaffold components and plastic roof lights.

In addition, moisture can freeze; increasing the slipperiness of surfaces and on many occasions the presence of ice is not easily visible.

Figure 10-1: Working above ground level.   *Source: RMS.*

Employees exposed to the cold can lose their dexterity and when hot, sweat may cause them to lose their grip.

FALLING MATERIALS

The risk of falling materials from work conducted at height is increased by:

- Poor housekeeping of people working above.
- Absence of toe boards or edge protection.
- Incorrect hooking and slinging.
- Incorrect assembly of gin wheels for raising materials.
- Surplus materials incorrectly stacked.
- Open, unprotected edges.
- Deterioration of structures causing crumbling masonry.

The risk of falling materials may also be increased by work platforms becoming cluttered with loose materials resulting from the work activity being conducted. In addition, if methods like toe boards, solid barriers and brick guards are not provided to prevent materials or other objects rolling, or being kicked off the edges of platforms the risk becomes significant.

The lack of control over removing materials from workplaces at a height can have a big influence on the risk of falling materials. If there are no suitable prescribed methods of removing materials employees may be tempted to improvise and throw materials, such as old slates, tiles and scaffold clips, to the ground. Even if enclosed debris chutes are provided, if they or the container materials go into becomes full employees may resort to throwing materials from height to the ground, putting people at risk.

Methods of avoiding working at height

WAH 2005 sets out a hierarchy for safe work at height. This requires the duty holder to:

- Avoid work at height where they can.
- Use work equipment or other measures to prevent falls where they cannot avoid working at height.
- Where they cannot eliminate the risk of fall, use work equipment or other measures to minimise the distance and consequence of a fall should one occur.

Figure 10-2: Using a pole to avoid work at height.
Source: HSE, HSG150

WAH 2005, Regulation 6 - Avoidance of risks from work at height, sets out the following requirements for dealing with risks from work at height:

"1) In identifying the measures required by this regulation, every employer shall take account of a risk assessment under regulation 3 of the Management Regulations.

2) *Every employer shall ensure that work is not carried out at height where it is reasonably practicable to carry out the work safely otherwise than at height.*

3) *Where work is carried out at height, every employer shall take suitable and sufficient measures to prevent, so far as is reasonably practicable, any person falling a distance liable to cause personal injury.*

4) *The measures required by paragraph (3) shall include:*

   a) *His ensuring that the work is carried out:*

      i) *From an existing place of work.*

      ii) *(In the case of obtaining access or egress) using an existing means; which complies with Schedule 1, where it is reasonably practicable to carry it out safely and under appropriate ergonomic conditions.*

   b) *Where it is not reasonably practicable for the work to be carried out in accordance with sub-paragraph (a), his providing sufficient work equipment for preventing, so far as is reasonably practicable, a fall occurring.*

5) *Where the measures taken under paragraph (4) do not eliminate the risk of a fall occurring, every employer shall:*

   a) *So far as is reasonably practicable, provide sufficient work equipment to minimise:*

      i) *The distance and consequences.*

      ii) *Where it is not reasonably practicable to minimise the distance, the consequences, of a fall.*

b) *Without prejudice to the generality of paragraph (3), provide such additional training and instruction or take other additional suitable and sufficient measures to prevent, so far as is reasonably practicable, any person falling a distance liable to cause personal injury".*

Where possible, work at height should be avoided by conducting the work at ground level. This means that organisations should review work done to determine a response to this requirement. This could be achieved by using different equipment or methods of work, for example, the pre-assembly of roof trusses, either before delivery or on the ground on site, instead of assembly at height. If materials are pre-painted or pre-drilled this can greatly reduce the work needed to be done at height, for example, decorative wooden panels for a building can be pre-treated to avoid weather treatment being brushed on at a height. Long reach devices can be used to allow cleaning or other tasks to be conducted from the ground. Where equipment, such as light units, requires maintenance an option may be to lower it sufficiently to enable bulbs to be changed and cleaning to be conducted from the ground.

Good planning arrangements, considering how fixtures/fittings, plant and services can be designed or installed can be utilised to avoid the need to work at height, both during construction and in ongoing cleaning or maintenance.

Main precautions necessary to prevent falls and falling materials

GOOD DESIGN

Good design should prevent the need to approach edges or provide built in fall prevention measures in order to prevent falls and falling materials; this will significantly reduce risk. If design anticipates the need for work at height it is possible to provide means of access that is integral with the building or structure, for example, the provision of cradles fitted to bridges to enable periodic inspection and maintenance. Similarly, a movable access system may be permanently fitted to the inside and outside of an atrium of an office block to enable cleaning and repair of the glass or other fittings. This not only provides a good work position for work to be carried out but also eliminates the time that employees may be exposed to risk while erecting and dismantling temporary means of access. Where possible, permanent means of access should be built into the design of buildings and structures to minimise risk. Good design for work at height may include consideration of access by means of a mobile elevating work platform (MEWP), which requires being stable when used. This might include providing a firm level surface around the building or structure and may cause the redesign of the layout of aesthetic features, such as ponds and shrubs, in order to achieve this.

Regulation 6 of WAH 2005 requires that, where reasonably practicable, work at height must be carried out from an existing place of work and the place of work must comply with the contents of Schedule 1 of WAH 2005 with regard to such things as its strength and prevention of people or materials falling through gaps. This will require designers to consider the provision of existing places of work that are suitable for work at height.

PROPER PLANNING AND SUPERVISION OF WORK

Fall of people

Regulation 4 of WAH 2005 states that all work at height must be properly planned, supervised and be carried out, so far as is reasonably practicable, safely. Planning must include the selection of suitable equipment; take account of emergencies and gives consideration to any weather conditions impacting on safety.

WAH 2005, Regulation 5, states that those engaged in any activity in relation to work at height must be competent; and, if under training, be supervised by a competent person.

WAH 2005, Regulation 6, states that work at height must only be carried out when it is not reasonably practicable to carry out the work otherwise. If work at height does take place, suitable and sufficient measures must be taken to prevent a fall of any distance, to minimise the distance and the consequences of any fall liable to cause injury. Employers must also make a risk assessment, as required by Regulation 3 of the Management of Health and Safety at Work Regulations (MHSWR) 1999.

Fall of materials

WAH 2005, Regulation 10, states that every employer shall take reasonably practicable steps to prevent injury to any person from the fall of any material or object; and where it is not reasonably practicable to do so, to take similar steps to prevent any person being struck by any falling material or object that is liable to cause personal injury. Also, that no material is thrown or tipped from height in circumstances where it is liable to cause injury to any person. Materials and objects must be stored in such a way as to prevent risk to any person arising from the collapse, overturning or unintended movement of the materials or objects.

WAH 2005, Regulation 11, states that every employer shall ensure that where an area presents a risk of falling from height or being struck from an item falling at height that the area is equipped with devices preventing unauthorised persons from entering such areas and the area is clearly indicated.

AVOIDING WORKING IN ADVERSE WEATHER CONDITIONS

Adverse weather can include wind, rain, sun, cold, snow and ice. Each of these conditions, particularly in extreme cases, can present a significant hazard to construction work. When long term projects are planned methods are often adjusted to minimise the effects. For example, road and walk routes that could quickly be affected by rain are made up into formal structures by the use of hardcore, concrete and tarmac. Work areas can be covered over at an early stage to enable work to be conducted in relative comfort.

Adverse weather must be considered formally and work may have to cease until conditions improve, for example, work on a roof in icy conditions or high winds. In some cases, it may be that work is organised in an order that predicts expected adverse weather, allowing tasks to be adjusted until short term weather conditions improve. Similar approaches may have to be taken for operating a mobile elevating work platform (MEWP) in windy conditions or entering a sewer during a rain storm.

Emergency rescue

When selecting work equipment for work at height, Regulation 7 of the WAH 2005 requires the employer to consider the additional risks that may arise from evacuation and rescue from it. This will include the need to establish clear emergency escape routes from major scaffold installations, rescue arrangements for employees where a mobile elevated work platform fails in its raised position and rescue for those in harnesses or on a fall arrest net. Steps must be taken to minimise the risk of injury due to the fall or contact with the safeguard. Even a short fall onto a net or other fall arresting safeguard could cause minor injuries or fractures. This should be anticipated and employees taught how to minimise the likelihood of injury.

Where an individual has fallen from height but has been protected by personal fall arrest equipment such as a harness, significant health effects known as suspension trauma may be experienced if they are not rescued quickly. This is mainly due to blood pooling in the legs, reducing the amount circulating through the rest of the body, which has consequential effects for vital organs such as the brain, heart and kidneys. Unless the individual is rescued very quickly the lack of oxygenated blood to vital organs can be fatal. Therefore, a rescue procedure and equipment must be available and practiced. The procedure should also take into account that a sudden transition from a vertical to a horizontal position when rescued and laid down, can lead to a massive amount of deoxygenated blood entering the heart, causing cardiac arrest.

Measures to minimise distance and consequences of a fall

Regulation 6 of WAH 2005 states a simple hierarchy for managing and selecting equipment for work at height. Duty holders must:

- Avoid work at height where they can.
- Use work equipment or other measures to prevent falls where they cannot avoid working at height.
- Where they cannot eliminate the risk of a fall, use work equipment or other measures to minimise the distance and consequences of a fall should one occur.
- Regulation 6 of WAH 2005, further requires that the employer or the self-employed provide such additional training and instruction or take other additional suitable and sufficient measures to prevent, so far as is reasonably practicable, any person falling a distance liable to cause personal injury.

PROVISION OF WORK EQUIPMENT TO PREVENT FALLS

Careful consideration during the risk assessment and planning phases for work at height should establish which equipment is best suited for the working environment and work to be done. There are various types of fall protection that should be evaluated in relationship to the activity and environment. This could be edge protection in the form of scaffolding or barriers (temporary or fixed), or consideration of the building of temporary walls.

Collective measures must be given priority over personal measures and account needs to be taken of such factors as:

- Working conditions and the risks to the safety of persons at the place where the work equipment is to be used.
- In the case of work equipment for access and egress, the distance to be negotiated.
- Distance and consequences of a potential fall.
- Duration and frequency of use.
- Need for easy and timely evacuation and rescue in an emergency.
- Any additional risk posed by the use, installation or removal of that work equipment or by evacuation and rescue from it.

To maintain safe access and egress, temporary staircases should be considered before the use of ladders. Where ladders are used it is more difficult to maintain a 'three-point contact' as employees may have to use their hands to carry or move items to different levels.

MITIGATING DISTANCE AND CONSEQUENCES OF A FALL

This is the third aspect in the work at height protection hierarchy set out in WAH 2005 and applies to situations where work equipment and other measures have not been able to provide sufficient means to prevent likely falls. Regulation 6(5) of WAH 2005 states:

> *"5) Where the measures taken under paragraph (4) do not eliminate the risk of a fall occurring, every employer shall:*
>
> *a) So far as is reasonably practicable, provide sufficient work equipment to minimise:*
>
> *i) The distance and consequences.*
>
> *ii) Where it is not reasonably practicable to minimise the distance, the consequences, of a fall."*

Figure 10-3: Avoidance of risks from work at height.   *Source: WAH 2005 Regulation 6(5).*

In mitigating the distance and consequences of a fall, two principal systems are used and considered by WAH 2005:

1) Fall arrest systems, for example, nets and air bags.
2) Personal fall protection systems, for example, work positioning systems, rope access and positioning techniques.

Fall arresting systems

Fall arrest systems include equipment designed to minimise the distance and consequence of falls, such as nets and air bags. Fall arresting systems are preferred to personal protection systems because they provide collective protection and, unlike a fall arrest harness, they do not rely on individual user discipline to guarantee acceptable safety standards.

WAH 2005 requires that a fall arresting safeguard may only be used if:

■ A risk assessment has demonstrated that the work activity can, so far as is reasonably practicable, be performed safely while using it and without affecting its effectiveness.
■ Use of other, safer work equipment is not reasonably practicable.
■ A sufficient number of available persons have received adequate training specific to the safeguard, including rescue procedures.

A fall arresting safeguard must be suitable and of sufficient strength to arrest safely the fall of any person who is liable to fall. In addition, it must:

■ In the case of a safeguard that is designed to be attached, be securely attached to all the required anchor points.
■ The anchors and the means of attachment must be suitable and of sufficient strength and stability for the purpose of supporting the foreseeable loading in arresting the fall and during any subsequent rescue.
■ In the case of an airbag, landing mat or similar safeguard, be stable.
■ In the case of a safeguard that distorts in arresting a fall, afford sufficient clearance.

Suitable and sufficient steps must be taken to ensure, so far as practicable, that in the event of a fall by any person the safeguard does not itself cause injury to that person. Fall arresting systems such as safety nets, air/bean bags or crash mats may be used to minimise the impact of falls through the gaps created within a structure. Safety netting is the preferred fall arrest option since it provides collective protection and, unlike a fall arrest harness, does not rely on individual user discipline to guarantee acceptable safety standards. They can simplify systems of work and can protect not only employees, but others such as supervisors.

Where safety nets are used, they must be installed as close as possible beneath the surface that people can fall from, securely attached and able to withstand a person falling onto them. These must be installed and maintained by competent personnel. If the work height increases, the nets must be repositioned at each higher level to ensure the minimum fall distance is maintained as the work progresses.

Personal fall protection systems

Personal fall protection systems include work positioning systems, rope access and positioning techniques, fall arrest systems and work restraint systems. Schedule 5, Part 1, WAH 2005 requires that a personal fall protection system may only be used if:

■ A risk assessment has demonstrated that:
  • Work can, so far as is reasonably practicable, be performed safely while using that system.
  • Use of other safer work equipment is not reasonably practicable.
■ The user and a sufficient number of available persons have received adequate training specific to the operations envisaged, including rescue procedures.

In addition, Schedule 5, Part 1, requires that a personal fall protection system must be:

■ Be suitable and of sufficient strength for the purposes for which it is being used, having regard to the work being carried out and any foreseeable loading.
■ Where necessary, fit the user.
■ Be correctly fitted.
■ Be designed to minimise injury to the user and, where necessary, be adjusted to prevent the user falling or slipping from it, should a fall occur.
■ Be so designed, installed and used as to prevent unplanned or uncontrolled movement of the user.

Each of the different personal fall protection systems (work positioning systems, rope access and positioning techniques, fall arrest systems and work restraint systems) has requirements related to their use set out in Schedule 5 of WAH 2005. Personal fall arrest systems (harnesses) are useful when other means of fall protection are not reasonably practicable. The harness itself may cause injury when the person comes to a sudden stop; therefore the use of an inertia reel harnesses (the same principle as a car seat belt) may be preferable.

In order to minimise the consequences of a fall when using personal fall arrest systems it is important to maintain a 'clear fall zone' that takes account of the likely movement of the person after the fall, including the pendulum effect. When using harnesses in a mobile elevating work platform (MEWP), the harness should always be fixed to the inside of the cradle.

INSTRUCTION AND TRAINING AND/OR OTHER MEANS

Where a risk of a fall remains, Regulation 6 of WAH 2005 requires that instruction, training and suitable and sufficient other measures must also be provided to prevent any person falling a distance liable to cause personal injury. This may include training employees in techniques that would limit the effect of the fall, controlling what equipment they use that might fall with them, ceasing processes in the area that may cause the worker to be disorientated/overcome leading to a fall, covering items that the person may fall onto and providing means to assist those that have fallen.

Employees should receive full training and instruction on the use of equipment and systems of working that will minimise the distance and consequences of a fall. Where harnesses are to be used, this should include how to wear the fall arrest harnesses, how to fit it to fixing points, what is a suitable fixing point and fixing at a height that minimises the fall (for example, above the head where possible).

Training should also include the checks that need to be made on fall arrest systems before they are used, this will include checks on the security of nets and the adequacy of airbags. Employees will also need to be trained in how to get off/out of this equipment safely when it has arrested a fall and on emergency arrangements for rescue, where employees cannot assist themselves.

This is supported by the general duty to provide training to those involved with work at height, set out in Regulation 5 of WAH 2005:

> *"Every employer shall ensure that no person engages in any activity, including organisation, planning and supervision, in relation to work at height or work equipment for use in such work unless he is competent to do so or, if being trained, is being supervised by a competent person."*

Figure 10-4: Provision of training.   *Source: WAH 2005 Regulation 5.*

Requirements for head protection

The Personal Protective Equipment Regulations (PPER) 1992 apply to the provision and wearing of head protection on construction sites following the revocation of the Construction (Head Protection) Regulations (CHPR) 1989. Hard hats are required where there is a foreseeable risk of injury to the head other than by a person falling, for example, the risk of being struck by falling materials or where people might hit their head. The exemption from wearing head protection for turban-wearing Sikhs working on construction sites (contained in the Employment Act 1989) now applies to the PPE Regulations. There is no such exemption for other religious groups or for Sikhs who choose not to wear a turban.

Hazards to consider:

- Loose material kicked into an excavation.
- Material falling from a scaffold platform.
- Material falling off a load being lifted by a crane or goods hoist or carried on a site dumper or truck.
- Dropping a fitting while erecting or dismantling a scaffold.

Decide on the areas of the site where hats have to be worn. Make site rules and tell everyone in the area. Provide employees with hard hats and make sure hats are worn and worn correctly. It is useful to ensure that a wide range of hats is available and to let employees try a few and decide which is most suitable for the job and for them. Some hats have extra features, including a sweatband for the forehead and a soft, or webbing harness. Although these hats are slightly more expensive, they are much more comfortable and therefore more likely to be worn.

Inspection requirements for work equipment

Inspection requirements for work equipment specified for use for work at height are set out in Regulation 12 of WAH 2005.

Requirements are:

- Where safety depends on how it is installed or assembled in any position - before used in that position.
- Where exposed to conditions causing deterioration which is liable to result in dangerous situations, to ensure that health and safety conditions are maintained and that any deterioration can be detected and remedied in good time - at suitable intervals and each time that exceptional circumstances which are liable to jeopardise the safety of the work equipment have occurred.
- Work platforms used for construction work in which a person could fall 2 metres or more - inspected in position, or if a mobile work platform inspected on the site, within the previous 7 days.

Result of an inspection must be recorded and kept until the next inspection. An inspection report containing the particulars set out below must be prepared before the end of the working period within which the inspection is completed and, within 24 hours of completing the inspection, be provided to the person it was carried out for.

The report must be kept at the site where the inspection was carried out until the construction work is completed and afterwards at an office of the person it was carried out for, for 3 months.

Reports on inspections must include the following particulars:

1) Name and address of person for whom the inspection is carried out.
2) Location of the work equipment.
3) Description of the work equipment.
4) Date and time of inspection.
5) Details of any matter identified that could give rise to a risk to the health and safety of any person.
6) Details of any action taken as a result of number (5) above.
7) Details of any further action considered necessary.
8) Name and position of the person making the report.

10.2 - Safe working practices for access equipment and roof work

Scaffolding

DESIGN FEATURES OF SCAFFOLDING

Independent tied

This type of scaffold typically uses two sets of standards; one near to the structure and the other set at the width of the work platform. It is erected so that it is independent from the structure and does not rely on it for its primary stability. However, as the name suggests, it is usual to tie the scaffold to the structure in order to prevent the scaffold falling towards or away from the structure.

Figure 10-5: Independent tied scaffold. *Source: RMS.*

Figure 10-6: Independent tied scaffold. *Source: RMS.*

Figure 10-7: Independent tied scaffold. *Source: HSE, HSG150.*

Putlog

This type of scaffold has a single set of standards erected at the width required for the work platform. The transoms have a flat end that is inserted into the mortar gap in the wall. The structure effectively provides the inner support for the work platform and therefore an inner set of standards is not needed.

Figure 10-8: Putlog scaffold.

Source: HSE, HSG150.

Figure 10-9: Putlog scaffold.   *Source: RMS.*

Figure 10-10: Putlog scaffold.   *Source: RMS.*

Fan

Fans are scaffold boards fixed on scaffold tubes set at an upward angle out from a scaffold in order to catch debris that may fall from the scaffold.

They may be provided at the entrances to buildings to protect persons entering and leaving the building that the scaffold is erected against.

They are also used where a scaffold is erected alongside a pedestrian walkway where there is a need to have an increased confidence that materials that might fall cannot contact people below.

In some cases it may be necessary for horizontal barriers to be erected to direct pedestrians under the fan.

Figure 10-11: Fans.   *Source: RMS.*

Cantilevered

A cantilever scaffold is assembled in the normal way then continued outwards by erecting a cantilever section from the inner vertical columns.

Care must be taken to ensure the structure remains safe and stable. Adding stabilisers to the main scaffold or tying-in to the building are normally essential safety precautions. The use of adjustable bases either under the main scaffold or cantilever or both is usually helpful in ensuring the cantilever section rests firmly on the building.

Mobile tower scaffolds

Mobile scaffold towers are widely used as they are convenient for work which involves frequent access to height over a short period of time in a number of locations that are spaced apart.

Figure 10-12: Wheels with brakes. *Source: RMS.*

However, they are often incorrectly erected or misused and accidents occur due to people/materials falling or the tower overturning/collapsing.

They must be erected and dismantled by trained, competent personnel, strictly in accordance with the supplier's instructions. All parts must be sound and from the same manufacturer.

- The height of an untied, independent tower must never exceed the manufacturer's recommendations. A 'rule of thumb' may be:
  - Outdoor use   -   3 times the minimum base width.
  - Indoor use   -   3.5 times the minimum base width.
- If the height of the tower is to exceed these maximum figures then the scaffold *must* be secured (tied) to the structure or outriggers used.
- Working platforms must only be accessed by safe means. Use internal stairs or fixed ladders only and never climb on the outside.
- Before climbing a tower the wheels must be turned outwards, the wheel brakes 'on', locked and kept locked.
- Never move a tower unless the platform is clear of people, materials, tools etc.
- Towers must only be moved by pushing them at base level. Instruct operators not to pull the tower along whilst on it. Pay careful attention to obstructions at base level and overhead.
- Never use a tower near live overhead power lines or cables.
- Working platforms must always be fully boarded out. Guardrails and toe boards must be fitted if there is a risk of a fall of more than two metres. Inspections must be carried out by a competent person - before first use, after substantial alteration and after any event likely to have affected its stability.

Figure 10-13: Mobile tower scaffold. *Source: RMS.*

Figure 10-14: Mobile tower scaffold. *Source: RMS.*

Scaffolding terms

Base plate	Distributes the load from a standard or a raker (scaffold standard used as an outrigger).
Brace	A tube fixed diagonally across two or more members in a scaffold for stability.

Guard rail	A tube incorporated in the structure to prevent personnel from falling.
Ledger	A tube spanning horizontally and tying the scaffold longitudinally. It may act as a support for putlogs or transoms.
Putlog	A tube with a flattened end, spanning from a horizontal member to a bearing in or on a brick wall. It may support scaffold boards.
Reveal pin	A tube wedged by means of a reveal screw between two opposite surfaces (for example, window reveals) to make a friction anchorage for tying a scaffold.
Standard/column	A vertical, or near vertical, supporting tube.
Tie	A tube used for fixing the scaffold to the building or other structure for stability.
Transom	A tube spanning across ledgers to tie a scaffold transversely. It may also support boards.

SAFETY FEATURES

Base plates and sole boards

Base plates and sole boards are used to spread the weight of the scaffold and to provide a firm surface on which to erect a scaffold. Sole boards are used with base plates where the ground is soft. The base plate spreads the load of the standard and helps to keep the standard vertical. Measures to ensure base plates and sole boards are effective include:

- A base plate must be used under every standard.
- Sole boards must be sound and should run under at least two standards at a time.

Figure 10-15: Base plates and sole boards. *Source: Lincsafe.*

Figure 10-16: Base plate and protection. *Source: RMS.*

Ties and bracing

Ensuring stability of a scaffold is critical. In the case of an independent tied scaffold the scaffold is set a small distance away from the structure and ties connect it to the structure and prevent the scaffold falling away from or towards the structure.

One of the ways to do this is to use a 'through tie' which is set into place through an opening in the structure such as a window. In addition to this, it is important that the scaffold is a rigid structure.

A scaffold comprising standards, transoms and ledgers alone may not be rigid enough, particularly in the case of tall scaffolds. In order to improve rigidity a system of braces, scaffold poles set at a diagonal angle, is used.

Figure 10-17: Tie through window. *Source: RMS.*

They are placed at the ends, in opposite diagonals for each level of scaffold, at intervals along the scaffold. In addition bracing is placed diagonally across the front of the scaffold.

Toe boards

Toe boards are scaffold boards placed against the standards at right angles to the surface of the working platform. They help prevent materials from falling from the scaffold and people slipping under rails. They must be suitable and sufficient to prevent the fall of any person or any material or object from a place of work.

Measures to ensure toe boards are effective include:

- The toe boards should be fixed to the inside of the standards with toe board clips.
- Typically a height of 150mm is needed.
- Joints must be as near as possible to a standard.

- Continuous around the platform where a guardrail is required.
- Any toe board that is removed temporarily for access or for any other reason must be replaced as soon as possible.

Figure 10-18: Guardrails and toe boards.　　　　　　　　*Source: HSE, HSG150.*

Guardrails

Guardrails are horizontal scaffold tubes which help to prevent people falling from a scaffold. Measures to ensure guardrails are effective include:

- They must be fitted to any working platform that is two metres or more above ground level.
- They must be fixed to the *inside* of the standards, at least 950mm from the platform.
- An intermediate guard rail must be no more than 470mm between the top guardrail and the toe boards.
- Guardrails must always be fitted with load-bearing couplers.

- Joints in guardrails must be near to a standard.
- Joints must be secured with sleeve couplers.
- Guardrail must go all round the work platform.
- If the gap between the structures is 300mm or more, then a guardrail must be fitted to the inside of the working platform as well as the outside.
- Guardrails must always be carried round the end of a scaffold, to make a 'stop end'.

Boarding

Boards provide the working platform of a scaffold and landings for access ladders. Boards supported by transoms or putlogs must be close fitting, free from cracks or splits or large knots, and must not be damaged in any way which could cause weakness.

Working platforms

However wide a working platform may be, if its height above ground or floor level is two metres or more, then it must be fitted with guardrails and toe boards. If it is also to carry materials, then the space between guardrails and toe boards must be reduced to a maximum 470mm. This can be done with an intermediate rail, mesh or similar material. The following additional points will assist in minimising risks from working at height on working platforms:

Figure 10-19: Scaffold boards - some defective.　　*Source: RMS.*

- General access must not be allowed to any working platform until the scaffold has been fully erected. Access must be blocked off to any section of any scaffold that is not yet finished.
- If a gap or opening is created in a working platform for any reason, then it must immediately be blocked off and a warning notice displayed.
- Where a ladder passes through a working platform, the access must be as small as practicable.

- Any access point through a working platform must be covered when it is not being used, and clearly marked to show its purpose.
- Trestles *must not* be put up on any working platform.
- If a working platform becomes covered with ice, snow, grease or any other slippery material, then suitable action must be taken to reduce the hazard, by sprinkling sand, salt, sawdust, etc.
- Rubbish or unused materials must not be left on working platforms.
- Platforms must not be used for 'storing' materials. All materials placed on a platform must be for immediate use only.
- Loadings must be evenly spread out over working platforms to the fullest extent possible.
- Where loading cannot be distributed evenly (as with bricklayers' materials) then the larger weights should be kept nearest to the standards.
- Any working platform positioned near to fragile items, such as glass, should be sheeted out to the full height of the guardrail.
- Everything loose must be taken off the working platforms before any start is made on dismantling.

Brick guards

Brick guards are designed to prevent material falling between the gaps in the guardrails and the toe board. Brick guards are not intended to protect against people falling. Therefore, brick guards should always be used in addition to the required fall protection, which consists of guard rails and toe boards or other similar barriers.

Figure 10-20: Brick guards.   *Source: HSE, HSG150.*

Debris netting

Debris netting is often fixed to the sides of a scaffold to limit the amount of debris escaping from the scaffold that may come from work being done on it. It provides a tough, durable and inexpensive method of helping to provide protection from the danger of falling debris and windblown waste. It allows good light transmission and reduces the effects of adverse weather.

Figure 10-21: Nets and sheets.   *Source: RMS.*

Figure 10-22: Nets.   *Source: RMS.*

WORKING AT HEIGHT - HAZARDS AND RISK CONTROL - **ELEMENT 10**

Debris netting may also be slung underneath steelwork or where roof work is being conducted to catch items that may fall. In this situation it should not be assumed that the debris netting is sufficient to hold the weight of a person who might fall.

REQUIREMENTS FOR SCAFFOLD ERECTORS

Scaffold erectors must erect and dismantle scaffold in a way that minimises the risk of falling. Where practicable they should erect intermediate platforms, with guardrails and toe boards, to enable them to build the next scaffold 'lift' safely.

If a platform is not practicable, falls must be prevented (or their effects minimised) by other means, such as the use of a safety harness or similar fall arrest equipment.

The National Access and Scaffolding Confederation (NASC) provide guidance for scaffold employees on the safe erection of scaffolds.

Figure 10-23: Fitting advanced guardrail system. *Source: NASC.*

Part 2 of Schedule 3 of the WAH 2005 requires that scaffolds only be erected by those that have received appropriate and specific training.

"12. Scaffolding may be assembled, dismantled or significantly altered only under the supervision of a competent person and by persons who have received appropriate and specific training in the operations envisaged which addresses specific risks which the operations may entail and precautions to be taken, and more particularly in -

(a) understanding of the plan for the assembly, dismantling or alteration of the scaffolding concerned;

(b) safety during the assembly, dismantling or alteration of the scaffolding concerned;

(c) measures to prevent the risk of persons, materials or objects falling;

(d) safety measures in the event of changing weather conditions which could adversely affect the safety of the scaffolding concerned;

(e) permissible loadings;

(f) any other risks which the assembly, dismantling or alteration of the scaffolding may entail."

Figure 10-24: Competency and training.   *Source: WAH Schedule 3 Part 2.*

MEANS OF ACCESS

"So far as is reasonably practicable as regards any place of work under the employer's control, the maintenance of it in a condition that is safe and without risks to health and the provision and maintenance of means of access to and egress from it that are safe and without such risks."

Figure 10-25: Means of access.   *Source: HASAWA 1974 s2(2)(d).*

General access must not be allowed to any scaffold until its erection has been fully completed. Access must be prevented to any subsequent sections of scaffold that are not completed and a 'scaffold incomplete' sign displayed. Ladders often provide access and egress to and from scaffolds where stairs cannot be provided.

Figure 10-26: Stair access.   *Source: RMS.*

Figure 10-27: Ladder access.   *Source: RMS.*

© RMS   295

Factors to be considered in the safe use of ladders for access include:

- They should be free from defect and not painted.
- The correct length used to reduce manual handling risks, flexing in use.
- Placed on a firm footing, with each stile equally supported.
- Positioned so that there is sufficient space at each rung to give an adequate foothold.
- Positioned approximately at an angle of 75° (1 unit horizontally to 4 units vertically).
- Extended to a height of 1 metre above the working platform (unless there is another adequate hand hold).
- When more than 3 metres in length, must be securely tied at the top or footed at the bottom to prevent slipping.
- Not be so long that it extends excessively past the stepping off point as this can cause the ladder to pivot around the tie/stepping off point and cause the user to fall.
- Positioned so that the vertical height of the ladder running between landings does not exceed 9 metres.
- Both hands should be free when climbing a ladder.

DESIGN OF LOADING PLATFORMS

Scaffold platforms that are used for loading of materials or equipment will need to be designed to take into account any concentration of heavy loads that will be placed upon them (for example, bricks, blocks, mortar or timber).

A loading platform is designed to withstand a weight that would be excessive on the normal working area of a scaffold.

Often this will be a separate scaffold structure, assembled adjacent to the main working scaffold, tied to both the building and the main scaffold and will consist of additional braces and sections to provide extra support.

The platform must be correctly signed as a loading area with a safe working load specified.

Employees must not be allowed to access the area directly below the platform where the loading and unloading will take place.

Figure 10-28: Loading platform.   Source: RMS.

SCAFFOLD HOISTS (PERSONS, MATERIALS)

The hoist should be protected by a substantial enclosure to prevent anyone from being struck by any moving part of the hoist or material falling down the hoist way. Gates must be provided at all access landings, including at ground level. The gates must be kept shut, except when the platform is at the landing.

The controls should be arranged so that the hoist can be operated from one position only. All hoist operators must be trained and competent. The hoist's safe working load must be clearly marked.

If the hoist is for materials only there should be a prominent warning notice on the platform or cage to stop people riding on it.

Figure 10-29: Loading platform.   Source: RMS.

The hoist should be inspected weekly, and thoroughly examined every six months by a competent person and the results of inspection recorded.

Inclined hoists are often used to transport materials. Inclined hoists should be erected and used by competent personnel. Additionally, there would need to be arrangements for its inspection, testing and regular maintenance and for ensuring the guarding of dangerous parts of the machinery and the integrity of any electrical installation.

Protection would need to be provided at the base and top of the hoist and means provided to ensure the security of the load as it travels to the top of the hoist. Relocation and or dismantling should only be carried out by competent persons.

See also - Element 4 - Musculoskeletal hazards and control - 'Lifts and hoists' - for further information.

ENSURING STABILITY

Effects of materials

Scaffold systems are a means of providing safe access when work at height cannot be avoided. They are not designed for storage of materials for long periods. It is however, acceptable to situate materials on scaffolds in small quantities to reflect the usage rate of the materials by the people using the scaffold. Provided the safe working load specified for the scaffold is not exceeded materials may be distributed evenly on the working platform.

Care should be taken to ensure the working platform is not reduced to a width that compromises access around the scaffold, the materials are distributed evenly and the safe working load specified for the scaffold is not exceeded.

Materials (bricks, mortar, timber, etc.) when placed on scaffold systems tend to be placed on the outer edge of the scaffold, creating an uneven balance and placing greater forces on the mechanical joints. These factors can contribute to failure of the joints, or buckling of the tube sections which may ultimately lead to a full or partial collapse of the structure. If this occurs, a host of other hazards become present (falls from height, falling materials).

All loading of scaffolds with materials should be well planned to prevent uneven loading and carried out under supervision. The scaffold should be checked to ensure the safe working load is adhered to at all times.

Weather

Adverse weather conditions not only affect the condition of structures and equipment but can also present dangers to those people who are exposed to them (cold weather can affect dexterity, awareness and morale). These need to be anticipated and suitable precautions taken. Rain, sleet or snow can make surfaces very slippery and in winter freeze to create ice or frost. Heavy rainfall can lead to soil being washed away from the base of the scaffold or the soil can subside leading to the scaffold becoming unstable. Scaffolds should always be inspected prior to work starting. If conditions have changed, checks should be made on whether it is safe to continue working.

A sudden gust of wind can cause loss of balance. This is usually exaggerated when working at height and handling large sheets of materials. In extreme circumstances, work should be stopped during windy weather as people can easily be thrown off balance while carrying out their work.

When deciding whether to continue or suspend work consider:

■ Wind speed.
■ The measures which have already been taken to prevent falls from the scaffold.
■ The position and height of the scaffold and the work being carried out.
■ The relationship of the work to other large structures as wind may be tunnelled and amplified at certain points.

Sheeting

Sheeting can be used on the outside of scaffold systems as a means of preventing materials, dust and other debris being blown from the working areas of the scaffold onto the construction site or possibly a public area, and it can also provide a means of restricting and controlling access. It is not a means of fall protection.

Whilst sheeting is relatively light and causes little stress on the scaffold system, the additional forces created by wind, rain or snow spread over the surface of the sheeting could cause sufficient force to affect the safe stability of the scaffold. It is also important that sheeting is securely fixed to the structure and not allowed to flail loosely as this could be snagged on site mobile plant resulting in the scaffold being pulled and causing it to collapse.

Protection from impact of vehicles

Construction sites quite often involve numerous types of vehicles of varying size and weight all presenting hazards to other people carrying out work within the site. Protection from impact should be applied to all aspects of work carried out, not just to scaffold structures in particular.

Measures that may be implemented in order to maintain a safe environment in relation to vehicles and scaffolds may include:

■ Providing signs warning of the presence of scaffolds.
■ Marking scaffolds with high-visibility tape or sheath around scaffold standards.
■ Closing routes past scaffolds to vehicles.
■ Ensuring adequate road width for the size of vehicle accessing the site.
■ Provision of one-way systems around sites or turning points (away from scaffold) to minimise the need for reversing.
■ Reversing vehicles properly controlled by trained banksmen. Competent drivers correctly trained.
■ Concrete or wooden impact blocks strategically placed around scaffold perimeter to limit proximity.
■ Providing lighting around the scaffold perimeter, scaffolds located near roads may be fitted with lighting to warn traffic of its presence.

Figure 10-30: Impact protection.   *Source: RMS.*

Figure 10-31: Lighting.   *Source: RMS.*

Inspection requirements

Inspection requirements for scaffolds are set out in Regulation 12 of WAH 2005 Regulations. All scaffolds used for construction work must be inspected by a competent person before being taken into use for the first time, after any substantial addition, dismantling or other alteration, after any event likely to have affected its strength or stability and where a person could fall 2 metres or more at regular intervals not exceeding 7 days since the last inspection. The result of an inspection must be recorded and kept until the next inspection. A report on the inspection must be completed before the end of the work period and a copy provided to the person on whose behalf it was carried out within 24 hours.

Figure 10-32: Marking.   *Source: RMS.*

Figure 10-33: Inspection 'Scaftag'. *Source: RMS.*

Reports on inspections to include the following details:

1) Name and address of the person for whom the inspection was carried out.
2) Location of the work equipment inspected.
3) Description of the work equipment.
4) Date and time of inspection.
5) Details of any matter identified that could give rise to a risk to the health and safety of any person.
6) Details of any action taken as a result of number 5) above.
7) Details of any further action considered necessary.
8) Name and position of the person making the report.

It is useful to indicate to those using the scaffold that the inspection has been conducted by the addition of a tag to the scaffold that shows basic details of the inspection. Employers must keep a copy of the inspection report at the site where it was carried out, until construction work is complete.

After this period they have to be kept at the employer's office for 3 months. It is useful to indicate to those using the scaffold that the inspection has been conducted by the addition of a tag to the scaffold that shows basic details of the inspection.

Mobile elevating work platforms

A mobile elevating work platform (MEWP) is, as the name suggests, a means of providing a work platform at height. The equipment is designed to be movable, under its own power or by being towed, so that it can easily be set up in a location where it is needed.

Various mechanical and hydraulic means are used to elevate the work platform to the desired height, including telescopic arms and scissor lifts.

The versatility of this equipment, enabling the easy placement of a platform at height, makes it a popular piece of access equipment. Often, to do similar work by other means would take a lot of time or be very difficult.

They are now widely available and, like other equipment such as fork-lift trucks there is a tendency for people to oversimplify their use and allow people to operate them without prior training and experience.

Figure 10-34: Mobile elevated work platform (MEWPs). *Source: RMS.*

This places users and others at high risk of serious injury. Some MEWPs can be used on rough terrain. This usually means that they are safe to use on uneven or undulating ground. The MEWP's limitations should always be checked in the manufacturer's handbook before moving on to unprepared or sloping ground and operates within the defined stability working area. Wearing a harness with a lanyard attached to the platform provides extra protection against falls especially when the platform is being raised or lowered. MEWPs and similar equipment used in poor lighting conditions on or near roads and walkways must use standard vehicle lighting.

Use of mobile elevating work platforms

Mobile elevating work platforms can provide excellent safe access to high level work. When using a MEWP make sure:

- Whoever is operating it is fully trained and competent.
- The work platform is fitted with guard rails and toe boards.
- It is used on suitable firm and level ground. The ground may have to be prepared in advance.
- Tyres are properly inflated.
- The work area is cordoned off to prevent access below the work platform.
- That it is well lit if being used on a public highway in poor lighting.
- Outriggers are extended and chocked as necessary before raising the platform.
- All involved know what to do if the machine fails with the platform in the raised position.

Figure 10-35: Mobile elevated work platform (MEWPs). *Source: RMS.*

Do not attach harnesses to a point outside platform!

Figure 10-36: Use of harness with a MEWP. *Source: HSE, HSG150.*

Figure 10-37: Scissor lift.   *Source: RMS.*

Figure 10-38: Scissor lift.   *Source: HSE, HSG150.*

Do not

- Operate MEWPs close to overhead cables or dangerous machinery.
- Allow a knuckle, or elbow, of the arm to protrude into a traffic route when working near vehicles.
- Move the equipment with the platform in the raised position unless the equipment is especially designed to allow this to be done safely (check the manufacturer's instructions).
- Overload or overreach from the platform.

Ladders

USE OF LADDERS

Ladders are primarily a means of vertical access to a workplace. However, they are often used to carry out work and this frequently results in accidents. Many accidents involving ladders happen during work lasting thirty minutes or less. Ladders are often used for short jobs when it would be safer to use other equipment, for example, mobile scaffold towers or MEWPs.

Generally, ladders should be considered as access equipment and use of a ladder as a work platform should be discouraged.

There are situations when working from a ladder would be inappropriate, for example:

- When two hands are needed or the work area is large.
- Where the equipment or materials used are large or awkward.
- Excessive height.
- Work of long duration.
- Where the ladder cannot be secured or made stable.
- Where the ladder cannot be protected from vehicles etc.
- Adverse weather conditions.

Figure 10-39: Ladder as access and workplace. *Source: RMS.*

Figure 10-40: Improper use.   *Source: RMS.*

Ladders can be used if after assessing the risks the use of more suitable work equipment is not justified because of the low risk and short duration.

Short duration is taken to be between fifteen and thirty minutes depending upon the task. Ladders can also be used for low risk work where there are features on the site that mean a ladder must be used.

The following measures should be taken before a ladder is put into use:

- Pre-use inspection. Make sure the ladder is in good condition. Check the rungs and stiles for warping, cracking or splintering, the condition of the feet, and for any other defects. Do not use defective or painted ladders.
- Position the ladder properly for safe access and out of the way of vehicles. Do not rest ladders against fragile surfaces.
- Ladders must stand on a firm, level base, be positioned approximately at an angle of 75° (1 unit horizontally to 4 units vertically) *(see figure ref 10-41)* (note means of securing omitted for clarity).
- If the ladder is being used to gain access to a landing place it should extend about 1 metre above the landing place.
- Ladders must be properly tied near the top, even if only in use for a short time, while being tied a ladder must be footed. If not tied, ladders must be secured near the bottom, footed or weighted. Footing is not considered effective on ladders longer than five metres.
- Both hands should be free to grip the ladder when climbing or descending, with only one person on the ladder at any time. Beware of wet, greasy or icy rungs and make sure soles of footwear are clean.
- Purpose designed roof ladders should be used to ensure safe access to sloping roofs.
- Ladders should be returned to the correct, secure storage location when they are not in use.

Figure 10-41: Correct 1 in 4 angle. *Source: HSE, HSG150.*

Figure 10-42: Poor storage.   *Source: Lincsafe.*

Figure 10-43: Use of roof ladders.   *Source: HSE, HSG150.*

STEP LADDERS

Stepladders require careful use. They are subject to the same general health and safety rules as ladders. However, in addition, they will not withstand any degree of side loading and overturn very easily.

When using a step ladder over-reaching should be avoided at all times and care should be taken avoid side loading.

Care should be taken to ensure it is placed on a firm level surface to minimise the possibility of it overturning sideways. Step ladder stays must be 'locked out' properly before use.

The top step of a stepladder should not be used as a working platform unless it has been specifically designed for that purpose.

Typically three clear steps should be left to ensure support and stability, depending on the size and design of the step ladder, *(see figure ref 10-45).*

Figure 10-44: Stepladder. *Source: RMS.*

Figure 10-45: Three steps clear. *Source: HSE, HSG150.*

Figure 10-46: Step platform. *Source: HSE, HSG150.*

Figure 10-47: Incorrect use of a step ladder. *Source: HSE, HSG150.*

Figure 10-48: Correct use of a step ladder. *Source: HSE, HSG150.*

TRESTLES

Trestles are pre-fabricated steel, aluminium or wood supports, of approximately 500mm to 1 metre width, that may be of fixed height or may be height adjustable by means of sliding struts with varying fixing points (pin method) or various cross bars to suit the height required. They are used to span scaffold boards from one to the other in order to make a work platform. ***These can only be used where work cannot be carried out from the ground but where a scaffold would be impracticable.*** A good example would be a plasterer who is installing and plastering a new ceiling.

Figure 10-49: Trestle handrail system.   *Source: London Tool Hire.*

Typical working heights when using a trestle system range from 300mm to 1 metre, but can be up to above 4 metres. Edge protection should be fitted wherever practical.

As with any work carried out above ground level, a risk assessment, as required by the Management of Health and Safety at Work Regulations (MHSWR) 1999, should be carried out and consideration given to the application of the WAH Regulations 2005 and/or the Construction (Design and Management) Regulations (CDM) 2015 and/or the Workplace (Health, Safety and Welfare) Regulations (WHSWR) 1992. There are many configurations of locking and adjustable trestles.

Platforms based on trestles should be fully boarded, adequately supported and provided with edge protection where appropriate. Safe means of access should be provided to trestle platforms, usually by stepladders.

Always

- Set up the equipment on a firm, level, non-slip surface.
- On soft ground, stand the equipment on boards to stop it sinking in.
- Place each trestle at 1.5m intervals which allows the scaffold boards to be adequately supported.
- Then open each up to the height required, ensure the locking pins are properly located.

Never

- Do anything that involves applying a lot of side force. The trestle could topple over.
- The maximum safe working load of a scaffold board is 150 Kg evenly spaced.
- The total weight of the user and tools must not exceed this.
- When moving to a new site, carry the equipment with care.
- Never use steps, boxes etc. to gain extra height.

STAGING PLATFORMS

Staging platforms can be made of metal alloy or wood and are often used for linking trestle systems or tower scaffolds together safely. They also provide a safe work platform when working at height, ***see figure ref 10-50***. They are produced in various lengths. The same rules apply for edge protection as with other scaffold platforms.

Ensure that the platform is:

- Of sufficient dimensions to allow safe passage and safe use of equipment and materials.
- Free from trip hazards or gaps through which persons or materials could fall.
- Fitted with toe boards and handrails. If toe boards and guardrails are not considered necessary for a specific platform, then this should be shown in the risk assessment, i.e. that not installing a toe board and/or a guard rail had been considered and why it was not necessary.
- Kept clean and tidy, for example, mortar and debris should not be allowed to build-up on platforms.
- Not loaded to the extent that there is a risk of collapse or deformation that could affect its safe use. This is particularly relevant in relation to block work loaded on platforms.
- Erected on firm level ground to ensure equipment remains stable during use.

Figure 10-50: Ladder staging platform. *Source: Ladder Safety Devices.*

LEADING EDGE PROTECTION SYSTEMS

Leading edges are created as new roof sheets are laid, or old ones are removed. Falls from a leading edge need to be prevented. Work at the leading edge requires careful planning to develop a safe system of work. Nets are the preferred method for reducing the risk of injury from falls at the leading edge, as they provide protection to everyone on the roof. Nets should be erected by trained riggers and be strong enough to take the weight of people.

Debris nets are only rigged to trap lightweight debris - therefore it is important to know which type is in use at a workplace. Staging platforms fitted with guardrails or suitable barriers and toe boards, in advance of the leading edge, can provide protection in some circumstances.

Figure 10-51: Edge protection and staging platforms. *Source: RMS.*

Staging platforms will need to be used in conjunction with harnesses attached to a suitable fixing. Close supervision of this system of work will be needed as it is difficult for the harness to remain safely clipped at all times throughout the work activity.

Other techniques for working at height

Where it is not possible to work from the existing structure and the use of a scaffold working platform is not appropriate, a range of mobile access equipment including boatswain's chairs or seats, suspended cradles, rope access equipment and mobile elevating work platforms (MEWPs) can be used. Those using this type of equipment should be trained and competent to operate it.

They should learn emergency and evacuation procedures so that they know what to do if, for example, the power to the platform fails or fire breaks out in the building being worked on. With many pieces of equipment, more than one person will be needed to ensure safe operation.

MAST CLIMBING WORK PLATFORM

Mast climbing work platforms (MCWPs) are often used when carrying out repairs or refurbishment to high-rise buildings. They provide excellent access to work positions at a height and enable work to be carried out at different heights as the work progresses.

They are not designed as materials hoists though they have a capacity for some work material and people to be on the platform to carry out the work required.

A particular advantage of using MCWPs is that employees on the platform and their tools/materials can be protected from adverse weather conditions by the provision of an enclosed work platform.

Figure 10-52: Mast climbing work platforms. *Source: HSE, HSG150.*

When using MCWPs it is important to ensure that:

- It is erected/installed by a competent specialist who is aware of the purpose of use, likely loadings and weather conditions it will be exposed to.
- Masts are rigidly connected to the structures against which they are operating and outriggers are used when necessary.
- The area below the platform guarded to prevent people from being struck by the platform or by objects that may fall from the platform.
- Working platforms are provided with suitable guardrails and toe boards.
- The controls only operate from the working platform.
- A handover document is provided by the erector/installer. The document should state its safe working load; cover how to operate the equipment, what checks and maintenance is required and how to deal with emergencies.
- There is a current report of thorough examination for the equipment.

BOATSWAIN'S CHAIR

Boatswains' chairs (commonly known as Bosun's chair) and seats can be used for light, short-term work. The chair is distinguished from a climbing harness by the inclusion of a rigid seat, providing more comfort than padded straps for long-term use. The boatswains chair does not allow the freedom of movement necessary for climbing, and the occupant is generally hoisted or lowered into place using the rope alone. They should only be used where it is not practicable to provide a working platform. When using a boatswain's chair it is important to ensure the following points, before, during and after use.

Before use

Before use ensure that:

- Installation and use of boatswain's chair to be supervised by trained, experienced and competent person.
- Chair and associated equipment carefully examined for defects.
- Confirm test/examination certificates are valid. Establish safe working load.
- Check that user is both trained and competent in the use of the chair.
- Warning notice displayed and notification of intention to carry out work given.
- Prohibit access to the area below the chair in case materials fall.

Figure 10-53: Boatswains chair. *Source: Photo, Pete Verdon.*

In use

When in use ensure that:

Chairs and ropes are free of material or articles which could interfere with the user's hand-hold.

- The fall rope must be properly tied off in use and always under or around a cleat to act as a brake.

After use

Chairs and ropes should be left in a safe condition:

- Top rope secured.
- Chair and rope secured to prevent swing.
- Raised when out of use or for overnight storage.
- Inspected for defects.
- Ropes (and chair, if timber) dried before storage.

CRADLES (INCLUDING SUSPENSION FROM CRADLES)

Before work starts using a cradle, check that:

- Equipment is installed, modified and dismantled only by competent specialists.
- There is a current report of thorough examination for the equipment.
- A handover certificate is provided by the installer. The certificate should cover how to deal with emergencies, operate, check and maintain the equipment, and state its safe working load.
- Areas of the site where people may be struck by the cradle or falling materials have been fenced off or similar. Debris fans or covered walkways may also be required.
- Systems are in place to prevent people within the building being struck by the cradle as it rises or descends and prevent the cradle coming into contact with open windows or similar obstructions which could cause it to tip.

Figure 10-54: Suspended cradle. *Source: Harsco Infrastructure.*

- Supports are protected from damage (for example, by being struck by passing vehicles or by interference from vandals).
- The equipment should not be used in adverse weather. High winds will create instability. Establish a maximum safe wind speed for operation. Storms and snow falls can also damage platforms, so they should be inspected before use after severe weather.
- Only trained personnel are to operate.

At the end of each day, check that:

- All power has been switched off and, where appropriate, power cables have been secured and made dead.
- The equipment is secured where it will not be accessible to vandals or trespassers.
- Notices are attached to the equipment warning that it is out of service and must not be used.
- Check the shift report for warnings of malfunction.

ROPE ACCESS

Often known as abseiling, this technique is usually used for inspection work rather than construction work.

Like a boatswain's chair, it should only be used when a working platform cannot be provided. If rope access is necessary, then check that:

- A competent person has installed the equipment.
- The user is fully trained.
- There is more than one point securing the equipment.
- Tools and equipment are securely attached or the area below cordoned off.
- The main rope and safety rope are attached to separate points.

Figure 10-55: Personal suspension equipment.   *Source: RMS.*

Fall arrest equipment

HARNESSES

There may be circumstances in which it is not practicable for guard rails etc. to be provided, for example, where guard rails are taken down for short periods to land materials. In this situation if people approach an open edge from which they would be liable to fall two metres or more, a suitably attached harness and temporary horizontal lifeline could allow safe working. When using harnesses and temporary horizontal lifelines, ensure:

- An emergency rescue system must be in place before a harness and lanyard is used to protect against a fall.
- A harness will not prevent a fall - it can only minimise the injury if there is a fall. The person who falls may be injured by the impact load to the body when the line goes tight or when they strike against parts of the structure during the fall. An energy absorber fitted to the energy-absorbing lanyard can reduce the risk of injury from impact loads.
- Where possible the energy-absorbing lanyard should be attached above the wearer to reduce the fall distance. Extra free movement can be provided by running temporary horizontal lifelines or inertia reels. Any attachment point must be capable of withstanding the impact load in the event of a fall. Consider how to recover anyone who does fall.
- Anyone who needs to attach themselves should be able to do so from a safe position. They need to be able to attach themselves before they move into a position where they are relying on the protection provided by the harness.
- To ensure that there is an adequate fall height to allow the system to operate and arrest the fall.
- A twin lanyard may be necessary in some cases where the wearer needs to move about. A twin lanyard allows the wearer to clip on one lanyard in a different position before unclipping the other lanyard.

Figure 10-56: Scaffolder using personal fall arrest device.
Source: NASC.

- Installation of equipment to which harnesses will be fixed, for example, a suitable anchor, must be inspected regularly.
- Everyone who uses a harness must be instructed in how to check, wear and adjust it before use and how to connect themselves to the structure or safety line as appropriate.
- They should be thoroughly examined at intervals of no more than every six months.
- Retractable type fall arresters tested against EN360 are tested with a 100Kg mass and have to produce an arrest force of less than 6kN. Therefore users greater than 100Kg (15 stone 10 lbs.) should refer to the manufacturer's instruction for use and if not covered within the instruction should contact the manufacturer for information for users weighing greater than 100Kg.

SAFETY NETS

Safety nets are used in a variety of applications where other forms of protection are not reasonably practicable - such as steel erecting and roof work where site personnel are at risk of falling through fragile roofs onto solid surfaces or structures (steel work) below.

Safety nets will arrest the fall of an individual preventing an impact that may cause injury or death. Safety nets must be installed beneath the work area, as a minimum, and consideration should be given to an extension of the protection to allow for people working outside the planned area. Safety nets are only to be installed under supervision by competent installers and are to be inspected weekly and checked daily as the build height progresses.

Figure 10-57: Safety nets. *Source: RMS.*

Relocation of the nets will be necessary if the build height increases to keep the fall distance to a minimum.

It should be remembered that nets are also used to collect debris that may fall. This may be rigged to take a lesser weight than that for protection of people. It is important to identify which type of net is in use in a workplace as reliance on the wrong type may have fatal consequences.

SOFT LANDING SYSTEMS

Soft landing systems normally consist of inflatable air bags or bean bags that are placed, prior to work commencing, under the work area.

Air bags

Airbags are shock absorption devices that can be employed to protect against the effects of falls from a height. They are made of a toughened nylon, or similar man-made material, and are usually inflated using a powered fan device.

They are designed so that should a person fall onto one, a volume of air is forced out of the bag creating a cushioning effect that does not bounce or deflect the person in another direction. This equipment must be matched to correspond to the fall height and as such must only be put into use by a competent person.

Figure 10-58: Soft fall arrest system. *Source: UK, HSE HSG150.*

Soft fall beanbags

Soft fall bean bags use a soft polymer bean to reduce the effect of a fall from up to two metres. The system is used in both traditional building and timber frame constructions.

CRASH DECKS

Collective fall prevention systems (including safety decking) are at the top of the HSE's hierarchy of controls for work at height.

Crash decks (passive, collective fall-protection) provide total protection from falls into the building for all trades at all build stages. For example, bricklayers can work directly off the decking for topping out.

Because they can be set out at a variety of heights they can remove the need for trestles. The decking can be installed concurrently with, or just before, external scaffold is lifted reducing build time.

Figure 10-59: Crash deck assembly. *Source: Bondeck Ltd.*

Figure 10-60: Passive, collective fall prevention. *Source: Bondeck Ltd.*

Figure 10-61: Crash deck designed for loading. *Source: Bondeck Ltd.*

EMERGENCY PROCEDURES INCLUDING RESCUE

It is essential that risk assessments are completed for work at height and they should include planned emergency procedures. Employees should be trained and competent in procedures. These procedures should be rehearsed, so that in the event of an actual incident, employees are competent. Emergency procedures should take account of the range of emergencies that may particularly affect those working at height, for example, loss of power to powered access equipment, loss of power in areas that need to be illuminated to ensure safety (for example, on a scaffold at night), possibilities of a fire or the occurrence of a fall of a person. In the case of equipment failure, the emergency procedures should include rescue from the work position. In situations where a person has fallen, emergency considerations should ensure that further injury is prevented by prompt rescue, using techniques that do not put the worker in further harm.

SUSPENSION TRAUMA IN THE USE OF ROPE AND HARNESSES

Use of harnesses and temporary horizontal lifelines; an emergency rescue system must be in place before a harness and lanyard is used to protect against a fall. The rescue team must be trained to carry out the rescue procedure and in how to deal with a person who is possibly unconscious. The rescue will need to be initiated rapidly (for example, within 15 minutes) to reduce the risk of suspension trauma, a postural hypertension which occurs when the blood pressure drops significantly (the trauma is primarily caused by gravity-induced blood pooling in the lower extremities, which in turn reduces venous return i.e. blood back to the heart, resulting in decreased cardiac output and subsequent lowering of arterial pressure).

Roof work

FLAT ROOFS

Work on a flat roof is high risk. People can fall:

- From the edge of a completed roof.
- From the edge where work is being carried out.
- Through openings or gaps.

Edge protection for flat roofs

Unless the roof parapet provides equivalent safety, temporary edge protection will be required during most work on flat roofs. Both the roof edge and any openings in it need to be protected. It will often be more appropriate to securely cover openings rather than put edge protection around them. Any protection should be:

- In place from start to finish of the work.
- Strong enough to withstand people and materials falling against it.

Where possible the edge protection should be supported at ground level, for example, by scaffold standards, so that there is no obstruction on the roof. If the building is too high for this, the roof edge up-stand can support the edge protection provided it is strong enough. Edge protection can also be supported by frames, counterweights or scaffolding on the roof. The protection should be in place at all times. Guarding systems are widely available that enable roof repair work to carry on without removing any guard rails.

Short-duration work on flat roofs

Short-duration means a matter of minutes rather than hours. It includes such jobs as brief inspections or adjusting a television aerial. Work on a flat roof is dangerous even if it only lasts a short time. Appropriate safety measures are essential. It may not be reasonably practicable to provide edge protection during short-duration work. In such cases, anyone working nearer than 2 metres to any unguarded edge should be using a safety harness.

Where safety harnesses are used they need to be:

- Appropriate for the user and in good condition - full harnesses are essential, safety belts are not sufficient.

- Securely attached to an anchorage point of sufficient strength.
- Fitted with as short a lanyard as possible that enables wearers to do their work (significant management discipline is needed to ensure this).

Demarcating safe areas

Full edge protection may not be necessary if limited work on a larger roof involves nobody going any closer than 2 metres to an open edge. In such cases demarcated areas can be set up to limit the area where work can be conducted safely.

Demarcated areas should be:

- Limited to areas from which nobody can fall.
- Indicated by an obvious physical barrier (full edge protection is not necessary but a painted line or bunting is not sufficient).
- Subject to a high level of supervision to make sure that nobody strays outside them (demarcation areas are unacceptable if this standard is not achieved).

SLOPING ROOFS

On traditional pitched roofs most people fall:

- From eaves.
- By slipping down the roof and then over the eaves.
- Through the roof internally, for example, during roof truss erection.
- From gable ends.

Edge protection for sloping roofs

Full edge protection at eaves level will normally be required for work on sloping roofs. The edge protection needs to be strong enough to withstand a person falling against it. The longer the slope and the steeper the pitch the stronger the edge protection needs to be. A properly designed and installed independent scaffold platform at eaves level will usually be enough. Less substantial scaffolding barriers (rather than platforms) may not be strong enough for work on larger or steeper roofs, especially slopes in excess of 30°.

On some larger roofs, the consequences of sliding down the whole roof and hitting the eaves edge protection may be such that intermediate platforms at the work site are needed to prevent this happening. If the work requires access within 2 metres of gable ends, edge protection will be needed there as well as at the eaves. Powered access platforms can provide good access as an alternative to fixed edge protection. They can be particularly useful in short-duration work.

Figure 10-62: Edge protection and access.　　*Source: RMS.*

Figure 10-63: Edge protection and roof ladder.　　*Source: RMS.*

MEANS OF ACCESS

Means of access for roof work is usually by means of a ladder or stair. Though, access may also be provided by using a scissor lift, which can also carry materials. If provided, a ladder should extend at least 1.05 metres above the edge of the roof, and it should be securely lashed in position, preferably with a wire bond or safety tie. All forms of access should enable employees to easily step onto a safe landing position on the roof or on a landing platform set to the side of the roof, for example, a scaffold tower built for this purpose.

EDGE AND LEADING EDGE PROTECTION

When working on a roof it is essential that edge protection be provided, usually in the form of toe boards and guard rails. When doing work on a roof that requires the worker to lie, fit or remove roof materials, such as insulation and cladding, this can cause the worker to be working at a leading edge.

The leading edge is the limit of the roof structure, on one side of the leading edge is an open height hazard and the other is the relatively safer roof. In order to provide protection at the leading edge it is necessary to provide a system of crawling boards that both spread the weight of the worker and provide fall protection in the form of guardrails. The crawling boards must be repeatedly re-set at the new leading edge as the work progresses.

Figure 10-64: Stair access to roof and edge protection.
Source: RMS.

Figure 10-65: Leading edge protection and crawling boards.
Source: RMS.

CRAWLING BOARDS

On any fragile or angled roof (greater than 30°) or on any roof that is considered hazardous because of its condition or because of the weather; suitable crawling boards must be used. They must be correctly positioned and secure. If it is obvious that the job requires a progression along the roof, extra crawling boards must be provided and no fewer than two such boards shall be taken on any job.

10.3 - Protection of others

DEMARCATION

When working at height is being carried out it is important to protect others from the hazards of items or objects falling onto them. A simple way of doing this is to identify hazardous zones with hazard tape and barriers. Inform those that may be affected by the work that is being undertaken and warn of the possible dangers that may arise within the demarcated area.

Clear demarcation of areas where construction work is being undertaken and where it is not will assist those not involved in the work to keep out of the area and avoid exposure to hazards. The area should be demarcated at a distance that relates to the hazards, such as materials or tools falling. A safety margin should always be built into the demarcation to ensure risks are controlled.

BARRIERS

Barriers are a physical means of preventing access to an area that is required to be restricted, for example, where work at height is being carried out. As such, they are particularly appropriate if people, such as the public, might stray past an area marked only with hazard tape.

These can be situated at a proximity that is relative to the hazards associated with the work being carried out. If necessary to ensure a demarcation zone the barriers may be 2 metre high fencing.

TUNNELS

Tunnels can be used to 'isolate' others from any surrounding hazards by enclosing an area (i.e. walkway) and thus preventing any contact with likely hazards until through the danger area.

An example of this could be the ground level of a scaffold on a shop front in a busy high street, being enclosed to form a tunnel that allows the public to pass through the works safely whilst allowing the work at height to continue above.

SIGNS

Safety signs are used to provide people with information relating to the works being carried out, to control or divert people and most importantly of any dangers or hazards.

Signs may be situated at a location in advance of the work area to give prior warning in addition to the works perimeter and actual work location. Signs may be used to prohibit public access to work areas where work at height is taking place.

Figure 10-66: Nets, signs and head protection. *Source: RMS.*

MARKING

Where equipment used to gain access to height may be collided with it should carry hazard marking. For example, the standards of a scaffold at ground level on a street may be marked with hazard tape. *See also the sections - Demarcation and Signs - previously in this element.*

LIGHTING

Suitable and adequate lighting should be provided to allow the works being carried out and any possible hazards to be seen clearly in advance and allow people to take the required actions to avoid interference with the site.

Scaffolds located near roads may be fitted with lighting to warn traffic of its presence. MEWPs and similar equipment used in poor lighting conditions on or near roads and walkways must use standard vehicle lighting.

SHEETING, NETTING AND FANS

Sheeting can protect other people at risk by preventing dust, materials or tools being ejected from work activities conducted at height. Sheeting provides a solid barrier to particles and spray that may result from some work and may be preferred for processes where building surfaces are being cleaned.

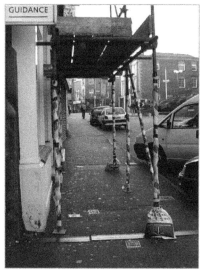

Figure 10-67: Marking.   *Source: RMS.*

However, for most construction activities the provision of fine netting is adequate, being lighter and offering less wind resistance it is often preferable to sheeting. Fans offer a robust means of collecting the material that may breach netting and fall onto the public, who would not be wearing head protection. The fans should extend sufficiently to provide protection over walk areas and be set at an angle that would deter material bouncing or rolling off the fan.

Fans add to the loading of the scaffold and consideration of this factor must be made at the time of scaffold design.

See also - 'Sheeting' - earlier in the section - 'Ensuring stability'.

Figure 10-68: Barriers, fans and netting.   *Source: RMS.*

HEAD PROTECTION

There is a need and legal duty to wear head protection on a construction site where there is a risk of injury from falling materials, this includes when people are working around people at height. This may necessitate the provision of head protection for people other than those involved in the work at height; this could include other employees, visitors to the site or client's employees.

However, it should be remembered that head protection, such as hard hats, provide the user with limited protection from objects falling from height. Therefore it is best, where practicable, to provide other collective means of protection from falling materials.

10.4 - Working over or near water

Prevention of drowning

CDM 2015, Part 4: Duties Relating to Health and Safety on Construction Sites, Regulation 26, states that:

> *"(1) Where, in the course of construction work, a person is at risk of falling into water or other liquid with a risk of drowning, suitable and sufficient steps must be taken to -*
>
> *(a) prevent, so far as is reasonably practicable, the person falling;*
>
> *(b) minimise the risk of drowning in the event of a fall; and*
>
> *(c) ensure that suitable rescue equipment is provided, maintained and, when necessary, used so that a person may be promptly rescued in the event of a fall.*
>
> *(2) Suitable and sufficient steps must be taken to ensure the safe transport of any person conveyed by water to or from a place of work.*

(3) Any vessel used to convey any person by water to or from a place of work must not be overcrowded or overloaded."

Figure 10-69: Prevention of drowning.   *Source: CDM 2015 Regulation 26.*

This means that prior to work above water being undertaken, a full risk assessment must be made that takes into account the conditions of the water being worked over or near (tidal, depth, temperature, fast flowing) and suitable control measures identified and implemented including emergency rescue plans and procedures.

Where possible and practicable, a scaffold system is the best method of safe working over water. Working above water brings an extra dimension to workplace safety and where the water is fast flowing additional risks need to be considered. Safety precautions will include protection for river traffic (advance warnings, lighting of obstructions and consultation with river authorities) and the need for the protection against the possibility of the structure being struck by such traffic.

There may also be the need for additional guardrails to working platforms or fall arrest equipment such as safety nets or harnesses; the provision of rescue equipment such as life belts and the availability of a rescue boat under the control of a competent person, should someone fall into the water. Scaffolds must be erected and inspected by competent persons with inspections required weekly. Employees who are required to work near to or over water are required to be properly trained with a provision made so that any person who does fall into water is able to float.

When working next to water in a MEWP, a harness should not be worn to prevent the risk of drowning by being pulled underwater if the MEWP falls into the water. Life jackets, however, should be worn *(see following section - Buoyancy Aids)*. Employees that fall into water should be recovered as quickly as possible.

Additional means of preventing falls into water may include floating stages, safety nets, safety harnesses and barriers.

Additional control measures

BUOYANCY AIDS

Buoyancy aids must be provided and their use enforced when working on or near water. However, a distinction between buoyancy aids and lifejackets needs to be noted. Both lifejackets and buoyancy aids are designed to keep the wearer afloat with the main difference that a buoyancy aid will provide sufficient buoyancy to keep a conscious person afloat in a reasonable flotation position. A lifejacket will support an unconscious person in a face upright flotation position, therefore reducing the likelihood of the wearer drowning.

Buoyancy aids and lifejackets can be used with safety harnesses so long as the items do not interfere with each other and reduce effectiveness. It is possible to obtain a combined piece of equipment. All staff that are required to use this equipment must be properly trained in its use and be fully aware of its functions and limitations.

Management systems must be in place that considers the use, inspection and storage of lifejackets and buoyancy aids.

The majority of drowning occurs close to the bank or water's edge, and this should be taken into account at the planning stage. Other equipment available to assist someone to remain afloat are life buoys or rescue lines. Life buoys are normally attached to approximately 30 metres of lifeline but can only be thrown a short distance of 6-8 metres. Rescue lines are available in various forms with life lines ranging from 25-40 metres in length. Rescue lines work by throwing a bag or capsule to the person in the water and the line deploying as the bag/capsule goes further out. The line, bag and capsule all stay afloat and allow the person in the water to grab the line and be pulled to safety. Care must be taken that the person deploying the line is secure at the bank and unable to be pulled into the water.

In fast flowing channels that have no water borne traffic, then 'safety nets' or 'safety lines' may be stretched across the width of the channel to allow the person in the water to hang on and wait for rescue. This is only effective if the person in the water remains conscious.

SAFETY BOATS

Where works are being carried out on fast flowing, or tidal waters then a rescue boat should be made available. Requirements state that it must have a reliable engine, carry oars, and the person that is operating the boat must be competent and experienced at handling small boats on flowing water.

It must be fitted with grab lines for persons who have fallen into the water and if any work is carried out in the hours of darkness, then the boat will be required to be fitted with high efficiency lighting. It may be a requirement to have two-way radio installed on the boat for communication between boat and shore.

Exam practice

1. Scaffolding that incorporates a powered hoist has been erected to the outside of an office block in order to undertake repairs to the external cladding of the building.

    Outline factors that could affect the stability of the scaffold. **(8)**

2. A flat roof of a shop in a busy town centre is to be repaired while the shop remains open.

    Outline the measures that could be taken to reduce the risk to workers involved in the roof repair work and others who may be affected by the work. **(8)**

3. **Outline** factors to consider when conducting a working at height risk assessment. **(8)**

4. **Outline** safe working practices associated with the use of a mobile elevating working platform. **(8)**

5. **Outline** safe working practices associated with work over water. **(8)**

Please refer to the back of the assessment section for answers.

This page is intentionally blank

Excavation work and confined spaces - hazards and risk control

Learning outcomes

On completion of this element, candidates should be able to demonstrate understanding of the content through the application of knowledge to familiar and unfamiliar situations. In particular they should be able to:

11.1   Explain the hazards and risk assessment of excavation work.

11.2   Explain the control measures for excavation work.

11.3   Explain the hazards and risks associated with confined space working.

11.4   Outline the control measures for confined space working.

Content

11.1 - Excavations hazards and assessment 317
   The hazards of work in and around excavations 317
   Risk assessment...320
11.2 - Control measures for excavation work 321
   Controls..321
   Particular requirements for contaminated ground 327
   Inspection requirements for excavation support systems...328
11.3 - Confined spaces hazards and risks...329
   Introduction and meaning of the term 'confined space' 329
   Typical confined spaces found during construction activities..329
   Hazards and risks associated with confined spaces 330
11.4 - Control measures for confined space working 331
   Precautions for safe entry...331
   Monitoring arrangements..334
   Emergency arrangements 334
Exam practice 335

Sources of reference

Reference information provided, in particular web links, is correct at time of publication, but may have changed.

Avoidance of danger from overhead electric power lines, Guidance Note GS6 (Fourth Edition), HSE Books, http://www.hse.gov.uk/pubns/gs6.pdf

Avoiding danger from underground services, HSG47, HSE Books, ISBN 978-0-7176-6584-6
http://www.hse.gov.uk/pubns/priced/hsg47.pdf

Managing Health and Safety in Construction, Construction (Design and Management) Regulations 2015, Guidance on Regulations, L153, HSE Books, ISBN: 978-0-7176-6626-3
http://www.hse.gov.uk/pubns/priced/L153.pdf

Personal Protective Equipment at Work (Guidance), L25, HSE Books, ISBN 978-07176-6139-3
http://www.hse.gov.uk/pubns/priced/l25.pdf

Protecting the public: Your next move, HSG151, HSE Books, ISBN 978-0-7176-6294-4
http://www.hse.gov.uk/pubns/priced/hsg151.pdf

Safe work in confined spaces. ACoP, regulations and guidance, L101, HSE Books, ISBN 978-0-7176-6233-3
http://www.hse.gov.uk/pubns/priced/l101.pdf

Relevant statutory provisions

Confined Spaces Regulations (CSR) 1997

Construction (Design and Management) Regulations (CDM) 2015

Personal Protective Equipment at Work Regulations (PPER) 1992

Work at Height Regulations (WAH) 2005

11.1 - Excavations hazards and assessment

The hazards of work in and around excavations

Work in excavations and trenches, basements, underground tanks, sewers, manholes etc., can involve high risks and each year construction employees are killed with some buried alive or asphyxiated.

Figure 11-1: Buried services.   *Source: RMS.*

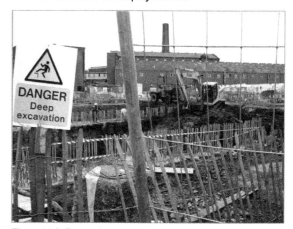

Figure 11-2: Excavation hazards.   *Source: RMS.*

BURIED SERVICES

Although electricity cables provide the most obvious risk, gas pipes, water mains, drains and sewers can all release dangerous substances. Gas is particularly dangerous if there is a potential ignition source close by. Fibre-optic cables may carry laser light, which could be damaging to the eyes if severed accidentally and are very expensive to repair.

Buried services (electricity, gas, water, etc.) may not be obvious at the time of conducting a site survey. This increases the likelihood of striking a service when excavating, drilling or piling. The results of striking an underground service are varied, and the potential to cause injury or a fatality is high. As with overhead power lines, any underground service should be treated as live until confirmed dead by an authority (utility provider). Incidents can include shock, electrocution, explosion and burns from power cables, explosion, burns or unconsciousness from gas, impact injury from dislodged stones or flooding from ruptured water mains.

Before groundwork is due to commence it is common and good practice to check for the presence of any of the previously mentioned services or hazards by using a detection device. A common device used regularly in the construction industry is a cable avoidance tool (CAT), more commonly known as a CAT scanner when utilised as a detection device in a particular area.

FALLS OF PERSONS/EQUIPMENT/MATERIAL INTO THE EXCAVATION

When people are working below ground in excavations, the problems are very similar to those faced when people are working at a height - falls and falling objects. Particular problems arise when:

- Materials, including spoil, are stored too close to the edge of the excavation.
- The excavation is close to another building and the foundations may be undermined.
- The edge of the excavation is not clear, especially if the excavation is in a public area.
- Absence of barriers or lighting.
- Poor positioning or the absence of access ladders allowing people to fall.
- Absence of organised crossing points.
- Badly constructed ramps for vehicle access which can cause the vehicle to topple.
- No stop blocks for back filling.
- Routing of vehicles too close to the excavation.

COLLAPSE OF SIDES

Often, the soil and earth that make up the sides of the excavation cannot be relied upon to support their own weight, leading to the possibility of collapse. The risk can be made worse if:

- The soil structure is loose or made unstable by water logging.
- Heavy plant or materials are too close to the edge of the excavation.
- Machinery or vehicles cause vibration.
- There is inadequate support for the sides.

The consequences of even a minor collapse can be very serious. A minor fall of earth can happen at high speed and bring with it anything (plant and machinery) that may be at the edge. Even if the arms and head of a person are not trapped in the soil, the material pressing on the person can lead to severe crush injuries to the lower body and asphyxiation due to restriction of movement of the chest.

COLLAPSE OF ADJACENT STRUCTURES

Excavations that are carried out within close proximity to existing buildings or structures may result in their foundations becoming undermined and create the potential for significant settling damage to occur or worse still, collapse. Consideration should be given to the effects that excavation work might have on foundations of neighbouring buildings or structures, and control measures implemented to ensure that foundations are not disturbed or undermined. Building foundations that are at a distance of less than twice the excavation depth from the face of the excavation are more likely to be affected by ground movement; underpinning or shoring of such structures may be required to prevent structural damage.

WATER INGRESS

Ingress of water may occur through rainfall, flood (river, sea) or when an excavation extends below the natural groundwater level. In deep excavations, where access is not readily available, the combined effect of water and mud could lead to difficulty in escape and risk of drowning. In addition, this can lead to the sides of the trench becoming soft and the integrity of the excavation supports can be undermined.

USE OF COFFERDAMS

A cofferdam is a retaining wall that is built into a river, lake, or other body of water and is commonly made of steel sheet piling, or concrete. The retaining wall is intended to provide a dry workplace in which work can be carried out.

Cofferdams are typically used in the construction of the foundations of bridges, docks, and piers. The principle hazard involved in the use of a cofferdam is the risk of failure of the retaining wall, allowing water ingress. If this happens gradually it can make the ground very wet and difficult to work in or travel around. Without the use of pumps to control water ingress slips and falls may become a major problem. If the failure of the wall is sudden, perhaps caused by severe tidal or storm water activity, there is a high risk of employees drowning.

Figure 11-3: Cofferdam.   Source: USA Army Corps Library.

The nature of the soil, depth of water, amount of water movement, depth of excavation and type of structure can all influence the stability and strength of the retaining wall and therefore its effectiveness in keeping water out.

USE OF CAISSONS

A caisson is a retaining, water tight structure that is constructed, floated or lowered into position where work needs to be conducted in a defined area, creating a type of 'box' to work in. Caissons are often made of concrete sections joined together to create the structure. When set in position, the water within the caisson is pumped out, providing a chamber as a workspace.

In the case of hollow caissons, if additional depth is required the earth can be mechanically excavated from the centre of the caisson and the weight of the caisson causes it to sink lower. This can be continued by adding additional caisson sections until a firm foundation is reached. Caissons are used for a wide variety of work, for example, to create or work on the foundations of a bridge pier that may be submerged in water.

Figure 11-4: Pressurised caisson.   Source: YK Times.

Pressurised (Pneumatic) caissons are shaped like an open box, turned upside down. They are placed where the work is needed and the bottom edges of the caisson sink into the earth, creating a seal. The inside is pressurised by compressed air to remove the water and prevent water ingress. Employees enter through an air lock. They remove earth from the bottom of the caisson by hand and place it in a (muck) tube connected to the surface, where it is removed by a crane and bucket. As with the hollow caisson, removing the earth at the bottom allows the caisson to sink deeper. When great strain or pressure is likely to be encountered in the construction of foundations or piers deep in a body of water, the pressurised caisson is generally used.

The principal hazard of work within caissons is the risk of water or slurry ingress and drowning. With hollow caissons, this may be because of failure of the sealing of joints between the sections that comprise the caisson. This failure could be due to damage at the time of assembly, the effects of water over time or the pressure due to the depth it is operating at overcoming the seal. Because caissons are frequently used in rivers and the sea there is the further hazard of service vessels colliding with the caisson, causing leaks or catastrophic failure.

In the case of pressurised caissons, they have the additional possibility of failure of the system maintaining pressure within the structure; this could lead to failure of seals or in the case of a homogenous structure the collapse of the sides. Work in pressurised conditions can be strenuous and employees leaving a pressurised caisson after hours of working under high pressure may suffer from a form of decompression sickness unless they are given special decompression treatment to accustom them to the lower atmospheric pressure.

CONTAMINATED GROUND

Digging may uncover buried materials that have the potential to be hazardous to health. Sites that once were used as steel works may contain arsenic and cyanide dating back many years; farmyards may have been used as graves for animals and to dispose of pesticides and organophosphates. Excavation may also involve removing old drums of chemicals and other buried debris that might be contaminated.

There is always the presence of vermin to consider - this can increase the risk of diseases such as leptospirosis.

TOXIC AND ASPHYXIATING ATMOSPHERES

Excavations can under different circumstances be subject to toxic, asphyxiating or explosive atmospheres. Chalk or limestone deposits when in contact with acidic groundwater can release carbon dioxide, and gases such as methane or hydrogen sulphide can seep into excavations from contaminated ground or damaged services in built-up areas. These atmospheres can accumulate at the bottom of an excavation and result in asphyxiation, poisoning, explosion or potential fatalities.

Figure 11-5: Water in excavation. *Source: RMS.*

MECHANICAL HAZARDS

Mechanical hazards of excavation work relate mainly to the equipment used to create the excavation and to lay equipment/materials in place. The principal mechanical hazard is the risk of being struck by this equipment as it moves its excavator arm or jib. The risk is greatly increased as people move close to the equipment, for example, employees or pedestrians passing by. People particularly at risk are those that place themselves in close proximity to the equipment when it is operating.

This would include people directing the equipment movement or those supervising the work, particularly if they stand in or close to the excavation at a position near to where work is going on. The closing movements of parts of this equipment, such as an excavator arm or bucket, present a significant crushing risk.

Figure 11-6: Mechanical hazard from excavator. *Source: RMS.*

In addition, as the plant is usually capable of mobility there is a risk of people working in close proximity receiving crush injuries to their feet.

OVERHEAD HAZARDS

The overhead hazards influencing excavation activities will depend upon where the excavation work is carried out. If the work is on a 'green field' site the only overhead hazards present are likely to be from overhead telephone and power lines or trees.

If the work is on an existing site, then the access and egress route, as well as the working area will need to be assessed for overhead hazards. Hazards may include overhead pipes and pipe racks/bridges, pedestrian walkways between buildings and power/telephone lines.

Work on or adjacent to the highway will present a number of overhead hazards, such as street lights, traffic signs/signal systems and bridges. The bridges may additionally carry utilities such as gas, water and sewage below them. Work near to water or railways will have similar overhead hazards to the highway.

Wherever the excavation is taking place, if the site is well developed there is the additional overhead hazard of scaffolds, MEWPS or parts of the structure.

Hazards of overhead power lines

Every year people are seriously hurt by coming into contact with overhead power lines. A high proportion, about one third, proves to be fatal. These fatalities occur at voltages ranging from 400 kV to 230 V. Any lines found on a site should always be treated as live until they are proved to be otherwise.

Overhead power lines usually consist of bare (uninsulated) conductors. These are often referred to as cables. They are supported overhead in a number of ways, the most common being wooden posts or metal towers. A common problem with the type supported by wooden posts is that they are mistaken for telephone cables, which may mean they are treated with less care than is deserved; an accidental contact with an excavators bucket could be fatal to the operator.

If the excavator comes into contact with an overhead line it may not discharge immediately to earth through the vehicle; this can be because the tyres offer some resistance. Operators of excavators have received fatal shocks in these circumstances when, on getting out of the vehicle, they make contact with the ground and provide a passage for the current to earth.

One of the other risks related with overhead power lines is that of arcing or, as it is sometimes called, a flashover. This occurs where the excavator approaches the conductor, but does not touch it. Instead, the electricity in the conductor bridges the air gap between the conductor and excavator as an arc; current then flows through the excavator. The risk of flashover increases significantly as the voltage applied to the conductor increases.

If excavators are brought closer than the following distances there is a significant risk of flashover:

- 15m of overhead lines supported by steel towers.
- 9m of overhead lines supported by wooden poles.

See also - Element 6 - Electrical safety - 'High risks associated with electricity' section.

Risk assessment

FACTORS TO CONSIDER

The depth of the excavation

Risks increase with the depth of excavation, risks from materials falling increase with the height they may fall and there is an increased risk of collapse at greater depths as the amount of material to support (comprising the excavation wall) increases. A collapse of an excavation deeper than the head height of a worker carries a high risk of suffocation.

It should be remembered that a worker may have to work low down in an excavation so a shallow excavation can present serious risks, depending on the work being carried out in it.

The type of soil being excavated

Clay presents specific risks of collapse due to it drying out or becoming more fluid when wet. If the soil is not compacted, for example, because of a previous excavation nearby, its strength may not be as higher as if it has had chance to settle and become compacted.

Soil changes its strength significantly when it becomes wet; presenting an added risk that water may make its way into the excavation and cause flooding. If the soil is chalky carbon dioxide may be liberated as part of the excavation process, similarly if it is in contaminated land there may be toxic substances and risks from methane.

The type of work being undertaken

If the work to be done to create and work in the excavation is to be done manually or mechanically the risks vary significantly. The task being conducted can increase the risks, for example, pipe jointing operations carried out manually will usually bring the head of the worker below the top of the excavation for a significant time. Additional risks may also be created by hot working or work in a confined space.

The use of mechanical equipment

Though this can reduce the risk to employees by not requiring them to enter the excavation to dig it they carry risks of their own. Where people work alongside this equipment there is a risk of contact or collision and as it carries a considerable amount of momentum major injuries or death would not be uncommon if contact was made.

Proximity of roadways and structures etc.

Where excavations are within close proximity of roadways and structures, vehicles should be segregated and excluded from excavation areas wherever possible. Brightly painted baulks or barriers and or fencing should be used where necessary to protect and clearly identify the excavation area.

If vehicles have to unload materials into excavations, then the use of stop blocks to prevent such vehicles falling into the excavation as a result of over-running is recommended. Special consideration should be given to the reinforcement of the sides of the excavation, which may need extra support, especially when adjacent to busy roads. Excavations should not be allowed to affect the footings of scaffolds or the foundations of nearby structures. Walls especially in older properties may have very shallow foundations, which could be undermined by small trenches, therefore some structures may need temporary support even before digging can commence. It is always best practice to conduct surveys of the foundations and gain the advice of a structural engineer in such cases.

Presence of public

Excavations in public areas should be fenced off, fitted with toe boards and stop block type barriers to prevent pedestrians and vehicles falling into them. Where children or trespassers might inadvertently get access to a site out of hours then certain precautions should be considered such as backfilling or securely covering excavations to reduce the potential of such people being injured.

The excavation should have suitable and sufficient identification and signage, with any pedestrian routes or detours clearly marked, fenced off and lit (if appropriate).

Weather

Heavy rain or fast melting snow may undermine the stability of the ground and therefore of the supports or sides of the excavation. Hence, careful consideration should be given to the type of shoring used, depending on the site and sub-soils.

Services

The presence or likelihood of services in the area of an excavation carries high risks of a different type. For example, contact with an electrical service may be immediately fatal to a worker or damage to a gas service may cause a risk of major explosion.

Material and vehicles

If materials are placed too close to excavations or vehicles pass nearby there is an increased risk of collapse or fall of materials/vehicle.

Required support equipment that may be needed

The risks from excavations may be reduced by using the correct support equipment. Care has to be taken to ensure that the right type and quantity is used if the risk is to be reduced effectively. For example, there may be a need to provide close shoring of the sides of an excavation to control a particular soil condition or where the effects of water are likely.

11.2 - Control measures for excavation work

Controls

IDENTIFICATION/DETECTION AND MARKING OF BURIED SERVICES

The Health and Safety Executive (HSE) guidance, HSG47; 'Avoiding danger from underground services', outlines the dangers that can arise from work near underground services and gives advice on how to reduce the risk.

The guidance defines 'service(s)' as all underground pipes, cables and equipment associated with the electricity, gas, water (including piped sewage) and telecommunications industries.

It also includes other pipelines that transport a range of petrochemical and other fluids. It does not include underground structures such as railway tunnels. The term 'service connection(s)' is used for pipes or cables between distribution mains and individual premises.

Identification

Excavation operations should not begin until all available service location drawings have been obtained and thoroughly examined to identify the location of services.

Location drawings should not be considered as totally accurate, but do serve as an indication of the likelihood of the presence of services, their location and depth.

It is possible for the position of an electricity supply cable to alter if previous works have been carried out in the location. This can be due to the flexibility of the cable and movement of surrounding features since the original installation of the cable.

In addition, location drawings often show a proposed position for the services that does not translate to the ground, such that services are placed in position only approximately where the plan says.

Detection

The main types of detection and locating devices are:

Hum detectors, which detect the magnetic field radiated by electricity cables that have a current flowing through. They do not detect where there is little or no current flowing, for example, service connection cables to unoccupied premises or street lighting cables in the daytime.

Radio frequency detectors, which generate a low frequency radio signal into a cable or pipe placed very close to it. The receiver can then detect this signal and locate the cable or pipe run.

Metal detectors, which usually locate flat metal covers, joint boxes etc., but may not detect round cables or pipes.

Ground probing radar, which is a method that is capable of detecting anomalies in the ground. When plotted into a continuous line they may indicate a cable, duct or pipe.

Commercially available instruments use more than one of the techniques listed and may also include a depth-measuring facility.

Figure 11-7: Using a cable locator. *Source: Allpipe Stoppers.*

It is important that 'service location devices', such as a cable avoidance tool (CAT) are used by competent, trained operatives to assist in the identification and marking of the actual location and position of buried services.

Marking

Markers may have been used to indicate the presence of services when they were laid, these include:

- Marker tiles, for example, to mark gas pipes when they have been laid at shallow depths.
- Coloured plastic, for example, tape laid to over an electric cable.
- Marker posts/plates, for example, to show the position and size of valves on gas mains or water mains.

Markers are useful in alerting caution with regard to excavation activities. However, these markers cannot be relied upon to accurately establish the position of the buried service, as they may have been disturbed in later work. Also, the absence of markers does not indicate that services are absent from the location.

Figure 11-8: Marking of services. *Source: RMS.*

When it is uncovered, the type of service may be identified by markings in the form of a colour coding, for example, blue for water and yellow for gas.

When services are identified it is essential that physical markings be placed on the ground to show where the services are located. This can include waterproof, biodegradable paint, applied to solid surfaces, or wooden (not metal) pegs, for un-surfaced areas.

The colour coding of paint/pegs and addition of tape indicators can help to identify the type of service present.

SAFE DIGGING METHODS

Safe digging methods should be implemented within 0.5 metres of a buried service. This involves the use of insulated hand tools such as a spade or shovel with curved edges (to be used with light force and not sudden blows).

Mechanical, probing or piercing tools and equipment such as excavator's, forks, picks or drills should ***not*** be used when in the vicinity of buried services, as these may cause damage to any service if they strike it. Careful hand digging using a spade or shovel should be used instead.

Example of a permit to dig

Contract:	Contract No: ....
Principal Contractor:	Sub Contractor: ....
Permit No:	Date: ....

1. Location: ....

2. Size, detail and depth of excavation: ....
   ....

3. Are Service Plans on site?   YES / NO
   Comments: ....

4. Has cable locating equipment been used to identify services?   YES / NO
   Comments: ....

5. Are all known services marked out? (site inspection by relevant statutory bodies)   YES / NO
   Comments: ....

6. Are trial holes required?   YES / NO
   Comments: ....

7. Have precautions been taken to prevent contact if overhead lines are in the vicinity of the operation or near approach to the operation?   YES / NO

8. Additional precautions, i.e. Shoring/Fencing/Access/Storage/Fumes/Record of setting out points to re-establish services routes
   Comments: ....

9. Sketch details or attach copy of plans

10. Date and time of excavation: ....

Signed:	Accepted by: ....
For and on behalf of issuing party	(Work shall not commence unless all persons involved are aware of the safe systems of work)

A new permit will be required for any further excavations. This permit is for guidance only.

Persons carrying out work must take reasonable precautions when working around services.

Figure 11-9: Permit to dig.   *Source: Reproduced by kind permission of Lincsafe.*

METHODS OF SUPPORTING EXCAVATIONS

"(1) All practicable steps must be taken to prevent danger to any person, including, where necessary, the provision of supports or battering, to ensure that:

(a) Any excavation or part of an excavation does not collapse.

(b) No material forming the walls or roof of, or adjacent to, any excavation is dislodged or falls.

(c) No person is buried or trapped in an excavation by material which is dislodged or falls."

Figure 11-10: Methods of shoring and battering.   *Source: CDM 2015 Regulation 22(1).*

Precautions must be taken to prevent collapse. An alternative method to the use of supports to prevent collapse is where soil and material is removed from the sides of the excavation so that a shallow slope is created in the sides, generally called battering, or steps are created in the sides of the excavation, generally called benching, *see figure ref 11-11*.

Battering relies on the material in the steps or slopes of the sides of the excavation creating minimal downward/sideways pressure, reducing the likelihood and effect of collapse.

The options available for providing support by shoring include closed boarding/sheeting *see figure refs 11-13 and 11-15*, open sheeting *see figure refs 11-14 and 11-16* and where the shoring needs to be repositioned frequently, such as where services are being laid, a trench box *see figure ref 11-12*.

The application of a particular method of prevention of collapse depends on the:

- Nature of the subsoil - for example, when wet it may require close shoring with sheets.
- Projected life of the excavation - a trench box may give ready-made access where it is only needed for short duration work.
- Work to be undertaken, including equipment used - for example, the use of a trench box for shoring where pipe joints are made.
- Possibility of flooding from ground water and heavy rain - close shoring would be required.
- Depth of the excavation - a shallow excavation may use battering instead of shoring, particularly where shoring may impede access.
- Number of people using the excavation at any one time - a lot of space may be required so cantilever sheet piling may be preferred.

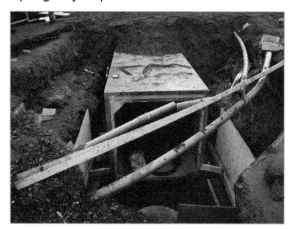

Figure 11-11: Benching.   *Source: RMS.*

Figure 11-12: Trench box - for shoring.   *Source: RMS.*

Figure 11-13: Close boarded excavation.   *Source: BS6031.*

Figure 11-14: Open sheeting.   *Source: BS6031.*

Figure 11-15: Close sheeting.   *Source: RMS.*

Figure 11-16: Open sheeting.   *Source: RMS.*

MEANS OF ACCESS

Ladders are the usual means of access and egress to excavations. They must be properly secured, in good condition and inspected regularly. The ladder should extend about one metre or three rungs above ground level to give a good handhold.

To allow for emergency egress it is recommended that a minimum requirement of one ladder every 15 metres be provided.

CROSSING POINTS

Crossing excavations should only be allowed at predetermined points. The crossing point should be able to withstand the maximum foreseeable load and be provided with guardrails and toe boards. The spacing or location of crossing points should be such that employees and others are encouraged to use them, rather than to attempt other means of crossing the excavation.

BARRIERS, LIGHTING AND SIGNS

Where people or materials can fall from height a form of edge protection must be provided. In some cases the shoring method used can provide this barrier by ensuring the top of the shoring extends sufficiently above the edge of the excavation, *see figure ref 11-17*.

Figure 11-17: Access and guardrails.   *Source: HSE, HSG150.*

Guardrails that are provided must meet the same standards as those for working platforms used for work at height. It is also good practice to cover shallow trenches when they are left unattended.

> *"(2) Suitable and sufficient steps must be taken to prevent any person, work equipment, or any accumulation of material from falling into any excavation."*

Figure 11-18: Prevention of falls into excavation.   *Source: CDM 2015 Regulation 22(2).*

The large pieces of mobile plant and equipment that are commonly used for excavation work have the potential to cause serious harm to site employees and members of the public. In order to keep people and vehicles apart, exclusion zones identified by barriers *(see figure ref 11-17)*, fencing *(see figure ref 11-19)*, warning signs and lights should be provided.

Concrete or wooden blocks (usually old railway sleepers) may be placed some distance from the edge of an excavation to prevent vehicles from getting too close, particularly when the excavation is being 'back filled'. In this case, the wooden blocks provide a 'stop block'.

Signs that comply with The Health and Safety (Signs and Signals) Regulations (SSSR) 1996 should be displayed to warn people of the excavation and any special measures to be taken. If working on a public highway, the police or the local authority must be consulted over the positioning of traffic lights. Appropriate lighting should be provided; it must provide sufficient illumination for those at work but should not create glare or other distractions for passers-by, especially motorists. Battery operated headlamps (to avoid trailing cables) may be considered for individual use. If excavations are present in dark conditions they must be suitably lit to prevent vehicles or people colliding or falling into them.

SAFE STORAGE OF SPOIL

Excavated material (spoil), other materials, plant and vehicles should never be stored or parked close to the sides of any excavation. The additional pressure distributed on the ground from spoil, vehicles, etc. significantly increases the likelihood of collapse occurring at the sides of the excavation. Though it will depend on the weight of the material, it would normally be kept to a minimum of 1 metre from the edge of the excavation. *See figure ref 11-19* which shows heavy pipes set away from the excavation and spoil set to the side.

In addition, spoil heaps consist of loose materials that present a risk of falling into the excavation, setting spoil away from the excavation reduces this risk. A means of preventing spillage of spoil into an excavation is by positioning scaffold boards as toe boards, fixed along the outside of trench sheets. This provides additional protection to combat the risk of loose materials spilling into the excavation. An alternative to this is to allow boards or sheeting to protrude above the top of the excavation sufficiently to act as toe boards and prevent materials falling from ground level into the excavation. Head protection in the form of a hard hat must be worn by employees working in excavations to provide protection from small pieces of material falling either from above or from the sides of the excavation and possible impact with obstructions.

If stored at a suitable distance away from an excavation and at a suitable height, spoil heaps can form an effective barrier against vehicles travelling around the construction site and assist in preventing falls of vehicles and plant into an excavation and onto employees.

Figure 11-19: Materials storage.   *Source: RMS.*

Figure 11-20: Preventing water ingress.   *Source: RMS.*

CONTROL OF WATER AND DEWATERING

Consideration must be given to the likelihood of water entering the excavation and the measures to be implemented in order to control water entering the excavation and water levels within it. Ingress of water may occur through rainfall, flood or when excavating below the natural groundwater level. When an excavation is liable to water ingress the stability of the excavation walls can be undermined, increasing the risk of collapse and possible drowning.

The first priority is to control the amount of water entering the excavation; this will influence the choice of shoring, for example, close sheeting may be used rather than open sheeting. In addition, it may be necessary to position flood or rain water barriers to direct water away from the excavation; this may include the use of sandbags or similar methods that provide a portable barrier, **see figure ref 11-20**.

Well points

Well point dewatering is often used to reduce the hydrostatic pressure from the back of a sheet pile wall, in conjunction with lowering the water table to the maximum excavation depth required for the construction site.

Figure 11-21: Well point schematic.   *Source: W J Groundwater Ltd.*

Figure 11-22: Well point trench installation.
Source: www.khansahebsykes.com.

Well point dewatering systems are installed around the perimeter of the site against excavation shoring and are coupled with a perimeter discharge line via a pump set. The system can effectively draw the water table down to between three and eight metres depending on the type of pump set used and the type of soil conditions. For a well point dewatering system to be effective, the ground sub-strata generally needs to be permeable, to allow the well points to draw the groundwater.

Sump points

Usually water in excavations is drained to sumps, from where it can be pumped out for disposal. The sump should be at the lowest point where the water collects. Typically a sump will be a minimum of 0.6 metres deep, so that the pump is covered by the water. This allows the pump to cycle on and off with rising and falling water levels within the sump.

It is normally permissible to distribute pumped groundwater from within an excavation over grassy areas where any silt deposits can be absorbed and not have a detrimental effect on the environment. However, when works are within close proximity to a watercourse, i.e. within 10 metres, then advice should be sought on the disposal of groundwater and a 'Consent for Works Affecting Watercourses' should be obtained from the Environment Agency.

SUBSTANCES

Excavations should be treated with similar caution to that applied to confined spaces, and an assessment should be carried out prior to work commencing in excavations to identify the risk of toxic gas, oxygen deficiency and fire or explosion. It should also identify the appropriate risk control measures required, such as:

- Type of gas monitoring equipment to be provided.
- Testing of the atmosphere before entry into the excavation.
- Provision of suitable ventilation equipment.
- Training of employees.
- Use of a sufficient number of people, including one at ground level.
- Procedures and equipment needed for an emergency rescue.

Figure 11-23: Substances in excavation.   Source: RMS.

POSITIONING AND ROUTING OF VEHICLES, PLANT AND EQUIPMENT

"(3) Suitable and sufficient steps must be taken, where necessary, to prevent any part of an excavation or ground adjacent to it from being overloaded by work equipment or material."

Figure 11-24: Overloading of excavation by work equipment or material.   Source: CDM 2015 Regulation 22(3).

To prevent objects falling into excavations, the following precautions should be taken:

- Spoil and construction materials must not be stacked near to the edge.
- The weight of stacks should not be enough to cause the sides to collapse.
- Designated operating areas for vehicles and equipment must be established.
- Unnecessary vehicles and equipment should be routed away from the excavation.
- Where vehicles have to approach the excavation, stop barriers must be provided to prevent overrunning.

PERSONAL PROTECTIVE EQUIPMENT

As well as the need for hard hats to limit the risks from falling materials, other personal protective equipment (PPE) may be necessary, such as:

- Breathing apparatus.
- Safety harnesses.
- Hearing protection.
- Clothing to protect from the rays of the sun.
- Masks and respirators.
- Face masks and gloves for welding and grinding.
- Gloves for contaminated materials.
- Footwear.

FILLING IN

On completion of use of the excavation, experienced people should remove support materials. A competent person should inspect the site to ensure that all people and materials have been removed. The excavation may need water pumping from it before filling.

Where vehicles approach the excavation to add materials it is essential that stop barriers are used at the edge of the excavation to avoid vehicles falling into it.

Materials added to the excavation must be sufficiently compacted to allow for the next use of the area, for example, as part of a roadway or to allow a scaffold to be placed on top of it. Only appropriate in-fill materials must be used. Uncontrolled tipping/burial is an offence.

Particular requirements for contaminated ground

Contaminated ground can give rise to various health hazards, including biological and chemical hazards. Exposure to the hazards can vary depending on the work to be carried out and assessments should be made to determine which controls are required.

Site preparation work which involves the removal of topsoil from land known to be contaminated with heavy metals will require specific arrangements in relation to personal protective equipment required and practices to be carried out. The work is likely to require the provision of gloves, overalls, eye protection and respirators. Additionally, the work will require campaigns of awareness training to ensure good levels of personal hygiene are maintained, with emphasis on ensuring that open cuts are covered with waterproof dressings whenever required. Consideration will need to be given to specific welfare facilities provision, for example, a decontamination unit. There should be arrangements in place in order to prevent contamination when eating and smoking. First-aid and emergency decontamination facilities should be made available located near to the place of work.

SOIL TESTING

Surveys should be undertaken, and a soil-testing programme implemented prior to works beginning. As each site is different and may involve various contaminant types, the methods of testing and analysis used should be suitable to the particular local needs of each site.

Usually, specialist contractors are used to carry out this type of work. Historical information such as land deeds, maps, building plans and any other information relating to the site provide useful assistance. Contaminants will usually be found in the top 0.5 - 1m layer (strata) of ground and soil samples should be at least to the greatest depth of any excavation, remembering that contamination may seep from one part of a site to another. As a minimum precaution, any proposed control measures chosen should adequately protect against the highest concentrations of contaminant found on site.

WELFARE FACILITIES

Ensuring good hygiene standards is one of the more important elements of protective measures to be taken when working on construction sites and in particular with contaminated ground. Whilst the level of risk that is identified will establish the range of measures that are to be provided, the principles outlined should always be followed when working on a contaminated site.

Installation of a sufficiently ventilated and lit hygiene facility must be provided. This may be purpose built or a smaller standard unit may be sufficient depending upon the number of personnel involved at the site. The installation of the hygiene/decontamination unit should be situated at the most convenient point to or from the dirty zone.

The hygiene/decontamination facility should generally be in three stages, but prior to entering the unit a boot wash point should be provided that includes running water and fixed or hand brushes for removing contaminated matter.

The hygiene facility should then be arranged in its three stages as follows:

Stage 1 Should provide storage for ordinary clothing not used whilst at work.

Stage 2 A high standard washing facility. This includes the provision of hot and cold water with taps preferably operated by the elbow or foot, detergent, nail brushes and disposable towels. In certain circumstances (toxic or corrosive contamination) showers may be the necessary means of cleansing. Both men and women may use showers (at separate times) provided that it is in a separate room with a lock on the inside of the door.

Stage 3 Should provide storage for contaminated work wear such as overalls, boots, etc.

In addition to the hygiene facility, toilets should be provided. The location of toilet units on contaminated sites must be situated so employees are directed through the hygiene facility prior to reaching the toilet for use. Daily cleaning and decontamination must be carried out on toilet facilities. Everyone who works on construction sites must have access to adequate toilet and washing facilities, a place for warming up and a clean room set aside for taking meals and refreshment. Secure storage for clothing and facilities for drying wet clothing. First-aid facilities should also be provided.

HEALTH SURVEILLANCE

The employer should decide about the need for health surveillance as part of the Control of Substances Hazardous to Health Regulations (COSHH) 2002 assessment. Health surveillance is appropriate where:

- A disease or adverse effect may be related to exposure.
- It is likely that this could arise in the circumstances of the work.
- There is valid techniques for detecting the disease or effect.

For example, work with cadmium, phenol, or arsenic, will normally need health surveillance including biological monitoring of employees.

Inspection requirements for excavation support systems

CDM 2015, Regulation 22, requires inspections and reports to be carried out for excavations.

A competent person must inspect excavations:

- At the start of each shift in which the work is to be carried out.
- After any event likely to have affected the strength or stability of the excavation.
- After any material unintentionally falls or is dislodged.

The competent person must:

- Inform the person, on whose behalf the inspection was carried out, before the end of the shift, of any matters that could give rise to a risk to the safety of any person. Work must not be carried out in the excavation until the matters have been remedied and the person who carried out the inspection is satisfied that construction work in the excavation can be safely carried out.
- Prepare a report and must, within 24 hours of completing the inspection to which the report relates, provide the report or a copy of it to the person on whose behalf the inspection was carried out.

CDM 2015, Regulation 24, requires that the inspection report must include the following information:

1) Name and address of person on whose behalf the inspection was carried out.

2) Location of the place of construction work inspected.

3) Description of the place of construction work or part of that place inspected (including any work equipment and materials).

4) Date and time of the inspection.

5) Details of any matter identified that could give rise to a risk to the safety of any person.

6) Details of any action taken as a result of any matter identified in the last point.

7) Details of any further action considered necessary.

8) The name and position of the person making the report.

The person receiving the inspection report must keep a copy of the report at the site where the inspection was carried out until the construction work is completed and after that for three months.

11.3 - Confined spaces hazards and risks

Introduction and meaning of the term 'confined space'

A failure to appreciate the dangers associated with confined spaces has led not only to the deaths of many employees, but also to the demise of some of those who have attempted to rescue them.

A confined space is a space that is substantially enclosed and where there will be a reasonably foreseeable risk of serious injury from substances or conditions. This therefore means not only a space that is small and difficult to enter, exit or work in, but one with limited or restricted access; or it can also be a space that is badly ventilated, for example, a tank or a large tunnel.

A place not usually considered to be a confined space may become one if there is a change in the conditions inside or a change in the degree of enclosure or confinement, which may occur intermittently. For example, an enclosed space may be free of contaminants and have a safe level of oxygen, but the work to be carried out in it may change this, such as:

■   Welding that would consume some of the oxygen.

■   Using chemicals for cleaning purposes which can add contaminants.

In these situations the space may be defined as a confined space while that work is taking place and the risk exists. Similarly, risks may change because of external factors, for example, heavy rain may present a foreseeable risk of drowning in a space not usually considered confined.

Typical confined spaces found during construction activities

Figure 11-25: Confined space - chamber.   *Source: RMS.*

Figure 11-26: Confined space - sewer.   *Source: RMS.*

The Confined Spaces Regulations (CSR) 1997 defines a confined space as any place, including the following or other similar spaces, in which, by virtue of its enclosed nature, there arises a reasonably foreseeable 'specified risk':

Cellar	An enclosed low level room or space below ground level usually found in old buildings or public houses
Chamber	Cellar, tunnel, caisson, cofferdam, water interception chamber or chamber for a pump
Flue	Exhaust chimney for disposal of waste gases
Pipe	Concrete, plastic, steel etc. fabrication used to carry liquids or gases

Pit	Excavations
Sewer	Brick or concrete structure for the carrying of liquid waste
Silo	May be an above the ground structure for storing cement or mortar
Tank	Storage tanks for solid or liquid chemical
Trench	A relatively shallow, narrow excavation, usually for utility laying provision or drainage facility
Vat	Process vessels, which may be open, but by its depth confines a person
Well	Deep source of water

A 'SPECIFIED RISK'

The Confined Spaces Regulations (CSR) 1997 apply to situations where there is a 'specified risk', this is defined as:

- Serious injury to any person at work arising from a fire or explosion.
- Loss of consciousness of a person at work arising from an increase in body temperature.
- Loss of consciousness or asphyxiation of any person at work arising from gas, fumes, vapour or lack of oxygen.
- Drowning of any person at work arising from an increase in the level of liquid.
- Asphyxiation of any person at work arising from a free flowing solid or the inability to reach a respirable environment due to entrapment by a free flowing solid.

Figure 11-27: Confined space - cement silo.   Source: RMS.

Figure 11-28: Confined space - open tank.   Source: RMS.

Hazards and risks associated with confined spaces

EXPOSURE TO TOXIC, EXPLOSIVE AND OXYGEN DEFICIENT ATMOSPHERES

Air in the confined space is made unbreathable either by toxic gases, fumes or by lack of oxygen. There is not enough natural ventilation to keep the air fit to breathe. In some cases the gases may be flammable, so there may also be a fire or explosion risk.

Some confined spaces are naturally dangerous, for example, because of:

- Gas build-up in sewers and manholes and pits connected to them.
- Gases leaking into trenches and pits in contaminated land such as old refuse tips and old gas works.
- Rust inside tanks and vessels which eat up the oxygen.
- Liquids and slurries which can suddenly fill the space or release gases into it when disturbed.
- Chemical reaction between some soils and air causing oxygen depletion or the action of ground water on chalk and limestone producing carbon dioxide.

Some places are made dangerous by vapours from the work done in them. Where possible, it is important to keep hazards out of confined spaces, for example, do not use petrol or diesel engines in or near to confined spaces, because exhaust gases can cause asphyxiation. Because paints and glues used in construction work processes may give off hazardous vapours it is essential to ensure the confined space has enough ventilation to make the air fit to breathe; mechanical ventilation might be needed.

HEAT

Confined spaces have limited natural ventilation and depending on the tasks being undertaken within the area may become hot and uncomfortable to work in. In extreme cases this may cause heat exhaustion which may lead to loss of consciousness. It may be necessary to implement a forced ventilation system to refresh and cool the air within the confined space.

WATER

Many confined spaces do not allow for ease of exit. If a large volume of water were to enter a confined space the consequences could be the drowning of employees due to the restrictions on space preventing rapid exit.

FREE-FLOWING SOLIDS

The term 'free flowing solid' means any substance consisting of solid particles and which is of, or is capable of being in, a flowing or running consistency. This includes flour, grain, sugar, sand or other similar material. These materials are usually stored in silos (enclosed tank), which are classed as a confined space. Silos are increasingly used on construction sites to store cement or mortar in bulk.

Asphyxiation can result as a consequence of falling into a free flowing solid such as grain, due to sinking into the material as it becomes displaced as weight is applied. Because the material can appear firm, possibly because a crust of material has formed, someone may be tempted to access and walk on the crust in order to dislodge it. It is common for such a crust to break up without warning causing the person to fall into the free-flowing solid.

RESTRICTED SPACE

Working space may be restricted, bringing employees into close contact with other hazards such as moving machinery, electricity or steam vents and pipes. The entrance to a confined space, for example, a small access hole, may make escape or rescue in an emergency more difficult.

11.4 - Control measures for confined space working

Precautions for safe entry

AVOIDANCE WHERE POSSIBLE

Employers have a duty to prevent employees, or others who are to any extent within the employer's control, such as contractors, from entering or working inside a confined space where it is reasonably practicable to undertake the work without entering the space. Similarly, the self-employed should not enter or work inside a confined space where it is reasonably practicable to undertake the work without entering it.

In every situation, the employer or the self-employed must consider what measures can be taken to enable the work to be carried out without the need to enter the confined space. The measures might involve modifying the confined space itself to avoid the need for entry, or to enable the work to be undertaken from outside the space. In many cases it will involve modifying working practices.

The following are examples of modified working practices avoiding the need for entry:

- It is usually possible to test the atmosphere or sample the contents of confined spaces from outside.
- Using appropriate long tools and probes to do work.
- In some cases you can clean a confined space, or remove residues from it, from the outside using water jetting, steam or chemical cleaning, long-handled tools, or in-place cleaning systems.
- Blockages can be cleared in silos where grain or other flowing solids can 'bridge' or where voids can form by the use of remotely-operated rotating flail devices, vibrators and air purgers which avoid the need to enter the space.
- In some cases, it is possible to see what is happening inside without going in by looking in through a porthole, sight glass, grille or hole. If a sight glass tends to become blocked, it can be cleaned with a wiper and washer. Lighting can be provided inside or by shining a light in through a window. The use of closed circuit television (CCTV) systems may be appropriate in some cases.

RISK ASSESSMENT AND PLANNING

There should be a safe system of work for operations inside confined spaces, and everyone should know and follow the system. A permit-to-work system may be required.

If entry is essential:

- Identify what work must be done in the confined space and the hazards involved.
- Consider if the space could be altered to make it permanently safe or if the work could be changed to make entry to the dangerous area unnecessary.
- Make sure employees have been trained in the dangers and precautions, including rescue procedures.
- Make sure the entrance to the space is big enough to allow employees wearing all the necessary equipment to climb in and out easily.
- Before entry, ventilate the space as much as possible, test the air inside the space and only enter if the test shows it is safe.
- After entry, continue to test the air for toxic substances, flammable gases and oxygen deficiency as necessary.
- If there is a flammable risk, the space must be ventilated until it is safe. When selecting equipment, remember heat or sparks from electrical or other equipment could ignite flammable vapours, so air-powered

tools may be required. The risk from flammable vapours is very high when work is carried out on the tanks of petrol service stations and similar sites. This is work that may be safer left to a specialist contractor.

■ Disturbing deposits and slurries in pipes and tanks may produce extra vapour, resulting in a greater risk, so clear deposits before entry where possible.

■ If the air inside the space cannot be made fit to breath because of the presence of a toxic risk or lack of oxygen, employees must wear breathing apparatus.

■ Never try to 'sweeten' the air in a confined space with oxygen as this can produce a fire and explosion risk.

■ Employees inside the confined space should wear rescue harnesses, with lifelines attached, which run back to a point outside the confined spaces.

■ Someone should be outside to keep watch and to communicate with anyone inside, raise the alarm in an emergency and take charge of rescue procedures if it becomes necessary. It is essential those outside the space know what to do in an emergency. They need to know how to use breathing apparatus if they are to effect a rescue. *See also - Emergency Arrangements - later in this element.*

PERMIT-TO-WORK PROCEDURES AND REQUIREMENTS

Permit-to-work procedure

A permit-to-work procedure is a formal written system and is usually required where there is a reasonably foreseeable risk of serious injury in entering or working in the confined space. The permit-to-work procedure is an extension of the safe system to work, not a replacement for it. The use of a permit-to-work procedure does not, by itself, make the job safe. It supports the safe system, providing a ready means of recording findings and authorisations required to proceed with the entry. It also defines information on control measures, for example, time limits on entry, results of the gas testing, and other information that may be required during an emergency. When the job is completed, historical information on original entry conditions can also provided. A permit-to-work procedure is appropriate, for example:

■ To ensure that the people working in the confined space are aware of the hazards involved and the identity, nature and extent of the work to be carried out.

■ To ensure there is a formal check undertaken confirming elements of a safe system of work are in place. This needs to take place before people are allowed to enter or work in the confined space.

■ Where there is a need to coordinate or exclude, using controlled and formal procedures, other people and their activities where they could affect work or conditions in the confined space.

■ If the work requires the authorisation of more than one person, or there is a time-limit on entry. It may also be needed if communications with the outside are other than by direct speech, or if particular respiratory protective and/or personal protective equipment is required.

Permit-to-work document

EXAMPLE ENTRY INTO CONFINED SPACES					
Possible Lay-Out For A Permit-To-Work Certificate **Permit-To-Work Certificate**					
PLANT DETAILS (Location, identifying number, etc.)			ACCEPTANCE OF CERTIFICATE Accepts all conditions of certificate		
WORK TO BE DONE				Signed Time	Date
WITHDRAWAL FROM SERVICE	Signed Time	Date	COMPLETION OF WORK All work completed - equipment returned for use	Signed Time	Date
ISOLATION Dangerous fumes Electrical supply Sources of heat	Signed Time	Date			
CLEANING AND PURGING Of all dangerous materials	Signed Time	Date	EXTENSION	Signed Time	Date
TESTING For contamination	Contaminations tested Results Signed Time	Date			
I CERTIFY THAT I HAVE PERSONALLY EXAMINED THE PLANT DETAILED ABOVE AND SATISFIED MYSELF THAT THE ABOVE PARTICULARS ARE CORRECT (1) THE PLANT IS SAFE FOR ENTRY WITHOUT BREATHING APPARATUS (2) BREATHING APPARATUS MUST BE WORN Other precautions necessary:			THIS PERMIT-TO-WORK IS NOW CANCELLED. A NEW PERMIT WILL BE REQUIRED IF WORK IS TO CONTINUE Signed Time	Date	
Time of expiry of certificate:	Signed		RETURN TO SERVICE	I accept the above plant back into service	
Delete (1) or (2) Time	Date		Signed	Date	Time

Figure 11-29: Example PTW document confined spaces.

Source: HSE Guidance note on permits to work.

Permit-to-work procedures will normally require a formal documented control system, including a permit-to-work document, to be used to:

- Describe (and restrict) the work to be done.
- Provide a process to determine the hazards.
- Define the controls to reduce the risk to an acceptable level.

A permit-to-work document should be cancelled once the operations to which it applies have finished.

Lock-off

Where there are distinct hazards presented by stored energy, such as plant and machinery or civil utilities, which would need to be disconnected and isolated in order for work to be conducted safely, then a lock off tag out regime should be in place. For example, if there could be residual energy or potential of harm from electrical systems, gas mains, high pressure water mains, heat or chemical carrying lines, then it would be essential that these hazardous sources of danger should be locked off at distribution boxes, control valves and supply lines.

A useful approach would be to have a multiple hasp type of lock off method. In this method all employees and the person managing the work have a padlock and attach it to the hasp, which is used to lock off the source of energy. In this way, a unified decision would have to be made in order to reinstate the energy supplies. Along with the lock off there should also be identification in the form of a tag notifying that the main energy control points have been isolated and by whom.

TRAINING AND THE USE OF COMPETENT PERSONS

To be competent to work safely in confined spaces adequate training and experience in the particular work involved is essential. Training standards must be appropriate to the task, and to the individual's roles and responsibilities, so that work can be carried out safely.

Where the risk assessment indicates that properly trained individuals can work for periods without supervision, a periodic check will need to be made to ensure that they are competent to follow the established safe system of work and have been provided with adequate information and instruction about the work to be done. It is important that those that issue and work under a permit-to-work for entry into confined spaces are trained and competent to do so in general and that consideration is given to whether this training is sufficient for a specific confined space being worked in. If necessary, because of special features of the confined space, further training may be required. Anyone providing emergency rescue must be trained and competent to do so.

It is likely that general training will need to cover:

- Awareness of the Confined Spaces Regulations (CSR) 1997.
- An understanding of the work to be done, the hazards and the necessary precautions.
- An understanding of safe systems of work and permits to work, where appropriate.
- How emergencies arise and the dangers, and prepared emergency arrangements.

Specific training will relate to the type of equipment used and the circumstances of use. Refresher training should be planned and conducted in order to maintain knowledge and skills.

ATMOSPHERIC TESTING

Testing of the atmosphere may be needed where the atmosphere might be contaminated or abnormal. The appropriate choice of testing equipment will depend on particular circumstances. For example, when testing for toxic atmospheres, chemical detector tubes or portable atmospheric monitoring equipment is appropriate. However there may be cases requiring monitoring equipment specifically designed to measure for flammable atmospheres. Only persons experienced and competent in the practice should carry out testing and records should be kept of the results of the tests.

MEANS OF ACCESS

Here a worker wearing full breathing apparatus is also wearing a harness with a lanyard connected to a winch so that he can be hauled to the surface in an emergency without others having to enter the manhole to rescue him.

Figure 11-30: Confined space.   *Source: HSE, HSG150.*

Figure 11-31: Entrance to a confined space.   *Source: RMS.*

Openings into confined spaces need to be sufficiently large and free from obstruction to allow the passage of employees wearing the necessary protective clothing and equipment and to allow access and egress for rescue purposes. Practice drills will help to check that the size of openings and entry procedures are satisfactory.

Where entry to a confined space is necessary, employers will need to ensure that the necessary safety features are provided to enable safe access and egress. For example, alongside openings there might be a safety sign warning against unauthorised entry and platforms may be provided to enable safe working within the confined space. In some situations, a permanent hoist may be installed to enable access and egress. In other cases, the site of the confined space may be fitted with bearing points for locating a portable hoist system.

PERSONAL PROTECTIVE EQUIPMENT

So far as is reasonably practicable, it should be ensured that a confined space is safe to work in without the need for personal protective equipment (PPE) and respiratory protective equipment (RPE) which should be a last resort, except for rescue work (including the work of the emergency services). Use of PPE and RPE may be identified as necessary in your risk assessment, in which case it needs to be suitable and should be provided and used by those entering and working in confined spaces.

Such equipment is in addition to engineering controls and safe systems of work. The type of PPE provided will depend on the hazards identified, but might include safety lines, harnesses and suitable breathing apparatus. It is important to take account of foreseeable hazards that might arise, and the need for emergency evacuation. Wearing respiratory protective equipment and personal protective equipment can contribute to heat stress. In extreme situations cooling air may be required for protective suits.

Monitoring arrangements

The system of work for confined space working must be monitored to ensure health and safety. This will include checking the permit-to-work document and the practical precautions related to it. It is important that the atmosphere be monitored to ensure it stays breathable; this can be done by using specific sampler equipment or personal sampler equipment. Personal gas detectors should be worn whenever appropriate to take account of the hazard of local pockets of contaminant.

The use of personal communication equipment or a communication line will assist with monitoring the progress of the activities within the confined space and the condition of the employees. This can help decide suitable breaks, the need to stop tasks or the need to instigate emergency rescue.

It is the duty of employers to ensure that any personal protective equipment provided to their employees is maintained (including replaced or cleaned as appropriate) in an efficient state, in efficient working order and in good repair. Arrangements should be in place to ensure that any PPE issued for confined space working is inspected, maintained and all findings recorded.

Emergency arrangements

The CSR 1997 prohibit any person to enter or carry out work in a confined space unless there are suitable and sufficient rescue arrangements in place.

The arrangements for emergency rescue will depend on the nature of the confined space, the risks identified and consequently the likely nature of an emergency rescue. Arrangements should not rely only on the public emergency services. The arrangements might need to cover:

- Rescue and resuscitation equipment.
- Special arrangements with local hospitals (for example, for foreseeable poisoning).
- Raising the alarm and rescue.
- Safeguarding the rescuers.
- Safeguarding the third parties.
- Firefighting.
- Control of plant.
- First-aid.
- Support of the public emergency services.
- Training.

Exam practice

1. Identify the main hazards associated with excavation work adjacent to a busy dual carriageway with a speed limit of 40mph. (8)

2. **Outline** the control measures that could be considered for excavation work on a construction site. **(8)**

3. (a) **Identify FOUR** examples of a confined space that may be encountered in construction activities. **(4)**

    (b) **Identify FOUR** hazards associated with work in a confined space encountered in construction activities. **(4)**

4. A leaking underground petrol tank has been emptied so that it can be visually inspected internally prior to repair.

    Outline the features of a safe system of work for the inspection team in order to satisfy the requirements of the Confined Spaces Regulations 1997. **(8)**

Please refer to the back of the assessment section for answers.

This page is intentionally blank

ELEMENT 11 - EXCAVATION WORK AND CONFINED SPACES - HAZARDS AND RISK CONTROL

Demolition and deconstruction - hazards and risk control

Learning outcomes

On completion of this element, candidates should be able to demonstrate understanding of the content through the application of knowledge to familiar and unfamiliar situations. In particular they should be able to:

12.1 Identify the main hazards of demolition and deconstruction work.

12.2 Outline the control measures for demolition and deconstruction work.

12.3 Identify the purpose and scope of a pre-demolition/refurbishment survey.

12.4 Outline the main control measures that a demolition/refurbishment method statement should include.

Content

12.1 - Demolition and deconstruction hazards and risk 339
   The meaning of terms 339
   The selection of the appropriate method 340
   Hazards relating to deconstruction and demolition...340
12.2 - Control measures...344
   Control measures for deconstruction and demolition work 344
12.3 - Pre-demolition, deconstruction or refurbishment surveys 350
   Purpose and scope of surveys 350
   Duties of the property owner for carrying out a pre-demolition survey..350
   Competent person to carry out investigations 350
   Identification of features of the structure 351
   Review of factors affecting the structure..353
12.4 - Method statements 354
   Control measures that a method statement should include 354
Exam practice 357

Sources of reference

Reference information provided, in particular web links, is correct at time of publication, but may have changed.

Asbestos: The survey guide, HSG264 (Second Edition), HSE Books, ISBN 978-07176-6502-0
http://www.hse.gov.uk/pubns/priced/hsg264.pdf

Code of practice for demolition, BS 6187, British Standards Institution, ISBN 978-0-5803-3206-7

Establishing exclusion zones when using explosives in demolition, HSE Construction information sheet No 45.
http://www.hse.gov.uk/pubns/cis45.pdf

Health and Safety in Construction, HSG150, HSE Books, ISBN 978-0-7176-6182-2
http://www.hse.gov.uk/pubns/priced/hsg150.pdf

Managing Health and Safety in Construction, Construction (Design and Management) Regulations 2015, Guidance on Regulations, L153, HSE Books, ISBN: 978-0-7176-6626-3
http://www.hse.gov.uk/pubns/priced/l153.pdf

Personal Protective Equipment at Work (Guidance), L25, HSE Books, ISBN: 978-0-7176-6139-3
http://www.hse.gov.uk/pubns/priced/l25.pdf

Protecting the public: Your next move, HSG151, HSE Books, ISBN 978-0-7176-6294-4
http://www.hse.gov.uk/pubns/priced/hsg151.pdf

Relevant statutory provisions

Construction (Design and Management) Regulations (CDM) 2015

Control of Explosives Regulations (CER) 1991

Environmental Protection Act (EPA) 1990

Personal Protective Equipment at Work Regulations (PPER) 1992

Provision and Use of Work Equipment Regulations (PUWER) 1998

12.1 - Demolition and deconstruction hazards and risk

The meaning of terms

DECONSTRUCTION

The term deconstruction is used to describe the taking apart and removal of a structure in such a way that it may be reused again. Reuse may be as before or in a different configuration. The term deconstruction may be related to any structure that is taken apart in an orderly way that enables reuse in part or whole, whether the structure was permanent or temporary.

The growth in environmental considerations has led to more permanent structures being deconstructed when redevelopment is needed, enabling the reuse of their component parts. Some industrial units are built in such a way that lends them to be deconstructed and used again elsewhere if they have not reached the end of their useful life, for example, when an industrial site grows units may have to be changed or relocated.

Temporary structures are one particular group of structures that are designed for ease of construction and deconstruction. Temporary structures include those used at events, such as concerts and sporting events. This will include structures for spectator seating, hospitality gatherings, communication (large screens) and accommodation facilities for performers or athletes. The events may take place indoors in arenas, for example, the National Exhibition Centre (NEC), Birmingham, or outdoors under temporary cover, such as in marquees, and in the open air on show grounds. In addition, temporary film/television sets and exhibitions are constructed and later deconstructed.

The risks of deconstruction include major risks related to managing and controlling an orderly deconstruction that does not cause overloading of a small number of load-bearing parts and the structure's sudden collapse. Particular difficulties may also be experienced in deconstructing parts that have been strained in use and resist being taken apart. Procedures need to be in place to deal with these anticipated difficulties without putting workers at risk.

The timing and order of deconstruction can have a significant bearing on the hazards and their control, for example, where more than one aspect of the structure is being deconstructed at the same time they can conflict with each other leading to increased risks. Similarly, it is important to organise the isolation of power sources in such a way that hazards workers are exposed to be controlled. It may be necessary to isolate all power sources from the structure and provide independent supplies to enable the safe deconstruction. Other than these issues, the general hazards of deconstruction are essentially the same as those that might be experienced in constructing structures.

Planning should also involve the recognition that some of the control measures within the structure may not be available for the protection of workers as deconstruction progresses, for example, smoke detection and fire alarm facilities may be disabled at an early point in deconstruction. This would mean that protection of workers would have to be provided by different means.

DEMOLITION

The term demolition is used to describe the tearing down, knocking down or blowing up of a structure that is no longer required. There are a number of techniques used in demolition processes, including piecemeal demolition, deliberate controlled collapse and explosive collapse.

Piecemeal demolition

Piecemeal demolition is carried out by hand using hand held tools and is sometimes a preliminary to other methods. It can be completed or begun by machines. For example, when demolishing a tall chimney with occupied buildings in close proximity, the job may commence with the painstaking task of dismantling by hand - brick by brick. When the structure has been reduced to about 10 metres, then conventional heavy equipment can be used.

Deliberate controlled collapse

Deliberate controlled collapse involves the pre-weakening of the structure or building. This involves removing key structural members so the remaining structure collapses under its own weight.

There are several problems associated with this method of demolition:

- The structure may collapse to a greater extent than was anticipated, affecting neighbouring buildings.
- The planned collapse may only be a partial collapse and could leave the structure hazardous and insecure.
- The resultant debris may be projected over a wider area than anticipated, particularly dust.
- The pile of debris that is left after the collapse of the structure may be in a dangerous condition, presenting a serious risk of injury to those who remove it, for example, contaminated with biological hazards or asbestos.

One method of removing the key structural members is overturning by wire rope pulling. Wires are attached to the main supports, which are pulled away using a heavy tracked vehicle or a winch to provide the motive power.

The area must be cleared of workers for this operation and there must be enough clearance for the vehicle to move the distance required to pull out the structural supports. Problems associated with this method arise when the wire becomes overstressed. If it breaks, then whiplash can occur which can have sufficient force to slice through the human body.

The forces applied may be enough to overturn the winch or the tracked vehicle. Another problem can occur when the action of pulling has begun and there is inadequate power to complete it.

Figure 12-1: Hydraulic demolition jaws. *Source: RMS.*

Figure 12-2: Hydraulic demolition grapple. *Source: RMS.*

Explosive collapse

Explosives may be used to bring about the collapse of structures, for example, where other means are not practicable. The technique uses explosive charges to weaken load-bearing parts of the structure, causing it to collapse under its own weight.

The selection of the appropriate method

A systematic approach to demolition and deconstruction projects is a team effort between many people, who all have responsibilities. Clients must appoint duty holders who are competent and adequately resourced. These will include a principal designer to survey the site and a principal contractor to plan effective site management that keeps people (site workers and the public) as far as possible from the risks and principal contractors with as much information as possible.

The selection of an appropriate method will need to take into account the method of construction used for the original building and its proximity to other buildings, structures and the general public. These factors, together with location, the cost and availability of waste disposal and the desirability and economics of reuse, must also be considered.

'As-built' drawings and structural details may often be unavailable or unreliable, consequently a site investigation will be necessary. This will ascertain the way in which the building was originally constructed, and identify the stresses and strains which exist within it.

Failure to establish these facts may result in risks to the safety of both those involved in the demolition and those in close proximity to the site.

Hazards relating to deconstruction and demolition

PREMATURE COLLAPSE

If a building selected for deconstruction or demolition comprises decaying materials and is unstable it may present an intrinsic hazard of premature collapse. In addition, the process of deconstruction or demolition can create a hazard of premature collapse or increase the risk if it is already there. Removal of part of a supporting wall could be sufficient to release cast concrete floor slabs to drop from one level to another, and the resultant kinetic energy can lead to the further collapse of floors below. The likelihood of premature collapse is a particular consideration when using the wrecking ball method or carrying out partial demolition. In some cases the façade of a building may be left intact for renovation and the rest of the structure removed. In these circumstances great care must be taken to avoid freestanding walls and in order to provide adequate support to the structure. When carrying out wrecking ball demolition the impact of the ball is designed to weaken the structure; if it is not used in a planned and careful manner the wrong parts of the structure or too much of it may be weakened leading to premature collapse.

Premature collapse can also be caused when carrying out systematic deconstruction or demolition by hand, particularly when load-bearing parts of the structure, such as beams, lintels, load-bearing walls and roof supports are removed. Premature collapse can occur in a similar way when carrying out building/structure undermining or dismantling.

FALLS AND FALLING MATERIALS

Depending on the type of building and method of deconstruction or demolition, workers may be expected to work at a significant height, for example, when demolishing a brick built structure by hand, and this can present a fall hazard. In the case of hand deconstruction/demolition it would be usual to remove parts of the structure in essentially the reverse order that it was erected. As such the same hazard of falling would exist as would be the case when constructing such a building. Fall hazards can often occur in the deconstruction/demolition process by the action of removing material, such as floors and stairs, or when access doors are not secured when part of the structure is removed. Part of the process may mean the removal of equipment built into the structure to prevent falls when in the structure was in normal use, thus exposing hazards, such as a rail and barrier around an atrium walkway. As with other construction work there is a risk of a worker falling outside the framework of a scaffold erected as part of the deconstruction/demolition process, particularly where workers over-reach. If the site is not well controlled there is a possibility of unauthorised people gaining access to the area, and in so doing they could be exposed to the risk of falling.

The process of deconstruction/demolition involves the movement of large quantities of material to ground level. If this is not carried out in an organised way and material is allowed to fall it may expose workers and passers-by to the hazard. This is particularly the case where workers are carrying out demolition above other workers or near to access routes.

In addition, mechanical or explosive demolition may eject material, which could fall significant distances from the demolition process. Even small items of material represent a significant hazard when they are allowed to fall from a great height. In demolition processes, depending on how well they are conducted, material may fall in significant quantities and unexpectedly.

Figure 12-3: Risk of falling or premature collapse. *Source: RMS.*

Figure 12-4: Falling materials. *Source: RMS.*

PLANT, VEHICLES AND OTHER EQUIPMENT OVERTURNING

Demolition processes create large quantities of material that accumulate at low level. As this builds up, demolition equipment may be working on top of it to gain access to part of a structure. This can cause the centre of gravity of the equipment to be moved towards the edge of or outside its stability base. Sudden movement or an unexpected heavy load can cause it to overbalance and overturn.

Other ways in which the hazard of overturning may present itself are:

- Weak ground support, for example, cellars, sump covers, soft ground, causing one side of the equipment to be lower than another.
- Operating outside the machine's capability, for example, too large a load at too great a distance.
- Striking or getting caught up in fixed obstructions.

MANUAL HANDLING

In demolition processes there are large quantities of a wide variety of materials to be moved. This presents a potential manual handling hazard, though, in many cases, much of the manual handling hazards have been removed by the use of mechanical handling equipment. In situations where deconstruction/demolition is carried out by hand there is usually a lot of debris to move which may also be carried out by hand as the structure is reduced. In some cases the distance debris moved is limited by the provision of chutes. Where material is being salvaged this can mean an increase in manual handling is necessary in order to safeguard the condition of the material.

DUST AND FUME

Dust can be a nuisance and a risk to health to the public as well as to the workers. It may contain fungal and bacterial matter, which is pathogenic to humans, or asbestos. Structures that are being demolished may contain materials used in the construction of the structure which present a hazard as a dust or fume, for example, asbestos as fire insulation, and lead as a protective paint for metalwork. In addition, the use of the structure may lead to the presence of chemical deposits in the form of contaminated dusts; this may include toxic substances such as arsenic. As structures fall out of use it is not uncommon for pigeons to take up residence; their droppings contain a biological hazard that can lead to a lung disease called psittacosis if the dust from the droppings are breathed in. The process of demolition may liberate these materials such that they are present in the air where people are working or the public is passing by. If the process is conducted in dry conditions and windy conditions the dust may be more mobile and therefore presents more of a risk. Workers may carry out deconstruction/demolition work that creates large quantities of dust, which may be considered a nuisance in the open air, such as brick dust, but when encountered in a confined area may be a hazard because of the quantity of dust in the air.

Carbon monoxide fumes present a chemical asphyxiant hazard and may be given off by equipment used to support the demolition process, for example, demolition plant or generators used to provide temporary power supply.

NOISE AND VIBRATION

Much of the equipment used in the deconstruction/demolition process can present a noise hazard. Not surprisingly explosive charges present a noise hazard, as does impact equipment such as wrecking ball plant. Crusher and manipulation equipment can also present a noise hazard as the hydraulic system draws its power from the equipment's engine. Debris crusher plant can emit a large amount of noise as debris such as bricks is reduced.

Hand deconstruction/demolition may be supplemented by the use of electric or pneumatic chisels which emit high noise levels. On a busy site this cumulative noise can have an effect on workers and people nearby. Neighbours or other residents of an adjoining property may be affected by deconstruction/demolition work in the form of ground borne vibration, surface shock wave, or air overpressure from demolition work. The use of hammer drills, pneumatic chisels, hammers and other similar equipment presents a vibration hazard that could lead to and arm vibration syndrome (HAVS). The operation of demolition equipment such as manipulation and bucket equipment can expose the operator to whole body vibration syndrome (WBVS).

Figure 12-5: Noise and dust.   *Source: Rollaston Council.*

Figure 12-6: Siting of plant.   *Source: RMS.*

EXISTENCE OF SERVICES SUCH AS GAS, ELECTRICITY AND WATER

Services that may be encountered during deconstruction/demolition present different hazards. Electricity may be still present in a building's mains supply because it had not been isolated and present a risk of electric shock. Sometimes there is a belief that mains circuits have been isolated but because it is fed from more than one route only part of the supply has been dealt with. Some buildings have backup systems in the form of batteries and/or capacitors which can present an unexpected electrical hazard when encountered. High voltage power supplies may pass underground or overhead, and these will present a significant hazard if not isolated before work commences.

Gas supplies routed into or under a building, if not isolated, may carry a risk of fire or explosion if they are disrupted. Residual quantities of gas left in isolated services within a building can present a lesser hazard but should not be ignored.

Water supplies that are damaged can present an indirect hazard in that they can lead to flooding of lower areas of a building where workers may be present. In addition, it may undermine part of the structure leading to premature collapse, increase the risk of slips trips and falls or aggravate a risk of electric shock.

HAZARDOUS SUBSTANCES

Hazardous substances may be present on the deconstruction/demolition site because they are left over from prior use. In industrial buildings this may mean such things as cadmium, arsenic, mercury, acids, alkalis and fuel oils and solvents (some of which may be prohibited by current good practices). In laboratory or hospital buildings that are to be demolished biological hazards may be present. Asbestos has been commonly used in buildings for many years and when the substance is broken up and fibres get into the air it can present a significant health risk. Asbestos fibres may get into the lungs and it can take many years (sometimes up to 40 years) before the symptoms of illnesses, like mesothelioma (cancer of the membrane lining the lungs), become apparent. The asbestos fibres may also be released into the air and contaminate clothing, which may pose an additional risk of harm to other workers and the public in the vicinity.

Asbestos cement drain pipe and cladding.

Decorative coating containing asbestos.

Asbestos cement flue in a ceiling void.

Figure 12-7: Asbestos use in buildings.
Source: HSE, HSG213.

The type of asbestos fibre used in the manufacture of different products and present in buildings today has varied over time, for example, white asbestos was the main form used in the manufacture of asbestos cement; blue asbestos was used from 1950–69 and brown asbestos between 1945 to around 1980. Asbestos cement containing blue or brown asbestos is more hazardous than that which contains white asbestos alone. Asbestos may be present in lagging of boilers and pipework, fire proofing of structures, decorative ceiling materials and roofing materials. Pigeon infestation is common with derelict buildings and if dried pigeon droppings become disturbed and airborne they may present the risk of respiratory disease to workers, such as psittacosis. During deconstruction/demolition sewers may become exposed and present a risk of biological contamination from substances within them, for example, leptospirosis or hepatitis. In addition, hazardous substances from the site could contaminate sewers. Where vehicles are being used to transport the demolition waste material to a disposal site, they may inadvertently carry hazardous substances that may come off their wheels or drop off when travelling. Deconstruction/demolition work also possesses the potential to generate waste substances, such as oils, which can leak away into the soil.

DILAPIDATION

Dilapidation is the state of disrepair of a building. Dilapidation of structures and building may occur for a number of reasons, for example, a coal fired power station may no longer be required and abandoned, the owner of a house may no longer be in occupancy or a building may not be maintained for economic reasons, such as a non-profitable Victorian pleasure pier at a sea resort. Dilapidation develops over time through lack of maintenance, resulting in decay of the outer fabric of the structure leading to water ingress, wind damage and ultimate weakening of the whole structure. Dilapidation presents particularly high risks to those conducting deconstruction/demolition work and may influence the decision for the structure to be demolished, rather than deconstructed, as it may be possible to demolish it from a safe distance.

Typical problems related to dilapidation include:

- Presence of weak/deteriorating materials and structural elements.
- Complex load paths, partial collapse may have caused additional load and stress on the remaining load-bearing parts.
- High levels of structural instability.
- Risk of premature collapse of part or the whole of the structure.

Difficulty with access to the structure as normal access may be blocked by fallen parts of the structure.

Premature structural collapses can occur with dilapidated structures for a variety of reasons. It can result from a major structural fault arising from dilapidation or smaller faults can contribute to a chain of events that leads to a collapse while work is being conducted.

Figure ref 12-8 shows the result of a sudden collapse of a three storey building in Berkhamsted High Street, Hemel Hempstead in February 2011. It is believed a structural fault in the building caused the collapse.

Figure 12-8: Building collapse. *Source: The Gazette.*

Collapses may be:

- Localised collapse, for example, a collapse confined to a small part of the structure, without damage elsewhere.
- Progressive collapse, for example, the isolated failure of a critical member or section initiates a sequence of events, causing failure of the entire structure.

12.2 - Control measures

Control measures for deconstruction and demolition work

The Construction (Design and Management) Regulations (CDM) 2015 apply to all construction projects, of which demolition is a part. CDM 2015 focuses on the responsibilities that make the management of construction projects effective in managing health and safety risks, for example, competence, co-operation, co-ordination, principles of prevention and the roles of those involved in the project.

In addition, CDM 2015, Part 4, sets out duties related to health and safety on construction sites, including - good order and site security, stability of structures, demolition and dismantling, explosives, excavations, energy distribution installations, traffic routes and vehicles.

Regulation 20, of Part 4, in CDM 2015 requires that:

"(1) *The demolition or dismantling of a structure must be planned and carried out in such a manner as to prevent danger or, where it is not practicable to prevent it, to reduce danger to as low a level as is reasonably practicable.*

(2) *The arrangements for carrying out such demolition or dismantling must be recorded in writing before the demolition or dismantling work begins.*"

Figure 12-9: Demolition or dismantling. *Source: CDM 2015 Regulation 20.*

AVOIDANCE OF PREMATURE COLLAPSE

Irrespective of which deconstruction/demolition process is used it is important that the deconstruction/demolition be conducted in a systematic way that prevents premature collapse of the structure. This will mean working with a good understanding of the building's strong and weak points. It is important that the deconstruction/demolition process does not leave unsupported walls or parts of a structure. Those controlling the deconstruction/demolition process should have a good understanding of building structure and mechanics, to avoid removing parts of the structure that can place an excessive load on other fragile parts. Modern machines can be fitted with scissor jaws that can break down a wall in small pieces. The use of this process reduces the likelihood of major structural damage or premature collapse.

When the wrecking ball method or partial demolition is conducted, as these processes often leave free standing structures, it is important that a careful deconstruction/demolition plan is adhered to. As part of this plan it is important to leave the structure in its most stable condition when not working on it. This may mean not starting a phase of deconstruction/demolition because it cannot be completed before the end of the day or providing shoring to the structure that is left. If a part of a building, such as a façade is to be left intact for renovation it is important to provide adequate longer term support.

PROTECTION FROM FALLS AND FALLING MATERIAL

The technical advances in mechanical plant have considerably reduced the risk to deconstruction/demolition workers of working at a height. For example, modern equipment enables a lot of demolition to be conducted by agile high reach equipment. Where it is necessary for people to work at height the same standards of protection from falls must be provided to deconstruction/demolition workers as are provided to other construction workers. This will include provision of safe work platforms, use of mobile elevating work platforms (MEWPs), nets and fall arrest equipment.

In order to prevent debris falling on to passers-by, protective screens, and where appropriate fans, should be set up around scaffolds erected around structures undergoing deconstruction/demolition. In addition, brick guards, debris nets and sheeting will help to contain falling materials and prevent them falling outside the framework of a scaffold erected as part of the deconstruction/demolition process. Areas of a structure under deconstruction/demolition that present a risk from falling material must be clearly demarcated from other areas. Where buildings are being deconstructed/demolished by hand a safe access route to the workplace must be maintained, which may include demarcated routes and temporary erection of covered areas. The use of audible and visual warnings will assist in removing people from hazard areas at times that they are at risk from a particular demolition task. Head protection is an essential last line of defence for workers in this environment.

SITING AND USE OF PLANT, VEHICLES AND OTHER EQUIPMENT

Access to the site should be established to enable the large plant and appliances to be taken or driven there safely. It may also be necessary to get permission to close roads or pathways for the duration of the work.

Any plant and equipment if used in the manner for which it was designed should not fall over and injure any person at work. In order to prevent overturning care should be taken to:

- Identify weak ground conditions.
- Avoid operating outside the machine's capability.
- Create space sufficient to manoeuvre to avoid striking obstructions.
- Maintain safe access to work areas by the prompt removal of demolition debris.

The key to preventing plant overturning is planning and control. The appointment of a competent person to organise the operation of the plant, vehicles and machinery is essential. Care with siting of plant is essential in order to prevent accidental contact with nearby structures, the structure being deconstructed/demolished, power lines or other overhead obstructions. In restricted areas tight control of the use of plant and vehicles is essential; this may include physical barriers to restrict movement, where practicable.

It is important to restrict access to plant, vehicles and other machinery to prevent unauthorised use, by, for example, children. This will include securing plant in compounds, locking doors and securing keys effectively. Taking steps to prevent unauthorised access to the deconstruction/demolition site by using barriers, fencing, and increased security is the responsibility of the principal contractor.

DUST AND FUME

Large volumes of dust can be dissipated when deconstruction/demolition work is conducted. This can be in the form of brick dust asbestos or cement based materials. Asbestos is a special case, and the substance should be identified and removed by specialists who are authorised and registered by the Health and Safety Executive (HSE) to remove asbestos material. All asbestos should be removed before any deconstruction/demolition work takes place. The liberation of other dusts can be limited and restricted by the amount of deconstruction/demolition activities conducted at any one time.

Consideration of when to demolish and dismantle is also a key factor as wind direction can play a significant role, affecting the direction of travel of dust and materials. Exclusion of workers while a dust producing activity is conducted and subsequent clean up processes can also control the exposure of workers to dust.

The build-up of fume emissions, typically from diesel powered equipment, can be reduced by limiting the amount of plant and equipment activities conducted at any one time. This can be combined with control measures or restrictions imposed to segregate plant and equipment from any person who is likely to come into contact with such fume emissions. The use of modern plant and equipment significantly reduces the level of emissions as they possess more efficient engines with cleaner exhaust systems.

Where fume may be emitted from the actual deconstruction/demolition process, for example, when demolishing some form of storage vessel, such as in a chemical plant or hospital. Then potential emission should be restricted by draining any system or vessel holding fume producing substances in a controlled and planned manner.

MANUAL HANDLING

Most of the deconstruction/demolition process should, where possible, be carried out by using mechanical equipment to prevent or reduce any potential manual handling hazards. Chutes and conveyors should be used to transport debris from the upper floors of the building into skips, thereby eliminating any manual handling between floors.

NOISE AND VIBRATION

Noise and vibration can be a major cause of harm to workers; therefore it is important that suitable and sufficient risk assessments are produced. Exposure to noise and vibration should be minimised by the careful selection and maintenance of equipment such that levels emitted are kept to a minimum. For example, vibration damped seats for cab operated equipment, vibration mats for areas where workers stand to operate crusher plant, and vibration damped handles for power tools.

Exposure levels can be controlled by the careful use of task rotation such that those exposed to high noise and vibration levels are periodically moved to tasks that have low exposure levels. Where levels of noise are above the action values hearing protection must be made available or provided, as appropriate and it is the duty of the employer to enforce and ensure that such protection is worn. A noise protected refuge may be required in order to allow workers to move out of noisy areas to limit their exposure during rest breaks.

PROTECTION OF THE ENVIRONMENT

Where vehicles are being used to transport the demolition waste material to a disposal site, then provision should be made for wheel washes and the cleaning of the highway by a road sweeper. Waste substances, such as oils, must not be allowed to leak away into the soil and must be disposed of in a controlled manner. During demolition sewers may become exposed and be at risk of contamination from substances, so care should be taken to identify and protect them from entry of such materials. In the same way, it may be necessary to establish interceptor pits to control water run-off into water courses and/or fit temporary pressure drain covers.

Figure 12-10: Doubtful competence of workers. *Source: Lincsafe.*

Figure 12-11: Use of demolition equipment. *Source: RMS.*

COMPETENCE OF WORKFORCE

It is the client's responsibility to check the competence of the principal contractor. In turn, the principal contractor must ensure the competence of contractors appointed to conduct demolition and dismantling. Competence checks can include taking up references on past work and reviewing contractor's health and safety policies and procedures. It is important to recognise that deconstruction/demolition contractors may not be competent to act as principal contractors on larger or more complex projects.

It is important that deconstruction/demolition work is controlled by someone with an understanding of buildings/structures and in turn that workers understand the effects on the building or structure that their work will make. In this way premature collapse may be prevented. Operators of plant and equipment must be competent to operate the specific items they use, in demolition circumstances. Operation in deconstruction/demolition work can be quite different to operation in other building work and is particularly affected by the terrain of the demolition work area.

PRE-DECONSTRUCTION/DEMOLITION INVESTIGATION/SURVEY

Before any deconstruction/demolition work begins a survey is carried out to ensure that the deconstruction/demolition can go ahead safely and that property surrounding the site is protected from the deconstruction/demolition work as it progresses.

The survey should give special consideration to the location of the intended deconstruction/demolition work, for example, if it is near a place of worship, school, hospital, shopping area, leisure centre, or housing estate then the survey may identify the need for extra provisions to control risks to members of the public. It is important to know the previous use of the building/structure; it may still contain toxic or flammable materials, biological hazards or even radioactive materials or sources. It is the client's responsibility to ensure that any building/structure to be deconstructed/demolished is adequately surveyed.

TYPE OF STRUCTURE

The survey should clearly identify the type of structure to be worked on, for example, high rise office blocks, chimneys or old buildings, as this will have a considerable impact on the method of deconstruction/demolition, the hazards present and the precautions to be taken.

Figure 12-12: Building structure. *Source: RMS.*

Figure 12-13: Structural condition and substances. *Source: RMS.*

METHOD OF CONSTRUCTION

The method of construction will also have a similar effect. The method of construction will particularly influence the method and order of deconstruction/demolition. Where buildings/structures contain pre-stressed or post-stressed concrete beams, this must be identified in the survey.

These buildings/structures have beams containing steel rods held under tension, which helps to bind the building/structure together. If part of the structure is deconstructed/demolished this may release the forces under tension and cause premature collapse.

STRUCTURAL CONDITION

The structural condition of the building/structure should be surveyed in order to identify any degradation of materials that might influence the method and order of deconstruction/demolition. The structural condition might present such risks that it is not safe to carry out demolition by entering inside the building/structure and other means, such as the use of mechanical demolition equipment, may be required.

When deconstruction/demolition work is carried out by hand it involves the workers moving about at height on materials that may have degraded and are not able to sustain their weight. In this type of operation full scaffolding and other platforms should be provided and the building deconstructed/demolished in the reverse order of erection.

PRESENCE OF CELLARS

Basements, cellars, wells or storage tanks need to be identified in order to apply control measures to the risks they create, such as falls from a height and drowning. Workers may fall through into underground areas, while tanks pose a special risk if they have held or still hold toxic or flammable materials.

IDENTIFICATION OF SERVICES

Details and location of all the public utility services must be identified in order to identify the hazards they present and to take action to isolate, divert or otherwise protect them. This will involve the examination of service location drawings held by the utility service organisations.

Most of these will be buried services, including gas pipes, electricity cables, water pipes and sewerage. This will be supported by visual examination, test equipment and, in some cases, test digging to establish the specific location and status of the services.

Figure 12-14: Hazardous substances. *Source: Scaftag.*

Figure 12-15: Proximity of other structures. *Source: D Hitchen.*

PRESENCE OF HAZARDOUS SUBSTANCES

A particular health hazard that should be identified at time of survey is possible exposure to asbestos, which can present a significant risk, especially if workers are unaware of its presence and no precautions have been taken. It is important to obtain details of any prior survey conducted on the building/structure by the owner/occupier, for consideration as part of the pre-demolition survey.

The Control of Asbestos Regulations (CAR) 2012 prohibits the importation, supply and use of all forms of asbestos. They also prohibit the second-hand use of asbestos products such as asbestos cement sheets and asbestos tiles. If existing asbestos containing materials (ACMs) are in good condition they may be left in place and their condition monitored and managed.

CAR 2012 sets out the following general requirements:

■ The presence of asbestos must be identified and must be labelled.
■ An assessment must be carried out of work which exposes employees to asbestos.
■ Training is mandatory for those that may be exposed to asbestos fibres at work, including deconstruction/demolition workers or others that may come into contact with or disturb asbestos.
■ A written plan of work is required for work with asbestos.

The CAR 2012, regulation 4, requires that duty holder, for example, the owner of a building, to provide information on the location and condition of ACMs to anyone who is liable to work on or disturb them. Demolition or deconstruction work would often mean the removal of ACMs or at the very least disturbance of them. The information on ACMs may be provided as part of information obtained during the pre-demolition survey. In the absence of this information it may be necessary for the duty holder or those involved in the demolition or deconstruction activity to conduct their own asbestos survey.

The CAR 2012, regulation 3, requires that employers who work with asbestos must be licensed unless the circumstances are that:

(a)   The exposure of employees to asbestos is sporadic and of low intensity.

(b)   It is clear from the risk assessment that the exposure of any employee to asbestos will not exceed the control limit.

(c)   The work involves:

   (i)   Short, non-continuous maintenance activities.

   (ii)   Removal of materials in which the asbestos fibres are firmly linked in a matrix.

   (iii)   Encapsulation or sealing of asbestos-containing materials which are in good condition.

   (iv)   Air monitoring and control, and the collection and analysis of samples to ascertain whether a specific material contains asbestos.

Other controls required by CAR 2012 related to asbestos include:

- Work with asbestos that requires a licence must be notified to the employer's enforcing authority.
- Exposure must be prevented or reduced by controls.
- Controls must be used and maintained.
- The employer is responsible for the cleaning of personal protective clothing.

CAR 2012 introduced a category of work called Notifiable Non-Licensed Work (NNLW). This required the appropriate enforcing authority to be notified if this category of work was to be carried out. Records of work carried out must be kept and workers must have a periodic medical examination.

There may be other health hazards present that could affect the deconstruction/demolition worker or others, for example, Weil's disease from rats, breathing difficulties from the dust of disturbed pigeon droppings or chemicals from the previous use of the building.

USE OF EXPLOSIVE

The use of explosives requires the expertise of an experienced explosives engineer. Also, the Health and Safety Executive (HSE) should be consulted to ensure compliance with the Control of Explosives Regulations (CER) 1991 and HSE Construction information sheet No 45.

When designing for demolition using explosives it is important to plan for the risk of possible ejection of projectiles. An exclusion zone should be established at a distance from and surrounding any structure that is being demolished using explosives. Everyone, with the possible exception of the shot-firer, should be outside the exclusion zone at the time of the blast. If the shot-firer needs to remain within the zone, a position of safety must be created.

An exclusion zone is built up from four areas:

1) Plan area - the plan area of the structure that is to be demolished.

2) Designed drop area - the area covered by the main debris pile.

3) Predicted debris area - the maximum area in which fragments can fall outside the designed debris area.

4) Buffer area - the area between the predicted debris area and the exclusion zone perimeter.

Consideration should also be given to services, for example, ground vibration which could damage services.

Figure 12-16: Demolition exclusion zone.   *Source: Adapted from HSE construction sheet No 45.*

Regulation 21, of Part 4, in CDM 2015 requires that:

"(1) So far as is reasonably practicable, explosives must be stored, transported and used safely and securely.

(2) An explosive charge may be used or fired only if suitable and sufficient steps have been taken to ensure that no person is exposed to risk of injury from the explosion or from projected or flying material caused by the explosion."

Figure 12-17: Explosives.   Source: CDM 2015 Regulation 21.

There are a number of factors to be considered for safe demolition with the use of explosives, which include:

- The local and structural conditions must be considered when fixing the size of the charges. The structure to be blasted can be divided into a number of sections and suitable charges applied to each section.
- Shot holes should be drilled electrically. Drilling pneumatically could cause vibration, which could result in premature collapse.
- Charges should not be placed near cast iron as it easily shatters into shrapnel.
- The area around the structure being demolished and the firing point should be barricaded and unauthorised persons not allowed to enter.
- The demolition engineer must be satisfied that no dangerous situation or condition has been left or created. The danger zone must be barricaded until rendered safe.

WASTE MANAGEMENT - ON SITE SEGREGATION AND OFF SITE DISPOSAL

The construction industry is one of the largest producers of waste in the UK. Construction and deconstruction/demolition waste can be broken down into the following:

- Concrete, bricks and tiles.
- Asphalt, tar and tar by-products.
- Metals.
- Soil and rubble.
- Wood.
- Soil from ground works (which may be contaminated, through the sites previous use).

This means that waste products should be identified before disturbance and an action plan developed to regulate how these products should be handled. Waste should be segregated in terms of type, identifying waste that may be re-used, recycled and recovered and segregating it from waste for disposal.

All waste products and residues in containers must be identified and clearly labelled and steps taken to prevent the combined storage of incompatible materials prior to disposal. Offsite disposal must be carried out by a licensed contractor and taken to a licensed waste disposal site. If necessary, waste removal should be planned to avoid rush hour traffic and steps taken such as wheel washing to prevent contamination on public roads.

ACCESS AND EGRESS FROM THE SITE

Access and egress for site vehicles is an essential part of site planning. Consideration should be given to:

- The appropriateness of public roads in the proximity of the site. Select routes of suitable width and schedule access to avoid times when large numbers of domestic vehicles may be parked in the road whenever possible.
- The nature of the surrounding buildings and their function, for example, the presence of schools or hospitals for which traffic and noise would be a problem.
- The number and size of vehicles expected to enter and leave the site should be determined and their arrival and departures scheduled to avoid back-up of waiting vehicles onto public highways.
- Speed limits should be imposed on site vehicles, limit signs should be displayed and the limit enforced.
- Reversing from the site must be avoided or if reversing is necessary a banksman should be used to control the process.

PROXIMITY AND CONDITION OF OTHER STRUCTURES AND ROADWAYS

The survey should seek to identify the proximity and condition of other structures to determine the influence they may have on the deconstruction/demolition process.

If a structure is close to the building/structure to be demolished and is in poor condition it may be necessary to shore it up and route demolition plant and equipment away from it.

The proximity and condition of roads to a site is an essential item to survey. If roads are good, and wide enough to take plant transport vehicles and debris vehicles, this will have a positive influence on the safety of the deconstruction/demolition activity.

Figure 12-18: Risk of collision due to close proximity with public road.
Source: HSE, HSG151.

If restrictions exist, it may be necessary to obtain police co-operation to clear roads and to time the delivery of plant when least disruption will occur.

A new, dedicated access may be necessary to provide access to a larger road nearby. This may influence the order of work to be conducted as part of the building/structure may need to be demolished to create better access. It is important to ensure that equipment and parts of equipment such as elbows of cranes, excavators, loaders etc. do not swing into the path of vehicles or pedestrians. Early identification of risk and nuisance to adjoining land, buildings or road users will enable early notification to those affected.

12.3 - Pre-demolition, deconstruction or refurbishment surveys

Purpose and scope of surveys

The purpose of a pre-demolition, deconstruction or refurbishment survey is to ensure that before any work begins the structure to be worked on is assessed to determine inherent hazards related to the structure and those hazards that are likely to emanate from the proposed work on the structure.

The scope of the survey will include the following hazards:

- Premature collapse.
- Falls and falling materials.
- Plant, vehicles and other equipment overturning.
- Access and egress restrictions.
- Manual handling.
- Dust and fumes.
- Noise and vibration.
- Existence of services.
- Hazardous substances.
- Dilapidation.
- Presence of fragile and sharp materials.
- Weak surfaces, for example, cellars.
- Proximity of other structures, vehicles and people that might be affected.
- Likely waste issues.

Figure 12-19: Dilapidation of a structure.   Source: RMS.

The information determined by the survey will be used to determine a method of working that ensures satisfactory control measures are in place and an orderly work process.

Duties of the property owner for carrying out a pre-demolition survey

Clients of projects that fall within the scope of CDM 2015 must provide all designers and contractors with suitable pre-construction (demolition is a form of construction work under CDM 2015) information that will allow hazards to be identified and work to be planned. It is not sufficient to state that "asbestos might be present".

The relevant information might be in an existing survey (for example, an asbestos survey) or in an existing health and safety file. If clients do not have sufficient information available, then they must make arrangements to obtain the information, for example, by arranging the necessary surveys to be carried out by a competent person.

When there is more than one contractor working on the project, the client must appoint a principal designer. The principal designer will assist the client in the provision of the pre-construction information to other designers and contractors (including the principal contractor).

Competent person to carry out investigations

STRUCTURAL ENGINEERS

The structural engineer can play a crucial part in reducing the hazards associated with deconstruction, demolition, refurbishment, dismantling and decommissioning. Presenting the structural risks clearly at the beginning of a project reduces accidents and saves time and money. Good communication helps ensure that the potential hazards are understood by the client team, site managers, supervisors and the workforce.

ASBESTOS SURVEYORS

Occupiers must have an asbestos management plan, such as that provided by an asbestos survey conducted on any non-domestic property that is over eight years old. Failure to do so could put the health of employees, visitors and, ultimately, deconstruction/demolition workers at risk.

Within an asbestos survey an asbestos surveyor must identify all materials either thought to contain asbestos or ones that could be mistaken for asbestos.

An independent expert/specialist organisation conducting asbestos surveys must:

- Have adequate training and be experienced in survey work.

- Be able to demonstrate independence, impartiality and integrity.
- Have an adequate quality management system.
- Carry out any asbestos survey work in accordance with recommended HSE guidance HSG264 'Asbestos: The survey'.

HSG264 states that organisations offering an asbestos survey service should be able to demonstrate their competence by holding United Kingdom Accreditation Service (UKAS) accreditation to ISO/IEC 17020 and individuals to ISO/IEC 17024.

In considering competence for assessment the HSE guidance 'Work with materials containing asbestos' states:

"Whoever carries out the assessment should:

Have adequate knowledge, training and expertise in understanding the risks from asbestos and be able to make informed and appropriate decisions about the risks and precautions needed.

Know how the work activity may disturb asbestos.

Be familiar with and understand the requirements of the Regulations ACOP.

Have the ability and the authority to collate all the necessary and relevant information.

Be able to assess other non-asbestos risks on site.

Be able to estimate the expected level of exposure to decide whether or not the control limit is likely to be exceeded."

Figure 12-20: Competence to carry out asbestos risk assessments.   *Source: HSE ACOP to CAR 2012.*

See also 'Element 8 - Chemical and biological health - hazards and risk control' - Health risks and controls associated with asbestos.

Identification of features of the structure

IDENTIFICATION OF KEY STRUCTURAL ELEMENTS

It is important that the survey identify the key structural elements in order to evaluate the effects on the structure of the proposed work. The location and condition of lintels, beams and other load-bearing members will need to be taken into account when planning how the work is to be carried out. The structural elements may be made of steel beams or concrete, which may be reinforced, pre-stressed or post stressed.

Reinforced concrete is poured around rods of steel that are formed to the shape of the structure being created.

Pre-stressed concrete is a method of overcoming the concrete's natural weakness in tension. It is used to produce beams, floors or bridges with a longer span than is practical with ordinary reinforced concrete. Pre-stressed tendons (generally of high tensile steel cable or rods) are used to provide a clamping force that produces a compressive stress to offset the tensile stress that the concrete compression member would otherwise experience due to bending load. Pre-tensioned concrete is cast around already tensioned tendons.

Post-tensioned concrete is the descriptive term for a method of applying compression after pouring and curing concrete and is conducted in situ. Tendons are passed through the duct that provides the proposed shape of the member and the concrete is poured. Once the concrete has hardened, the tendons are tensioned by hydraulic jacks; when the tendons have stretched sufficiently they are locked in position and continue to transfer pressure to the concrete.

Demolishing reinforced concrete does not present any unusual hazards. However, demolishing pre-tensioned and post tensioned structures can be difficult because of the energy stored in the stressing tendons, which are under constant tensile stress. The uncontrolled release of this stored energy can cause a concrete component to fly through the air; care needs to be taken when they are cut. The tendons in tensioned structures are generally made of high tensile steel so there will be fewer to cut compared to standard reinforced concrete.

IDENTIFICATION OF LOCATION AND TYPE OF SERVICES

The location and type of services connected to the structure being worked on should be identified. Consideration should be given to both over ground, including, for example, pipe racks, power lines and telephone wires; and underground, such as pipes, cables and equipment associated with the electricity, gas, water (including piped sewage) and telecommunications industries. This will also include the identification of other pipelines that may transport a range of petrochemical and other fluids through the site.

See also 'Element 11.2 - Control measures for excavation work' - Identification and detection of buried services.

IDENTIFICATION, SIGNIFICANCE AND EXTENT OF DILAPIDATION OF THE STRUCTURE

The state of dilapidation can cause a wide variety of problems during demolition/deconstruction of a structure.

The survey should determine the extent of the dilapidation and its significance to the health and safety of those that will be affected by the work to be conducted. The dilapidation may mean that asbestos materials have become damaged and are exposed.

Floors may have collapsed and stairs that could have been able to be used for access may have become rotten as they became affected by water ingress. If part of the roof has collapsed this may add stress to other members holding up the remainder of the roof.

Fixtures and fittings may become damaged or parts stolen, leaving electrical services in a poor condition. Though power should have been removed from them this is not always the case.

Fungal and other harmful growth

Fungal growth occurs when there is moisture content in the walls of a structure. It flourishes in an environment of high humidity with lack of ventilation.

Fungal growth may indicate the level of decline in the integrity of the structure.

Figure 12-21: Dilapidation of buildings.   *Source: RMS.*

Harmful growth includes creeping ivy and plants that can grow either on walls, roofs or gutters. Roots can go deep into the existing holes causing cracks and water penetration that lead to the erosion of mortar joints and dampness, which weaken the structure.

Figure 12-22: Black mould. *Source: Premier preservation Ltd.*

Figure 12-23: Ivy.   *Source: Daily Mail.*

Cracking of walls and leaning walls

Vertical or diagonal cracks in the wall are common symptoms of structural instability. The survey should identify these cracks as symptoms and try to diagnose the cause.

This may be poor foundations, weak materials and joints; or any shrinkage or thermal movements such as those of timber window frames.

Diagonal cracks, usually widest at the foundations and terminating at the corner of a building, often occur when shallow foundations are laid on shrinkable sub-soil that is drier than normal.

They may also be caused by a physical uplifting action of a large tree's main roots close to the walls.

Figure 12-24: Settlement diagonal wall cracking. *Source: diynot.com.*

Common causes of leaning walls include a spreading roof, which forces the weight of a roof down towards the walls, sagging due to soil movement, weak foundations due to the presence of dampness, shrinkable clay soil or decayed building materials; and disturbance of nearby mature trees with roots expanding to the local settlement.

Decayed floorboards

Timber floorboards were widely used in many older buildings including churches, schools, and railway stations. Some timber floorboards will have been subjected to surface abuse and subsequently deteriorated to the extent that they can no longer hold the weight of workers walking on them.

The main natural causes of decay are pest attacks, such as dry rot or hidden cavities caused by death watch beetle.

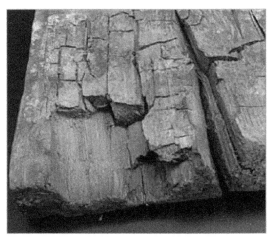

Figure 12-25: Dry rot - characteristic cuboidal cracking.
Source: Safeguard Europe Ltd.

Figure 12-26: Timber damaged by death watch beetle.
Source: Rudders and Paynes Ltd.

Weakened or split boards may be caused by damage by occupants, loss of natural preservatives and the effects of corroded nails.

Roof defects

Common defects of roof tiles include corrosion of nails that fix the tiles to battens and rafters, the decay of battens, and the cracking of tiles caused by harmful growth. Another aspect to be considered is the mortar applied for ridge tiles, which tends to decay or flake off over the years. Roof light materials often deteriorate on exposure to sunlight and become brittle, lose structural strength and are easily fractured. Often they are covered with felt to prevent leaks or become obscured from the rest of the roof by the growth of moss. Hidden roof lights present a risk to workers of falling through.

Unstable foundations

Most of the common problems associated with foundations depend on the geology of the ground upon which a building stands. For example, settlement or subsidence may result if it is built prematurely on made up ground or the water table height is causing the ground to expand or contract.

The leaning Tower of Pisa is perhaps the most famous example of building subsidence. The tower began to sink after construction had progressed to the second floor in 1178. This was due to a shallow three-metre foundation, set in weak, unstable sandy subsoil, a design that was flawed from the beginning.

Unstable foundations may occur due to traffic vibrations, deterioration of building materials and through change of use, for example, increased floor loading.

Problems with unstable foundations may lead to an unstable building structure, which increases the risks of premature collapse during deconstruction or demolition.

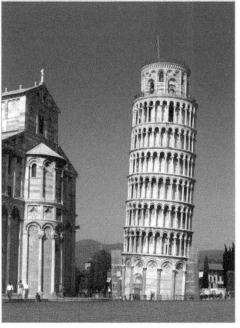

Figure 12-27: The leaning tower of Pisa, Italy. *Source: Marshaü.*

Review of factors affecting the structure

DRAWINGS, STRUCTURAL CALCULATIONS, HEALTH AND SAFETY

Before work commences every effort should be made to find the original design drawings, together with the calculations made by the architect. If the building is of recent construction these will be found in the health and safety file related to the structure.

This will provide information on how the structure was built, for example, reinforced concrete frame or steel frame. If it is a large structure, it will be important to identify any pre-stressed or post-stressed concrete beams present within the structure and whether any floor slabs or piles were involved in the build. It is also important to determine the age of the structure and its previous use.

It is the client's responsibility to provide such information to the contractor. Prior to deconstruction/demolition, any structural alterations that might affect the load-bearing capacity of walls and floors should be reviewed to avoid premature collapse.

STRUCTURAL ALTERATIONS CARRIED OUT ON THE STRUCTURE IN THE PAST

The pre-demolition survey should consider past alterations. This is particularly important to identify any changes, for example, the addition of doors or windows or the removal of walls, which may have compromised the building's original structural stability.

12.4 - Method statements

Control measures that a method statement should include

After completion of the survey it is possible to consider how the work is to be carried out and to establish a method statement to define and manage the work.

The method statement should include consideration of:

- Services.
- Soft strip requirements.
- Working at height.
- Protection of the public and neighbours.
- Emergency arrangements.
- Waste management.
- Competence of workforce.
- Communications.

- Asbestos.
- Control measures for identified hazards.
- Plant and equipment.
- Access and egress from site.
- Training and welfare arrangements.
- Named responsible person.
- Coordination of work activities.

SERVICES

Isolations

The method statement should define the actions necessary to establish isolations that are adequate and secure. It is important to isolate services at the furthest point practicable from the structure to be demolished, for example, at the site boundary.

This may include gas or water services isolated in the pavement outside the demolition site. This will help to remove the hazard at source and is preferable to local isolation of the services within the building. It should be remembered that some systems will store energy from services and should not be presumed safe merely by isolating the service. This includes electricity stored in capacitors and batteries, stored water in tanks, and compressed oils/air in pressure systems.

Temporary services

The method statement should set out any arrangements for temporary services that may be required. It may be necessary to install temporary services such as electricity, lighting and fresh air. These services must be installed by competent people and, in the case of fresh air supply; there must be an audible and visual warning of failure.

SOFT STRIP REQUIREMENTS

Often, the exterior of a building has to be preserved intact whilst the interior is completely stripped of partitioning, flooring and internal walls ready for refurbishment or redevelopment. The extent of soft strip should be clarified, as this work requires careful control and management because it often reveals unexpected aspects of the building's structural design, such as the presence of asbestos and weaknesses in the structure such as cracks that may have been hidden by plaster.

WORKING AT HEIGHT ACCESS INCLUDING SCAFFOLDING

If work at height cannot be avoided by the use of pusher arms or 'nibblers', details of how those working at height will be protected will need to be determined and set out in the method statement. This will include details of competent scaffold erectors and the inspection arrangements for scaffolds to be used or other access equipment such as mobile elevating work platforms (MEWPS).

PROTECTION OF PUBLIC, THIRD PARTIES AND SURROUNDING STRUCTURES

The protection of the public, third parties and surrounding structures is an essential pre deconstruction/demolition or refurbishment control measure. The method statement should specify the measures to remove and prevent people accessing the building/structure, such as children, persons sleeping rough and those who wish to salvage materials, as well as people who are just passing by. The boundaries of the demolition site need to provide an effective barrier to persons not involved with the work, typically 2.5 metres high fencing with warning signs posted around it.

Fencing must be maintained to a good standard and checks should be made at the end of each day to ensure it is in place, and continues to be effective. Where the work is close to where the public may pass they should be protected from falling materials by the use of sheeting, brick guards, nets, fans and covered areas. In some cases, work in such an area may have taken place at a specified time and the public prevented from accessing the area.

Figure 12-28: Demolition - separate entrance for workers and protected pedestrian route.   *Source: HSE, HSG151.*

Figure 12-29: Protection of public.   *Source: RMS.*

Figure 12-30: Disposal of waste.   *Source: RMS.*

EMERGENCY ARRANGEMENTS

The method statement should set out emergency procedures and arrangements. These should be sufficient for dealing with foreseeable emergencies, for example, fire, explosions, chemical leaks and premature collapse of the structure. Fire detection, fire alarms, fire-fighting equipment, first-aid provisions, site evacuation, and rescue plans should form part of these arrangements. The method statement should specify necessary training in the use of emergency techniques and equipment.

WASTE MANAGEMENT - ON-SITE SEGREGATION AND OFF SITE DISPOSAL

It is important that the method statement detail arrangements for waste management. Taking into account the size of the site, waste material must not be allowed to accumulate. This means controlling build-up of waste at local points around the site, particularly where they impede access and egress, as well as any major accumulation points. The disposal of building materials must be controlled by consignment certificates and taken to a recognised licensed landfill site. Asbestos waste should only be handled by trained and qualified workers and disposed of in accordance with current local environmental requirements.

COMPETENCE OF WORKFORCE

Details of the competencies of those involved in the work the method statement relates to should be clearly stated. The importance of adequate training in the demolition industry has been recognised by the introduction of the 'Scheme for the Certification of Competence of Demolition Operatives' (CCDO) by the National Demolition Training Group. The CCDO scheme is for anyone whose job entails on-site demolition. The scheme applies to new entrants, temporary workers, and existing operatives with site experience. It is partly NVQ based, with the Demolition Site Operative and Demolition Operative 1 (Labourer) being the only jobs not requiring proof of an NVQ.

There are seven different cards available that confirm the holder of the card is competent. The appropriate card is issued under the scheme depending on qualifications and experience. All cards require a health and safety test in either demolition or demolition and plant in order to be issued or reissued, which takes place every five years.

Similar schemes operate through the CITB (provided by the Construction Skills organisation) and the ECITB (provided by the Client/Contractor National Safety Group) and may be relevant to refurbishment work.

COMMUNICATIONS

The method statement should include details of what meetings are planned (pre-start, weekly, progress, etc.) and who will attend.

ASBESTOS

Before work can begin an asbestos survey should be carried out by a qualified surveyor. The purpose of the survey is to help identify and manage any asbestos in the duty holder's premises.

The survey has to provide sufficient information for:

- An asbestos register and plan to be prepared.
- A suitable risk assessment to be carried out.
- A written plan to manage the risks to be produced.

The duty to manage asbestos is covered by Regulation 4 of the Control of Asbestos Regulations (CAR) 2012.

The method statement should establish the way in which asbestos is to be managed. If refurbishment is to be carried out this may mean leaving ACMs in place, ensuring it is identified and adding it to the register. If deconstruction or demolition is intended the method statement should set out the arrangements for removal and disposal.

CONTROL MEASURES FOR IDENTIFIED HAZARDS

Measures that will be taken to control hazards must be detailed, for example, noise nuisance, by the use of silencers, remote location of noisy equipment from neighbouring properties, avoidance of work at night. If dust nuisance is expected the method statement may set out arrangements for sheeting of the area, damping down of materials or avoidance of work on very windy days.

PLANT AND EQUIPMENT

The method statement should specify the type and capacity of equipment to be used at different stages in the demolition process, in order that it can be used within its capability and for the right purpose. The equipment specified should match the factors identified at time of survey. Due to the dangerous nature of demolition work all equipment should only be used by trained, competent and authorised workers. The method statement should take account of this and the availability of suitable operators at the demolition site.

ACCESS AND EGRESS FROM SITE

The method statement should give consideration to the movement of vehicles and people on and around the site. Arrangements for access and egress for loading and unloading materials should be considered. Segregation of vehicle and pedestrian traffic should be specified.

Access and egress routes should be kept clear of any obstructions, with traffic and pedestrian routes clearly marked and signed. Emergency routes may have unique signage. All routes should be inspected on a regular basis for compliance. Where possible, it is good practice to operate a one-way traffic management system.

TRAINING AND WELFARE ARRANGEMENTS

Adequate training and information must be provided to visitors, new workers, transferred employees from another site and contractors. This should take the form of an induction course and include the following:

- Outline of the work.
- Key personnel and line managers.
- Site rules.
- Sites health and safety risks - for example, transport, any site contamination, hazardous substances and manual handling.
- Safe systems of work, permits-to-work systems.
- Security arrangements.
- Hearing protection zones.
- Personal protective equipment (PPE) provision, storage and cleaning stations.
- Housekeeping, material storage and waste.
- First-aid arrangements.
- Reporting of accidents or incidents.
- Emergency procedures.
- Welfare arrangements - for example, personal clothing storage, drying facilities, showers/toilets and rest areas.

The method statement should set out details of welfare facilities suitable for the work activity. This may include specialist decontamination facilities for workers dealing with contaminated materials or asbestos.

NAMED RESPONSIBLE PERSON

The client has the ultimate responsibility for the work being carried out. The principal contractor/contractor conducts the work on the client's behalf and should appoint a named responsible person (individual or agent) to control the work.

COORDINATION OF WORK ACTIVITIES

The method statement should specify measures for co-operation and coordination between people involved in the work, for example, client, principal designer, designers, principal contractor and contractors. The work process should follow the approved method statement produced in conjunction with the client, principal designer/designers and the principal contractor/contractors.

The principal contractor or contractor has overall control and coordination of the work. They must take into account any changes or new hazards identified, liaising with employees or sub-contractors and updating any health and safety requirements.

Exam practice

1. A multi-storey car park in a city centre is to be demolished.

    (a) **Identify FOUR** possible hazards to the environment that could be caused by the demolition. **(4)**

    (b) **Outline** measures to reduce the risk to the environment during the demolition work. **(4)**

2. **Outline** the control measures that should be considered when demolishing a group of ten terraced houses in a series of twenty terraced houses in an occupied street. **(8)**

3. **Outline** the main issues to be addressed in a pre-demolition survey of a three storey office block in a city centre. **(8)**

4. A steel framed warehouse that was part of a large factory is to be demolished. **Identify** the main control measures to be included in a demolition method statement. **(8)**

Please refer to the back of the assessment section for answers.

This page is intentionally blank

ELEMENT 12 - DEMOLITION AND DECONSTRUCTION - HAZARDS AND RISK CONTROL

This page is intentionally blank

Relevant statutory provisions

Content

Classification Labelling and Packaging of Substances (CLP) EC Regulation 360
Confined Spaces Regulations (CSR) 1997...362
Construction (Design and Management) Regulations (CDM) 2015 363
Control of Artificial Optical Radiation at Work Regulations (CAOR) 2010 372
Control of Asbestos Regulations (CAR) 2012..372
Control of Noise at Work Regulations (CNWR) 2005 375
Control of Substances Hazardous to Health Regulations (COSHH) 2002 377
Control of Substances Hazardous to Health (Amendment) Regulations (COSHH) 2004 381
Control of Vibration at Work Regulations (CVWR) 2005 381
Dangerous Substances and Explosive Atmospheres Regulations (DSEAR) 2002...382
Electricity at Work Regulations (EWR) 1989 384
Fire Safety (Scotland) Regulations (FSSR) 2006 386
Fire (Scotland) Act (FSA) 2005..386
Hazardous Waste (England and Wales) Regulations (HWR) 2005 (as amended) 387
Health and Safety (Display Screen Equipment) Regulations (DSE) 1992 (as amended) 389
Health and Safety (First-Aid) Regulations (FAR) 1981 (as amended) 390
Health and Safety (Miscellaneous Amendments) Regulations (MAR) 2002 390
Health and Safety (Miscellaneous Repeals, Revocations and Amendments) Regulations (MRRA) 2013 392
Health and Safety (Safety Signs and Signals) Regulations (SSSR) 1996 392
Ionising Radiations Regulations (IRR) 1999 392
Lifting Operations and Lifting Equipment Regulations (LOLER) 1998 (as amended) 394
Management of Health and Safety at Work Regulations (MHSWR) 1999 394
Manual Handling Operations Regulations (MHOR) 1992 (as amended) 398
New Roads and Street Works Act (NRSWA) 1991 399
Personal Protective Equipment at Work Regulations (PPER) 1992 (as amended) 400
Provision and Use of Work Equipment Regulations (PUWER) 1998 (as amended)...401
Registration, Evaluation, Authorisation and Restriction of Chemicals (REACH) EC Regulation 403
Regulatory Reform (Fire Safety) Order (RRFSO) 2005..406
Road Traffic Act (RTA) 1991 407
Supply of Machinery (Safety) Regulations (SMSR) 2008 409
Work at Height Regulations (WAH) 2005 410
Workplace (Health, Safety and Welfare) Regulations (WHSWR) 1992 412

RMS technical publications refer to the principal legislation relevant to the subjects covered by the publication. This is provided in context in the sections that comprise the publication. In addition, an outline of the main points of the legislation is provided in this relevant statutory provisions section. Here the outline relates to the main points of the legislation relevant to construction health and safety issues. This is provided to aid understanding and 'signpost' further reading and research.

RMS publications are widely used by students to support their professional studies and by qualified practitioners to maintain their continual professional development or to develop new skills.

This section to the guide provides an excellent reference source for those undergoing the following learning programmes:

- To meet the requirements of the NEBOSH National Certificate in Construction Health and Safety syllabus.
- To develop the knowledge of managers and supervisors working in construction.
- To develop and enhance competency and skills needed for facilities managers.
- To develop and enhance competency and skills needed for those who construct and disassemble temporary structures for outdoor events, music or theatre production and trade or other exhibitions.

The source documents used in this section may be obtained, free of charge, from www.legislation.gov.uk and www.hse.gov.uk/pubns/books.

Classification Labelling and Packaging of Substances (CLP) EC Regulation

Law considered in context and more depth in Element 8.

European Regulation (EC) No 1272/2008 on classification, labelling and packaging of substances and mixtures came into force on 20 January 2009 in all EU Member States, including the UK. It is known by its abbreviated form, 'the CLP Regulation' or 'CLP'.

The CLP Regulation adopts the United Nations' Globally Harmonised System (GHS) on the classification and labelling of chemicals across all European Union countries, including the UK. As the GHS is a voluntary agreement rather than a law, it has to be adopted through a suitable national or regional legal mechanism to ensure it becomes legally binding. That is what the CLP Regulation does.

As GHS was heavily influenced by the old EU system, the CLP Regulation is very similar in many ways. The duties on suppliers are broadly the same and cover classification, labelling and packaging. The process suppliers have to follow when they are classifying substances and mixtures has changed and a new set of hazard pictograms are used.

Explosive	Flammable	Corrosive	Toxic	Human health	Gas bottles	Environmental	Oxidizing

Figure RSP-1: GHS hazard pictograms.

Source: RMS.

Arrangement of Regulation

TITLE I - GENERAL ISSUES

Article 1   Purpose and scope

Article 2   Definitions

Article 3   Hazardous substances and mixtures and specification of hazard classes

Article 4   General obligations to classify, label and package

TITLE II - HAZARD CLASSIFICATION

Chapter 1 - Identification and examination of information

Article 5   Identification and examination of available information on substances

Article 6   Identification and examination of available information on mixtures

Article 7   Animal and human testing

Article 8   Generating new information for substances and mixtures

Chapter 2 - Evaluation of hazard information and decision on classification

Article 9   Evaluation of hazard information for substances and mixtures

Article 10   Concentration limits and M-factors for classification of substances and mixtures

Article 11   Cut-off values

Article 12   Specific cases requiring further evaluation

Article 13   Decision to classify substances and mixtures

Article 14   Specific rules for the classification of mixtures

Article 15   Review of classification for substances and mixtures

Article 16   Classification of substances included in the classification and labelling inventory

TITLE III - HAZARD COMMUNICATION IN THE FORM OF LABELLING

CHAPTER 1 - CONTENT OF THE LABEL

Article 17   General rules

Article 18   Product identifiers

Article 19   Hazard pictograms

Article 20   Signal words

Article 21   Hazard statements

Article 22   Precautionary statements

Article 23   Derogations from labelling requirements for special cases

Article 24   Request for use of an alternative chemical name

Article 25   Supplemental information on the label

Article 26   Principles of precedence for hazard pictograms

Article 27   Principles of precedence for hazard statements

Article 28   Principles of precedence for precautionary statements

Article 29   Exemptions from labelling and packaging requirements

Article 30   Updating information on labels

CHAPTER 2 - APPLICATION OF LABELS

Article 31   General rules for the application of labels

Article 32   Location of information on the label

Article 33   Specific rules for labelling of outer packaging, inner packaging and single packaging

Article 34   Report on communication on safe use of chemicals

TITLE IV - PACKAGING

Article 35   Packaging

TITLE V - HARMONISATION OF CLASSIFICATION AND LABELLING OF SUBSTANCES AND THE CLASSIFICATION AND LABELLING INVENTORY

CHAPTER 1 - ESTABLISHING HARMONISED CLASSIFICATION AND LABELLING OF SUBSTANCES

Article 36   Harmonisation of classification and labelling of substances

Article 37   Procedure for harmonisation of classification and labelling of substances

Article 38   Content of opinions and decisions for harmonised classification and labelling in Part 3 of Annex VI; accessibility of information

CHAPTER 2 - CLASSIFICATION AND LABELLING INVENTORY

Article 39   Scope

Article 40   Obligation to notify the Agency

Article 41   Agreed entries

Article 42   The classification and labelling inventory

TITLE VI - COMPETENT AUTHORITIES AND ENFORCEMENT

Article 43   Appointment of competent authorities and enforcement authorities and co-operation between authorities

Article 44   Helpdesk

Article 45   Appointment of bodies responsible for receiving information relating to emergency health response

Article 46   Enforcement and reporting

Article 47   Penalties for non-compliance

TITLE VII - COMMON AND FINAL PROVISIONS

Article 48   Advertisement

Article 49   Obligation to maintain information and requests for information

Article 50   Tasks of the Agency

Article 51   Free movement clause

Article 52   Safeguard clause

Article 53   Adaptations to technical and scientific progress

Article 54   Committee procedure

Article 55   Amendments to Directive 67/548/EEC

Article 56   Amendments to Directive 1999/45/EC

Article 57   Amendments to Regulation (EC) No 1907/2006 from the entry into force of this Regulation

Article 58   Amendments to Regulation (EC) No 1907/2006 from 1 December 2010

Article 59   Amendments to Regulation (EC) No 1907/2006 from 1 June 2015

Article 60   Repeal

Article 61   Transitional provisions

Article 62   Entry into force

ANNEX I - CLASSIFICATION AND LABELLING REQUIREMENTS FOR HAZARDOUS SUBSTANCES AND MIXTURES

This annex sets out the criteria for classification in hazard classes and in their differentiations and sets out additional provisions on how the criteria may be met.

PART 1 - GENERAL PRINCIPLES FOR CLASSIFICATION AND LABELLING

1.1. Classification of substances and mixtures

1.2. Labelling (General rules for the application of labels required by Article 31)

1.3. Derogations from labelling requirements for special cases

1.4. Request for use of an alternative chemical name

1.5. Exemptions from labelling and packaging requirements

PART 2 - PHYSICAL HAZARDS

Including explosive and flammable hazards

PART 3 - HEALTH HAZARDS

Including acute toxicity and respiratory/skin sensitisation hazards

PART 4 - ENVIRONMENTAL HAZARDS

Including hazards to the aquatic environment

PART 5 - ADDITIONAL HAZARDS

Including hazards to the ozone layer

Annex ii - Special rules for labelling and packaging of certain substances and mixtures

Annex iii - List of hazard statements, supplemental hazard information and supplemental label elements

Annex iv - List of precautionary statements

Annex v - Hazard pictograms

Annex vi - Harmonised classification and labelling for certain hazardous substances

Annex vii - Translation table from classification under directive 67/548/EEC to classification under this regulation

Outline of main points

The CLP Regulation ensures that the hazards presented by chemicals are clearly communicated to workers and consumers in the European Union, including the UK, through classification and labelling of chemicals. Before placing chemicals on the market, the industry must establish the potential risks to human health and the environment of such substances and mixtures, classifying them in line with the identified hazards. The hazardous chemicals also have to be labelled according to a standardised system so that workers and consumers know about their effects before they handle them. Suppliers must label a substance or mixture contained in packaging according to CLP before placing it on the market. CLP defines the content of the label and the organisation of the various labelling elements. This process ensures the hazards of chemicals are communicated through standard statements and pictograms on labels.

For example, when a supplier identifies a substance as 'acute toxicity category 1 (oral)', the labelling will include the hazard statement 'fatal if swallowed', the word 'Danger' and a pictogram with a skull and crossbones. CLP provides certain exemptions for substances and mixtures contained in packaging that is small (typically less than 125ml) or is otherwise difficult to label.

The exemptions allow the supplier to omit the hazard and/or precautionary statements or the pictograms from the label elements normally required under CLP. The label includes:

- The name, address and telephone number of the supplier.
- The nominal quantity of a substance or mixture in the packages made available to the general public (unless this quantity is specified elsewhere on the package).
- Product identifiers.
- Where applicable, hazard pictograms, signal words, hazard statements, precautionary statements and supplemental information required by other legislation.

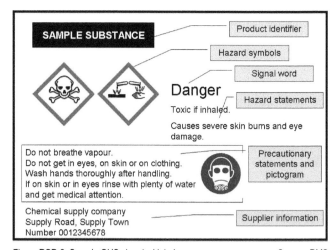

Figure RSP-2: Sample GHS chemical labels.   Source: RMS.

Confined Spaces Regulations (CSR) 1997

Law considered in context/more depth in Element 11.

Arrangement of Regulations

1) Citation, commencement and interpretation.

2) Disapplication of Regulations.

3) Duties.

4) Work in confined spaces.

5) Emergency arrangements.

6) Exemption certificates.

7) Defence in proceedings.

8) Extension outside Great Britain.

9) Repeal and revocations.

Outline of main points

The Confined Spaces Regulations (CSR) 1997 repeal and replace earlier provisions contained in s.30 of the Factories Act 1961.

A failure to appreciate the dangers associated with confined spaces has led not only to the deaths of many workers, but also to the demise of some of those who have attempted to rescue them. A confined space is not only a space which is small and difficult to enter, exit or work in; it can also be a large space, but with limited/restricted access. It can also be a space which is badly ventilated for example, a tank or a large tunnel.

The Confined Spaces Regulations (CSR) 1997, define a confined space as any place, including any chamber, tank, vat, silo, pit, pipe, sewer, flue, well, or other similar space, in which, by virtue of its enclosed nature, there arises a reasonably foreseeable specified risk.

The CSR 1997 sets out duties on employers and the self-employed in regard to work carried out in confined spaces. Entry into confined spaces is prohibited unless it is not reasonably practicable to do the work without entering. Work conducted must be carried out in accordance with a safe system of work and arrangements must be in place to deal with emergencies that may arise and to effect a rescue.

Construction (Design and Management) Regulations (CDM) 2015

Law considered in context/more depth in Element 1.

The Construction (Design and Management) Regulations (CDM) 2015 came in to force in April 2015. CDM 2015 re-emphasises the health, safety and broader business benefits of a well-managed and coordinated approach to the management of health and safety in construction that were introduced in earlier versions of this Regulation.

Arrangement of Regulations

PART 1 - COMMENCEMENT, INTERPRETATION AND APPLICATION

1) Citation and commencement.
2) Interpretation.
3) Application.

PART 2 - CLIENT DUTIES

4) Client duties in relation to managing projects.
5) Appointment of the principal designer and the principal contractor.
6) Notification.
7) Application to domestic clients.

PART 3 - HEALTH AND SAFETY DUTIES AND ROLES

8) General duties.
9) Duties of designers.
10) Designs prepared or modified outside Great Britain.
11) Duties of a principal designer in relation to health and safety at the pre-construction phase.
12) Construction phase plan and health and safety file.
13) Duties of a principal contractor in relation to health and safety at the construction phase.
14) Principal contractor's duties to consult and engage with workers.
15) Duties of contractors.

PART 4 - GENERAL REQUIREMENTS FOR ALL CONSTRUCTION SITES

16) Application of Part 4.
17) Safe places of construction work.
18) Good order and site security.
19) Stability of structures.
20) Demolition or dismantling.
21) Explosives.
22) Excavations.
23) Cofferdams and caissons.
24) Reports of inspections.
25) Energy distribution installations.
26) Prevention of drowning.
27) Traffic routes.
28) Vehicles.
29) Prevention of risk from fire, flooding or asphyxiation.
30) Emergency procedures.
31) Emergency routes and exits.
32) Fire detection and firefighting.
33) Fresh air.
34) Temperature and weather protection.

35) Lighting.

PART 5 - GENERAL

36) Enforcement in respect of fire.

37) Transitional and saving provisions.

38) Revocation and consequential amendments.

39) Review.

SCHEDULES

Schedule 1 (Regulation 6) - Particulars to be notified under Regulation 6

Schedule 2 (Regulation 4 (2)(b), 13(4)(c) and 15(11)) - Minimum welfare facilities required for construction sites

1) Sanitary conveniences.

2) Washing facilities.

3) Drinking water.

4) Changing rooms and lockers.

5) Facilities for rest.

Schedule 3 (Regulation 12(2)) - Work involving particular risk

Schedule 4 (Regulation 37) - Transitional and saving provisions

Schedule 5 (Regulation 38) - Amendments

Appendix 1 The general principles of prevention

Appendix 2 Pre-construction information

Appendix 3 The construction phase plan

Appendix 4 The health and safety file

Appendix 5 How different types of information relate to and influence each other in a construction project involving more than one contractor: A summary

Appendix 6 Working for a domestic client

Outline of main points

PART 2 - CLIENT DUTIES

Regulation 4 - Client duties for managing projects

(1) A client must make suitable arrangements for managing a project, including the allocation of sufficient time and other resources.

(2) Arrangements are suitable if they ensure that:

(a) The construction work can be carried out, so far as is reasonably practicable, without risks to the health or safety of any person affected by the project.

(b) The facilities required by Schedule 2 are provided in respect of any person carrying out construction work.

(3) A client must ensure that these arrangements are maintained and reviewed throughout the project.

(4) A client must provide pre-construction information as soon as is practicable to every designer and contractor appointed, or being considered for appointment, to the project.

(5) A client must ensure that -

(a) Before the construction phase begins, a construction phase plan is drawn up by the contractor if there is only one contractor, or by the principal contractor.

(b) The principal designer prepares a health and safety file for the project, which:

(i) Complies with the requirements of Regulation 12(5).

(ii) Is revised from time to time as appropriate to incorporate any relevant new information.

(iii) Is kept available for inspection by any person who may need it to comply with the relevant legal requirements.

(6) A client must take reasonable steps to ensure that -

(a) The principal designer complies with any other principal designer duties in Regulations 11 and 12.

(b) The principal contractor complies with any other principal contractor duties in Regulations 12 to 14.

(7) If a client disposes of the client's interest in the structure, the client complies with the duty in paragraph (5)(b)(iii) by providing the health and safety file to the person who acquires the client's interest in the structure and ensuring that that person is aware of the nature and purpose of the file.

(8) Where there is more than one client in relation to a project:

(a) One or more of the clients may agree in writing to be treated for the purposes of these Regulations as the only client or clients.

(b) Except for the duties specified in sub-paragraph (c) only the client or clients agreed in paragraph (a) are subject to the duties owed by a client under these Regulations.

(c) The duties in the following provisions are owed by all clients:

(i) Regulation 8(4).

(ii) Paragraph (4) and Regulation 8(6) to the extent that those duties relate to information in the possession of the client.

Regulation 5 - Appointment of the principal designer and the principal contractor

(1) Where there is more than one contractor, or if it is reasonably foreseeable that more than one contractor will be working on a project at any time, the client must appoint in writing -

    (a) A designer with control over the pre-construction phase as principal designer.

    (b) A contractor as principal contractor.

(2) The appointments must be made as soon as is practicable, and in any event, before the construction phase begins.

(3) If the client fails to appoint a principal designer, the client must fulfil the duties of the principal designer in Regulations 11 and 12.

(4) If the client fails to appoint a principal contractor, the client must fulfil the duties of the principal contractor in Regulations12 to 14.

Regulation 6 - Notification

(1) A project is notifiable if the construction work on a construction site is scheduled to -

    (a) Last longer than 30 working days and have more than 20 workers working simultaneously at any point in the project.

    (b) Exceed 500 person days.

(2) Where a project is notifiable, the client must give notice in writing to the Executive as soon as is practicable before the construction phase begins.

(3) The notice must -

    (a) Contain the particulars specified in Schedule 1.

    (b) Be clearly displayed in the construction site office in a comprehensible form where it can be read by any worker engaged in the construction work.

(c) If necessary, be periodically updated.

Regulation 7 - Application to domestic clients

(1) Where the client is a domestic client the duties in Regulations 4(1) to (7) and 6 must be carried out by:

    (a) The contractor for a project where there is only one contractor.

    (b) The principal contractor for a project where there is more than one contractor.

    (c) The principal designer where there is a written agreement that the principal designer will fulfil those duties.

(2) If a domestic client fails to make the appointments required by Regulation 5 -

    (a) The designer in control of the pre-construction phase of the project is the principal designer.

    (b) The contractor in control of the construction phase of the project is the principal contractor.

(3) Regulation 5(3) and (4) does not apply to a domestic client.

PART 3 - HEALTH AND SAFETY DUTIES AND ROLES

Regulation 8 - General duties

(1) A designer (including a principal designer) or contractor (including a principal contractor) appointed to work on a project must have the skills, knowledge and experience and, if they are an organisation, the organisational capability, necessary to fulfil the role that they are appointed to undertake, in a manner that secures the health and safety of any person affected by the project.

(2) A designer or contractor must not accept an appointment to a project unless they fulfil the conditions in paragraph (1).

(3) A person who is responsible for appointing a designer or contractor to carry out work on a project must take reasonable steps to satisfy themselves that the designer or contractor fulfils the conditions in paragraph (1).

(4) A person with a duty or function under these Regulations must co-operate with any other person working on or in relation to a project at the same or an adjoining construction site to the extent necessary to enable any person with a duty or function to fulfil that duty or function.

(5) A person working on a project under the control of another must report to that person anything they are aware of in relation to the project which is likely to endanger their own health or safety or that of others.

(6) Any person who is required by these Regulations to provide information or instruction must ensure the information or instruction is comprehensible and provided as soon as is practicable.

(7) To the extent that they are applicable to a domestic client, the duties in paragraphs (3), (4) and (6) must be carried out by the person specified in Regulation 7(1).

Regulation 9 - Duties of designers

(1) A designer must not commence work in relation to a project unless satisfied that the client is aware of the duties owed by the client under these Regulations.

(2) When preparing or modifying a design the designer must take into account the general principles of prevention and any pre-construction information to eliminate, so far as is reasonably practicable, foreseeable risks to the health or safety of any person:

    (a) Carrying out or liable to be affected by construction work.

    (b) Maintaining or cleaning a structure.

    (c) Using a structure designed as a workplace.

(3) If it is not possible to eliminate these risks, the designer must, so far as is reasonably practicable:

    (a) Take steps to reduce or, if that is not possible, control the risks through the subsequent design process.

    (b) Provide information about those risks to the principal designer.

    (c) Ensure appropriate information is included in the health and safety file.

(4)   A designer must take all reasonable steps to provide, with the design, sufficient information about the design, construction or maintenance of the structure, to adequately assist the client, other designers and contractors to comply with their duties under these Regulations.

Regulation 10 - Designs prepared or modified outside Great Britain

(1)   Where a design is prepared or modified outside Great Britain for use in construction work to which these Regulations apply:

(a) The person who commissions it, if established within Great Britain.

(b) If that person is not so established, the client for the project, must ensure that Regulation 9 is complied with.

(2)   This Regulation does not apply to a domestic client.

Regulation 11 - Duties of a principal designer in relation to health and safety at the pre-construction phase

(1)   The principal designer must plan, manage and monitor the pre-construction phase and coordinate matters relating to health and safety during the pre-construction phase to ensure that, so far as is reasonably practicable, the project is carried out without risks to health or safety.

(2)   In fulfilling the duties in paragraph (1), and in particular when:

(a) Design, technical and organisational aspects are being decided in order to plan the various items or stages of work which are to take place simultaneously or in succession.

(b) Estimating the period of time required to complete such work or work stages, the principal designer must take into account the general principles of prevention and, where relevant, the content of any construction phase plan and health and safety file.

(3)   In fulfilling the duties in paragraph (1), the principal designer must identify and eliminate or control, so far as is reasonably practicable, foreseeable risks to the health or safety of any person:

(a) Carrying out or liable to be affected by construction work.

(b) Maintaining or cleaning a structure.

(c) Using a structure designed as a workplace.

(4)   In fulfilling the duties in paragraph (1), the principal designer must ensure all designers comply with their duties in Regulation 9.

(5)   In fulfilling the duty to coordinate health and safety matters in paragraph (1), the principal designer must ensure that all persons working in relation to the pre-construction phase co-operate with the client, the principal designer and each other.

(6)   The principal designer must:

(a) Assist the client in the provision of the pre-construction information required by Regulation 4(4).

(b) So far as it is within the principal designer's control, provide pre-construction information, promptly and in a convenient form, to every designer and contractor appointed, or being considered for appointment, to the project.

(7)   The principal designer must liaise with the principal contractor for the duration of the principal designer's appointment and share with the principal contractor information relevant to the planning, management and monitoring of the construction phase and the coordination of health and safety matters during the construction phase.

Regulation 12 - Construction phase plan and health and safety file

(1)   During the pre-construction phase, and before setting up a construction site, the principal contractor must draw up a construction phase plan or make arrangements for a construction phase plan to be drawn up.

(2)   The construction phase plan must set out the health and safety arrangements and site rules taking account, where necessary, of the industrial activities taking place on the construction site and, where applicable, must include specific measures concerning work which falls within one or more of the categories set out in Schedule 3.

(3)   The principal designer must assist the principal contractor in preparing the construction phase plan by providing to the principal contractor all information the principal designer holds that is relevant to the construction phase plan including -

(a) Pre-construction information obtained from the client.

(b) Any information obtained from designers under Regulation 9(3)(b).

(4)   Throughout the project the principal contractor must ensure that the construction phase plan is appropriately reviewed, updated and revised from time to time so that it continues to be sufficient to ensure that construction work is carried out, so far as is reasonably practicable, without risks to health or safety.

(5)   During the pre-construction phase, the principal designer must prepare a health and safety file appropriate to the characteristics of the project which must contain information relating to the project which is likely to be needed during any subsequent project to ensure the health and safety of any person.

(6)   The principal designer must ensure that the health and safety file is appropriately reviewed, updated and revised from time to time to take account of the work and any changes that have occurred.

(7)   During the project, the principal contractor must provide the principal designer with any information in the principal contractor's possession relevant to the health and safety file, for inclusion in the health and safety file.

(8)   If the principal designer's appointment concludes before the end of the project, the principal designer must pass the health and safety file to the principal contractor.

(9)   Where the health and safety file is passed to the principal contractor under paragraph (8), the principal contractor must ensure that the health and safety file is appropriately reviewed, updated and revised from time to time to take account of the work and any changes that have occurred.

(10)   At the end of the project, the principal designer, or where there is no principal designer the principal contractor, must pass the health and safety file to the client.

Regulation 13 - Duties of a principal contractor in relation to health and safety at the construction phase

(1) The principal contractor must plan, manage and monitor the construction phase and coordinate matters relating to health and safety during the construction phase to ensure that, so far as is reasonably practicable, construction work is carried out without risks to health or safety;

(2) In fulfilling the duties in paragraph (1), and in particular when:

(a) Design, technical and organisational aspects are being decided in order to plan the various items or stages of work which are to take place simultaneously or in succession.

(b) Estimating the period of time required to complete the work or work stages; the principal contractor must take into account the general principles of prevention.

(3) The principal contractor must:

(a) Organise co-operation between contractors (including successive contractors on the same construction site).

(b) Coordinate implementation by the contractors of applicable legal requirements for health and safety; (c) ensure that employers and, if necessary for the protection of workers, self-employed persons.

(i) Apply the general principles of prevention in a consistent manner, and in particular when complying with the provisions of Part 4.

(ii) Where required, follow the construction phase plan.

(4) The principal contractor must ensure that:

(a) A suitable site induction is provided.

(b) The necessary steps are taken to prevent access by unauthorised persons to the construction site.

(c) Facilities that comply with the requirements of Schedule 2 are provided throughout the construction phase.

(5) The principal contractor must liaise with the principal designer for the duration of the principal designer's appointment and share with the principal designer information relevant to the planning, management and monitoring of the pre-construction phase and the coordination of health and safety matters during the pre-construction phase.

Regulation 14 - Principal contractor's duties to consult and engage with workers

The principal contractor must -

(a) Make and maintain arrangements which will enable the principal contractor and workers engaged in construction work to co-operate effectively in developing, promoting and checking the effectiveness of measures to ensure the health, safety and welfare of the workers.

(b) Consult those workers or their representatives in good time on matters connected with the project which may affect their health, safety or welfare, in so far as they or their representatives have not been similarly consulted by their employer.

(c) Ensure that those workers or their representatives can inspect and take copies of any information which the principal contractor has, or which these Regulations require to be provided to the principal contractor, which relate to the health, safety or welfare of workers at the site, except any information:

(i) The disclosure of which would be against the interests of national security.

(ii) Which the principal contractor could not disclose without contravening a prohibition imposed by or under an enactment.

(iii) Relating specifically to an individual, unless that individual has consented to its being disclosed.

(iv) The disclosure of which would, for reasons other than its effect on health, safety or welfare at work, cause substantial injury to the principal contractor's undertaking or, where the information was supplied to the principal contractor by another person, to the undertaking of that other person.

(v) Obtained by the principal contractor for the purpose of bringing, prosecuting or defending any legal proceedings.

Regulation 15 - Duties of contractors

(1) A contractor must not carry out construction work in relation to a project unless satisfied that the client is aware of the duties owed by the client under these Regulations.

(2) A contractor must plan, manage and monitor construction work carried out either by the contractor or by workers under the contractor's control, to ensure that, so far as is reasonably practicable, it is carried out without risks to health and safety.

(3) Where there is more than one contractor working on a project, a contractor must comply with:

(a) Any directions given by the principal designer or the principal contractor.

(b) The parts of the construction phase plan that are relevant to that contractor's work on the project.

(4) If there is only one contractor working on the project, the contractor must take account of the general principles of prevention when -

(a) Design, technical and organisational aspects are being decided in order to plan the various items or stages of work which are to take place simultaneously or in succession.

(b) Estimating the period of time required to complete the work or work stages.

(5) If there is only one contractor working on the project, the contractor must draw up a construction phase plan, or make arrangements for a construction phase plan to be drawn up, as soon as is practicable prior to setting up a construction site.

(6) The construction phase plan must fulfil the requirements of Regulation 12(2).

(7) A contractor must not employ or appoint a person to work on a construction site unless that person has, or is in the process of obtaining, the necessary skills, knowledge, training and experience to carry out the tasks allocated to that person in a manner that secures the health and safety of any person working on the construction site.

(8) A contractor must provide each worker under their control with appropriate supervision, instructions and information so that construction work can be carried out, so far as is reasonably practicable, without risks to health and safety.

(9)   The information provided must include:

(a) A suitable site induction, where not already provided by the principal contractor.

(b) The procedures to be followed in the event of serious and imminent danger to health and safety.

(c) Information on risks to health and safety.

(i) Identified by the risk assessment under Regulation 3 of the Management Regulations.

(ii) Arising out of the conduct of another contractor's undertaking and of which the contractor in control of the worker ought reasonably to be aware.

(d) Any other information necessary to enable the worker to comply with the relevant statutory provisions.

(10) A contractor must not begin work on a construction site unless reasonable steps have been taken to prevent access by unauthorised persons to that site.

(11) A contractor must ensure, so far as is reasonably practicable, that the requirements of Schedule 2 are complied with so far as they affect the contractor or any worker under that contractor's control.

PART 4 - GENERAL REQUIREMENTS FOR ALL CONSTRUCTION SITES

Part 4 of CDM 2015 sets out general health, safety and welfare requirements that apply to all construction sites involved in construction work.

The Regulations in Part 4 apply to places of work in the ground, at ground level and at height. In essence they require that arrangements are made to ensure risks to health and safety are minimised and appropriate welfare facilities are provided.

Safe place of work, good order and site security (Regulations 17 and 18)

- Safe access to and egress from places of work and other places that workers have access to within a construction site.
- The site must be safe and healthy for those that work there.
- The site must have sufficient working space and be arranged so that it is suitable for those working on it, taking into account any work equipment that is being used.
- The site should be kept in a reasonable state of cleanliness and in good order.
- Depending on the level of risk, the site must have its perimeter identified by signs or be fenced off.
- Removal of material with projecting nails or similar sharp objects that could be a source of danger.

Work on structures (Regulations 19, 20 and 21)

- Prevent accidental collapse of new, existing structures or those under construction.
- Not to load structures unsafely.
- Make sure any dismantling or demolition of any structure is planned and carried out in a safe manner.
- Arrangements for carrying out demolition or dismantling must be recorded in writing.
- Explosive charges must be stored, transported and used safely and securely. Explosive charges can only be fired after steps have been taken to ensure that no one is exposed to risk or injury from the explosion.

Every year there are structural collapses which have the potential to cause serious injury. Demolition or dismantling are recognised as high risk activities. In any cases where this work presents a risk of danger to anyone, it should be planned and carried out under the direct supervision of a competent person.

Excavations, cofferdams and caissons (Regulations 22, 23 and 24)

- Prevent collapse of ground both in and above excavations by the use of supports or battering.
- Prevent people, equipment and materials falling in to excavations.
- Ensure cofferdams and caissons are properly designed, constructed and maintained.
- Inspections of excavations, cofferdams and caissons, and any work equipment/materials that may affect its safety, by a competent person. Prevent work in excavations that have been inspected and found to be unsafe, until they have been made safety.
- Inform the responsible person of the outcome of inspections and provide reports of the inspection, containing the specified details, to the responsible person before the end of the shift. The report must include:

  - The name and address of the person on whose behalf the inspection was carried out.
  - The location of the place of construction work inspected.
  - A description of the place of construction work or part of that place inspected (including any work equipment and materials).
  - The date and time of the inspection.
  - The details of any matter identified that could give rise to a risk to the safety of any person.
  - Details of any action taken as a result of any matter identified above.
  - The details of any further action considered necessary.
  - The name and position of the person making the report.

- Provide the report or a copy of it, to the person on whose behalf the inspection was carried out, within 24 hours of completing the inspection.
- No further inspection reports are required for subsequent inspection of that place within a 7 day period.

From the outset, and as work progresses, any excavation which has the potential to collapse unless supported should have suitable equipment immediately available to provide such support.

Regular inspection of excavations, cofferdams and caissons is an important aspect of assuring that they are safe to be worked in. When inspections identify problems with them it is essential that they are resolved before people work in them.

Energy distribution installations (Regulation 25)

- Where necessary to prevent danger, energy distribution installations must be suitably located, checked and clearly indicated.
- Where there is a risk from overhead electric power cables, they must be directed away from the area of risk or the power cut off or, if it is not reasonably practicable, provide:

- Barriers suitable for excluding work equipment which is not needed.
- Suspended protections where vehicles need to pass beneath the cables.
- Measures achieving an equivalent level of safety.
- Take suitable and sufficient steps to prevent construction work creating a risk to health or safety from underground services, or from damage to or disturbance of it.

Prevention or avoidance of drowning (Regulation 26)

- Take steps to prevent people from falling into water or other liquid with a risk of drowning and to minimise the risk of drowning in the event of a fall.
- Ensure rescue equipment is immediately available for use and is maintained.
- Make sure safe transport by water is provided and is not overcrowded or overloaded.

Traffic routes and vehicles (Regulations 27 and 28)

- Ensure construction sites are organised so that pedestrians and vehicles can both move safely and without risks to health.
- Make sure traffic routes are suitable and sufficient for the people or vehicles using them.
- Ensure separation between vehicles and pedestrians, including at doors and gate.
- Ensure loading bays have at least one exit for the exclusive use of pedestrians.
- Ensure a separate pedestrian door is provided where gates are used primarily for vehicles.
- Ensure traffic routes are identified, checked and maintained.
- Ensure traffic routes are free from obstruction and wide enough for use.
- Prevent or control the unintended movement of any vehicle.
- Make arrangements for giving a warning of any possible dangerous movement, for example, reversing vehicles.
- Ensure vehicles are loaded and driven safely. Including prohibiting people from remaining on vehicles loading loose materials and riding on vehicles, unless they are in a safe place.
- Ensure measures are taken to prevent vehicles falling into excavations, pits or water.

Fresh air, temperature and lighting (Regulations 33, 34, and 35)

- Ensure sufficient fresh or purified air is available at every workplace. Where plant is used to provide fresh or purified air it must give a visible or audible warning of its failure.
- Make sure a reasonable working temperature is maintained at indoor work places during working hours.
- Provide facilities for protection against adverse weather conditions.
- Make sure suitable and sufficient lighting is available (preferably natural light), including providing secondary lighting where there would be a risk to health or safety if primary or artificial lighting failed.

Prevention and control of emergencies (Regulations 29, 30, 31, 32 and 36)

- Prevent risk from fire, explosion, flooding and asphyxiation.
- Make arrangements for dealing with emergencies, including procedures for evacuating the site and the testing of these procedures.
- Provide emergency routes and exits, which have emergency lighting and are indicated by signs.
- Where necessary, provide firefighting equipment, fire detectors and alarm systems.

These Regulations require the prevention of risk as far as it is reasonably practicable to achieve. However, there are times when emergencies do arise and planning is needed to ensure, for example, that emergency routes are provided and evacuation procedures are in place. These particular Regulations (as well as those on traffic routes, welfare, cleanliness and signing of sites) apply to construction work which is carried out on construction sites. However, the rest of the Regulations apply to all construction work.

The HSE continues to be responsible for inspection of means of escape and firefighting for most sites. However, fire authorities have enforcement responsibility in many premises which remain in normal use during construction work. This continues the sensible arrangement which ensures that the most appropriate enforcement authority regulates fire safety.

PART 5 - GENERAL

Regulation 36 - Enforcement in respect of fire

The enforcing authority for Regulations 30 and 31 (so far as those Regulations relate to fire) and Regulation 32, in respect of a construction site which is contained within or forms part of premises occupied by persons other than those carrying out construction work, or any activity related to this work, is:

- In England and Wales the enforcing authority enforcing the Regulatory Reform (Fire Safety) Order 2005 in the premises.
- In Scotland the enforcing authority enforcing the Fire (Scotland) Act 2005 in the premises.

Regulation 37 - Transitional and saving provisions

Schedule 4, sets out transitional arrangements for projects established before CDM 2015 came into force.

Regulation 38 - Revocation and consequential amendments

1. The 2007 Regulations are revoked.
2. The amendments affecting other legislation are set out in Schedule 5 of CDM 2015.

SCHEDULES

SCHEDULE 1 (Regulation 6) Particulars to be notified under Regulation 6

Regulation 6 requires the notification of specified categories of project to the enforcing authority, usually the HSE. The particulars to be included in the notification are:

1. The date of forwarding the notice.
2. The address of the construction site or precise description of its location.
3. The name of the Local Authority where the construction site is located.

4.   A brief description of the project and the construction work that it entails.

5.   The following contact details of the client: name, address, telephone number and (if available) an email address.

6.   The following contact details of the principal designer: name, address, telephone number and (if available) an email address.

7.   The following contact details of the principal contractor: name, address, telephone number and (if available) an email address.

8.   The date planned for the start of the construction phase.

9.   The time allocated by the client under Regulation 4(1) for the construction work.

10. The planned duration of the construction phase.

11. The estimated maximum number of people at work on the construction site.

12. The planned number of contractors on the construction site.

13. The name and address of any contractor already appointed.

14. The name and address of any designer already appointed.

15. A declaration signed by or on behalf of the client that the client is aware of the client duties under these Regulations.

SCHEDULE 2 (Regulation 4(2)(b), 13(4)(c) and 15(11)) Minimum welfare facilities

Sanitary conveniences

■   Provide suitable and sufficient sanitary conveniences or make them available at readily accessible places.

■   Provide rooms containing sanitary conveniences that are adequately ventilated and lit.

■   Keep the sanitary conveniences and the rooms containing them in a clean and orderly condition.

■   Provide separate rooms containing sanitary conveniences for men and women, except where each convenience is in a separate room and the door to the room is capable of being secured from the inside.

Washing facilities

■   Provide suitable and sufficient washing facilities, including showers if required by the nature of the work or for health reasons, or make them available at readily accessible places. This includes near sanitary conveniences and changing rooms.

■   Provide washing facilities with a supply of clean hot and cold, or warm, running water; soap or other suitable means of cleaning; towels or other suitable means of drying.

■   Provide ventilation and lighting for washing facilities and ensure they are kept clean and in an orderly condition.

■   Provide separate washing facilities for men and women, except where they are provided in a room and the door to the room can be secured from inside and the facilities in each room are intended to be used by only one person at a time.

■   Separate washing facilities are not required where they are only provided for washing hands, forearms and face.

Drinking water

■   Provide an adequate supply of wholesome drinking water or make it available at readily accessible and suitable places.

■   Mark every supply of drinking water with an appropriate sign where necessary for reasons of health and safety.

■   Provide a sufficient number of suitable cups or other drinking vessels, unless the supply of drinking water is in a jet from which people can drink easily.

Changing rooms and lockers

■   Provide suitable and sufficient changing rooms or make them available at readily accessible places if a worker has to wear special clothing for the purposes of work and cannot, for reasons of health or propriety, be expected to change elsewhere.

■   Where necessary for reasons of propriety, provide separate rooms for men and women.

■   Provide changing rooms with seating and, where necessary, facilities to enable the drying of any special clothing and the worker's own clothing and personal effects.

■   Provide, where necessary, suitable and sufficient facilities or make them available at readily accessible places to enable persons to lock away any such special clothing which is not taken home, their own clothing which is not worn during working hours, their personal effects.

Facilities for rest

■   Provide suitable and sufficient rest rooms or rest areas must be provided or made available at readily accessible places.

■   Ensure rest rooms and rest areas:

(a) Are equipped with an adequate number of tables and adequate seating with backs for the number of persons at work likely to use them at any one time.

(b) Where necessary, include suitable facilities for any person at work who is a pregnant woman or nursing mother to rest lying down.

(c) Include suitable arrangements to ensure that meals can be prepared and eaten.

(d) Include the means for boiling water.

(e) Be maintained at an appropriate temperature.

SCHEDULE 3 (Regulation 12(2)) - Work involving particular risks

Regulation 12 requires that special account be taken of work involving risks specified in Schedule 3 when setting out health and safety arrangements in the construction phase plan.

The risks specified in Schedule 3 are:

1.   Work which puts workers at risk of burial under earthfalls, engulfment in swampland or falling from a height, where the risk is particularly aggravated by the nature of the work or processes used or by the environment at the place of work or site.

2.   Work which puts workers at risk from chemical or biological substances constituting a particular danger to the safety or health of workers or involving a legal requirement for health monitoring.

3. Work with ionizing radiation requiring the designation of controlled or supervised areas under Regulation 16 of the Ionising Radiations Regulations 1999.

4. Work near high voltage power lines.

5. Work exposing workers to the risk of drowning.

6. Work on wells, underground earthworks and tunnels.

7. Work carried out by divers having a system of air supply.

8. Work carried out by workers in caissons with a compressed air atmosphere.

9. Work involving the use of explosives.

10. Work involving the assembly or dismantling of heavy prefabricated components.

SCHEDULE 4 Transitional provisions

This schedule established arrangements for projects that were in place at the time the Regulations came into force and provided transitional provisions for this.

They cover situations where a CDM coordinator had been appointed and ones where they had not.

Projects with no existing CDM coordinator or principal contractor

Where no CDM coordinator or principal contractor is appointed, there is or is likely to be more than one contractor and the construction phase has started:

- The client may appoint a principal designer and must appoint a principal contractor and ensure the principal contractor draws up a construction phase plan.
- If the client, other than a domestic client, does not appoint a principal designer the principal must prepare a health and safety file, ensure it is reviewed, updated and revised as the project proceeds.
- Where the client, other than a domestic client, fails to appoint a principal contractor, the client must fulfil the principal contractor duties. If the client is a domestic client the contractor in control of the construction phase is the principal contractor.

Projects with an existing CDM coordinator

Where a CDM coordinator is appointed:

- The appointment of CDM coordinator continues to have effect until a principal designer is appointed or the project comes to an end. Duties in these Regulations to liaise with the principal designer will mean liaising with the CDM coordinator.
- The client may appoint a principal designer for the project before 6th October 2015.

Duties of CDM coordinator during the transitional period

The CDM coordinator must:

- Co-operate with any other person working on or in relation to a project at the same or an adjoining construction site, to the extent necessary to enable any person with a duty or function under these Regulations to fulfil that duty or function.
- Where the CDM coordinator works under the control of another, report to that person anything they are aware of in relation to the project which is likely to endanger their own health or safety or that of others.
- Ensure that suitable arrangements are made and implemented for the coordination of health and safety measures during the planning and preparation for the construction phase, including facilitating:
  (i)   Co-operation and coordination between all persons working on the pre-construction phase of the project.
  (ii) The application of the general principles of prevention.
- Liaise with the principal contractor over:
  (i)   The content of the health and safety file.
  (ii) The information which the principal contractor needs to prepare the construction phase plan.
  (iii) Any design development which may affect planning and management of the construction work.
- Where no or partial pre-construction information has been supplied to the CDM coordinator by the client under Regulation 10 of the 2007 Regulations, assist the client to comply with Regulation 4(4) of these Regulations.
- Unless the information has already been provided under Regulation 20(2)(b) of the 2007 Regulations, provide any pre-construction information that is in the possession or control of the CDM coordinator, promptly and in a convenient form, to every designer and contractor appointed, or being considered for appointment, to the project.
- Take all reasonable steps to ensure that designers comply with their duties under Regulation 9 of these Regulations.
- Take all reasonable steps to ensure co-operation between designers and the principal contractor during the construction phase in relation to any design or change to a design.
- If a health and safety file has not been prepared under Regulation 20(2)(e) of the 2007 Regulations, prepare a health and safety file that complies with the requirements of Regulation 12(5) of these Regulations.
- Review, update and revise the health and safety file from time to time to take account of the work and any changes that have occurred.
- If the CDM coordinator's appointment continues to have effect immediately before the project ends, pass the health and safety file to the client at the end of the project.
- If a principal designer is appointed, pass the health and safety file and all other relevant health and safety information in the CDM coordinator's possession to the principal designer, as soon as is practicable after the appointment.
- The CDM coordinator must not arrange for or instruct a worker to carry out or manage design or construction work unless the worker is competent or under the supervision of a competent person.

Projects with one contractor

Where a relevant project has only one contractor and the construction phase has started, the contractor must draw up a construction phase plan, or make arrangements for a construction phase plan to be drawn up as soon as is practicable.

Control of Artificial Optical Radiation at Work Regulations (CAOR) 2010

Law considered in context/more depth in Element 9.

Arrangement of Regulations

1) Citation, commencement and interpretation.
2) Application of these Regulations.
3) Assessment of the risk of adverse health effects to the eyes or skin created by exposure to artificial optical radiation at the workplace.
4) Obligations to eliminate or reduce risks.
5) Information and training.
6) Health surveillance and medical examinations.
7) Extension outside Great Britain.

Outline of main points

The Regulations came into force on 27 April 2010. The employer has duties to employees and any other person at work who may be affected by the work carried out.

ASSESSMENT OF THE RISK OF ADVERSE HEALTH EFFECTS TO THE EYES OR SKIN

The employer must make a suitable and sufficient assessment of risk for the purpose of identifying the measures it needs to take to meet the requirements of these Regulations where:

(a) The employer carries out work which could expose any of its employees to levels of artificial optical radiation that could create a reasonably foreseeable risk of adverse health effects to the eyes or skin of the employee.

(b) That employer has not implemented any measures to either eliminate or, where this is not reasonably practicable, reduce to as low a level as is reasonably practicable, that risk based on the general principles of prevention set out in Schedule 1 to the Ionising Radiation (IRR) Regulations 1999.

OBLIGATIONS TO ELIMINATE OR REDUCE RISKS

An employer must ensure that any risk of adverse health effects to the eyes or skin of employees as a result of exposure to artificial optical radiation which is identified in the risk assessment is eliminated or, where this is not reasonably practicable, reduced to as low a level as is reasonably practicable.

INFORMATION AND TRAINING

If the risk assessment indicates that employees could be exposed to artificial optical radiation which could cause adverse health effects to the eyes or skin of employees, the employer must provide its employees and representatives with suitable and sufficient information and training relating to the outcome of the risk assessment, and this must include the following:

(a) The technical and organisational measures taken in order to comply with the requirements of Regulation 4.
(b) The exposure limit values.
(c) The significant findings of the risk assessment, including any measurements taken, with an explanation of those findings.
(d) Why and how to detect and report adverse health effects to the eyes or skin.
(e) The circumstances in which employees are entitled to appropriate health surveillance.
(f) Safe working practices to minimise the risk of adverse health effects to the eyes or skin from exposure to artificial optical radiation.
(g) The proper use of personal protective equipment.

The employer must ensure that any person, whether or not that person is an employee, who carries out work in connection with the employer's duties under these Regulations has suitable and sufficient information and training.

HEALTH SURVEILLANCE AND MEDICAL EXAMINATIONS

If the risk assessment indicates that there is a risk of adverse health effects to the skin of employees, as a result of exposure to artificial optical radiation, the employer must ensure that such employees are placed under suitable health surveillance.

Control of Asbestos Regulations (CAR) 2012

Law considered in context/more depth in Element 8.

Arrangement of Regulations

PART 1 - PRELIMINARY

1) Citation and commencement.
2) Interpretation.
3) Application of these Regulations.

PART 2 - GENERAL REQUIREMENTS

4) Duty to manage asbestos in non-domestic premises.
5) Identification of the presence of asbestos.
6) Assessment of work which exposes employees to asbestos.
7) Plans of work.
8) Licensing of work with asbestos.

9) Notification of work with asbestos.

10) Information, instruction and training.

11) Prevention or reduction of exposure to asbestos.

12) Use of control measures etc.

13) Maintenance of control measures etc.

14) Provision and cleaning of protective clothing.

15) Arrangements to deal with accidents, incidents and emergencies.

16) Duty to prevent or reduce the spread of asbestos.

17) Cleanliness of premises and plant.

18) Designated areas.

19) Air monitoring.

20) Standards for air testing.

21) Standards for analysis.

22) Health records and medical surveillance.

23) Washing and changing facilities.

24) Storage, distribution and labelling of raw asbestos and asbestos waste.

PART 3 - PROHIBITIONS AND RELATED PROVISIONS

25) Interpretation of prohibitions.

26) Prohibitions of exposure to asbestos.

27) Labelling of products containing asbestos.

28) Additional provisions in the case of exceptions and exemptions.

PART 4 MISCELLANEOUS

29) Exemption certificates.

30) Exemptions relating to the Ministry of Defence.

31) Extension outside Great Britain.

32) Existing licences and exemption certificates.

33) Revocations and savings.

34) Defence.

35) Review.

SCHEDULE 1

Particulars to be included in a notification.

SCHEDULE 2

Appendix 7 to Annex XVII of the REACH Regulation – special provisions on the labelling of articles containing asbestos.

SCHEDULE 3

Amendments.

Outline of main points

SUMMARY

The **Control of Asbestos Regulations (CAR) 2012** place emphasis on assessment of exposure; exposure prevention, reduction and control; adequate information, instruction and training for employees; monitoring and health surveillance. The Regulations also apply to incidental exposure. The section on prohibitions is now covered by REACH. The amendments in these Regulations have introduced an additional category of work with asbestos. The three categories are: Licensed, Non-Licensed and a new category of Notifiable Non-Licensed (NNLW). A summary of the requirements of each category is detailed below:

Non-licenced work	Notifiable non-licenced work	Licenced work
■ Carry out and comply with a risk assessment. ■ Control exposure. ■ Provide training and information.	■ Notify before work starts. ■ Provide medical examinations every three years. ■ Keep health records of employees. ■ Carry out and comply with a risk assessment. ■ Control exposure. ■ Provide training and information.	■ Licencing. ■ Notify fourteen days in advance. ■ Develop emergency arrangements. ■ Designate of asbestos areas. ■ Provide medical examination every two years. ■ Keep health records of all employees. ■ Carry out and comply with a risk assessment. ■ Control exposure. ■ Provide training and information.

In order to achieve the required changes the Regulations provide a separate definition of licensable work and set out the scope of the work which is exempt from the various requirements as now. Several other amendments have also been necessary and as a result there are changes to the notification requirements and those relating to health records and medical surveillance to distinguish between licensed and non-licensed work and amendments to permit a wider range of medical professionals to carry out the required medical examinations.

The work for which a licence is required is defined as 'Licensable work with asbestos' and is work:

(a)   Where the exposure to asbestos of employees is not sporadic and of low intensity.

(b)   In relation to which the risk assessment cannot clearly demonstrate that the control limit will not be exceeded.

(c)   On asbestos coating.

(d)   On asbestos insulating board or asbestos insulation for which the risk assessment:

    (i)   Demonstrates that the work is not sporadic and of low intensity.

    (ii)   Cannot clearly demonstrate that the control limit will not be exceeded.

    (iii)   Demonstrates that the work is not short duration work.

Regulation 3(2) sets out the exemptions for non-licensable work as follows:

Regulations 9 (notification of work with asbestos), 18(1)(a) (designated areas) and 22 (health records and medical surveillance) do not apply where:

(a)   The exposure to asbestos of employees is sporadic and of low intensity.

(b)   It is clear from the risk assessment that the exposure to asbestos of any employee will not exceed the control limit.

(c)   The work involves:

    (i)   Short, non-continuous maintenance activities in which only non-friable materials are handled.

    (ii)   Removal without deterioration of non-degraded materials in which the asbestos fibres are firmly linked in a matrix.

    (iii)   Encapsulation or sealing of asbestos-containing materials which are in good condition.

    (iv)   Air monitoring and control, and the collection and analysis of samples to ascertain whether a specific material contains asbestos.

Whether a type of asbestos work is either licensable, NNLW or non-licensed work has to be determined in each case and will depend on the type of work being carried out, the type of material being worked on and its condition. The identification of the type of asbestos-containing material (ACM) to be worked on and an assessment of its condition are important parts of your risk assessment, which needs to be completed before work starts. It is the responsibility of the person in charge of the job to assess the ACM to be worked on and decide if the work is NNLW or non-licensed work. This will be a matter of judgement in each case, dependent on consideration of the above factors. A decision flow chart is available from the HSE at www.hse.gov.uk/asbestos/essentials/index.htm.

Duty to manage asbestos in non-domestic premises (Regulation 4)

The Regulations include the 'duty to manage asbestos' in non-domestic premises. Guidance on the duty to manage asbestos can be found in the Approved Code of Practice, Work with Materials Containing Asbestos, L143 (Second Edition), ISBN 9780717662067.

Information, instruction and training (Regulation 10)

The Regulations require mandatory training for anyone liable to be exposed to asbestos fibres at work. This includes maintenance workers and others who may come into contact with or who may disturb asbestos (for example, cable installers) as well as those involved in asbestos removal work.

Prevention or reduction of exposure to asbestos (Regulation 11)

When work with asbestos or which may disturb asbestos is being carried out, the Control of Asbestos Regulations require employers and the self-employed to prevent exposure to asbestos fibres. Where this is not reasonably practicable, they must make sure that exposure is kept as low as reasonably practicable by measures other than the use of respiratory protective equipment. The spread of asbestos must be prevented. The Regulations specify the work methods and controls that should be used to prevent exposure and spread.

Control limits

Worker exposure must be below the airborne exposure limit (Control Limit). The Asbestos Regulations have a single Control Limit for all types of asbestos of 0.1 fibres per cm^3. A Control Limit is a maximum concentration of asbestos fibres in the air (averaged over any continuous 4 hour period) that must not be exceeded. In addition, short term exposures must be strictly controlled and worker exposure should not exceed 0.6 fibres per cm^3 of air averaged over any continuous 10 minute period using respiratory protective equipment if exposure cannot be reduced sufficiently using other means.

Respiratory protective equipment

Respiratory protective equipment is an important part of the control regime but it must not be the sole measure used to reduce exposure and should only be used to supplement other measures. Work methods that control the release of fibres such as those detailed in the **Asbestos Essentials task sheets** (available on the HSE website) for non-licensed work should be used. Respiratory protective equipment must be suitable, must fit properly and must ensure that worker exposure is reduced as low as is reasonably practicable.

Asbestos removal work undertaken by a licensed contractor

Most asbestos removal work must be undertaken by a licensed contractor but any decision on whether particular work is licensable is based on the risk. Work is only exempt from licensing if:

■   The exposure of employees to asbestos fibres is sporadic and of low intensity (but exposure cannot be considered to be sporadic and of low intensity if the concentration of asbestos in the air is liable to exceed 0.6 fibres per cm3 measured over 10 minutes).

■   It is clear from the risk assessment that the exposure of any employee to asbestos will not exceed the control limit.

■   The work involves:

    •   Short, non-continuous maintenance activities. Work can only be considered as short, non-continuous maintenance activities if any one person carries out work with these materials for less than one hour in a seven-day period. The total time spent by all workers on the work should not exceed a total of two hours*.

- Removal of materials in which the asbestos fibres are firmly linked in a matrix. Such materials include: asbestos cement; textured decorative coatings and paints which contain asbestos; articles of bitumen, plastic, resin or rubber which contain asbestos where their thermal or acoustic properties are incidental to their main purpose (for example, vinyl floor tiles, electric cables, roofing felt) and other insulation products which may be used at high temperatures but have no insulation purposes, for example gaskets, washers, ropes and seals.
- Encapsulation or sealing of asbestos-containing materials which are in good condition.
- Air monitoring and control, and the collection and analysis of samples to find out if a specific material contains asbestos.

It is important that the amount of time employees spend working with asbestos insulation, asbestos coatings or asbestos insulating board (AIB) is managed to make sure that these time limits are not exceeded. This includes the time for activities such as building enclosures and cleaning.

Under the Asbestos Regulations, anyone carrying out work on asbestos insulation, asbestos coating or AIB needs a licence issued by HSE unless they meet one of the exemptions above. *Although you may not need a licence to carry out a particular job, you still need to comply with the rest of the requirements of the Asbestos Regulations.*

Licensable work - additional duties

If the work is licensable there are a number of additional duties.

The need to:

- Notify the enforcing authority responsible for the site where you are working (for example, HSE or the Local Authority).
- Designate the work area (see Regulation 18 for details).
- Prepare specific asbestos emergency procedures.
- Pay for your employees to undergo medical surveillance.

Non-notifiable licensable work - additional duties

If work is determined to be NNLW, the duties are:

- To notify the enforcing authority responsible for the site where the work is before work starts. (There is no minimum period).
- By 2015 all employees will have to undergo medical examinations which are repeated every three years.
- To have prepared procedures which can be put into effect should an accident, incident or emergency occur.
- To keep a register of all NNLW work for all employees.
- To record the significant findings of and comply with a risk assessment.
- To prevent or reduce exposure so far as is reasonably practicable and to take reasonable steps that all control measures are used.
- To ensure that adequate information, instruction and training is given to employees.

Air monitoring (Regulation 19)

The Asbestos Regulations require any analysis of the concentration of asbestos in the air to be measured in accordance with the 1997 WHO recommended method.

Standards for air testing and site clearance certification (Regulation 20)

From 06 April 2007, a clearance certificate for re-occupation may only be issued by a body accredited to do so. At the moment, such accreditation can only be provided by the United Kingdom Accreditation Service (UKAS). You can find more details of how to undertake work with asbestos containing materials, the type of controls necessary, what training is required and analytical methods in the following HSE publications:

- Approved Code of Practice Work with Materials containing Asbestos, L143, ISBN: 978-0-717662-06-7.
- Asbestos: the Licensed Contractors Guide, HSG 247, ISBN: 978-0-717628-74-2.
- Asbestos: the analysts' guide for sampling, analysis and clearance procedures, HSG 248, ISBN: 978-0-717628-75-9.
- Asbestos Essentials, HSG 210, ISBN: 978-0-717662-63-0. (See also the 'Asbestos Essentials Task Sheets' available on the HSE website).

Other health and safety legislation must be complied with.

Source: HSE Website: www.hse.gov.uk.

Control of Noise at Work Regulations (CNWR) 2005

Law considered in context/more depth in Element 9.

Arrangement of Regulations

1) Citation and commencement.
2) Interpretation.
3) Application and transition.
4) Exposure limit values and action values.
5) Assessment of the risk to health created by exposure to noise at the workplace.
6) Elimination or control of exposure to noise at the workplace.
7) Hearing protection.
8) Maintenance and use of equipment.
9) Health surveillance.
10) Information, instruction and training.
11) Exemption certificates from hearing protection.
12) Exemption certificates for emergency services.

13) Exemption relating to the Ministry of Defence etc.

14) Extension outside Great Britain.

15) Revocations, amendment and savings.

Outline of main points

CHANGES TO THE ACTION LEVELS (REGULATION 4)

The values of the actions levels associated with noise at work have been lowered and their names have been changed. The first action level is reduced from *85 dB(A) down to 80 dB(A)* and is known as the *lower exposure action value*. Meanwhile, the section level is reduced from *90 dB(A) down to 85 dB(A)* and is known as the *upper exposure action value*. The Regulations also allow the employer to average out the exposure to noise over a one week period instead of the previous normal eight hour period, in situations where the noise exposure varies on a day-to-day basis.

When determining noise levels for the purposes of determining exposure action levels, the noise exposure reducing effects of hearing protection may not be taken in to account. Where exposure is at, or above, the *lower exposure action value* (80 dB(A)) the employer has a duty to provide hearing protection to those employees that request it. The employer also has a duty to information, instruction and training on the risks posed by exposure to noise and the control measures to be used. Where the exposure is at, or above, the *upper exposure action value* (85 dB(A)) the employer is also required to introduce a formal programme of control measures. The measures to be taken as part of this programme of control measures will depend on the findings of the noise risk assessment *(see below)*. The Control of Noise at Work Regulations 2005 also introduces a new value known as the *exposure limit value*. These are limits set both in terms of daily (or weekly) personal noise exposure (*LEP,d* of 87 dB) and in terms of peak noise (*LCpeak* of 140 dB). The exposure action values, take account of the protection provided by personal hearing protection (unlike the two exposure limit values).

If an employee is exposed to noise at or above the exposure limit value, then the employer must take immediate action to bring the exposure down below this level.

SUMMARY OF EXPOSURE LIMIT VALUES AND ACTION VALUES

The lower exposure action values are:	A daily or weekly personal noise exposure of 80 dB (A-weighted)
	A peak sound pressure of 135 dB (C-weighted)
The upper exposure action values are:	A daily or weekly personal noise exposure of 85 dB (A-weighted)
	A peak sound pressure of 137 dB (C-weighted)
The exposure limit values are:	A daily or weekly personal exposure of 87 dB (A-weighted)
	A peak sound pressure of 140 dB (C-weighted)

NOISE RISK ASSESSMENT AND CONTROL MEASURES (REGULATIONS 5 AND 6)

The requirement for a noise risk assessment carries through from the Noise at Work Regulations 1989 into the Control of Noise at Work Regulations 2005. Employers are required (in accordance with the general risk assessment and general principles of prevention contained in Schedule 1 to the Management of Health and Safety at Work Regulation 1999) to ensure that the risks associated with employees' exposure to noise are eliminated where this is reasonably practicable. Where elimination is not reasonably practicable, then the employer must reduce the risks down to as low a level as is reasonably practicable. Regulation 6(2) of the Control of Noise at Work Regulations 2005 introduces the requirement for a formal programme of control measures. If any employee is likely to be exposed to noise at or above an upper exposure action value, the employer shall reduce exposure to a minimum by establishing and implementing a programme of organisational and technical measures, excluding the provision of personal hearing protectors, which is appropriate to the activity and consistent with the risk assessment, and shall include consideration of:

(a) Other working methods which eliminate or reduce exposure to noise.

(b) Choice of appropriate work equipment emitting the least possible noise, taking account of the work to be carried out.

(c) The design and layout of workplaces, work stations and rest facilities.

(d) Suitable and sufficient information and training for employees, such that work equipment may be used correctly, in order to minimise their exposure to noise.

(e) Reduction of noise by technical means including:

(i) In the case of airborne noise the use of shields, enclosures, and sound-absorbent coverings.

(ii) In the case of structure-borne noise by damping and isolation.

(f) Appropriate maintenance programmes for work equipment, the workplace and workplace systems.

(g) Limitation of the duration and intensity of exposure to noise.

(h) Appropriate work schedules with adequate rest periods.

If the risk assessment indicates an employee is likely to be exposed to noise at or above an upper exposure action value, the employer shall ensure that:

■ The area is designated a Hearing Protection Zone.

■ The area is demarcated and identified by means of the sign specified for the purpose of indicating 'ear protection must be worn' (to be consistent with the Health and Safety (Safety Signs and Signals) Regulations 1996).

■ The sign shall be accompanied by text that indicates that the area is a Hearing Protection Zone and that employees must wear personal hearing protectors while in that area.

■ Access to the area is restricted where this is technically feasible and the risk of exposure justifies it and shall make every effort to ensure that no employee enters that area unless they are wearing personal hearing protectors.

MAINTENANCE AND USE OF EQUIPMENT (REGULATION 8)

There is a duty on the employer to maintain the control introduced to protect employees. This will include maintenance of acoustic enclosures, etc. as well as the maintenance of machinery (as required under the Provision and Use of Work Equipment Regulations 1998) to control noise at source.

HEALTH SURVEILLANCE (REGULATION 9)

Under the Control of Noise at Work Regulations 2005, employees who are regularly exposed to noise levels of 85 dB(A) or higher must be subject to health surveillance, including audiometric testing. This constitutes a big change from the previous Regulations that only required an employer to carry out health surveillance where the employee was subject to noise levels of 95 dB(A) or higher.

Where exposure is between 80 dB and 85 dB, or where employees are only occasionally exposed above the upper exposure action values, health surveillance will only be required if information comes to light that an individual may be particularly sensitive to noise induced hearing loss.

SUMMARY

The Control of Noise at Work Regulations 2005 became part of UK health and safety law in April 2006. They introduced levels for employees to control exposure down to, including a new exposure limit value, above which employers are obliged to take immediate action to reduce exposure. These new lower limits mean that about a further million workers will be afforded protection by these Regulations. The requirements for risk assessments, control measures and health surveillance have been updated, but are broadly similar to previous requirements.

Source: www.lrbconsulting.com and www.hse.gov.uk.

Control of Substances Hazardous to Health Regulations (COSHH) 2002

Law considered in context/more depth in Element 8.

Amendments to these Regulations were made by the Control of Substances Hazardous to Health (Amendment) Regulations 2004. The main change being that MELs and OESs were replaced by workplace exposure limits (WELs).

Arrangement of Regulations

1) Citation and commencement.
2) Interpretation.
3) Duties under these Regulations.
4) Prohibitions on substances.
5) Application of Regulations 6 to 13.
6) Assessment of health risks created by work involving substances hazardous to health.
7) Control of exposure.
8) Use of control measures etc.
9) Maintenance of control measures.
10) Monitoring exposure.
11) Health surveillance.
12) Information etc.
13) Arrangements to deal with accidents, incidents and emergencies.
14) Exemption certificates.
15) Extension outside Great Britain.
16) Defence in proceedings for contravention of these Regulations.
17) Exemptions relating to the Ministry of Defence etc.
18) Revocations, amendments and savings.
19) Extension of meaning of 'work'.
20) Modification of section 3(2) of the Health and Safety at Work etc. Act (HASAWA) 1974.

Schedule 1 - Other substances and processes to which the definition of 'carcinogen' relates.

Schedule 2 - Prohibition of certain substances hazardous to health for certain purposes.

Schedule 3 - Special provisions relating to biological agents.

Schedule 4 - Frequency of thorough examination and test of local exhaust ventilation plant used in certain processes.

Schedule 5 - Specific substances and processes for which monitoring is required.

Schedule 6 - Medical surveillance.

Schedule 7 - Legislation concerned with the labelling of containers and pipes.

Schedule 8 - Fumigations excepted from Regulation 14.

Schedule 9 - Notification of certain fumigations.

Appendix 1 - Control of carcinogenic substances.

Annex 1 - Background note on occupational cancer.

Annex 2 - Special considerations that apply to the control of exposure to vinyl chloride.

Appendix 2 - Additional provisions relating to work with biological agents.

Appendix 3 - Control of substances that cause occupational asthma.

Outline of main points

REGULATIONS

Reg. 2   **Interpretation**

'Substance hazardous to health' includes:

1) Substances which under the Chemicals (Hazard Information and Packaging) Regulations (CHIP 3) 2002 are in categories of very toxic, toxic, harmful, corrosive or irritant.
2) A substance listed in Schedule 1 to the Regulations or for which the HSE (*formerly HSC*) have approved a maximum exposure limit or an occupational exposure standard.
3) A biological agent.
4) Dust in a concentration in air equal to or greater than:
   - 10 mg/m3 inhalable dust as an 8hr TWA.
   - 4mg/m3 respirable dust as an 8hr TWA.
5) Any other substance which creates a health hazard comparable with the hazards of the substances in the other categories above.

Reg. 3   **Duties**

Are on employer to protect:

- Employees.

Any other person who may be affected, except:

- Duties for health surveillance do not extend to non-employees.
- Duties to give information may extend to non-employees if they work on the premises.

Reg. 4   **Prohibitions on substances**

Certain substances are prohibited from being used in some applications. These are detailed in Schedule 2.

Reg. 5   **Application of Regulations 6-13**

Regulations 6-13 are made to protect a person's health from risks arising from exposure. They do not apply if:

The following Regulations already apply:

- The Control of Lead at Work Regulations (CLAW) 2002.
- The Control of Asbestos at Work Regulations (CAWR) 2002.

The hazard arises from one of the following properties of the substance:

- Radioactivity, explosive, flammable, high or low temperature, high pressure.
- Exposure is for medical treatment.
- Exposure is in a mine.

Reg. 6   **Assessment**

Employers must not carry out work that will expose employees to substances hazardous to health unless they have assessed the risks to health and the steps that need to be taken to meet the requirements of the Regulations. The assessment must be reviewed if there are changes in the work and at least once every 5 years.

A suitable and sufficient assessment should include:

- An assessment of the risks to health.
- The practicability of preventing exposure.
- Steps needed to achieve adequate control.

An assessment of the risks should involve:

- Types of substance including biological agents.
- Where the substances are present and in what form.
- Effects on the body.
- Who might be affected?
- Existing control measures.

Reg. 7   **Control of exposure**

1) Employer shall ensure that the exposure of employees to substances hazardous to health is either prevented or, where this is not reasonably practicable, adequately controlled.
2) So far as is reasonably practicable (1) above except to a carcinogen or biological agent shall be by measures other than personal protective equipment (PPE).
3) Where not reasonably practicable to prevent exposure to a carcinogen by using an alternative substance or process, the following measure shall apply:

- Total enclosure of process.
- Use of plant, process and systems which minimise generation of, or suppress and contain, spills, leaks, dust, fumes and vapours of carcinogens.
- Limitation of quantities of a carcinogen at work.
- Keeping of numbers exposed to a minimum.
- Prohibition of eating, drinking and smoking in areas liable to contamination.
- Provision of hygiene measures including adequate washing facilities and regular cleaning of walls and surfaces.
- Designation of areas/installations liable to contamination and use of suitable and sufficient warning signs.
- Safe storage, handling and disposal of carcinogens and use of closed and clearly-labelled containers.

       © RMS

4) If adequate control is not achieved, then employer shall provide suitable PPE to employees in addition to taking control measures.

5) PPE provided shall comply with the Personal Protective Equipment at Work Regulations (PPER), 2002 (dealing with the supply of PPE).

6&7) For substances which have a maximum exposure limit (MEL), control of that substance shall, so far as inhalation is concerned, only be treated if the level of exposure is reduced as far as is reasonably practicable and in any case below the MEL.

Where a substance has an occupational exposure standard (OES), control of that substance shall, so far as inhalation is concerned, only be treated as adequate if the OES is not exceeded or if it is, steps are taken to remedy the situation as soon as reasonably practicable.

8) Respiratory protection must be suitable and of a type or conforming to a standard approved by the HSE.

9) In the event of failure of a control measure which may result in the escape of carcinogens, the employer shall ensure:

- Only those who are responsible for repair and maintenance work are permitted in the affected area and are provided with PPE.
- Employees and other persons who may be affected are informed of the failure forthwith.

Reg. 8

Employer shall take all reasonable steps to ensure control measures, PPE, etc. are properly used/applied.

Employee shall make full and proper use of control measures, PPE etc. and shall report defects to employer.

Reg. 9 **Maintenance of control measures**

Employer providing control measures to comply with Reg.7 shall ensure that it is maintained in an efficient state, in efficient working order and in good repair and in the case of PPE in a clean condition, properly stored in a well-defined place checked at suitable intervals and when discovered to be defective repaired or replaced before further use.

- Contaminated PPE should be kept apart and cleaned, decontaminated or, if necessary destroyed.
- Engineering controls - employer shall ensure thorough examination and tests.
- Local exhaust ventilation (LEV) - once every 14 months unless process specified in Schedule 4.
- Others - at suitable intervals.
- Respiratory protective equipment - employer shall ensure thorough examination and tests at suitable intervals.
- Records of all examinations, tests and repairs kept for 5 years.

Reg. 10 **Monitoring exposure**

Employer shall ensure exposure is monitored if:

- Needed to ensure maintenance of adequate control.
- Otherwise needed to protect health of employees.
- Substance/process specified in Schedule 5.

Records kept if:

- There is an identified exposure of identifiable employee - 40 years.
- Otherwise - 5 years.

Reg. 11 **Health surveillance**

1) Where appropriate for protection of health of employees exposed or liable to be exposed, employer shall ensure suitable health surveillance.

2) Health surveillance is appropriate if:

- Employee exposed to substance/process specified in Schedule 6.
- Exposure to substance is such that an identifiable disease or adverse health effect can result, there is a reasonable likelihood of it occurring and a valid technique exists for detecting the indications of the disease or effect.

3) Health records kept for at least 40 years.

4) If employer ceases business, HSE notified and health records offered to HSE.

5) If employee exposed to substance specified in Schedule 6, then health surveillance shall include medical surveillance, under Employment Medical Adviser (EMA) at 12 monthly intervals - or more frequently if specified by EMA.

6) EMA can forbid employee to work in process, or specify certain conditions for him to be employed in a process.

7) EMA can specify that health surveillance is to continue after exposure has ceased. Employer must ensure.

8) Employees to have access to their own health record.

9) Employee must attend for health/medical surveillance and give information to EMA.

10) EMA entitled to inspect workplace.

11) Where EMA suspends employee from work exposing him to substances hazardous to health, employer of employee can apply to HSE in writing within 28 days for that decision to be reviewed.

Reg. 12 **Information etc.**

Employer shall provide suitable and sufficient information, instruction and training for him to know:

- Risks to health.
- Precautions to be taken.

This should include information on:

- Results of monitoring of exposure at workplace.
- Results of collective health surveillance.

If the substances have been assigned a maximum exposure limit, then the employee/Safety Representative must be notified forthwith if the MEL has been exceeded.

Reg. 13 **Arrangements to deal with accidents, incidents and emergencies**

To protect the health of employees from accidents, incidents and emergencies, the employer shall ensure that:

- Procedures are in place for first-aid and safety drills (tested regularly).
- Information on emergency arrangements is available.
- Warning, communication systems, remedial action and rescue actions are available.
- Information made available to emergency services: external and internal.
- Steps taken to mitigate effects, restore situation to normal and inform employees.
- Only essential persons allowed in area.

These duties do not apply where the risks to health are slight or measures in place Reg 7(1) are sufficient to control the risk. The employee must report any accident or incident which has or may have resulted in the release of a biological agent which could cause severe human disease.

NOTE the main impact to the latest version of the COSHH Regs concern the control of substances that cause occupational asthma.

APPENDIX 3 CONTROL OF SUBSTANCES THAT CAUSE OCCUPATIONAL ASTHMA

This relates certain Regulations specifically to substances with the potential to cause asthma.

- Regulation 6 - Assessment of risk to health created by work involving substances hazardous to health, (i.e. substances that may cause asthma).
- Regulation 7 - Prevention or control of exposure to substances hazardous to health, (i.e. substances that may cause occupational asthma).
- Regulation 11 - Health surveillance, (for employees who are or may be exposed to substances that may cause occupational asthma).
- Regulation 12 - Information, instruction and training for persons who may be exposed to substances hazardous to health, to include: typical symptoms of asthma, substances that may cause it, the permanency of asthma and what happens with subsequent exposures, the need to report symptoms immediately and the reporting procedures.

Training should be given, including induction training before they start the job.

SCHEDULE 3 ADDITIONAL PROVISIONS RELATING TO WORK WITH BIOLOGICAL AGENTS

Regulation 7(10) Part I Provision of general application to biological agents:

1) **Interpretation**

2) **Classification of biological agents**

   The HSC shall approve and publish a 'Categorisation of Biological Agents according to hazard and categories of containment' which may be revised or re-issued. Where no approved classification exists, the employer shall assign the agent to one of four groups according to the level of risk of infection.

   Group 1 - unlikely to cause human disease.

   Group 2 - can cause human disease.

   Group 3 - can cause severe disease and spread to community.

   Group 4 - can cause severe disease, spread to community and there is no effective treatment.

3) **Special control measures for laboratories, animal rooms and industrial processes**

   Every employer engaged in research, development, teaching or diagnostic work involving Group 2, 3 or 4 biological agents; keeping or handling laboratory animals deliberately or naturally infected with those agents, or industrial processes involving those agents, shall control them with the most suitable containment.

4) **List of employees exposed to certain biological agents**

   The employer shall keep a list of employees exposed to Group 3 or 4 biological agents for at least 10 years. If there is a long latency period then the list should be kept for 40 years.

5) **Notification of the use of biological agents**

   Employers shall inform the HSE at least 20 days in advance of first time use or storage of Group 2, 3 or 4 biological hazards. Consequent substantial changes in procedure or process shall also be reported.

6) **Notification of the consignment of biological agents**

   The HSE must be informed 30 days before certain biological agents are consigned.

Part II Containment measures for health and veterinary care facilities, laboratories and animal rooms. Part III Containment measures for industrial processes. Part IV Biohazard sign. The biohazard sign required by Regulation 7(6) (a) shall be in the form shown. Part V Biological agents whose use is to be notified in accordance with paragraph 5(2) of Part I of this Schedule.

- Any Group 3 or 4 agent.
- Certain named Group 2 agents.

Figure RSP-3: Biohazard sign. *Source: COSHH 2002.*

Control of Substances Hazardous to Health (Amendment) Regulations (COSHH) 2004

These Regulations make minor amendments to the Control of Substances Hazardous to Health Regulations (COSHH) 2002 and came into force on 17th January 2005 and 6th April 2005.

Arrangement of Regulations

1) Citation and commencement.
2) Amendments of the Control of Substances Hazardous to Health (Amendment) Regulations 2004.
3) Amendment of the Chemicals (Hazard Information and Packaging for Supply) Regulations 2002.
4) Amendments of the Control of Lead at Work Regulations 2002.

Outline of main points

The main changes are that maximum exposure limits (MEL) and occupational exposure standards (OES) have been replaced by the new workplace exposure limits (WELs) and schedule 2a has been introduced.

Reg 2(a)(v) workplace exposure limit for a substance hazardous to health means the exposure limit approved by the Health and Safety Commission for that substance in relation to the specified reference period when calculated by a method approved by the Health and Safety Commission, as contained in HSE publication 'EH/40 Workplace Exposure Limits 2005' as updated from time to time.

Reg 7(7) Schedule 2a - Principles of good practice for the control of exposure to substances hazardous to health.

(a) Design and operate processes and activities to minimise emission, release and spread of substances hazardous to health.
(b) Take into account all relevant routes of exposure - inhalation, skin absorption and ingestion - when developing control measures.
(c) Control exposure by measures that are proportionate to the health risk.
(d) Choose the most effective and reliable control options which minimise the escape and spread of substances hazardous to health.
(e) Where adequate control of exposure cannot be achieved by other means, provide, in combination with other control measures, suitable personal protective equipment.
(f) Check and review regularly all elements of control measures for their continuing effectiveness.
(g) Inform and train all employees on the hazards and risks from the substances with which they work and the use of control measures developed to minimise the risks.
(h) Ensure that the introduction of control measures does not increase the overall risk to health and safety.

Control of Vibration at Work Regulations (CVWR) 2005

Considered in context in Element 9.

Hand-arm vibration (HAV) and whole body vibration (WBV) are caused by the use of work equipment and work processes that transmit vibration into the hands, arms and bodies of employees in many industries and occupations. Long-term, regular exposure to vibration is known to lead to permanent and debilitating health effects such as vibration white finger, loss of sensation, pain, and numbness in the hands, arms, spine and joints. These effects are collectively known as hand-arm or whole body vibration syndrome. These Regulations introduce controls, which aim substantially to reduce ill-health caused by exposure to vibration. These Regulations came into force on 6th July 2005.

Arrangement of Regulations

1) Citation and commencement.
2) Interpretation.
3) Application and transition.
4) Exposure limit values and action values.
5) Assessment of the risk to health created by vibration at the workplace.
6) Elimination or control of exposure to vibration at the workplace.
7) Health surveillance.
8) Information, instruction and training for persons who may be exposed to risk from vibration.
9) Exemption certificates for emergency services.
10) Exemption certificates for air transport.
11) Exemption relating to the Ministry of Defence etc.
12) Extension outside Great Britain.
13) Amendment.

Outline of main points

Regulation 3 makes provision for transition arrangements affecting equipment provided for use before 6th July 2007 and does not permit compliance with the exposure limits, taking into account technical advances and organisational measures to respond to the Regulations, the Regulations shall not apply until 6th July 2010.

Duties under most of these Regulations extend not only to employees but to others, whether or not at work that may be affected. The duty does not include Regulation 7 (health surveillance) or Regulation 8 (information instruction and training), these are limited to employees.

Regulation 4 states the personal daily exposure limits and daily exposure action values normalised over an 8-hour reference period.

	Daily exposure action values	Daily exposure limits
Hand arm vibration	2.5 m/s^2	5 m/s^2
Whole body vibration	0.5 m/s^2	1.15 m/s^2

Regulation 5 requires the employer to make a suitable and sufficient assessment of the risk created by work that is liable to expose employees to risk from vibration. The assessment must observe work practices, make reference to information regarding the magnitude of vibration from equipment and if necessary measurement of the magnitude of the vibration. Consideration must also be given to the type, duration, effects of exposure, exposures limit/action values, effects on employees at particular risk, the effects of vibration on equipment and the ability to use it, manufacturers' information, availability of replacement equipment, and extension of exposure at the workplace (for example, rest facilities), temperature and information on health surveillance. The risk assessment should be recorded as soon as is practicable after the risk assessment is made and reviewed regularly.

Regulation 6 states that the employer must seek to eliminate the risk of vibration at source or, if not reasonably practicable, reduce it to as low a level as is reasonably practicable. Where the personal daily exposure limit is exceeded the employer must reduce exposure by implementing a programme of organisational and technical measures. Measures include the use of other methods of work, ergonomics, maintenance of equipment, design and layout, rest facilities, information, instruction and training, limitation by schedules and breaks and the provision of personal protective equipment to protect from cold and damp. Measures must be adapted to take account of any group or individual employee whose health may be of particular risk from exposure to vibration.

Regulation 7 states that health surveillance must be carried out if there is a risk to the health of employees liable to be exposed to vibration. This is in order to prevent or diagnose any health effect linked with exposure to vibration. A record of health shall be kept of any employee who undergoes health surveillance. The employer shall, providing reasonable notice is given, provide the employee with access to their health records and provide copies to an enforcing officer on request. If health surveillance identifies a disease or adverse health effect, considered by a doctor or other occupational health professional to be a result of exposure to vibration, the employer shall ensure that a qualified person informs the employee and provides information and advice. The employer must ensure they are kept informed of any significant findings from health surveillance, taking into account any medical confidentiality. In addition the employer must also:

- Review risk assessments.
- Review the measures taken to comply.
- Consider assigning the employee to other work.

- Review the health of any other employee who has been similarly exposed and consider alternative work.

Regulation 8 states that employers must provide information, instruction and training to all employees who are exposed to risk from vibration and their representatives. This includes any organisational and technical measures taken, exposure limits and values, risk assessment findings, why and how to detect injury, entitlement to and collective results of health surveillance and safe working practices. Information instruction and training shall be updated to take account of changes in the employers work or methods. The employer shall ensure all persons, whether or not an employee, who carries out work in connection with the employer's duties has been provided with information, instruction and training.

Dangerous Substances and Explosive Atmospheres Regulations (DSEAR) 2002

Law considered in context/more depth in Element 7.

Arrangement of Regulations

1) Citation and commencement.
2) Interpretation.
3) Application.
4) Duties under these Regulations.
5) Risk assessment.
6) Elimination or reduction of risks from dangerous substances.
7) Places where explosive atmospheres may occur.
8) Arrangements to deal with accidents, incidents and emergencies.
9) Information, instruction and training.
10) Identification of hazardous contents of containers and pipes.
11) Duty of coordination.
12) Extension outside Great Britain.
13) Exemption certificates.
14) Exemptions for Ministry of Defence etc.
15) Amendments.
16) Repeals and revocations.
17) Transitional provisions.

Schedule 1 - General safety measures.
Schedule 2 - Classification of places where explosive atmospheres may occur.
Schedule 3 - Criteria for the selection of equipment and protective systems.
Schedule 4 - Warning sign for places where explosive atmospheres may occur.
Schedule 5 - Legislation concerned with the marking of containers and pipes.
Schedule 6 - Amendments.
Schedule 7 - Repeal and revocation.

Outline of main points

These Regulations aim to protect against risks from fire, explosion and similar events arising from dangerous substances that are present in the workplace.

DANGEROUS SUBSTANCES

These are any substances or preparations that due to their properties or the way in which they are being used could cause harm to people from fires and explosions. They may include petrol, liquefied petroleum gases, paints, varnishes, solvents and dusts.

APPLICATION

DSEAR applies in most workplaces where a dangerous substance is present. There are a few exceptions where only certain parts of the Regulations apply, for example:

- Ships.
- Medical treatment areas.
- Explosives/chemically unstable substances.
- Mines.
- Quarries.
- Boreholes.
- Offshore installations.
- Means of transport.

MAIN REQUIREMENTS

You must:

- Conduct a risk assessment of work activities involving dangerous substances.
- Provide measures to eliminate or reduce risks.
- Provide equipment and procedures to deal with accidents and emergencies.
- Provide information and training for employees.
- Classify places into zones and mark zones where appropriate.

The risk assessment should include:

- The hazardous properties of substance.
- The way they are used or stored.
- Possibility of hazardous explosive atmosphere occurring.
- Potential ignition sources.
- Details of zoned areas.
- Coordination between employers.

SAFETY MEASURES

Where possible eliminate safety risks from dangerous substances or, if not reasonably practicable to do this, control risks and reduce the harmful effects of any fire, explosion or similar event.

Substitution - Replace with totally safe or safer substance (best solution).

Control measures - If risk cannot be eliminated apply the following control measures in the following order:

- Reduce quantity.
- Avoid or minimise releases.
- Control releases at source.
- Prevent formation of explosive atmosphere.
- Collect, contain and remove any release to a safe place, for example, ventilation.
- Avoid ignition sources.
- Avoid adverse conditions, for example, exceeding temperature limits.
- Keep incompatible substances apart.

Mitigation measures - Apply measures to mitigate the effects of any situation.

- Prevent fire and explosions from spreading to other plant, equipment or other parts of the workplace.
- Reduce number of employees exposed.
- Provide process plant that can contain or suppress an explosion, or vent it to a safe place.

ZONED AREAS

In workplaces where explosive atmospheres may occur, areas should be classified into zones based on the likelihood of an explosive atmosphere occurring. Any equipment in these areas should ideally meet the requirements of the Equipment and Protective Systems Intended for Use in Potentially Explosive Atmospheres Regulations (ATEX) 1996. However equipment in use before July 2003 can continue to be used providing that the risk assessment says that it is safe to do so. Areas may need to be marked with an 'Ex' warning sign at their entry points. Employees may need to be provided with appropriate clothing, for example, anti-static overalls. Before use for the first time, a person competent in the field of explosion protection must confirm hazardous areas as being safe.

ACCIDENTS, INCIDENTS AND EMERGENCIES

DSEAR builds on existing requirements for emergency procedures, which are contained in other Regulations. These may need to be supplemented if you assess that a fire, explosion or significant spillage could occur, due to the quantities of dangerous substances present in the workplace. You may need to arrange for:

- Suitable warning systems.
- Escape facilities.
- Emergency procedures.
- Equipment and clothing for essential personnel who may need to deal with the situation.
- Practice drills.
- Make information, instruction and training available to employees and if necessary liaise with the emergency services.

Electricity at Work Regulations (EWR) 1989

Law considered in context/more depth in Element 6.

Arrangement of Regulations

PART I - INTRODUCTION

1) Citation and commencement.
2) Interpretation.
3) Persons on whom duties are imposed by these Regulations.

PART II - GENERAL

4) Systems, work activities and protective equipment.
5) Strength and capability of electrical equipment.
6) Adverse or hazardous environments.
7) Insulation, protection and placing of conductors.
8) Earthing or other suitable precautions.
9) Integrity of referenced conductors.
10) Connections.
11) Means for protecting from excess of current.
12) Means for cutting off the supply and for isolation.
13) Precautions for work on equipment made dead.
14) Work on or near live conductors.
15) Working space, access and lighting.
16) Persons to be competent to prevent danger and injury.

PART III - REGULATIONS APPLYING TO MINES ONLY

17) Provisions applying to mines only.
18) Introduction of electrical equipment.
19) Restriction of equipment in certain zones below ground.
20) Cutting off electricity or making safe where firedamp is found either below ground or at the surface.
21) Approval of certain equipment for use in safety-lamp mines.
22) Means of cutting off electricity to circuits below ground.
23) Oil-filled equipment.
24) Records and information.
25) Electric shock notices.
26) Introduction of battery-powered locomotives and vehicles into safety-lamp mines.
27) Storage, charging and transfer of electrical storage batteries.
28) Disapplication of section 157 of the Mines and Quarries Act 1954.

PART IV - MISCELLANEOUS AND GENERAL

29) Defence.
30) Exemption certificates.
31) Extension outside Great Britain.
32) Disapplication of duties.
33) Revocations and modifications.

Schedule 1 - Provisions applying to mines only and having effect in particular in relation to the use below ground in coal mines of film lighting circuits.

Schedule 2 - Revocations and modifications.

Outline of main points

SYSTEMS, WORK ACTIVITIES AND PROTECTIVE EQUIPMENT (REGULATION 4)

The system and the equipment comprising it must be designed and installed to take account of all reasonably foreseeable conditions of use.

- The system must be maintained so as to prevent danger.
- All work activities must be carried out in such a manner as to not give rise to danger.
- Equipment provided to protect people working on live equipment must be suitable and maintained.

STRENGTH AND CAPABILITY OF ELECTRICAL EQUIPMENT (REGULATION 5)

Strength and capability refers to the equipment's ability to withstand the effects of its load current and any transient overloads or pulses of current.

ADVERSE OR HAZARDOUS ENVIRONMENTS (REGULATION 6)

This Regulation requires that electrical equipment is suitable for the environment and conditions that might be reasonably foreseen. In particular, attention should be paid to:

- Mechanical damage caused by, for example; vehicles, people, vibration, etc.
- Weather, natural hazards, temperature or pressure. Ice, snow, lightning, bird droppings, etc.
- Wet, dirty, dusty or corrosive conditions. Conductors, moving parts, insulators and other materials may be affected by the corrosive nature of water, chemicals and solvents. The presence of explosive dusts must be given special consideration.
- Flammable or explosive substances. Electrical equipment may be a source of ignition for liquids, gases, vapours etc.

INSULATION, PROTECTION AND PLACING OF CONDUCTORS (REGULATION 7)

The purpose of this Regulation is to prevent danger from direct contact. Therefore, if none exists, no action is needed. Conductors though will normally need to be insulated and also have some other protection to prevent mechanical damage.

EARTHING OR OTHER SUITABLE PRECAUTIONS (REGULATION 8)

The purpose of this Regulation is to prevent danger from indirect contact. Conductors such as metal casings may become live through fault conditions. The likelihood of danger arising from these circumstances must be prevented by using the techniques described earlier in this section i.e. earthing, double insulation, reduced voltages etc.

INTEGRITY OF REFERENCED CONDUCTORS (REGULATION 9)

In many circumstances the reference point is earthed because the majority of power distribution installations are referenced by a deliberate connection to earth at the generators or distribution transformers. The purpose of this Regulation is to ensure that electrical continuity is never broken.

CONNECTIONS (REGULATION 10)

As well as having suitable insulation and conductance, connections must have adequate mechanical protection and strength. Plugs and sockets must conform to recognised standards as must connections between cables. Special attention should be paid to the quality of connections on portable appliances.

MEANS FOR PROTECTING FROM EXCESS CURRENT (REGULATION 11)

Faults or overloads can occur in electrical systems and protection must be provided against their effects. The type of protection depends on several factors but usually rests between fuses and circuit breakers.

MEANS FOR CUTTING OFF THE SUPPLY AND FOR ISOLATION (REGULATION 12)

Means must be provided to switch off electrical supplies together with a means of isolation so as to prevent inadvertent reconnection.

PRECAUTIONS FOR WORK ON EQUIPMENT MADE DEAD (REGULATION 13)

Working dead should be the norm. This Regulation requires that precautions be taken to ensure that the system remains dead and to protect those at work on the system. Any or all of the following steps should be considered:

- Identify the circuit. Never assume that the labelling is correct.
- Disconnection and isolation. These are the most common methods: isolation switches, fuse removal and plug removal.
- Proving dead. The test device itself must also be tested before and after testing.
- Earthing.
- Permits-to-work.
- Notices and barriers.

WORK ON OR NEAR LIVE CONDUCTORS (REGULATION 14)

Live work must only be carried out if it is unreasonable for it to be carried out dead. If live work must be carried out then any or all of the following precautions should be taken:

- Competent staff (see Reg. 16).
- Adequate information.
- Suitable tools. Insulated tools, protective clothing.
- Barriers or screens.
- Instruments and test probes. To identify what is live and what is dead.
- Accompaniment.
- Designated test areas.

WORKING SPACE, ACCESS AND LIGHTING (REGULATION 15)

Space. Where there are dangerous live exposed conductors, space should be adequate to:

- Allow persons to pull back from the hazard.
- Allow persons to pass each other.

Lighting. The first preference is for natural lighting then for permanent artificial lighting.

PERSONS TO BE COMPETENT TO PREVENT DANGER AND INJURY (REGULATION 16)

The object of this Regulation is to 'ensure that persons are not placed at risk due to a lack of skills on the part of themselves or others in dealing with electrical equipment'.

In order to meet the requirements of this Regulation a competent person would need:

- An understanding of the concepts of electricity and the risks involved in work associated with it.
- Knowledge of electrical work and some suitable qualification in electrical principles.
- Experience of the type of system to be worked on with an understanding of the hazards and risks involved.
- Knowledge of the systems of work to be employed and the ability to recognise hazards and risks.
- Physical attributes to be able to recognise elements of the system, for example, colour blindness and wiring.

Advice and queries regarding qualifications and training can be directed to the IEE - Institute of Electrical Engineers, London.

DEFENCE (REGULATION 29)

In any Regulation where the absolute duty applies, a defence in any criminal proceedings shall exist where a person can show that: *"He took all reasonable steps and exercised due diligence to avoid the commission of the offence."* Is there a prepared procedure (steps), is the procedure being followed (diligence) and do you have the records or witness to prove it retrospectively?

Fire Safety (Scotland) Regulations (FSSR) 2006

Law considered in context/more depth in Element 7.

The Fire Safety (Scotland) Regulations 2006 ('FSSR') are Regulations that were made by Scottish Ministers under the powers contained in the Fire (Scotland) Act 2005, and further build upon the requirements of that act.

Arrangement of Regulations

PART 1 - PRELIMINARY

1) Citation and commencement.
2) Interpretation.

PART 2 - ASSESSMENTS

3) Duty to review.
4) Duty in respect of young persons.
5) Assessment and review duty in respect of young persons.
6) Assessment and review duty in respect of dangerous substances.
7) New work activities where dangerous substances are present.
8) Duty to record information.
9) Specified information.

PART 3 - FIRE SAFETY

10) Fire safety arrangements.
11) Elimination or reduction of risks from dangerous substances.
12) Means for fighting fire and means for giving warning in the event of fire.
13) Means of escape.
14) Procedures for serious and imminent danger from fire and for danger areas.
15) Additional emergency measures in respect of dangerous substances.
16) Maintenance.
17) Safety assistance.
18) Provision of information to employees.
19) Provision of information to employers and the self-employed from outside undertakings.
20) Training.
21) Co-operation and coordination.
22) Duties of employees.

PART 4 - MISCELLANEOUS

23) Maintenance of measures provided in relevant premises for protection of firefighters.
24) Maintenance of measures provided in the common areas of private dwellings for protection of firefighters.
25) Arrangements with the Office of Rail Regulation.
26) Nominated person's act or omission not to afford employer defence.
27) Service of documents: further provision.
28) Disapplication of certain provisions.

Schedule - Measures to be taken in respect of dangerous substances.

Please refer to the Regulatory Reform (Fire Safety) Order 2005 for the equivalent legislation for England and Wales.

Fire (Scotland) Act (FSA) 2005

Law considered in context/more depth in Element 7.

Arrangement of Act

PART 1 - FIRE AND RESCUE AUTHORITIES

1) Fire and Rescue Authorities.
2) Joint fire and rescue boards.
3) Meaning of 'relevant authority'.

PART 2 - FIRE AND RESCUE SERVICES

Chapter 1 - Appointment of chief officer.
Chapter 2 - Principal fire and rescue functions.
Chapter 3 - Ancillary functions.

Chapter 4 - Water supply.

Chapter 5 - Powers of employees and constables.

Chapter 6 - Mutual assistance etc.

Chapter 7 - Assaulting or impeding employees and others.

Chapter 8 - Central supervision and support.

Chapter 9 - Employment.

Chapter 10 - Interpretation.

PART 3 - FIRE SAFETY

Chapter 1 - Fire safety duties.

Chapter 2 - Enforcement.

Chapter 3 - Miscellaneous.

Chapter 4 - Offences.

Chapter 5 - General.

PART 4 - MISCELLANEOUS

1)   Inquiries.

2)   Consultation requirements.

3)   Pre-commencement consultation.

4)   Advisory bodies.

5)   Payments in respect of advisory bodies.

6)   Abolition of Scottish Central Fire Brigades Advisory Council.

7)   False alarms.

8)   Disposal of land.

PART 5 - GENERAL

1)   Ancillary provision.

2)   Orders and Regulations.

3)   Minor and consequential amendments and repeals.

4)   Commencement.

5)   Short title.

Schedule 1 - Joint fire and rescue boards: supplementary provision.

Schedule 2 - Fire safety measures.

Schedule 3 - Minor and consequential amendments.

Schedule 4 - Repeals.

Outline of main points

The Act is targeted at reducing the number of workplace fires by imposing far reaching responsibilities on all employers, as well as those who have control to any extent of non-domestic premises, to assess and reduce the risks from fire. Fire certificates were abolished under the Act and have been replaced by a new fire safety regime based upon the principles of risk assessment and the requirement to take steps to mitigate the detrimental effects of a fire on relevant premises. The new regime applies to all employers as well as to anyone who has control of non-domestic premises to any extent including building owners, tenants, occupiers and factors. The overriding duty is to ensure, so far as is reasonably practicable, safety in respect of harm caused by fire in the workplace and is supplemented by a number of prescriptive duties:

- To carry out a fire safety risk assessment of the premises. If you have 5 or more employees, the risk assessment must be recorded in writing.
- Not to employ a young person (a person under 18) unless an assessment of the risks of fire to young persons has been undertaking.
- To appoint a competent person to assist with the discharge of fire safety duties.
- To identify the fire safety measures necessary.
- To put in place arrangements for the planning, organisation, control, monitoring and review of the fire safety measures that are put in place.
- To implement these fire safety measures using risk reduction principles.
- To inform employees of the fire safety risks and provide fire safety training.
- To coordinate and co-operate with other duty holders in the same premises.
- To review the risk assessment.

Hazardous Waste (England and Wales) Regulations (HWR) 2005 (as amended)

INTRODUCTION

These Regulations replaced the Special Waste Regulations 1996 (as amended); the Regulations came into force from 16th July 2005 and were subsequently amended by the Hazardous Waste (England and Wales) (Amendment) Regulations 2009 SI 507, which came into force in England on 6th April 2009. The Regulations are outlined in their amended form.

Outline of main points

1) The term 'special waste' has been replaced by 'hazardous waste'.
2) The European Waste Catalogue (EWC) and the Hazardous Waste List (part of the EWC) have been formally transposed into UK legislation. All wastes need to be characterised by their EWC code. *(See following section on the List of Wastes (England) Regulations 2005).*
3) Some wastes which were not classified as special waste will now be classified as hazardous waste by virtue of their EWC code, as a result more waste will need to be consigned.
4) Hazardous waste movements will continue to require a consignment note. However, additional information will be required.
5) 200 additional wastes have been added to the Hazardous Waste List. Among them are everyday items such as fluorescent tubes, fridges, TVs, computer monitors and end of life vehicles. There are new requirements on hazardous waste producers (registration, inspections, consignment notes, record keeping):

 - All producers of hazardous waste are required to annually register each of their sites with the Environment Agency, for which there is a fee.
 - Some sites will be exempt from registration such as those producing less than 500kg (200kg before amendment) of hazardous waste per annum.
 - The requirement to pre-notify the Environment Agency for every consignment of hazardous waste will be abolished, as will the consignment note charge.
 - Consignees, disposal and transfer sites, are required to provide quarterly returns that will form the basis of the new consignment charge.

6) Mixing of hazardous wastes with other hazardous wastes and with non-hazardous wastes is not permitted, except under license.
7) Fixed penalty charges of £300.00 for minor offences.

All Hazardous Waste producers must be registered; it will be an offence for companies to move the waste if the producers are not registered. From 16th July 2005 all treated hazardous waste accepted into hazardous or special 'cells' of a non-hazardous landfill site must comply with the full Waste Acceptance Criteria (WAC), as required by the Landfill Regulations 2002.

EXCLUSIONS

The only hazardous waste type excluded from the Regulations will be 'domestic wastes', arising from households. If you are a contractor dealing with asbestos waste from domestic premises the Regulations affect you, but not the occupier.

THE NEED TO REGISTER WITH THE ENVIRONMENT AGENCY AS A HAZARDOUS WASTE PRODUCER

If hazardous waste is produced (as defined in the Hazardous Waste List of the EWC) the production site will be classed as a producer of hazardous waste. Each hazardous waste production site must be registered annually with the Environment Agency. Registration applies to sites where separately collected fractions of domestic waste are bulked up (CA site, transfer station, etc). These sites are classed as sites of production with appropriate notification fees.

THE RULES FOR NOTIFICATION AND RECORD KEEPING

1) Consignment Notes are used as before under the Special Waste Regulations, but a 72 hour pre-notification to the Environment Agency will be required before hazardous waste is moved.
2) Quarterly consignee returns have replaced the system of the consignee copying each Consignment Note to the Environment Agency. Electronic transfer is encouraged.
3) Sites exempt from waste management licensing need to send quarterly returns to the Environment Agency.
4) The consignee must send returns to waste producers notifying them of the receipt of their wastes. It is an offence to collect hazardous waste from non-notified premises if the producer is not exempt.

HOW THE CHANGES AFFECT THE COLLECTION OF WASTE

Waste producers cannot mix different categories of hazardous waste or mix hazardous waste with non-hazardous waste, except under license. If multiple hazardous waste streams from industrial or commercial premises are deposited within a single container, all the individual EWC codes must accompany the consignment note, which must contain the relevant EWC codes. Both individual and multiple collections of hazardous wastes can be arranged. There is one consignment note for multiple collections with space in an annex for the details of individual loads rather than completely separate consignment notes for each collection. For waste collections using multi-lift vehicles and single compartment tankers, a transfer note will exist for each waste producer. Differences in the contents of the individual containers must be recorded in the individual written descriptions.

DUTIES RELATING TO THE WASTE ACCEPTANCE CRITERIA

From 16th July 2005 all hazardous and non-hazardous wastes destined for disposal in landfill have to meet the WAC before they can be deposited. WAC contains the 'quality standards' wastes have to comply with before they are allowed to be placed in inert, non-hazardous or hazardous landfills. The waste producer is under a duty of care to ensure the characterisation of the waste to establish its main characteristics as specified in the Regulations. That is, to assess the physical and chemical properties to identify if they classify as hazardous, non-hazardous or inert waste. In particular, details of the chemical composition and leaching behaviour of the waste are required. This assessment takes the form of sample testing, whereby a representative sample of waste arising is sent away for scientific analysis.

THE INSPECTION REGIME

The Environment Agency will periodically inspect hazardous waste producing premises and assess the following:

(a) Does the site produce hazardous waste?
(b) Has the site been notified (i.e. registered)?
(c) Is mixing carried out?
(d) Are the Consignment Note records complete?

(e)   Is the waste moved by a registered carrier…

(f)   …and taken to a permitted consignee?

(g)   If going to landfill how are the Waste Acceptance Criteria being met?

The Environment Agency issues fixed penalties (spot fines) for:

■   Failing to notify premises.
■   Failing to complete consignment notes.
■   Failing to apply for review of existing permit.

Source: www.sita.co.uk. Document code M141, Review of the Hazardous Waste (England) Regulations 2005 and the introduction of the Waste Acceptance Criteria.

List of Wastes (England) Regulations (LoWR) 2005

OUTLINE OF MAIN POINTS

Includes the European Waste Catalogue (EWC) and the Hazardous Waste List (part of the EWC); all wastes need to be characterised by their EWC code. These Regulations include Chapters of the List numbered 01-20. The Chapters are broken down into specific materials or substances which are further identified as 'wastes' or 'hazardous wastes'; *a waste marked with an asterisk in the List of Wastes is considered listed as a hazardous waste*, whereas those without an asterisk are considered as a waste. The different types of wastes in the List of Wastes are fully defined by the six-digit code for the waste and the respective two-digit and four-digit chapter headings, and accordingly, for purposes connected with the Regulation of waste or hazardous waste:

(a)   Any reference to a waste by its six-digit code as specified in the List of Wastes is to be treated as a reference to that waste.

(b)   A reference to wastes by the respective two-digit or four-digit chapter heading is a reference to the wastes listed in the List of Wastes under that chapter heading.

Source: The List of Wastes (England) Regulations 2005.

The Regulations set out a list of hazardous waste properties, wastes on the List of Wastes are hazardous if they have one or more of the listed hazardous properties, for example:

H1	**Explosive:** substances and preparations which may explode under the effect of flame or which are more sensitive to shocks or friction than dinitrobenzene.
H2	**Oxidizing:** substances and preparations which exhibit highly exothermic reactions when in contact with other substances, particularly flammable substances.
H3A	**Highly flammable:** ■ Liquid substances and preparations having a flash point below 21°C (including extremely flammable liquids). ■ Substances and preparations which may become hot and finally catch fire in contact with air at ambient temperature without any application of energy. ■ Solid substances and preparations which may readily catch fire after brief contact with a source of ignition and which continue to burn or to be consumed after removal of the source of ignition. ■ Gaseous substances and preparations which are flammable in air at normal pressure. ■ Substances and preparations which, in contact with water or damp air, evolve highly flammable gases in dangerous quantities.

Figure RSP-4: Hazardous properties.   *Source: Environment Agency, HWR01, What is a Hazardous Waste?*

See the Regulations for specific details.

Health and Safety (Display Screen Equipment) Regulations (DSE) 1992 (as amended)

See also - Health and Safety (Miscellaneous Amendments) Regulations (MAR) 2002.

Arrangement of Regulations

2)   Every employer shall carry out suitable and sufficient analysis of workstations.

3)   Employers shall ensure that equipment provided meets the requirements of the schedule laid down in these Regulations.

4)   Employers shall plan activities and provide such breaks or changes in work activity to reduce employees' workload on that equipment.

5)   For display screen equipment (DSE) users, the employer shall provide, on request, an eyesight test carried out by a competent person.

6&7) Provision of information and training.

Outline of main points

WORKSTATION ASSESSMENTS (REG 2)

Workstation assessments should take account of:

■   Screen   -   positioning, character definition, character stability etc.
■   Keyboard   -   tilt able, character legibility etc.
■   Desk   -   size, matt surface etc.
■   Chair   -   adjustable back and height, footrest available etc.
■   Environment   -   noise, lighting, space etc.
■   Software   -   easy to use, work rate not governed by software.

INFORMATION AND TRAINING (REGS 6&7)

Information and training should include:

■   Risks to health.   ■   How to recognise problems.

- Precautions in place (for example, the need for regular breaks).
- How to report problems.

Health and Safety (First-Aid) Regulations (FAR) 1981 (as amended)

See also - Health and Safety (Miscellaneous Amendments) Regulations (MAR) 2002.

Law considered in context/more depth in Element 2.

Arrangement of Regulations

1) Citation and commencement.
2) Interpretation.
3) Duty of employer to make provision for first-aid.
4) Duty of employer to inform his employees of the arrangements.
5) Duty of self-employed person to provide first-aid equipment.
6) Power to grant exemptions.
7) Cases where these Regulations do not apply.
8) Application to mines.
9) Application offshore.
10) Repeals, revocations and modification.

Schedule 1 - Repeals.

Schedule 1 - Revocations.

Outline of main points

1) Regulation 2 defines first-aid as: '...treatment for the purpose of preserving life and minimising the consequences of injury or illness until medical (doctor or nurse) help can be obtained. Also, it provides treatment of minor injuries which would otherwise receive no treatment, or which do not need the help of a medical practitioner or nurse'.
2) Requires that every employer must provide equipment and facilities which are adequate and appropriate in the circumstances for administering first-aid to his employees.
3) Employer must inform their employees about the first-aid arrangements, including the location of equipment, facilities and identification of trained personnel.
4) Self-employed people must ensure that adequate and suitable provision is made for administering first-aid while at work.

Health and Safety (Miscellaneous Amendments) Regulations (MAR) 2002

See also - FAR 1981, DSE 1992, MHOR 1992, PPER 1992, WHSWR 1992, PUWER and LOLER.

These Regulations made minor amendments to UK law to come into line with the requirements of the original Directives and came into force on 17th September 2002. In relation to this publication, the Regulations that are affected by the amendments are:

- Health and Safety (First-Aid) Regulations (FAR) 1981.
- Health and Safety (Display Screen Equipment) Regulations (DSE) 1992.
- Manual Handling Operations Regulations (MHOR) 1992.
- Personal Protective Equipment at Work Regulations (PPER) 1992.
- Workplace (Health, Safety and Welfare) Regulations (WHSWR) 1992.
- Provision and Use of Work Equipment Regulations (PUWER) 1998.
- Lifting Operations and Lifting Equipment Regulations (LOLER) 1998.

Arrangement of Regulations

1) Citation and commencement.
2) Amendment of the Health and Safety (First-Aid) Regulations 1981.
3) Amendment of the Health and Safety (Display Screen Equipment) Regulations 1992.
4) Amendment of the Manual Handling Operations Regulations 1992.
5) Amendment of the Personal Protective Equipment at Work Regulations 1992.
6) Amendment of the Workplace (Health, Safety and Welfare) Regulations 1992.
7) Amendment of the Provision and Use of Work Equipment Regulations 1998.
8) Amendment of the Lifting Operations and Lifting Equipment Regulations 1998.
9) Amendment of the Quarries Regulations 1999.

Outline of main points

REGULATION 3 - AMENDMENT OF THE HEALTH AND SAFETY (FIRST-AID) REGULATIONS 1981

The Health and Safety (First-Aid) Regulations 1981 are amended by adding the additional requirements that any first-aid room provided under requirements of these Regulations must be easily accessible to stretchers and to any other equipment needed to convey patients to and from the room and that the room be sign-posted by use of a sign complying with the Health and Safety (Safety Signs and Signals) Regulations 1996.

REGULATION 3 - AMENDMENT OF THE HEALTH AND SAFETY (DISPLAY SCREEN EQUIPMENT) REGULATIONS 1992

The Health and Safety (Display Screen Equipment) Regulations 1992 were amended to cover workstations 'used for the purposes of' an employer's undertaking, which includes workstations provided by the employer and others. The Health and Safety (Display Screen Equipment) Regulations 1992 were amended to provide for people that are users of display screen equipment in an employers undertaking but are not employees of the employer, for example, staff provided through an employment agency. This extension of duty relates to requests for eye site tests from the person. The employer who carries on the undertaking must ensure an eyesight test is carried out, as soon as is practicable after the request for those currently a user and before they become a user for those who become users. The Health and Safety (Display Screen Equipment) Regulations 1992 were similarly amended with regard to health and safety training for users.

REGULATION 4 - AMENDMENT OF THE MANUAL HANDLING OPERATIONS REGULATIONS 1992

Regulation 4 of the Manual Handling Operations Regulations 1992 were amended by adding the requirement to, when determining whether manual handling operations at work involve a risk of injury and the appropriate steps to reduce that risk, have regard to:

- Physical suitability of the employee to carry out the operations.
- Clothing, footwear or other personal effects they are wearing.
- Knowledge and training.
- Results of any relevant risk assessment conducted for the Management of Health and Safety at Work Regulations.
- Whether the employee is within a group of employees identified by that assessment as being especially at risk.
- Results of any health surveillance provided under the Management of Health and Safety Regulations.

REGULATION 5 - AMENDMENT OF THE PERSONAL PROTECTIVE EQUIPMENT AT WORK REGULATIONS 1992

The Personal Protective Equipment at Work Regulations 1992 were amended so that personal protective equipment (PPE) must also be suitable for the period for which it is worn and account is taken of the characteristics of the workstation of each person.

Provision of personal issue of PPE needs to take place in situations where it is necessary to ensure it is hygienic and free of risk to health. Where an assessment of PPE is made this must consider whether it is compatible with other personal protective equipment that is in use and which an employee would be required to wear simultaneously.

The amendments require that information provided to satisfy Regulation 9 for the provision of information, instruction and training must be kept available to employees. A new, additional duty is created requiring the employer, where appropriate, and at suitable intervals, to organise demonstrations in the wearing of PPE.

REGULATION 6 - AMENDMENT OF THE WORKPLACE (HEALTH, SAFETY AND WELFARE) REGULATIONS 1992

The Workplace (Health, Safety and Welfare) Regulations 1992 have been amended to improve clarity, include additional Regulations and make provision for the disabled.

An additional Regulation (4A) sets out a requirement where a workplace is in a building, the building shall have a stability and solidity appropriate to the nature of the use of the workplace. The range of things requiring maintenance under these Regulations is extended to equipment and devices intended to prevent or reduce hazards. A new duty requires workplaces to be adequately thermally insulated where it is necessary, having regard to the type of work carried out and the physical activity of the persons carrying out the work. In addition, excessive effects of sunlight on temperature must be avoided.

The Regulations were amended with regard to facilities for changing clothing in that the facilities need to be easily accessible, of sufficient capacity and provided with seating. Requirements were amended such that rest rooms and rest areas must include suitable arrangements to protect non-smokers from discomfort caused by tobacco smoke. They also must be equipped with an adequate number of tables and adequate seating with backs for the number of persons at work likely to use them at any one time and seating which is adequate for the number of disabled persons at work and suitable for them.

A new Regulation (25A) was added requiring, where necessary, those parts of the workplace (including in particular doors, passageways, stairs, showers, washbasins, lavatories and workstations) used or occupied directly by disabled persons at work to be organised to take account of such persons.

AMENDMENT OF THE PROVISION AND USE OF WORK EQUIPMENT REGULATIONS 1998

The Regulations have a small number of amendments affecting 3 main Regulations. Regulation 10, which deals with equipment's conformity with community requirements, is amended such that the requirement to conform to 'essential requirements' is no longer limited to the point at which the equipment was designed and constructed - equipment must now conform at 'all times'. The 'essential requirements' are those that were applicable at the time it was put into first service. Regulation 11 was amended to remove the opportunity of reliance on information, instruction, training and supervision as a separate option in the hierarchy of control of dangerous parts of machinery. The requirement to provide information, instruction, training and supervision is now amended to apply to each stage of the dangerous parts of machinery control hierarchy. Regulation 18, which deals with control systems, carries a small but important amendment which means the requirement that all control systems of work equipment are 'chosen making due allowance for the failures, faults and constraints to be expected in the planned circumstances of use' is modified from an absolute duty to one of so far as is reasonably practicable.

AMENDMENT OF THE LIFTING OPERATIONS AND LIFTING EQUIPMENT REGULATIONS 1998

Minor changes to the definitions in the Lifting Operations and Lifting Equipment Regulations 1998 were made by these Regulations.

(a)   In the definition of 'accessory for lifting' in Regulation 2(1), by substituting for the word 'work' the word 'lifting'.

(b)   In Regulation 3(4), by substituting for the words '(5) (b)' the words '(3) (b)'.

Health and Safety (Miscellaneous Repeals, Revocations and Amendments) Regulations (MRRA) 2013

See also - PPER 1992 and WHSWR 1992.

These Regulations repeal one Act and revoke twelve instruments (plus a related provision in the Factories Act 1961) and came into force on 6th April 2013. The Regulations, applicable to this award, that are affected by the amendments are detailed below.

Arrangement of Regulations

1) Citation and commencement.
2) Repeals and revocations.
3) Consequential amendments to the Dangerous Substances (Notification and Marking of Sites) Regulations (NAMOS) 1990.
4) Consequential amendments to the Workplace (Health, Safety and Welfare) Regulations (WHSWR) 1992.

Outline of main points

CONSEQUENTIAL AMENDMENTS TO THE PERSONAL PROTECTIVE EQUIPMENT AT WORK REGULATIONS (PPE) 1992

The Personal Protective Equipment at Work Regulations 1992 have been amended so that they cover the provision and use of head protection on construction sites thus maintaining the level of legal protection when the Construction (Head Protection) Regulations were revoked as part of the Health and Safety (Miscellaneous Repeals, Revocations and Amendments) Regulations 2013. These measures are being removed because they have either been overtaken by more up to date Regulations, are redundant or do not deliver the intended benefits.

AMENDMENT OF THE WORKPLACE (HEALTH, SAFETY AND WELFARE) REGULATIONS (WHSWR) 1992

The Workplace (Health, Safety and Welfare) Regulations 1992 have been amended to include the requirement for adequate lighting and safe access for workers on ships in a shipyard or harbour undergoing construction, repair or maintenance.

Health and Safety (Safety Signs and Signals) Regulations (SSSR) 1996

Law considered in context/more depth in Element 2.

Arrangement of Regulations

1) Citation and commencement.
2) Interpretation.
3) Application.
4) Provision and maintenance of safety signs.
5) Information, instruction and training.
6) Transitional provisions.
7) Enforcement.
8) Revocations and amendments.

Outline of main points

The Regulations require employers to provide specific safety signs whenever there is a risk which has not been avoided or controlled by other means, for example, by engineering controls and safe systems of work. Where a safety sign would not help to reduce that risk, or where the sign is not significant, there is no need to provide a sign. They require, where necessary, the use of road traffic signs within workplaces to regulate road traffic.

They also require employers to:

- Maintain the safety signs which are provided by them.
- Explain unfamiliar signs to their employees and tell them what they need to do when they see a safety sign.

The Regulations cover 4 main types of signs:

1) **Prohibition** - circular signs, prime colours red and white, for example, no pedestrian access.
2) **Warning** - triangular signs, prime colours black on yellow, for example, overhead electrics.
3) **Mandatory** - circular signs, prime colours blue and white, for example, safety helmets must be worn.
4) **Safe condition** - oblong/square signs, prime colours green and white, for example, fire assembly point, first-aid etc.

Supplementary signs provide additional information. Supplementary signs with yellow/black or red/white diagonal stripes can be used to highlight a hazard, but must not substitute for signs as defined above. Firefighting, rescue equipment and emergency exit signs have to comply with a separate British Standard.

Ionising Radiations Regulations (IRR) 1999

Arrangement of Regulations

PART I - INTERPRETATION AND GENERAL

1) Citation and commencement.
2) Interpretation.
3) Application.

4)   Duties under the Regulations.

PART II - GENERAL PRINCIPLES AND PROCEDURES

5)   Authorisation of specified practices.

6)   Notification of specified work.

7)   Prior risk assessment etc.

8)   Restriction of exposure.

9)   Personal protective equipment.

10)   Maintenance and examination of engineering controls etc. and personal protective equipment.

11)   Dose limitation.

12)   Contingency plans.

PART III - ARRANGEMENTS FOR THE MANAGEMENT OF RADIATION PROTECTION

13)   Radiation protection adviser.

14)   Information, instruction and training.

15)   Co-operation between employers.

PART IV - DESIGNATED AREAS

16)   Designation of controlled or supervised areas.

17)   Local rules and radiation protection supervisors.

18)   Additional requirements for designated areas.

19)   Monitoring of designated areas.

PART V - CLASSIFICATION AND MONITORING OF PERSONS

20)   Designation of classified persons.

21)   Dose assessment and recording.

22)   Estimated doses and special entries.

23)   Dosimetry for accidents etc.

24)   Medical surveillance.

25)   Investigation and notification of overexposure.

26)   Dose limitation for overexposed employees.

PART VI - ARRANGEMENTS FOR THE CONTROL OF RADIOACTIVE SUBSTANCES, ARTICLES AND EQUIPMENT

27)   Sealed sources and articles containing or embodying radioactive substances.

28)   Accounting for radioactive substances.

29)   Keeping and moving of radioactive substances.

30)   Notification of certain occurrences.

31)   Duties of manufacturers etc. of articles for use in work with ionising radiation.

32)   Equipment used for medical exposure.

33)   Misuse of or interference with sources of ionising radiation.

PART VII - DUTIES OF EMPLOYEES AND MISCELLANEOUS

34)   Duties of employees.

35)   Approval of dosimetry services.

36)   Defence on contravention.

37)   Exemption certificates.

38)   Extension outside Great Britain.

39)   Transitional provisions.

40)   Modifications relating to the Ministry of Defence.

41)   Modification, revocation and saving.

SCHEDULES

Schedule 1 - Work not required to be notified under Regulation 6.

Schedule 2 - Particulars to be provided in a notification under Regulation 6(2).

Schedule 3 - Additional particulars that the Executive may require.

Schedule 4 - Dose limits.

Schedule 5 - Matters in respect of which radiation protection adviser must be consulted by a radiation employer.

Schedule 6 - Particulars to be entered in the radiation passbook.

Schedule 7 - Particulars to be contained in a health record.

Schedule 8 - Quantities and concentrations of radionuclides.

Schedule 9 - Modifications.

Outline of main points

The Regulations supersede and consolidate the Ionising Radiations Regulations 1985 and the Ionising Radiation (Outside Workers) Regulations 1993. They impose duties on employers to protect employees and other persons against ionising radiation arising from work with radioactive substances and other sources of ionising radiation; and also impose certain duties on employees.

Lifting Operations and Lifting Equipment Regulations (LOLER) 1998 (as amended)

See also - Health and Safety (Miscellaneous Amendments) Regulations (MAR) 2002.

Law considered in context/more depth in Element 4.

Arrangements of Regulations

1) Citation and commencement.

2) Interpretation.

3) Application.

4) Strength and stability.

5) Lifting equipment for lifting persons.

6) Positioning and installation.

7) Marking of lifting equipment.

8) Organisation of lifting operations.

9) Thorough examination and inspection.

10) Reports and defects.

11) Keeping of information.

12) Exemption for the armed forces.

13) Amendment of the Shipbuilding and Ship-repairing Regulations 1960.

14) Amendment of the Docks Regulation 1988.

15) Repeal of provisions of the Factories Act 1961.

16) Repeal of section 85 of the Mines and Quarries Act 1954.

17) Revocation of instruments.

Schedule 1 - Information to be contained in a report of a thorough examination.

Schedule 2 - Revocation of instruments.

Outline of main points

The Lifting Operations and Lifting Equipment Regulations (LOLER) 1998 impose health and safety requirements with respect to lifting equipment (as defined in Regulation 2(1)). They are not industry specific and apply to almost all lifting operations.

The Regulations place duties on employers, the self-employed, and certain persons having control of lifting equipment (of persons at work who use or supervise or manage its use, or of the way it is used, to the extent of their control (Regulation 3(3) to (5)).

The Regulations make provision with respect to:

- The strength and stability of lifting equipment (Regulation 4).
- The safety of lifting equipment for lifting persons (Regulation 5).
- The way lifting equipment is positioned and installed (Regulation 6).
- The marking of machinery and accessories for lifting, and lifting equipment which is designed for lifting persons or which might so be used in error (Regulation 7).
- The organisation of lifting operations (Regulation 8).
- The thorough examination (defined in (Regulation 2(1)) and inspection of lifting equipment in specified circumstances, (Regulation 9(1) to (3)).
- The evidence of examination to accompany it outside the undertaking (Regulation 9(4)).
- The exception for winding apparatus at mines from Regulation 9 (Regulation 9(5)).
- Transitional arrangements relating to Regulation 9 (Regulation 9(6) and (7)).
- The making of reports of thorough examinations and records of inspections (Regulation 10 and Schedule 1).
- The keeping of information in the reports and records (Regulation 11).

Management of Health and Safety at Work Regulations (MHSWR) 1999

Law considered in context/more depth in Element 1.

Arrangement of Regulations

1) Citation, commencement and interpretation.

2) Disapplication of these Regulations.

3) Risk assessment.

4) Principles of prevention to be applied.

5) Health and safety arrangements.

6) Health surveillance.

7) Health and safety assistance.

8) Procedures for serious and imminent danger and for danger areas.

9) Contacts with external services.

10) Information for employees.

11) Co-operation and coordination.

12) Persons working in host employers' or self-employed persons' undertakings.

13) Capabilities and training.

14) Employees' duties.

15) Temporary workers.

16) Risk assessment in respect of new or expectant mothers.

17) Certificate from a registered medical practitioner in respect of new or expectant mothers.

18) Notification by new or expectant mothers.

19) Protection of young persons.

20) Exemption certificates.

21) Provisions as to liability.

22) Exclusion of civil liability.

23) Extension outside Great Britain.

24) Amendment of the Health and Safety (First-Aid) Regulations 1981.

25) Amendment of the Offshore Installations and Pipeline Works (First-Aid) Regulations 1989.

26) Amendment of the Mines Miscellaneous Health and Safety Provisions Regulations 1995.

27) Amendment of the Construction (Health, Safety and Welfare) Regulations 1996.

28) Regulations to have effect as health and safety Regulations.

29) Revocations and consequential amendments.

30) Transitional provision.

Schedule 1 - General principles of prevention.

Schedule 2 - Consequential amendments.

Outline of main points

Management of Health and Safety at Work Regulations (MHSWR) 1999 set out some broad general duties that apply to almost all kinds of work. They are aimed mainly at improving health and safety management. The Regulations work in a similar way to the broad health and safety requirements set out in the Health and Safety at Work Act (HASAWA) 1974, and can be seen as a way of fleshing out what is already in the HASAWA 1974. The 1999 Regulations replace the Management of Health and Safety at Work Regulations 1992, the Management of Health and Safety at Work (Amendment) Regulations 1994, the Health and Safety (Young Persons) Regulations 1997 and Part III of the Fire Precautions (Workplace) Regulations 1997. The principal Regulations are discussed below.

RISK ASSESSMENT (REGULATION 3)

The Regulations require employers (and the self-employed) to assess the risk to the health and safety of their employees and to anyone else who may be affected by their work activity. This is necessary to ensure that the preventive and protective steps can be identified to control hazards in the workplace. Where an employer is employing or about to employ young persons (under 18 years of age) he must carry out a risk assessment which takes particular account of:

- The inexperience, lack of awareness of risks and immaturity of young persons.
- The layout of the workplace and workstations.
- Exposure to physical, biological and chemical agents.
- Work equipment and the way in which it is handled.
- The extent of health and safety training to be provided.
- Risks from agents, processes and work listed in the Annex to Council Directive 94/33/EC on the protection of young people at work.

Where 5 or more employees are employed, the significant findings of risk assessments must be recorded in writing (the same threshold that is used in respect of having a written safety policy). This record must include details of any employees being identified as being especially at risk.

PRINCIPLES OF PREVENTION TO BE APPLIED (REGULATION 4)

Regulation 4 requires an employer to implement preventive and protective measures on the basis of general principles of prevention specified in Schedule 1 to the Regulations.

These are:

1) Avoiding risks.

2) Evaluating the risks which cannot be avoided.

3) Combating the risks at source.

4) Adapting the work to the individual, especially as regards the design of workplaces, the choice of work equipment and the choice of working and production methods, with a view, in particular, to alleviating monotonous work and work at a predetermined work-rate and to reducing their effect on health.

5) Adapting to technical progress.

6) Replacing the dangerous by the non-dangerous or the less dangerous.

7) Developing a coherent overall prevention policy which covers technology, organisation of work, working conditions, social relationships and the influence of factors relating to the working environment.

8) Giving collective protective measures priority over individual protective measures.

9) Giving appropriate instructions to employees.

HEALTH AND SAFETY ARRANGEMENTS (REGULATION 5)

Appropriate arrangements must be made for the effective planning, organisation, control, monitoring and review of preventative and protective measures (in other words, for the management of health and safety). Again, employers with five or more employees must have their arrangements in writing.

HEALTH SURVEILLANCE (REGULATION 6)

In addition to the requirements of other specific Regulations, consideration must be given to carrying out health surveillance of employees, where there is a disease or adverse health condition identified in risk assessments.

HEALTH AND SAFETY ASSISTANCE (REGULATION 7)

The employer must appoint one or more competent persons to assist him in complying with the legal obligations imposed on the undertaking. The number of persons appointed should reflect the number of employees and the type of hazards in the workplace.

If more than one competent person is appointed, then arrangements must be made for ensuring adequate co-operation between them. The competent person(s) must be given the necessary time and resources to fulfil their functions. This will depend on the size the undertaking, the risks to which employees are exposed and the distribution of those risks throughout the undertaking.

The employer must ensure that competent person(s) who are not employees are informed of the factors known (or suspected) to affect the health and safety of anyone affected by business activities.

Competent people are defined as those who have sufficient training and experience or knowledge and other qualities to enable them to perform their functions. Persons may be selected from among existing employees or from outside. Where there is a suitable person in the employer's employment, that person shall be appointed as the 'competent person' in preference to a non-employee.

PROCEDURES FOR SERIOUS AND IMMINENT DANGER AND FOR DANGER AREAS (REGULATION 8)

Employers are required to set up emergency procedures and appoint **competent persons** to ensure compliance with identified arrangements, to devise control strategies as appropriate and to limit access to areas of risk to ensure that only those persons with adequate health and safety knowledge and instruction are admitted.

The factors to be considered when preparing a procedure to deal with workplace emergencies such as fire, explosion, bomb scare, chemical leakage or other dangerous occurrence should include:

- The identification and training requirements of persons with specific responsibilities.
- The layout of the premises in relation to escape routes etc.
- The number of persons affected.
- Assessment of special needs (disabled persons, children etc.).
- Warning systems.
- Emergency lighting.
- Location of shut-off valves, isolation switches, hydrants etc.
- Equipment required to deal with the emergency.
- Location of assembly points.
- Communication with emergency services.
- Training and/or information to be given to employees, visitors, local residents and anyone else who might be affected.

CONTACTS WITH EXTERNAL SERVICES (REGULATION 9)

Employers must ensure that, where necessary, contacts are made with external services. This particularly applies with regard to first-aid, emergency medical care and rescue work.

INFORMATION FOR EMPLOYEES (REGULATION 10)

Employees must be provided with relevant information about hazards to their health and safety arising from risks identified by the assessments. Clear instruction must be provided concerning any preventative or protective control measures including those relating to serious and imminent danger and fire assessments. Details of any competent persons nominated to discharge specific duties in accordance with the Regulations must also be communicated as should risks arising from contact with other employer's activities (see Regulation 11).

Before employing a child (a person who is not over compulsory school age) the employer must provide those with parental responsibility for the child with information on the risks that have been identified and preventative and protective measures to be taken.

CO-OPERATION AND COORDINATION (REGULATION 11)

Employers who work together in a common workplace have a duty to co-operate to discharge their duties under relevant statutory provisions. They must also take all reasonable steps to inform their respective employees of risks to their health or safety which may arise out of their work. Specific arrangements must be made to ensure compliance with fire legislation.

PERSONS WORKING IN HOST EMPLOYERS' OR SELF EMPLOYED PERSONS' UNDERTAKINGS (REGULATION 12)

This Regulation extends the requirements of Regulation 11 to include employees working as sole occupiers of a workplace under the control of another employer.

Such employees would include those working under a service of contract and employees in temporary employment businesses under the control of the first employer.

CAPABILITIES AND TRAINING (REGULATION 13)

Employers need to take into account the capabilities of their employees before entrusting tasks. This is necessary to ensure that they have adequate health and safety training and are capable enough at their jobs to avoid risk.

To this end, consideration must be given to recruitment including job orientation when transferring between jobs and work departments. Training must also be provided when other factors such as the introduction of new technology and new systems of work or work equipment arise.

Training must:

- Be repeated periodically where appropriate.
- Be adapted to take account of any new or changed risks to the health and safety of the employees concerned.
- Take place during working hours.

EMPLOYEES' DUTIES (REGULATION 14)

Employees are required to follow health and safety instructions by using machinery, substances, transport etc. in accordance with the instructions and training that they have received.

They must also inform their employer (and other employers) of any dangers or shortcoming in the health and safety arrangements, even if there is no risk of imminent danger.

TEMPORARY WORKERS (REGULATION 15)

Consideration is given to the special needs of temporary workers. In particular to the provision of particular health and safety information such as qualifications required to perform the task safely or any special arrangements such as the need to provide health screening.

RISKS ASSESSMENT IN RESPECT OF NEW OR EXPECTANT MOTHERS (REGULATION 16)

Where the work is of a kind which would involve risk to a new or expectant mother or her baby, then the assessment required by Regulation 3 should take this into account. If the risk cannot be avoided, then the employer should take reasonable steps to:

- Adjust the hours worked.
- Offer alternative work.
- Give paid leave for as long as is necessary.

CERTIFICATE FROM A REGISTERED MEDICAL PRACTITIONER IN RESPECT OF NEW OR EXPECTANT MOTHERS (REGULATION 17)

Where the woman is a night shift worker and has a medical certificate identifying night shift work as a risk then the employer must put her on day shift or give paid leave for as long as is necessary.

NOTIFICATION BY NEW OR EXPECTANT MOTHERS (REGULATION 18)

The employer need take no action until he is notified in writing by the woman that she is pregnant, has given birth in the last six months, or is breastfeeding.

PROTECTION OF YOUNG PERSONS (REGULATION 19)

Employers of young persons shall ensure that they are not exposed to risk as a consequence of their lack of experience, lack of awareness or lack of maturity.

No employer shall employ young people for work which:

- Is beyond his physical or psychological capacity.
- Involves exposure to agents which chronically affect human health.
- Involves harmful exposure to radiation.
- Involves a risk to health from extremes of temperature, noise or vibration.
- Involves risks which could not be reasonably foreseen by young persons.

This Regulation does not prevent the employment of a young person who is no longer a child for work:

- Where it is necessary for his training.
- Where the young person will be supervised by a competent person.
- Where any risk will be reduced to the lowest level that is reasonably practicable.

(Note: Two HSE publications give guidance on these topics. HSG122 - New and expectant mothers at work: A guide for employers and HSG165 - Young people at work: A guide for employers).

EXEMPTION CERTIFICATES (REGULATION 20)

The Secretary of State for Defence may, in the interests of national security, by a certificate in writing exempt the armed forces, any visiting force or any headquarters from certain obligations imposed by the Regulations.

PROVISIONS AS TO LIABILITY (REGULATION 21)

Employers cannot submit a defence in criminal proceedings that contravention was caused by the act or default either of an employee or the competent person appointed under Regulation 7.

EXCLUSION OF CIVIL LIABILITY (REGULATION 22)

As amended by Health and Safety at Work etc. Act 1974 (Civil Liability) (Exceptions) Regulations 2013:

Regulation 22 specifies:

"(1) Breach of a duty imposed by Regulation 16, 16A, 17 or 17A shall, so far as it causes damage, be actionable by the new or expectant mother.

(2) Any term of an agreement which purports to exclude or restrict any liability for such a breach is void."

REVOCATIONS AND AMENDMENTS (REGULATIONS 24-29)

The Regulations:

- Revoke Regulation 6 of the Health and Safety (First-Aid) Regulations (FAR) 1981 which confers power on the Health and Safety Executive to grant exemptions from those Regulations.

- Amend the Offshore Installations and Pipeline Works (First-Aid) Regulations 1989.
- Amend the Mines Miscellaneous Health and Safety Provisions Regulations 1995.

The Regulations also make amendments to the statutory instruments as specified in Schedule 2.

Manual Handling Operations Regulations (MHOR) 1992 (as amended)

See also - Health and Safety (Miscellaneous Amendments) Regulations (MAR) 2002.

Law considered in context/more depth in Element 4.

Arrangement of Regulations

1) Citation and commencement.
2) Interpretation.
3) Disapplication of Regulations.
4) Duties of employers.
5) Duty of employees.
6) Exemption certificates.
7) Extension outside Great Britain.
8) Repeals and revocations.

Outline of main points

CITATION AND COMMENCEMENT (1)

INTERPRETATION (2)

'Injury' does not include injury caused by toxic or corrosive substances which:

- Have leaked/spilled from load.
- Are present on the surface but not leaked/spilled from it.
- Are a constituent part of the load.

'Load' includes any person or animal.

'Manual Handling Operations' means transporting or supporting a load including:

- Lifting and putting down.
- Pushing, pulling or moving by hand or bodily force.
- Shall as far as is reasonably practicable.

DISAPPLICATION OF REGULATIONS (3)

DUTIES OF EMPLOYERS (4)

AVOIDANCE OF MANUAL HANDLING (4) (1) (A)

The employer's duty is to avoid the need for manual handling operations which involve a risk of their employees being injured - as far as is reasonably practicable.

ASSESSMENT OF RISK (4) (1) (B) (I)

Where not reasonably practicable make a suitable and sufficient assessment of all such manual handling operations.

REDUCING THE RISK OF INJURY (4) (1) (B) (II)

Take appropriate steps to reduce the risk of injury to the lowest level reasonably practicable.

THE LOAD - ADDITIONAL INFORMATION (4) (1) (B) (III)

Employers shall provide information on general indications or where reasonably practicable precise information on:

- The weight of each load.
- The heaviest side of any load whose centre of gravity is not central.

REVIEWING THE ASSESSMENT (4) (2)

Assessment review:

- Where there is reason to believe the assessment is no longer valid.
- There is sufficient change in manual handling operations.

DUTY OF EMPLOYEES (5)

Employees shall make full and proper use of any system of work provided for his use by his employer.

EXEMPTION CERTIFICATES (6)

EXTENSION OUTSIDE GREAT BRITAIN (7)

REPEALS AND REVOCATIONS (8)

SCHEDULES

Schedule 1 - Factors to which the employer must have regard and questions he must consider when making an assessment of manual handling operations.

Schedule 2 - Repeals and revocations.

Appendix 1 - Numerical guidelines for assessment.

Appendix 2 - Example of an assessment checklist.

Thus the Regulations establish a clear hierarchy of measures:

1) Avoid hazardous manual handling operations so far as is reasonably practicable.

2) Make a suitable and sufficient assessment of any hazardous manual handling operations that cannot be avoided.

3) Reduce the risk of injury so far as is reasonably practicable.

New Roads and Street Works Act (NRSWA) 1991

Arrangement of Act

PART I - NEW ROADS IN ENGLAND AND WALES
- Concession agreements.
- Toll orders.
- Further provisions with respect to tolls.
- Annual report.
- Miscellaneous.
- General.

PART II - NEW ROADS IN SCOTLAND
- Toll roads.
- Further provision with respect to tolls.
- Report.
- Supplementary provisions.

PART III - STREET WORKS IN ENGLAND AND WALES
- Introductory provisions.
- The street works register.
- Notice and coordination of works.
- Streets subject to special controls.
- General requirements as to execution of street works.
- Reinstatement.
- Charges, fees and contributions payable by undertakers.
- Duties and liabilities of undertakers with respect to apparatus.
- Apparatus affected by highway, bridge or transport works.
- Provisions with respect to particular authorities and undertakings.
- Power of street authority or district council to undertake street works.
- Supplementary provisions.

PART IV - ROAD WORKS IN SCOTLAND
- Introductory provisions.
- The road works register.
- Notice and coordination of works.
- Roads subject to special controls.
- General requirements as to execution of road works.
- Reinstatement.
- Charges, fees and contributions payable by undertakers.
- Duties and liabilities of undertakers with respect to apparatus.
- Apparatus affected by road, bridge or transport works.
- Provisions with respect to particular authorities and undertakings.
- Power of road works authority or district council to undertake road works.
- Supplementary provisions.

PART V - GENERAL

SCHEDULES

Schedule 1 - Supplementary provisions as to termination of concession.

Schedule 2 - Procedure in connection with toll orders.

Schedule 3 - Street works licences.

Schedule 4 - Streets with special engineering difficulties.

Schedule 5 - Procedure for making certain orders under Part III.

Schedule 6 - Roads with special engineering difficulties.

Schedule 7 - Procedure for making certain orders under Part IV.

Schedule 8 - Minor and consequential amendments.

Schedule 9 - Repeals.

Outline of main points

One of the most important elements of the street works legislation is the duty on street authorities to coordinate all works in the highway. As important is the parallel duty on undertakers to co-operate in this process. It is essential that both street authorities and undertakers take these responsibilities seriously. The New Roads and Street Works Act 1991 spells out the objectives of the coordination function.

They are to:

- Ensure safety.
- Minimise inconvenience to people using a street, including a specific reference to people with a disability.
- Protect the structure of the street and apparatus in it.

These objectives should be taken into account by everyone responsible for planning and carrying out works in the highway.

The NRSWA 1991 sets out three requirements for a successful coordination framework:

- The notice system - the notices themselves provide vital information to aid the coordination process, while the notice periods provide time within which appropriate steps can be taken. The best method of exchanging notices is electronically.
- Streets subject to special controls - these designation procedures provide a mechanism by which attention can be focused on particularly sensitive streets.
- The coordination tools - the Act provides a range of tools to facilitate the coordination process. These include: the power to direct the timing of street works, the power to restrict street works following substantial road works and the requirement on undertakers to avoid unnecessary delay and obstruction.

There are three important principles to which undertakers and street authorities must adhere if coordination is to be effective. They are:

- The need to balance the potentially conflicting interests of road users and undertakers' customers.
- The importance of close co-operation and liaison between street authorities and undertakers.
- An acknowledgement on all sides of the fact that works programmes and practices may have to be adjusted in order to ensure that the objectives of the coordination provisions are achieved.

In carrying out their responsibilities under the NRSWA 1991 street authorities and undertakers should endeavour to ensure that their works are planned in such a way as to minimise inconvenience to all road users including disability groups.

Authorities and undertakers are expected to work particularly closely in relation to 'urgent work', which is that work that falls short of emergencies as defined by the NRSWA 1991.

These works will need to be executed in circumstances where planning and coordination time is limited. Where work is needed in traffic sensitive streets considerable disruption may result and both parties are expected to take an objective but balanced view on the necessity of the work and arrangements surrounding it.

Personal Protective Equipment at Work Regulations (PPER) 1992 (as amended)

See also - Health and Safety (Miscellaneous Amendments) Regulations (MAR) 2002 and Health and Safety (Miscellaneous Repeals, Revocations and Amendments) Regulations (MRRA) 2002.

Law considered in context/more depth in Element 2.

Arrangement of Regulations

1) Citation and commencement.
2) Interpretation.
3) Disapplication of these Regulations.
4) Provision of personal protective equipment.
5) Compatibility of personal protective equipment.
6) Assessment of personal protective equipment.
7) Maintenance and replacement of personal protective equipment.
8) Accommodation for personal protective equipment.
9) Information, instruction and training.
10) Use of personal protective equipment.
11) Reporting loss or defect.
12) Exemption certificates.
13) Extension outside Great Britain.
14) Modifications, repeal and revocations directive.

Schedule 1 - Relevant Community.

Schedule 2 - Modifications.

Part I   Factories Act 1961.

Part II   The Coal and Other Mines (Fire and Rescue) Order 1956.

Part III   The Shipbuilding and Ship-Repairing Regulations 1960.

Part IV   The Coal Mines (Respirable Dust) Regulations 1975.

Part V   The Control of Lead at Work Regulations 1980.

Part VI   The Ionising Radiations Regulations 1985.

Part VII   The Control of Asbestos at Work Regulations 1987.

Part VIII   The Control of Substances Hazardous to Health Regulations 1988.

Part IX   The Noise at Work Regulations 1989.

Part X   The Construction (Head Protection) Regulations 1989.

Schedule 3 - Revocations.

Outline of main points

2)   Personal protective equipment (PPE) means all equipment (including clothing provided for protection against adverse weather) which is intended to be worn or held by a person at work and which protects him against risks to his health or safety.

3)   These Regulations do not apply to:

- Ordinary working clothes/uniforms.
- Offensive weapons.
- Portable detectors which signal risk.
- Equipment used whilst playing competitive sports.
- Equipment provided for travelling on a road.

The Regulations do not apply to situations already controlled by other Regulations i.e.

- Control of Lead at Work Regulations 2002.
- Ionising Radiation Regulations 1999.
- Control of Asbestos at Work Regulations 2002.
- CoSHH Regulations 2002 (as amended).
- Noise at Work Regulations 2005.
- Construction (Head Protection) Regulations 1989.

4)   Suitable PPE must be provided when risks cannot be adequately controlled by other means. Reg. 4 requires that PPE will not be suitable unless it:

- Is appropriate for the risk and conditions.
- It takes account of ergonomic requirements.
- It takes account of the state of health of users.
- It takes account of the characteristics of the worker's workstation.
- Is capable of fitting the wearer, if required after adjustment.
- Is effective in controlling risks, without increase in overall risk.
- Complies with EU directives.

Where it is necessary to ensure hygiene or prevention of health risk personal issue will be made.

5)   Equipment must be compatible with any other PPE which has to be worn.

6)   Before issuing PPE, the employer must carry out a risk assessment to ensure that the equipment is suitable.

- Assess risks not avoided by other means.
- Define characteristics of PPE and of the risk of the equipment itself.
- Compare characteristics of PPE to defined requirement.
- Repeat assessment when no longer valid, or significant change has taken place.

7)   PPE must be maintained.

- In an efficient state.
- In efficient working order.
- In good repair.

8)   Accommodation must be provided for equipment when it is not being used.

9)   Information, instruction and training must be given on:

- The risks PPE will eliminate or limit.
- Why the PPE is to be used.
- How the PPE is to be used.
- How to maintain the PPE.

Information and instruction must be comprehensible to the wearer/user and kept available to them.

10)   Employers shall take reasonable steps to ensure PPE is worn.

- Every employee shall use PPE that has been provided.
- Every employee shall take reasonable steps to return PPE to storage.

11)   Employees must report any loss or defect.

The Guidance on the Regulations points out:

"Whatever PPE is chosen, it should be remembered that, although some types of equipment do provide very high levels of protection, none provides 100%."

Provision and Use of Work Equipment Regulations (PUWER) 1998 (as amended)

See also - Health and Safety (Miscellaneous Amendments) Regulations (MAR) 2002.

Law considered in context/more depth in Elements 3 and 5.

Arrangement of Regulations

PART I - INTRODUCTION

1) Citation and commencement.

2) Interpretation.

3) Application.

PART II - GENERAL

4)   Suitability of work equipment.

5)   Maintenance.

6)   Inspection.

7)   Specific risks.

8)   Information and instructions.

9)   Training.

10) Conformity with community requirements.

11) Dangerous parts of machinery.

12) Protection against specified hazards.

13) High or very low temperature.

14) Controls for starting or making a significant change in operating conditions.

15) Stop controls.

16) Emergency stop controls.

17) Controls.

18) Control systems.

19) Isolation from sources of energy.

20) Stability.

21) Lighting.

22) Maintenance operations.

23) Markings.

24) Warnings.

PART III - MOBILE WORK EQUIPMENT

25) Employees carried on mobile work equipment.

26) Rolling over of mobile work equipment.

27) Overturning of fork-lift trucks.

28) Self-propelled work equipment.

29) Remote-controlled self-propelled work equipment.

30) Drive shafts.

PART IV - POWER PRESSES

31) Power presses to which Part IV does not apply.

32) Thorough examination of power presses, guards and protection devices.

33) Inspection of guards and protection devices.

34) Reports.

35) Keeping of information.

PART V - MISCELLANEOUS

36) Exemption for the armed forces.

37) Transitional provision.

38) Repeal of enactment.

39) Revocation of instruments.

Schedule 1 - Instruments which give effect to Community directives concerning the safety of products.

Schedule 2 - Power presses to which Regulations 32 to 35 do not apply.

Schedule 3 - Information to be contained in a report of a thorough examination of a power press, guard or protection device.

Schedule 4 - Revocation of instruments.

Outline of main points

GENERAL REQUIREMENTS

These Regulations impose health and safety requirements with respect to the provision and use of work equipment, which is defined as 'any machinery, appliance, apparatus, tool or installation for use at work (whether exclusively or not)'.

These Regulations:

- Place general duties on employers.
- Certain persons having control of work equipment, of persons at work who use or supervise or manage its use or of the way it is used, to the extent of their control.
- List minimum requirements for work equipment to deal with selected hazards whatever the industry.
- 'Use' includes any activity involving work equipment and includes starting, stopping, programming, setting, transporting, repairing, modifying, maintaining, servicing and cleaning.

The general duties require the employer to:

- Make sure that equipment is suitable for the use that will be made of it.
- Take into account the working conditions and hazards in the workplace when selecting equipment.
- Ensure equipment is used only for operations for which, and under conditions for which, it is suitable.
- Ensure that equipment is maintained in an efficient state, in efficient working order and in good repair.
- Ensure the inspection of work equipment in specified circumstances by a competent person; keep a record of the result for specified periods; and ensure that evidence of the last inspection accompany work equipment used outside the undertaking.
- Give adequate information, instruction and training.
- Provide equipment that conforms to EU product safety directives.

SPECIFIC REQUIREMENTS COVER

- Guarding of dangerous parts of machinery.
- Protection against specified hazards i.e. articles and substances falling/ejected, rupture/disintegration of work equipment parts, equipment catching fire or overheating, unintended or premature discharge of articles and substances, explosion.
- Work equipment parts and substances at high or very low temperatures.
- Control systems and control devices.
- Isolation of equipment from sources of energy.
- Stability of equipment.
- Lighting.
- Maintenance operations.
- Warnings and markings.

MOBILE WORK EQUIPMENT

Mobile work equipment must have provision as to:

- Its suitability for carrying persons and its safety features.
- Means to minimise the risk to safety from its rolling over.
- Means to reduce the risk to safety from the rolling over of a fork-lift truck.
- The safety of self-propelled work equipment and remote-controlled self-propelled work equipment.
- The drive shafts of mobile work equipment.

POWER PRESSES

The Regulations provide for:

- The thorough examination (defined in Regulation 2(1)) of power presses and their guards and protection devices (Regulation 32).
- Their inspection after setting, re-setting or adjustment of their tools, and every working period (Regulation 33).
- The making (Regulation 34 and Schedule 3) and keeping (Regulation 35) of reports.
- The Regulations implement an EU directive aimed at the protection of workers. There are other directives setting out conditions which new equipment (especially machinery) will have to satisfy before it can be sold in EU member states.

Registration, Evaluation, Authorisation and Restriction of Chemicals (REACH) EC Regulation

Law considered in context/more depth in Element 8.

REACH (Registration, Evaluation, Authorisation and restriction of CHemicals) is the system for controlling chemicals in the EU. REACH is an EU Regulation that applies throughout the EU, including the UK. It has been adopted to improve the protection of human health and the environment from the risks that can be posed by chemicals. In principle, REACH applies to all chemical substances; not only those used in industrial processes, but also used by the public, for example in cleaning products, paints as well as in articles such as clothes, furniture and electrical appliances. Therefore, the Regulation has an impact on most companies across the EU. It also promotes alternative methods for the hazard assessment of substances in order to reduce the number of tests on animals. REACH provides a common EU system to gather hazard information, assess risks, classify, label, and restrict the marketing and use of individual chemicals and mixtures. This is known as the REACH system:

R egistration of basic information of substances to be submitted by companies, to a central database.

E valuation of the registered information to determine hazards and risks.

A uthorisation and restriction requirements imposed on the use of substances of very high concern.

CH emicals.

REACH establishes procedures for collecting and assessing information on the properties and hazards of substances. Companies need to register their substances and to do this they need to work together with other companies who are registering the same substance. The European Chemicals Agency (the Agency; ECHA) receives and evaluates individual registrations for their compliance, and the EU Member States evaluate selected substances to clarify initial concerns for human health or for the environment. Authorities in member states and ECHA's scientific committees assess whether the risks of substances can be managed. Authorities can ban hazardous substances if their risks are unmanageable. They can also decide to restrict a use or make it subject to a prior authorisation. If the risks cannot be managed, authorities can restrict the use of substances in different ways. In time, the most hazardous substances should be substituted with less dangerous ones. REACH requires information, in the form of Safety data sheets, to be provided to users by those that supply chemicals. 'Supply' means making a chemical available to another person. Manufacturers, importers, distributors, wholesalers and retailers are all examples of suppliers.

Arrangement of Regulations

TITLE I - GENERAL ISSUES

Chapter 1 - Aim, scope and application.

Chapter 2 - Definitions and general provision.

TITLE II - REGISTRATION OF SUBSTANCES

Chapter 1 - General obligation to register and information requirements.

Chapter 2 - Substances regarded as being registered.

Chapter 3 - Obligation to register and information requirements for certain types of isolated intermediates.

Chapter 4 - Common provisions for all registrations.

Chapter 5 - Transitional provisions applicable to phase-in substances and notified substances.

TITLE III - DATA SHARING AND AVOIDANCE OF UNNECESSARY TESTING

Chapter 1 - Objectives and general rules.

Chapter 2 - Rules for non-phase-in substances and registrants of phase-in substances who have not pre-registered.

Chapter 3 - Rules for phase-in-substances.

TITLE IV - INFORMATION IN THE SUPPLY CHAIN

TITLE V - DOWNSTREAM USERS

TITLE VI - EVALUATION

Chapter 1 - Dossier evaluation.

Chapter 2 - Substance evaluation.

Chapter 3 - Evaluation of intermediates.

Chapter 4 - Common provisions.

TITLE VII - AUTHORISATION

Chapter 1 - Authorisation requirement.

Chapter 2 - Granting of authorisations.

Chapter 3 - Authorisations in the supply chain.

TITLE VIII - RESTRICTIONS ON THE MANUFACTURING, PLACING ON THE MARKET AND USE OF CERTAIN DANGEROUS SUBSTANCES AND MIXTURES

Chapter 1 - General issues.

Chapter 2 - Restrictions process.

TITLE IX - FEES AND CHARGES

TITLE X - AGENCY

TITLE XII - INFORMATION

TITLE XIII - COMPETENT AUTHORITIES

TITLE XIV - ENFORCEMENT

TITLE XV - TRANSITIONAL AND FINAL PROVISIONS

Annex I - General provisions for assessing substances and preparing chemical safety reports.

Annex II - Requirements for the compilation of safety data sheets.

Annex III - Criteria for substances registered in quantities between 1 and 10 tonnes.

Annex IV - Exemptions from the obligation to register in accordance with article 2(7)(a).

Annex V - Exemptions from the obligation to register in accordance with article 2(7)(b).

Annex VI - Information requirements referred to in article 10.

Annex VII - Standard information requirements for substances manufactured or imported in quantities of one tonne or more.

Annex VIII - Standard information requirements for substances manufactured or imported in quantities of 10 tonnes or more.

Annex IX - Standard information requirements for substances manufactured or imported in quantities of 100 tonnes or more.

Annex X - Standard information requirements for substances manufactured or imported in quantities of 1,000 tonnes or more.

Annex XI - General rules for adaptation of the standard testing regime set out in annexes VII to X.

Annex XII - General provisions for downstream users to assess substances and prepare chemical safety reports.

Annex XIII - Criteria for the identification of persistent, bioaccumulative and toxic substances, and very persistent and very bioaccumulative substances.

Annex XIV - List of substances subject to authorisation.

Annex XV - Dossiers.

Annex XVI - Socio-economic analysis.

Annex XVII - Restrictions on the manufacture, placing on the market and use of certain dangerous substances, mixtures and articles.

Outline of main points

Scope and exemptions

REACH applies to substances manufactured or imported into the EU in quantities of 1 tonne or more per year. Generally, it applies to all individual chemical substances on their own, in preparations or in articles (if the substance is intended to be released during normal and reasonably foreseeable conditions of use from an article).

Some substances are specifically excluded:

- Radioactive substances.
- Substances under customs supervision.
- The transport of substances.
- Non-isolated intermediates.
- Waste.
- Some naturally occurring low-hazard substances.

Some substances, covered by more specific legislation, have tailored provisions, including:

- Human and veterinary medicines.
- Food and foodstuff additives.
- Plant protection products and biocides.

Other substances have tailored provisions within the REACH legislation, as long they are used in specified conditions:

- Isolated intermediates.
- Substances used for research and development.

REACH places the burden of proof of compliance on companies. To comply with the Regulation, companies must identify and manage the risks linked to the substances they manufacture and supply in the EU. They have to demonstrate to ECHA how the substance can be safely and healthily used, and they must communicate the risk management measures to the users.

Registration

Companies have the responsibility of collecting information on the properties and the uses of substances that they manufacture or import at or above one tonne per year. They also have to make an assessment of the hazards and potential risks presented by the substance. They have to register this by submitting a dossier to ECHA, based in Helsinki. The dossier contains details of the substance's properties, other relevant information about risks and how these risks can be managed. They will not be able to manufacture or import a substance within the EU, or import an article that intentionally releases a substance, unless the substance has been registered.

Evaluation

ECHA and the Member States evaluate the information submitted by companies to examine the quality of the registration dossiers and the testing proposals and to clarify if a given substance constitutes a risk to human health or the environment. REACH promotes the use of alternative methods for the assessment of the hazardous properties of substances in order to reduce the number of tests on animals, for example, quantitative structure-activity relationships (QSAR) and read across.

Authorisation

The authorisation procedure aims to assure that the risks from Substances of Very High Concern (SVHC) are properly controlled and that these substances are progressively replaced by suitable alternatives, while ensuring the good functioning of the EU internal market. SVHCs will need to be authorised for specific uses if they appear in Annex XIV of REACH. There will not be a 'blanket' authorisation for a substance to be used generally. Instead, applications for authorisation for a specific use may be made by companies that register the substances, or by those that use them. When a substance is placed on Annex XIV of REACH, a 'sunset date' will be set after which its use will be prohibited, unless an authorisation has been granted.

Restriction

Restrictions are set to protect human health and the environment from unacceptable risks posed by chemicals. Restrictions may limit or ban the manufacture, placing on the market or use of a substance. This is a direct means of controlling the risks associated with any given hazardous substance. Restriction will be used when it is felt that action at the European level is needed. Restriction decisions will also be made by the European Commission based on advice from the ECHA and consultation with EU Member States and others. Restrictions in place already from previous legislation are carried over into REACH in Annex XVII of REACH; further restrictions will be added to this Annex as necessary.

Information

The passage of information up and down the supply chain is one of the important features of REACH - users should be able to understand what manufacturers and importers know about the dangers involved in using chemicals, and they can also pass information back up the supply chain. REACH adopts and builds on the existing system for passing information in a structured way down to chemicals users - the Safety Data Sheet (SDS). This should accompany materials down through the supply chain, providing the information that users need to ensure chemicals are safely managed. REACH will also allow for information on uses of chemicals to be passed back up the supply chain, so that these can be reflected in the SDS.

Users of chemicals - Article 37 - 39 particularly

REACH aims to reduce the use of (and risks from) hazardous chemicals. Certain substances will be identified as substances of very high concern (SVHC), and may become subject to 'authorisation'. Substances that are subject to authorisation cannot be used in the EU unless a company (and their identified users) have been authorised to do so. This will mean that these substances are eventually phased out of all non-essential uses. Other substances are subject to a 'restriction'. Restrictions limit or ban the manufacture, placing on the market or use of substances that pose an unacceptable risk to human health and the environment. REACH may make things better for users of chemicals as it is designed to provide more information on chemicals and increase confidence in their safe and healthy use. In particular, better information on the hazards of chemicals and how to use them safely and healthily will be passed down the supply chain by chemical manufacturers and importers through improved Safety Data Sheets. Users have a duty to apply risk reduction measures identified in Safety Data Sheets provided to them form chemicals (Article 37(5)).

If users of chemicals use a chemical in a novel way that is perhaps not expected, then they will need to consider letting their supplier know. This use will need to be considered for registration by the supplier. If users do not want to let your supplier know about this use (for example, because of commercial concerns) then they do not have to, but it will mean that they will have to let ECHA know about this use and possibly have to submit their own risk assessment. Once the chemical has been registered and they have been provided with a safety data sheet listing the registration number, they have a maximum of 6 months to provide information about their use to

ECHA if it is not included in the supplier's registration. The user's supplier should be able to tell them which uses are covered by the registration. Users of hazardous substances should check whether any of the substances they use are subject to a 'restriction'. This information should be communicated to users in the safety data sheet or other communication given to them by their supplier. If users use restricted substances, they will need to ensure their use of the substance meets the conditions of the restriction. Users are able to contribute to the public consultations whenever a new restriction is proposed, or an existing restriction is amended. Users of hazardous substances should check whether any of the substances they use are subject to authorisation, or are likely to become subject to authorisation in the future. If a substance is subject to authorisation, users will only be able to use the substance if they, or someone else further up the supply chain, have been granted an authorisation for that use. Information about whether a substance is subject to authorisation, and whether an authorisation has been granted or refused, should be communicated to users in the safety data sheet or other communication given by the supplier.

Safety data sheets under REACH - Article 31 particularly

Once chemicals are registered, safety data sheets will list registration numbers. Safety data sheets may also include exposure scenarios. An exposure scenario describes the operating conditions and risk management measures that have been identified by the supplier as necessary to use the chemical safely and healthily in the users processes. Under Article 31 of REACH the supplier of a substance or mixture must provide 'the recipient', including end users, with a safety data sheet compiled in accordance with Annex II of REACH. Safety Data Sheets need not be supplied where substances are provided to the general public and they are provided with sufficient information to enable them to take the necessary measures, unless they are requested by a distributor or user. REACH requires users to follow the advice on risk management measures given in the exposure scenario attached to the safety data sheet. If users use different risk management measures to those described in the exposure scenario, then they should be able to justify why their measures offer an equivalent (or better) level of protection for human health and the environment to those described in the exposure scenario. If users need to change the risk management measures used at their workplace in order to comply with the exposure scenario then they have a maximum of 12 months (after they have received a safety data sheet listing a registration number for a chemical) to do this.

REACH, Article 31 and Annex II, specifies the scope of the content of safety data sheets for chemicals:

1. Identification of the substance/mixture and of the company/undertaking.
2. Hazards identification.
3. Composition/information on ingredients.
4. First-aid measures.
5. Firefighting measures.
6. Accidental release measures.
7. Handling and storage.
8. Exposure controls/personal protection.
9. Physical and chemical properties.
10. Stability and reactivity.
11. Toxicological information.
12. Ecological information.
13. Disposal considerations.
14. Transport information.
15. Regulatory information.
16. Other information.

Regulatory Reform (Fire Safety) Order (RRFSO) 2005

Law considered in context/more depth in Element 7.

INTRODUCTION

The amount of legislation covering the risk of fire has grown considerably over time. The situation was identified as unwieldy; many different Regulations existed, often with conflicting definitions and requirements.

In order to simply this and remove confusion the Regulatory Reform (Fire Safety) Order 2005 was introduced. There were 4 principal pieces of legislation that covered fire safety in the workplace that have been affected by the RRFSO:

- Fire Precautions Act (FPA).
- Fire Precautions (Workplace) Regulations (FPWR).
- Management of Health and Safety at Work Regulations (MHSWR).
- Dangerous Substances and Explosive Atmosphere Regulations (DSEAR).

FIRE PRECAUTIONS ACT

This legislation is has been repealed by the RRFSO 2005.

FIRE PRECAUTIONS WORKPLACE REGULATIONS

These Regulations outlined the fire safety measures that need to be achieved via the risk assessment of fire and management of fire safety within a workplace. These Regulations have been repealed by the implementation of the RRFSO, however their content has been incorporated within the RRFSO 2005.

MANAGEMENT OF HEALTH AND SAFETY AT WORK REGULATIONS

It is this Regulation that makes the legal requirement for risk assessments. In addition, it made various requirements for the management of fire safety within workplaces, which have now been revoked.

This Regulation will continue as a stand-alone health and safety Regulation as the relevant fire aspects of this Regulation have been incorporated within the RRFSO 2005.

DANGEROUS SUBSTANCES AND EXPLOSIVE ATMOSPHERE REGULATIONS

This Regulation outlines the safety and control measures that need to be taken if dangerous or flammable/explosive substances are present.

This Regulation will continue as a stand-alone health and safety Regulation. Again the relevant fire aspects of this Regulation have been incorporated within the RRFSO 2005.

REGULATORY REFORM (FIRE SAFETY) ORDER 2005

This is a new, all encompassing, fire safety order, which came into force in England and Wales on 01 October 2006. As shown above it has aspects of other legislation within it and has been compiled in such a way as to present a cohesive structure for fire safety legislation.

The order is split into 5 parts, each part is then subdivided into the individual points, or articles as they are called in the order:

- Part 1   General.
- Part 2   Fire safety duties.
- Part 3   Enforcement.
- Part 4   Offences and appeals.
- Part 5   Miscellaneous.

Outline of main points

PART 1 - GENERAL

This part covers various issues such as the interpretation of terminology used, definition of responsible person, definition of general fire precautions, duties under the order, and its application.

PART 2 - FIRE SAFETY DUTIES

This part imposes a duty on the responsible person to carry out a fire risk assessment to identify what the necessary general fire precautions should be. It also outlines the principles of prevention that should be applied and the necessary arrangements for the management of fire safety.

The following areas are also covered:

- Firefighting and fire detection.
- Emergency routes and exits.
- Procedures for serious and imminent danger and for danger areas.
- Additional emergency measures re dangerous substances.
- Maintenance.
- Safety assistance.
- Provision of information to employees, employers and self-employed.
- Capabilities and training.
- Co-operation and coordination.
- General duties of employees.

PART 3 - ENFORCEMENT

This part details who the enforcing authority is, (which in the main is the Fire Authority), and it states they must enforce the order. It also details the powers of inspectors.

It also details the different types of enforcement that can be taken:

- Alterations notice.
- Enforcement notice.
- Prohibition notice.

PART 4 - OFFENCES AND APPEALS

This part details the 13 offences that may occur and the subsequent punishments and appeals procedure. It also explains that the legal onus for proving that an offence was not committed is on the accused. A new disputes procedure is also outlined within this part.

PART 5 - MISCELLANEOUS

Various matters are covered within this part, the principal points being:

- 'Firefighters switches' for luminous tube signs etc.
- Maintenance of measures provided for the protection of firefighters.
- Civil liability.
- Duty to consult employees.
- Special provisions for licensed premises.
- Application to crown premises.

There is then a schedule that covers the risk assessment process.

Road Traffic Act (RTA) 1991

Law considered in context/more depth in Element 3.

Arrangement of main part of Act

PART 1 - GENERAL

Driving Offences

1) Offences of dangerous driving.
2) Careless, and inconsiderate, driving.

Drink and drugs

3) Causing death by careless driving when under influence of drink or drugs.

4) Driving under influence of drink or drugs.

Motoring events

5) Disapplication of sections 1 to 3 of the Road Traffic Act 1988 for authorised motoring events.

Danger to road-users

6) Causing danger to road-users.

CYCLING

7) Cycling offences.

Construction and use

8) Construction and use of vehicles.

9) Vehicle examiners.

10) Testing vehicles on roads.

11) Inspection of vehicles.

12) Power to prohibit driving of unfit vehicles.

13) Power to prohibit driving of overloaded vehicles.

14) Unfit and overloaded vehicles: offences.

15) Removal of prohibitions.

16) Supply of unroadworthy vehicles etc.

Licensing of drivers

17) Requirement of licence.

18) Physical fitness.

19) Effects of disqualification.

Insurance

20) Exception from requirement of third-party insurance.

Information

21) Information as to identity of driver etc.

Trial

22) Amendment of Schedule 1 to the Road Traffic Offenders Act 1988.

23) Speeding offences etc. admissibility of certain evidence.

24) Alternative verdicts.

25) Interim disqualification.

Penalties

26) Amendment of Schedule 2 to the Road Traffic Offenders Act 1988.

27) Penalty points to be attributed to offences.

28) Penalty points to be taken into account on conviction.

29) Disqualification for certain offences.

30) Courses for drink-drive offenders.

31) Experimental period for section 30.

32) Disqualification until test is passed.

33) Short periods of disqualification.

34) Conditional offer of fixed penalty.

Miscellaneous

35) Disabled persons' badges.

36) Forfeiture of vehicles.

37) Forfeiture of vehicles: Scotland.

38) Disqualification where vehicle used for assault.

39) Disqualification in Scotland were vehicle used to commit offence.

40) Power to install equipment for detection of traffic offences.

41) Variation of charges at off-street parking places.

42) Variation of charges at designated parking places.

43) Permitted and special parking areas outside London.

44) Parking attendants.

45) Variable speed limits.

46) Tramcars and trolley vehicles.

47) Application for licences to drive hackney carriages etc.

Outline of main points

SECTION 2 - CARELESS, AND INCONSIDERATE, DRIVING

"If a person drives a vehicle on a road or other public place without due care and attention, or without reasonable consideration for other persons using the road or place, he is guilty of an offence."

SECTION 3 - DRINK AND DRUGS

Causing death by careless driving when under influence of drink or drugs - if a person causes the death of another person by driving a vehicle on a road or other public place without due care and attention, or without reasonable consideration for other persons using the road or place:

- At the time of driving is unfit to drive through drink or drugs.
- Has consumed so much alcohol that the proportion of it in his breath, blood or urine at that time exceeds the prescribed limit.
- Is within 18 hours after that time, required to provide a specimen in pursuance of section 7 of this Act, but without reasonable excuse fails to provide it, he is guilty of an offence.

For the purposes of this section a person shall be taken to be unfit to drive at any time when his ability to drive properly is impaired.

SECTION 6 - DANGER TO ROAD-USERS

Causing danger to road-users - a person is guilty of an offence if he intentionally and without lawful authority or reasonable cause.

- Causes anything to be on or over a road.
- Interferes with a motor vehicle, trailer or cycle.
- Interferes (directly or indirectly) with traffic equipment, in such circumstances that it would be obvious to a reasonable person that to do so would be dangerous.

SECTION 8 - CONSTRUCTION AND USE OF VEHICLES

A person is guilty of an offence if he uses, or causes or permits another to use, a motor vehicle or trailer on a road when:

- The condition of the motor vehicle or trailer.
- Its accessories or equipment.
- The purpose for which it is used.
- The number of passengers carried by it, or the manner in which they are carried.
- The weight, position or distribution of its load, or the manner in which it is secured.

…..is such that the use of the motor vehicle or trailer involves a danger of injury to any person.

Breach of requirement as to weight (goods and passenger vehicles) - a person who:

- Contravenes or fails to comply with a construction and use requirement as to any description of weight applicable to:
- A goods vehicle.
- A motor vehicle or trailer adapted to carry more than eight passengers.
- Uses on a road a vehicle which does not comply with such a requirement, or causes or permits a vehicle to be so used, is guilty of an offence.

SECTION 21 - INFORMATION AS TO THE DRIVER ETC

Where the driver of a vehicle is alleged to be guilty of an offence to which this section applies:

- The person keeping the vehicle shall give such information as to the identity of the driver as he may be required to give by or on behalf of a chief officer of police.
- Any other person shall if required as stated above give any information which it is in his power to give and may lead to identification of the driver.

Supply of Machinery (Safety) Regulations (SMSR) 2008

Law considered in context/more depth in Element 5.

Outline of main points

Previously the Supply of Machinery (Safety) Regulations 1992 as amended by the Supply of Machinery (Safety) (Amendment) Regulations 1994 and the Supply of Machinery (Safety) (Amendment) Regulations 2005.

The SMSR 2008 imposes duties upon those who place machinery and safety components onto the market, or put them into service (this includes second-hand machinery which is 'new' to Europe). They set out the essential requirements which must be met before machinery or safety components may be placed on the market or put into service in the UK. They implement the latest version of the Machinery Directive 2006/42/EC and came into force on 29 December 2009, replacing the previous Supply of Machinery (Safety) Regulations 1992, as amended in 1994 and 2005.

MEETING THE REQUIREMENTS

The duty to meet the requirements mainly falls to the 'responsible person' who is defined as the manufacturer or the manufacturer's representative. If the manufacturer is not established in the EEA, the person who first supplies the machinery in the EEA may be the responsible person, which can be a user who manufactures or imports a machine for their own use.

Conformity assessment

The responsible person should ensure that machinery and safety components satisfy the ***Essential Health and Safety Requirements (EHSRs)***, see Schedule 2, Part 1 of the Regulations, and that appropriate conformity assessment procedures have been carried out. These requirements are intended to ensure that all machinery throughout the EC is constructed to the same safety standards. In addition, the responsible person must draw up a technical file ***(see below)***. For certain classes of dangerous machine and safety component, a more rigorous procedure is required. The new SMSR place even greater emphasis on the EHSR requirements. However, still extant are the requirements of primary legislation by way of the Health and Safety at Work Act 1974

(HASAWA), which makes a specific reference to the duties of manufacturers and suppliers of workplace machinery (including second hand machinery).

Section 6 of HASAWA (general duties of manufacturers) states:

"It shall be the duty of any person who designs, manufactures, imports or supplies any article for use at work....

(a)   To ensure , so far as is reasonably practicable, that the article is so designed and constructed that it will be safe and without risks to health at all times when it is being set, used, cleaned or maintained by a person at work."

HASAWA is reinforced by the duties under Part 3 of SMSR 2008 (general prohibitions and obligations), which states: *"No responsible person shall place machinery on the market or put it into service unless it is safe; and before machinery is placed on the market or put into service, the responsible person must:*

(a)   Ensure that the applicable essential health and safety requirements are satisfied in respect of it...."

Declaration procedure

The responsible person must issue one of two forms of declaration.

Declaration of conformity

This declaration should be issued with the finished product so that it is available to the user. It will contain various details such as the manufacturer's address, the machinery type and serial number, and Harmonised European or other Standards used in design.

Declaration of Incorporation

Where machinery is intended for incorporation into other machinery, the responsible person can draw up a declaration of incorporation. This should state that the machinery must not be put into service until the machinery into which it is to be incorporated has been given a Declaration of Conformity. A CE mark is not affixed at this intermediate stage.

Marking

When the first two steps have been satisfactorily completed, the responsible person or the person assembling the final product should affix the CE mark.

ENFORCEMENT

In the UK the Health and Safety Executive is responsible for enforcing these Regulations in relation to machinery and safety components designed for use at work. Trading Standards Officers are responsible for enforcing these Regulations in relation to consumer goods.

DETAILED ADVICE FOR THE DESIGNER AND MANUFACTURER

Technical file contents

The responsible person (defined above) is required to draw up a technical file for all machinery and safety components covered by these Regulations. The file or documents should comprise:

a)   An overall drawing of the product together with the drawings of the control circuits.

b)   Full detailed drawings, accompanied by any calculation notes, test results etc. required to check the conformity of the product with the essential health and safety requirements.

c)   A list of the essential health and safety requirements, transposed harmonised standards, national standards and other technical specifications which were used when the product was designed.

d)   A description of methods adopted to eliminate hazards presented by the machinery or safety component.

e)   If the responsible person so desires, any technical report or certificate obtained from a component body or laboratory.

f)   If the responsible person declares conformity with a transposed harmonised standard, any technical report giving the results of tests.

g)   A copy of the instructions for the product.

For series manufacture, the responsible person must also have available documentation on the necessary administrative measures that the manufacturer will take to ensure that the product meets requirements.

Technical file procedure

The technical file document need not be on a permanent file, but it should be possible to assemble and make them available to an enforcement authority.

The technical file documents should be retained and kept available for at least ten years following the date of manufacture of the product or of the last unit produced, in the case of a series manufacture. If the technical file documents are drawn up in the United Kingdom, they should be in English unless they are to be submitted to an Approved/Notified Body in another Member State, in which case they should be in a language acceptable to that approved Body. In all cases the instructions for the machinery should be in accordance with the language requirements of the EHSRs.

Work at Height Regulations (WAH) 2005

Law considered in context/more depth in Elements 5 and 10. See also - PUWER 1998 and WHSWR 1992.

Arrangement of Regulations

1)   Citation and commencement.

2)   Interpretation.

3)   Application.

4)   Organisation and planning.

5)   Competence.

6)   Avoidance of risks from work at height.

7) Selection of work equipment for work at height.

8) Requirements for particular work equipment.

9) Fragile surfaces.

10) Falling objects.

11) Danger areas.

12) Inspection of work equipment.

13) Inspection of places of work at height.

14) Duties of persons at work.

15) Exemption by the Health and Safety Executive.

16) Exemption for the Armed Forces.

17) Amendment to the Provision and Use of Work Equipment Regulations (PUWER) 1998.

18) Repeal of section 24 of the Factories Act 1961.

19) Revocation of instruments.

SCHEDULES

Schedule 1 - Requirements for existing places of work and means of access or egress at height.

Schedule 2 - Requirements for guard-rails, toe-boards, barriers and similar collective means of protection.

Schedule 3 - Requirements for working platforms.

Part 1 - Requirements for all working platforms.

Part 2 - Additional requirements for scaffolding.

Schedule 4 - Requirements for collective safeguards for arresting falls.

Schedule 5 - Requirements for personal fall protection systems.

Part 1 - Requirements for all personal fall protection systems.

Part 2 - Additional requirements for work positioning systems.

Part 3 - Additional requirements for rope access and positioning techniques.

Part 4 - Additional requirements for fall arrest systems.

Part 5 - Additional requirements for work restraint systems.

Schedule 6 - Requirements for ladders.

Schedule 7 - Particulars to be included in a report of inspection.

Schedule 8 - Revocation of instruments.

Outline of main points

The final version of the Regulations, designated the **Work at Height Regulations (WAH) 2005** came into force 6th April 2005.

Under these Regulations the interpretation of 'work at height' includes any place of work at ground level, above or below ground level that a person could fall a distance liable to cause personal injury and includes places for obtaining access or egress, except by staircase in a permanent workplace.

AMENDMENTS TO OTHER REGULATIONS AS A RESULT OF THE WORK AT HEIGHT REGULATIONS 2005

WAH 2005 makes an amendment to the Provision and Use of Work Equipment Regulations 1998; they also replace certain Regulations in the Workplace (Health and Safety) Regulations; and amend definitions in the Construction (Health, Safety and Welfare) Regulations:

Regulation 17 - Amendment of the Provision and Use of Work Equipment Regulations (PUWER) 1998. There shall be added to Regulation 6(5) of the Provision and Use of Work Equipment Regulations 1998 the following sub-paragraph:

(f) *"Work equipment to which Regulation 12 of the Work at Height Regulations 2005 applies."*

Schedule 8 - Revocation of instruments

Workplace (Health and Safety) Regulations 1992 - extent of revocation: Regulation 13(1) to (4).

Construction (Health, Safety and Welfare) Regulations 1996 - extent of revocation: in Regulation 2(1), the definitions of 'fragile material', 'personal suspension equipment' and 'working platform'; Regulations 6 to 8; in Regulation 29(2) the word 'scaffold' in both instances; Regulation 30(5) and (6) (a); Schedules 1 to 5; and the entry first mentioned in columns 1 and 2 of Schedule 7.

WORK AT HEIGHT (AMENDMENT) REGULATIONS 2007

These Regulations amended WAH 2005 to remove the dis-application of WAH 2005 to certain work concerning the provision of instruction or leadership to people engaged in caving or climbing by way of sport, recreation, team building or similar activities. They introduce a new duty under Regulation 14A that takes into account the special circumstances of work at height in caving and climbing.

Under these Regulations the interpretation of 'work at height' includes any place of work at ground level, above or below ground level that a person could fall a distance liable to cause personal injury and includes places for obtaining access or egress, except by staircase in a permanent workplace.

Regulation 4 states that all work at height must be properly planned, supervised and be carried out so far as is reasonably practicable safe. Planning must include the selection of suitable equipment, take account of emergencies and give consideration to weather conditions impacting on safety.

Regulation 5 states that those engaged in any activity in relation to work at height must be competent; and, if under training, are supervised by a competent person.

Regulation 6 states that work at height must only be carried out when it is not reasonably practicable to carry out the work otherwise. If work at height does take place, suitable and sufficient measures must be taken to prevent a fall of any distance, to minimise the distance and the consequences of any fall liable to cause injury. Employers must also make a risk assessment, as required by Regulation 3 of the Management of Health and Safety at Work Regulations.

Regulation 7 states that when selecting equipment for use in work at height the employer shall take account of working conditions and any risk to persons in connection with the place where the equipment is to be used. The selection of work equipment must have regard in particular to the purposes specified in Regulation 6.

Regulation 8 sets out requirements for particular equipment to conform to standards expressed in schedules to the Regulations. It includes guard-rails, toe-boards, working platforms, nets, airbags, personal fall arrest equipment rope access and ladders.

Regulation 9 states that every employer shall ensure that suitable and sufficient steps are taken to prevent any person at work falling through any fragile surface; and that no work may pass across or near, or work on, from or near, fragile surfaces when it is reasonably practicable to carry out work without doing so. If work has to be from a fragile roof then suitable and sufficient means of support must be provided that can sustain foreseeable loads. No person at work should be allowed to pass or work near a fragile surface unless suitable and sufficient guard rails and other means of fall protection is in place. Signs must be situated at a prominent place at or near to works involving fragile surfaces, or persons are made aware of the fragile roof by other means.

Regulation 10 states that every employer shall take reasonably practicable steps to prevent injury to any person from the fall of any material or object; and where it is not reasonably practicable to do so, to take similar steps to prevent any person being struck by any falling material or object which is liable to cause personal injury. Also, that no material is thrown or tipped from height in circumstances where it is liable to cause injury to any person. Materials and objects must be stored in such a way as to prevent risk to any person arising from the collapse, overturning or unintended movement of the materials or objects.

Regulation 11 states that every employer shall ensure that where an area presents a risk of falling from height or being struck from an item falling at height that the area is equipped with devices preventing unauthorised persons from entering such areas and the area is clearly indicated.

Regulation 12 states that every employer shall ensure that, where the safety of work equipment depends on how it is installed or assembled, it is not used after installation or assembly in any position unless it has been inspected in that position.

Also, that work equipment is inspected at suitable intervals and each time that exceptional circumstances which are liable to jeopardise the safety of the work equipment occur. Specific requirements exist for periodic (every 7 days) inspection of a working platform where someone could fall 2 metres or more.

Regulation 13 states that every employer shall ensure that fall protection measures of every place of work at height are visually inspected before use.

Regulation 14 states the duties of persons at work to report defects and use equipment in accordance with training/instruction.

Workplace (Health, Safety and Welfare) Regulations (WHSWR) 1992

See also - Health and Safety (Miscellaneous Amendments) Regulations (MAR) 2002 and Health and Safety (Miscellaneous Repeals, Revocations and Amendments) Regulations (MRRA) 2002.

Law considered in context/more depth in Element 2.

Arrangement of Regulations

1) Citation and commencement.
2) Interpretation.
3) Application of these Regulations.
4) Requirements under these Regulations.
5) Maintenance of workplace, and of equipment, devices and systems.
6) Ventilation.
7) Temperature in indoor workplaces.
8) Lighting.
9) Cleanliness and waste materials.
10) Room dimensions and space.
11) Workstations and seating.
12) Condition of floors and traffic routes.
13) Falls or falling objects (Revoked in part by WAH 2005).
14) Windows, and transparent or translucent doors, gates and walls.
15) Windows, skylights and ventilators.
16) Ability to clean windows etc. safely.
17) Organisation etc. of traffic routes.
18) Doors and gates.
19) Escalators and moving walkways.
20) Sanitary conveniences.
21) Washing facilities.
22) Drinking water.
23) Accommodation for clothing.
24) Facilities for changing clothing.

25) Facilities for rest and to eat meals.
26) Exemption certificates.
27) Repeals, saving and revocations.
Schedule 1 - Provisions applicable to factories which are not new workplaces, extensions or conversions.
Schedule 2 - Repeals and revocations.

Outline of main points

SUMMARY

The main requirements of the Workplace (Health, Safety and Welfare) Regulations (WHSWR) 1992 are:

1) **Maintenance** of the workplace and equipment.
2) **Safety** of those carrying out maintenance work and others who might be at risk (for example, segregation of pedestrians and vehicles, provision of handrails etc.).
3) Provision of **welfare** facilities (for example, rest rooms, changing rooms etc.).
4) Provision of a safe **environment** (for example, lighting, ventilation etc.).

ENVIRONMENT

Reg 1   New workplaces, extensions and modifications must comply.

Reg 4   Requires employers, persons in control of premises and occupiers of factories to comply with the Regulations.

Reg 6   Ventilation - enclosed workplaces should be ventilated with a sufficient quantity of fresh or purified air (5 to 8 litres per second per occupant).

Reg 7   Temperature indoors - this needs to be reasonable and the heating device must not cause injurious fumes. Thermometers must be provided. Temperature should be a minimum of 16°C or 13°C if there is physical effort.

Reg 8   Lighting - must be suitable and sufficient. Natural light if possible. Emergency lighting should be provided if danger exists.

Reg 10 Room dimensions and space - every room where persons work shall have sufficient floor area, height and unoccupied space (min 11 cu. m per person).

Reg 11 Workstations and seating have to be suitable for the person and the work being done.

SAFETY

Reg 12 Floors and traffic routes must be of suitable construction. This includes absence of holes, slope, uneven or slippery surface. Drainage where necessary. Handrails and guards to be provided on slopes and staircases.

Reg 13 Tanks and pits containing dangerous substances to be covered or fenced where people could fall into them and traffic routes fenced.

Reg 14 Windows and transparent doors, where necessary for health and safety, must be of safety material and be marked to make it apparent.

Reg 15 Windows, skylights and ventilators must be capable of opening without putting anyone at risk.

Reg 17 Traffic routes for pedestrians and vehicles must be organised in such a way that they can move safely.

Reg 18 Doors and gates must be suitably constructed and fitted with any necessary safety devices.

Reg 19 Escalators and moving walkways shall function safely, be equipped with any necessary safety devices and be fitted with emergency stop.

HOUSEKEEPING

Reg 5   Workplace and equipment, devices and systems must be maintained in efficient working order and good repair.

Reg 9   Cleanliness and waste materials - workplaces must be kept sufficiently clean. Floors, walls and ceilings must be capable of being kept sufficiently clean. Waste materials shall not be allowed to accumulate, except in suitable receptacles.

Reg 16 Windows etc. must be designed so that they can be cleaned safely.

FACILITIES

Reg 20 Sanitary conveniences must be suitable and sufficient and in readily accessible places. They must be adequately ventilated, kept clean and there must be separate provision for men and women.

Reg 21 Washing facilities must be suitable and sufficient. Showers if required (a table gives minimum numbers of toilets and washing facilities).

Reg 22 Drinking water - an adequate supply of wholesome drinking water must be provided.

Reg 23 Accommodation for clothing must be suitable and sufficient.

Reg 24 Facilities for changing clothes must be suitable and sufficient, where a person has to use special clothing for work.

Reg 25 Facilities for rest and eating meals must be suitable and sufficient.

The WHSWR 1992 were amended by the Health and Safety (Miscellaneous Amendments) Regulations 2002 to establish specific requirements that rest rooms be equipped with:

- An adequate number of tables and adequate seating with backs for the number of persons at work likely to use them at any one time.
- Seating which is adequate for the number of disabled persons at work and suitable for them.

In addition, WHSWR 1992 were amended to take account of disability arrangements. Where necessary, those parts of the workplace used or occupied directly by disabled persons at work, including in particular doors, passageways, stairs, showers, washbasins, lavatories and workstations, must be organised to take account of such persons.

Assessment

Content

Assessments of understanding 416
Sample practical application (NCC2) 419
Exam practice – answer guidance 428

Assessments of understanding

It is understood that those using this publication may be doing so to broaden their understanding of this important topic, management of health and safety in construction, and others will be studying in order to obtain a specific construction related award. The approach taken by those assessing such awards will vary. This element provides information on how one such award is assessed, the NEBOSH National Certificate in Construction Health and Safety Management. The questions and related answers provided in this element may prove useful for those that want to assess their understanding for this award and for more general reasons.

The inspection observation sheets and accompanying report, provided in the section 'construction health and safety review' below, will be of great use to those studying for the NEBOSH award and will prove particularly useful to those that wish to develop and use their own means of assessing construction management in their workplace.

Written assessment - Paper NCC1

To assist students understanding of the assessment requirements for the NEBOSH National Certificate in Construction Health and Safety award, paper NCC1, some short answer questions that are typical of the type used in an award at this level have been included at the end of each element. This is accompanied by the following observations related to the success of candidates taking examinations of this type.

At every examination a number of candidates - including some good ones - perform less well than they might because of poor examination technique. It is essential that candidates practice answering both essay-type and short answer questions and learn to manage their time according to the number of marks allocated to questions (and parts of questions) as shown on the paper.

A common fault is that candidates may fail to pay attention to the command word (for example, identify, give, outline, describe and explain) in each question. The need to understand the meaning of the 'command word' and to read the question carefully is explained in the section 'Revision and Examination Guidance'.

ANSWERS TO EXAM PRACTICE

Typical answers are provided on pages 428-450.

GENERAL CONFIRMATION OF UNDERSTANDING

Those not taking examinations related to health and safety may find the questions and answers useful to check and confirm their understanding of some of the issues covered by this publication.

Construction health and safety workplace review

NEBOSH UNIT NCC2

The aim of this unit is to assess a candidate's ability to complete successfully a construction health and safety review of their workplace and to provide a report to management with justified recommendations. The questionnaire has been produced by NEBOSH as part of their practical assessment of the above award, their origination and copyright is acknowledged. In order to understand how the questionnaire may be used and the type of report produced by candidates studying this award, a completed questionnaire and report is provided.

In summary the proforma and report should clearly identify:

- The nature, and if appropriate, the location of each health and safety at work issue.
- Review findings with prioritisation and justification.
- Clear links to strengths and weaknesses in the way that health and safety at work is managed, with relevant prioritisation.

Creating workplace templates

The NEBOSH template is an excellent starting point for those wishing to develop and create their own templates to carry out reviews of their construction health and safety standards at work.

PROCEDURE

The assessment must take place within 14 days of (before or after) the date of the written papers (date of the examination). Please make sure you are clear about when you will carry out the assessment.

The time allowed by NEBOSH to complete the assessment is not restricted, but NEBOSH advise that candidates should aim to complete the inspection and report in two hours. This indicates an acceptable amount of time that could produce an acceptable result. The actual time taken will depend on the student, the type of workplace and the method used to produce the observations sheet and report, particularly if whether they are produced in hand written or word processed format.

You are advised to spend no more than 45 minutes making an inspection of the workplace in order to leave enough time to finish your observation notes and prepare the management report. NEBOSH advise that you should aim to complete the management report in one hour. If it is necessary to take longer than this time this is allowed. Once you have completed your practical assessment (observation sheets and management report) - you must sign a declaration that shows the submission is your own work. If this declaration is not submitted then your result may be declared void.

The whole assessment must be carried out under as near examination conditions as possible and you must not use anything previously prepared or gain assistance from other people while conducting the assessment. The practical assessment must be completed using forms based on the NEBOSH forms provided and take place in a workplace of your choice. It must not contain extraneous material such as drawings and photographs.

NEBOSH provide a sample observation sheet for use during the inspection of the workplace. There are three columns on the form; observations, control measures and timescales.

Observations	Control measures	Timescale
Hazards and consequences	Immediate and longer-term actions	

This form can be adapted by adding to it in order to aid the recording process. This can be done by you at the time of the assessment. The sample observation sheet provided by RMS Publishing in the following pages has been adapted by the addition of a column to structure a consistent record of the observations and the identification of actions.

Observations	Control measures		Timescale
Hazards and consequences	Immediate and longer-term actions		
	I		
	M		
	L		

Copies of the observation sheet provided by your learning centre should be used during your inspection. The forms must be completed during the inspection and must be included with your covering management report for marking by the assessor. Both the observation sheet and management report may be submitted in the student's handwriting or word processed. Whilst poor spelling and grammar are not penalised if the assessor cannot read or understand what the candidate has written good marks are less likely to be achieved.

When conducting the inspection of the workplace you are expected to recognise physical, health and environmental hazards. Good work practices as well as bad work practices should be observed, though the emphasis for this assessment should be on uncontrolled hazards. You should cover as wide a range of hazards as possible, but at least five different types. It is important that the candidate describes the hazard that they have observed; care should be taken as short general comments like 'poor housekeeping in the store' does not convey what the hazard is.

The sample provided uses an approach that encourages a better description of the hazard, for example, '*Risk of* trip in the walkway outside the office *due to* trailing electrical cables ....". Hazards that are well controlled should be observed and noted in a similar way, for example, '*Risk of* trip in walkway outside office *controlled by* ....".

While only short notes on each hazard are required, it is important that the assessor is able to identify from your notes in the observation column:

- Where the hazard was located.
- The type and nature of the hazard.
- In what way, if any, the hazard was being controlled.

Welfare and environmental issues may also be observed and noted, for example:

- Availability and standard of washing and toilet facilities.
- Adequacy of heating, lighting and ventilation.
- Condition of floors and gangways.
- Cleanliness of structures.
- If workers are present in the workplace, are they aware of the actions to take in the event of an emergency?

In the time advised for the inspection it should be possible to make 24 good observations and record what was seen. In order to gain good marks it is necessary to observe and describe at least 20 hazards that are not controlled.

For each observation you should comment on any actions necessary to control the hazards in the 'Control measures' column. Experience shows that some candidates do this part of the assessment in an inconsistent way. The addition of a column to the left of the 'Control measures' part of the observation form and the use of a key to remind you to consider immediate, medium and long term actions would be useful and improve consistency. This is not a NEBOSH requirement, but candidates have found that it prompts them to be more consistent.

It is important to consider each of the immediate, medium and long term actions for each observation to gain good marks. This will require the candidate to note actions to take immediate control of the hazard and control measures to deal with the causes of the hazard and improve the management of them to prevent a reoccurrence. Where hazards are currently controlled, medium and longer term actions should be considered in order to maintain or improve control.

Care should be taken to describe the action proposed sufficiently and avoid over simple statements like 'Monitor'; you should indicate what should be monitored and perhaps how. Actions proposed should be practical and cost effective, in that they should relate to the level of risk. Candidates should remember that if observations noted are unclear it will not be possible to gain full credit for the actions suggested as their suitability in relation to the hazard cannot be determined by the assessor.

The 'Timescales' column should be completed for each action to indicate an acceptable completion date, for example, immediately, 1 week, 1 month, 3 months etc.

An example of completed observation sheets that would obtain good marks are provided on pages 419-427. Please study this document as it will help to indicate the approach the candidate should take and support the explanation already provided.

When completing the management report it should follow the structure set out by NEBOSH:
- Introduction, including overview of area inspected and activities taking place.
- Executive summary.
- Main findings of the inspection.
- Conclusions.
- Recommendations - action plan.

Deviation from this structure will make the report less effective and will usually lead to reduced marks. NEBOSH allows the candidate to consult reference books when preparing the management report, but plagiarism is treated seriously. The report should be written persuasively, so that a manager would be encouraged and be able to take action. Only copying the notes from the observation sheet would not usually be persuasive enough and not gain good marks. NEBOSH advise that the report should be approximately 700 to 1,000 words. There is no penalty based on word count, but marks are available for the quality of interpretation of findings and persuasiveness. Experience shows that a word processor word count of approximately 2,000 words will be necessary to explain well and provide motivation for the reader, depending on the number and complexity of main findings.

The executive summary should be written after completion of the other parts of the report to enable an overview of the positive and negative findings, with a summary of the conclusions and indicate actions recommend. It can be difficult for the candidate to provide a concise executive summary, but they should keep in mind that it should only be long enough to indicate the outcome of the inspection and the content of the report.

The main findings are an important part of a report of this type and attract nearly a third of the marks. Observations from the observation sheets should be selected for specific comments in the findings. This may be on the basis of the highest risk or on their prevalence. A large number of small risks may be a significant problem, if this is the case this should be made clear in the report. It would be common to find that four significant findings are necessary; care should be taken to ensure that the findings do not become just a copy of all the observations. The notes in the observation sheet should further explain to ensure the manager understands the hazard, the significance of the risk and the likely outcomes, in terms of harm to people, cost and breach of legal standards. Where breaches of legal standards exist the candidate should explain what causes the breach and what the breach is. Stating the name of the legal standard alone will not be sufficient. The actions proposed should be explained and emphasis made of the cost effectiveness of the actions relative to the risk, reasonable practicability.

The conclusions and recommendations are also important and attract nearly one third of the available marks. The conclusions should be drawn from and reflect the findings of the report. Care should be taken not to introduce new items not discussed in the report. Conclusions should be clear, concise and convince management to take action.

Sample practical application (NCC2)

NEBOSH NATIONAL CERTIFICATE IN CONSTRUCTION HEALTH AND SAFETY

UNIT NCC2 - CONSTRUCTION HEALTH AND SAFETY PRACTICAL APPLICATION

Candidate's observation sheet

Sheet number 1 **of** 5

Student name:	J Grealish	Student number:	********
Place inspected:	************ site	Date of Inspection:	01/06/20**

Observations	Control measures		Timescale
Hazards and consequences	Immediate and longer-term actions		
1. Risk of falling from height due to missing edge protection	I	Stop work	1 hour
	M	Reinstall edge protection	1 day
	L	Instigate toolbox talk	1 week
2. Risk of person falling due to use of damaged step ladder by electrician	I	Stop work and remove ladder	1 hour
	M	Provide new ladder	1 day
	L	Set up a recorded system of testing, inspections labelling	1 week
3. Risk of being struck by moving objects due to lack of barriers around material lifting machine	I	Install barrier tape	1 hour
	M	Install permanent barrier	1 Week
	L	Inspect barrier weekly	1 month then weekly
4. Risk of falling controlled by secure ladder when accessing control room roof	I	None	N/A
	M	Commend good practice	Immediate
	L	Commend good practice at toolbox talks	1 month
5. Risk of fall from height due to incorrect barrier between MCC room and corridor	I	Remove barrier and stop work in MCC room	1 hour
	M	Install correct barrier	1 day
	L	Install correct door	1 week

Actions: I = Immediate, M = Medium, L = Long term, N/A = Not applicable.

NEBOSH NATIONAL CERTIFICATE IN CONSTRUCTION HEALTH AND SAFETY

UNIT NCC2 - CONSTRUCTION HEALTH AND SAFETY PRACTICAL APPLICATION

Candidate's observation sheet

Sheet number 2 **of** 5

Student name: J Grealish   Student number: ********

Place inspected: *********** site   Date of Inspection: 01/06/20**

Observations Hazards and consequences	Control measures Immediate and longer-term actions		Timescale
6. Risk of electric shock or fire controlled by regular PAT testing	I	None	
	M	Continue regular testing	On going
	L	Ensure competence of electricians	6 months
7. Risk of falling loads due to damaged lifting sling	I	Remove sling from site	1 hour
	M	Replace with new sling	1 day
	L	Instigate system of regular checks	1 week
8. Risk of respiratory problems due to not wearing respirator when cutting ducting insulation board	I	Issue appropriate PPE to include dust mask/respirator	1 hour
	M	Implement recorded inspections to ensure PPE is being worn	1 day
	L	Review cutting process to determine if dust can be reduced at source	1 month
9. Risk of skin problems controlled by availability of clean washing facilities and provision of barrier creams	I	None	
	M	Instigate weekly inspections	1 day
	L	Review other welfare facilities	1 month
10. Risk of collision with vehicles due to pedestrian route not clearly signed	I	Stop pedestrian access	Immediately
	M	Install permanent demarcation barriers	1 day
	L	Erect clear signs	1 week

Actions: I = Immediate, M = Medium, L = Long term, N/A = Not applicable.

NEBOSH NATIONAL CERTIFICATE IN CONSTRUCTION HEALTH AND SAFETY

UNIT NCC2 - CONSTRUCTION HEALTH AND SAFETY PRACTICAL APPLICATION

Candidate's observation sheet

Sheet number 3 **of** 5

Student name: J Grealish   Student number: ********

Place inspected: *********** site   Date of Inspection: 01/06/20**

Observations Hazards and consequences		Control measures Immediate and longer-term actions	Timescale
11. Risk of fire/explosion due to incorrect storage of oxyacetylene bottles when in use. Wheel broken on trolley.	I	Stop using cutting gear	Immediate
	M	Inspect and repair trolley	1 day
	L	Inspect other similar equipment	1 month
12. Risk of fire/explosion due to wood and timber being stored where grinding work is being done	I	Remove timber to dedicated storage area	Immediate
	M	Remind employees of need for good housekeeping at next toolbox talk	1 week
	L	Include item on workplace inspection checklist	1 week
13. Risk of sprains due to poor storage of materials, uneven floor and poor lighting.	I	Move all excess materials to store or waste bin	1 week
	L	Install more lights	1 month
	M	Inspect light levels regularly and review floor condition	3 months
14. Risk of injury from fire due to alarm bell covered in concrete splashes making it in-audible in the event of a fire	I	Remove from use and clean	1 hour
	M	Replace with new bell	1 week
	L	Regular tests and inspection and record findings	1 month
15. Risk of building material falling from height controlled by good edge protection on scaffold	I	N/A	
	M	Commend good practice at next toolbox talk	1 week
	L	Continue regular statutory inspections	Weekly

Actions: I = Immediate, M = Medium, L = Long term, N/A = Not applicable.

NEBOSH NATIONAL CERTIFICATE IN CONSTRUCTION HEALTH AND SAFETY

UNIT NCC2 - CONSTRUCTION HEALTH AND SAFETY PRACTICAL APPLICATION

Candidate's observation sheet

Sheet number 4 **of** 5

Student name: J Grealish

Student number: ********

Place inspected: ************ site

Date of Inspection: 01/06/20**

Observations	Control measures		Timescale
Hazards and consequences	Immediate and longer-term actions		
16. Risk of fire controlled by present use of fire extinguisher during hot work	I	None	
	M	Commend good practice	1 week
	L	Review permit to work system	2 weeks
17. Risk of cuts due to threaded bar protruding into walkway from cast section of concrete	I	Put tape barrier around protruding obstacle	1 day
	M	Ensure that rods are not cut too long in future	1 week
	L	Review design of clamp for concrete pouring	Annual
18. Risk of trips due to poor lighting in mezzanine area. 30% of lights not working	I	Provide temporary lighting in dark areas	2 days
	M	Repair broken lights	1 week
	L	Implement regular inspection	1 month
19. Risk of eye injury due to damaged socket on 22mm nut runner. Could cause flying debris	I	Remove tool from use	Immediate
	M	Replace with new tool	1 week
	L	Implement regular inspections	1 month
20. Risk of trips due to trailing electrical leads	I	Provide cable covers	1 day
	M	Review cable management systems	1 week
	L	Provide more power sockets	3 months

Actions: I = Immediate, M = Medium, L = Long term, N/A = Not applicable.

NEBOSH NATIONAL CERTIFICATE IN CONSTRUCTION HEALTH AND SAFETY

UNIT NCC2 - CONSTRUCTION HEALTH AND SAFETY PRACTICAL APPLICATION

Candidate's observation sheet

Sheet number 5 **of** 5

Student name: J Grealish

Student number: ********

Place inspected: ************ site

Date of Inspection: 01/06/20**

Observations Hazards and consequences		Control measures Immediate and longer-term actions	Timescale
21. Risk of unauthorised access to the site controlled by signing and guarding	I	None	N/A
	M	Regular checks of fence line	Daily
	L	Review fencing requirements as project progresses	Monthly
22. Risk of delayed first aid treatment due to eye wash being out of date	I	Replace eye wash	1 day
	M	Implement system of weekly checks	1 week
	L	Toolbox talk on procedure for replacing first aid equipment	1 month
23. Risk of hearing damage when using disc cutter without protection.	I	Provide appropriate PPE	1 day
	M	Implement regular inspections to ensure PPE is being worn	1 week
	L	Set up regular audiometric tests	3 months
24. Risk of dermatitis from diesel fuel when refuelling vehicles	I	Provide suitable gloves	1 day
	M	Remind local supervisor of need to ensure staff wear PPE when refuelling vehicles	1 week
	L	Refresher training on personal hygiene	6 months

Actions: I = Immediate, M = Medium, L = Long term, N/A = Not applicable.

MANAGEMENT REPORT

1. Introduction

This report is based on the findings by the author J Grealish, during a recent workplace inspection that was completed on Thursday 1st June 20**. The workplace inspected was a construction site at **** Limited, Anytown, Someplace, where a new extension is being constructed.

The new building consists of two floors; the ground floor area is where all the services are being installed i.e., electrics, hydraulics and gas. The upper floor is where the main equipment is being installed. There is a new roof and side wall cladding on the new building. The roof is three meters high.

The work being carried out is moving very quickly, especially the sides of the building being installed and lots of concrete being poured inside the extension. There is a lot of activity in the basement (ground floor) with electricians and pipe fitters working to install new services which will supply all the new machinery.

In total, there are fifty eight people working on the site.

2. Executive Summary

Whilst carrying out this workplace inspection I was impressed to find that generally the construction site area was very tidy due to a good level of housekeeping. All inspections of portable appliances and scaffolding was in date and storage areas for gas bottles well maintained. All welfare facilities were in good order.

However, a number of items were noticed which, on further investigation, require your attention in order to prevent the risk of injury or ill-health. Immediate consideration should be given to matters such as the use of frayed lifting slings and the lack of edge protection when pouring concrete.

Further details can be found in the main body of this report and in the "observations" section.

3. Main Findings of the inspection

3.1. Observation No 1. Falling from height

When pouring concrete to the south side of the main foundation, a part of the installed edge protection had been removed so that access could be gained for the concrete pour. After the work had been completed, the edge protection had not been replaced. All work was stopped until edge protection had been reinstalled and inspected. The immediate remedy to this problem was quite straightforward but, for a short period, ten people were standing idle.

This situation creates a breach of the Work at Height Regulations (WAH) 2005 which require the employer to take suitable and sufficient steps to prevent people falling from height. Employees must be reminded that the organisation will not tolerate unauthorised interference with safety equipment and that it is a possible breach of section 7 of the Health and Safety at Work Act (HASWA) 1974 if they do.

Further recommendations are that the situation should be discussed in toolbox talks, prominent signs erected and that the barriers are subject to a daily inspection by management.

There are no direct costs to these recommendations. However, failure to implement them could lead to a prosecution and civil action.

3.2. Observation No 7. Damaged lifting sling

The pipefitters installing the main six inch gas pipe were using a five ton capacity lifting sling which was clearly damaged and could have had very serious consequences had it failed whilst lifting a very heavy pipe. Employers have a duty under the Lifting Operations and Lifting Equipment (LOLER) Regulations 1998 to ensure that all lifting equipment and accessories are of adequate strength and regularly inspected.

The sling was immediately removed from site and replaced by a new, fully certified sling from stores. Regular inspection of lifting equipment is a legal requirement and must take place at approved intervals. I estimate that a new sling to replace the one damaged and calibration certificate will cost about £250.

3.3. Observation No 10. Traffic route demarcation

The concrete mixing wagons were being manoeuvred into an area which is a designated pedestrian area. HSE statistics show that collision with vehicles is one of the most common causes of death in the workplace. This is a possible breach of the Construction (Design and Management) Regulations (CDM) 2015 under which employers have a duty to ensure that all traffic routes are organised so that pedestrians can move safely without risk.

The pedestrian route was closed and re-routed away from the danger by using concrete blocks and warning tape. Drivers and pedestrians need to be reminded at toolbox talks of the dangers caused by site traffic.

The cost of moving the concrete blocks and erecting new signs is about £350.

3.4. Observation No 18. Poor lighting

The lighting level in the lower mezzanine basement was not very good on account of about 30% of the lights not working. As the project progresses, more and more people are working in this area. The poor quality of the lighting significantly increases the likelihood of accidents such as tripping.

CDM 2015 requires that all workplaces have suitable and sufficient lighting. Therefore, to avoid a breach, the lighting must be repaired as soon as possible. Some of the fittings will have to repositioned to prevent them being obscured by the new pipework.

The cost to reposition the light fittings will be about £550.

3.5. Observation No's 6, 9 and 15. Good practice

It must be stated that, whilst carrying out the inspection, several examples of good practice were identified. Notably, all portable appliances that were inspected had indate test stickers on them which assists with compliance with the Electricity at Work (EWR) Regulations 1989.

All welfare facilities were clean and in good order as required by CDM 2015.

Similarly, all scaffolds were clearly identified by a green "scafftag" to show that it was safe to use. This, again, suggests compliance with the WAH 2005.

4. Conclusions

The removal of edge protection is an indication that employees are not aware of their responsibilities to themselves and fellow workers. It also suggests a lax approach to health and safety on the part of site management. The inclusion of this subject in future toolbox talks is an immediate remedy but the message has to be consistently reinforced.

The damaged sling would have been identified and taken out of service much earlier if a system of regular inspections had been in place and records kept. To comply with the minimum requirements set out in LOLER 1998, the whole inspection system must be reviewed.

The concrete mixer encroaching on the pedestrian area was totally avoidable. Planning by the vehicle co-ordination team should have taken into account the long term development of the site and the constant evolution of the traffic routes as the project progressed. As stated in the main body, uncontrolled vehicle movements are one of the most common causes of fatal accidents in the workplace. The moral aspect of these serious incidents is something that should be at the forefront of everyone's mind.

The poor lighting levels are a concern. Once again, as building work has progressed, it has become apparent that there was a lack of planning when positioning the fittings. The present lights are only in place temporarily. So, when permanent lighting is installed, thought should be given to the layout of pipework and other fixtures to prevent a recurrence of the problem.

I suggest that my recommendations are implemented at the earliest opportunity according to the priority allocated to them in the next section of this report. By doing this, the organisation will openly demonstrate to all employees that their health and safety is being taken seriously at all levels of management. Also, it will show that, in the long term, a positive safety culture is being developed which will reduce the sizeable costs attributed to accidents and enhance the reputation of the business in a very competitive market place.

Several items of good practice were noted during the inspection. It is important that complacency does not creep into these areas and that the systems that have brought about these good standards are maintained and improved throughout the project.

5. Recommendations

Ref No	Recommendation	Likely resource implications	Priority	Target date
3.1	Display prominent warning signs	£20	Immediate	One week
	Regular inspection	30 minutes of management time	Immediate	One week
3.2	Inspect all lifting equipment and replace damaged items	£250	Medium	One month
3.3	Replace barriers and erect signs	£350	Immediate	One week
3.4	Redesign and move light fittings	£550	Low	One month
3.5	Review management system to ensure continued good practice	No immediate implications	Low	Six months

Candidate and course provider declarations:

For completion by the Candidate:

I declare that the work submitted for this practical application assessment is my own work. I recognise that contravention of this statement constitutes malpractice and may result in my being subject to the penalties set out in the NEBOSH malpractice policy.

Name (Print) _ J GREALISH_____

Signature _J Grealish_____

Date _01/06/XX_____

For completion by a course provider representative (e.g. internal practical assessor):

I declare that the work marked is identical to that received from the candidate. I recognise that contravention of this statement constitutes malpractice and may result in my being subject to the penalties set out in the NEBOSH malpractice policy.

Name (Print) _ C HEMSWORTH_____

Signature _ C Hemsworth_____

Date _10/06/XX_____

For completion by the course provider's internal practical assessor:

I declare that I have marked this work and am both qualified and approved by NEBOSH to do so. I recognise that contravention of this statement constitutes malpractice and may result in my being subject to the penalties set out in the NEBOSH malpractice policy.

Name (Print) _R STEWART_____

Signature _ R Stewart_____

Date _15/06/XX_____

Exam practice - answer guidance

ELEMENT 1

1. **Identify** the duties placed upon the principal contractor under the Construction (Design and Management) Regulations 2015. **(8)**

The principal contractor's duties are mainly specified in regulations 13 and 14 of CDM 2015 and include:

- *Not accept an appointment to a project unless they have the skills, knowledge and experience, and, if they are an organisation, the organisational capability, necessary to fulfil their role in a manner that secures the health and safety of any person affected by the project.*
- *Planning, managing and monitoring the construction phase to ensure that it is carried out, so far as is reasonably practicable, without risks to health and safety. In particular when design, technical and organisational decisions are being made or the time to complete stages of work is being estimate.*
- *Draw up a construction phase plan and ensure it is reviewed, updated and revised as construction work is carried out.*
- *Take into account the general principles of prevention.*
- *Liaise and share with the principal designer information relevant to the planning, management and monitoring of the construction phase and coordination of the pre-construction phase.*
- *Organising co-operation between contractors (including successive contractors on the same construction site).*
- *Ensuring that employers and self-employed persons apply the general principles of prevention and follow the construction phase plan.*
- *Where the project is notifiable, display the notification details in a prominent place so that workers can read them.*
- *Taking the necessary steps to prevent access by unauthorised persons to the construction site.*
- *Ensuring a suitable site induction is provided.*
- *Ensuring that welfare facilities that comply with the requirements of Schedule 2 of CDM 2015 are provided throughout the construction phase.*
- *Liaising and sharing comprehensive information with the principal designer, including providing the principal designer with information relevant to the health and safety file.*
- *Co-operate with others in relation to the project.*
- *Consulting workers or their representatives on matters that may affect their health, safety or welfare.*
- *Ensuring that workers or their representatives can inspect and take copies of any information which is held by the principal contractor.*

2. (a) **Outline FOUR** of the designer's duties under the Construction (Design and Management) Regulations 2015. **(4)**

    (b) Providing an example in **EACH** case, **outline TWO** ways in which failures on the part of designers to comply with their duties can cause health and safety problems during the construction phase of a project. **(4)**

a) Designer's duties are mainly specified in Regulation 9 of CDM 2015.

- *Not accept an appointment to a project unless they have the skills, knowledge and experience, and, if they are an organisation, the organisational capability, necessary to fulfil their role in a manner that secures the health and safety of any person affected by the project (general duties).*
- *Not commencing work unless the client is aware of the duties a client has under CDM 2015.*
- *Apply the principles of prevention and any pre-construction information when preparing or modifying a design to eliminate risks.*
- *Providing information to the principal designer on residual risks that could not be eliminated by design.*
- *Ensuring appropriate information related to residual risks is included in the health and safety file.*
- *Providing information to the client, other designers and contractors.*
- *Ensure information or instruction is comprehensible and provided as soon as is practicable (general duties).*
- *Co-operate with others in relation to the project.*
- *To report to the person in control of the work anything they are aware of in relation to the project which is likely to endanger their own health or safety or that of others.*

b) Examples could include:

- *The sequence of construction not being considered so that stairs between floors were not installed until the end of the project.*
- *Risks had not been properly addressed at the design stage, for example, the design created the residual risk of working at height to complete assembly of components that could have been avoided.*

- *Insufficient thought being given to specifying safer materials such as the use of water-based paints as opposed to solvent-based paints.*
- *Build-ability issues had not being addressed so that work could not be done safely without the use of specialist equipment for lifting loads into place.*
- *Insufficient information being given with the design to enable risks to be recognised, for example, a failure to indicate the safe working loads on floors.*

3. **Outline** the information that could be included within a construction phase plan as required by the Construction (Design and Management) Regulations 2015. **(8)**

a) *Advice regarding the information to be included in the construction phase plan can be found in Appendix 3 of the Guidance on CDM 2015.*

b) *The plan might include the following:*

- *A description of the project such as key dates and names of key team members.*

c) *Management of the work to include:*

- *Health and safety aims.*
- *Site rules.*
- *Arrangements to ensure co-operation between project team members and co-ordination of their work, for example, regular site meetings.*
- *Arrangements for involving workers.*
- *Site induction.*
- *Welfare facilities.*
- *Fire and emergency arrangements.*
- *Control of specific risks listed in Schedule 3 of CDM 2015.*

4. **Identify** the duties of a non-domestic client for a construction project under the Construction (Design and Management) Regulations 2015. **(8)**

Regulations 4 and 5 of CDM 2015 set out the duties of clients and include:

- *Ensure suitable arrangements for managing a project, including the allocation of sufficient time and other resources.*
- *Take reasonable steps to ensure designers and contractors are competent.*
- *Ensure that pre-construction information is provided to every designer and contractor appointed.*
- *Provide information and instruction as soon as is practicable.*
- *Co-operate with others in relation to the project.*
- *Ensure that a construction phase plan is drawn up before the construction phase begins.*
- *Ensure that the principal designer prepares a health and safety file for the project.*
- *Ensure that the health and safety file is kept up to date and is available for inspection.*
- *Ensure that the principal designer and the principal contractor comply with their duties.*
- *Ensure that where there is more than one contractor, the client must appoint in writing a principal designer and a principal contractor.*
- *If the project is classed as notifiable, notify the enforcing agency, which is usually the Health and Safety Executive.*
- *Ensure a copy of the notification is displayed in a prominent position at the site for workers to read.*
- *Ensure the health and safety file is passed on if the client no longer has an interest in the structure to which it relates.*
- *Ensure that adequate welfare facilities are provided.*

5. (a) **Identify** the criteria that have to be considered for a project to be notifiable to the Health and Safety Executive under the Construction (Design and Management) Regulations 2015. **(2)**

    (b) **Identify** the information that must be notified to the HSE. **(6)**

a) *A project is notifiable to the HSE if:*

- *It is scheduled to last longer than 30 working days and have more than 20 workers working simultaneously at any point in the project.*
- *It will exceed 500 person days.*

b) *Details of information that must be notified to the HSE can be found in Schedule 1 of CDM 2015 and includes:*

- *Date of forwarding.*
- *Exact address of the construction site.*

- *The name of the local authority where the site is located.*
- *A brief description of the project and the construction work which it includes.*
- *Contact details of the client (name, address, telephone number and any e-mail address).*
- *Contact details of the principal designer (name, address, telephone number and any e-mail address).*
- *Contact details of the principal contractor (name, address, telephone number and any e-mail address).*
- *Date planned for the start of the construction phase.*
- *The time allowed by the client under regulation 4(1) for the construction work.*
- *Planned duration of the construction phase.*
- *Estimated maximum number of people at work on the construction site.*
- *Planned number of contractors on the construction site.*
- *Name and address of any contractor already appointed.*
- *Name and address of any designer already engaged.*
- *A declaration signed by or on behalf of the client that the client is aware of the client duties under CDM 2015.*

ELEMENT 2

1. An old factory building has been demolished and the ground cleared ready for the construction of a four story office block. The construction of the office block involves over 40 construction workers employed by the principal contractor being on site at any one time.

   Identify the welfare facilities that should be provided for the 40 construction workers involved in this work. **(8)**

The welfare facilities that should be provided for the employees include:

- *A sufficient number of sanitary conveniences, WC's and urinals.*
- *Washing facilities, including wash basins and showers with hot and cold or warm running water, with soap and towels made available.*
- *An adequate supply of drinking water.*
- *Provision of changing rooms with separate storage for dirty and clean clothing.*
- *Facilities for drying clothing.*
- *A rest room or rest area, including tables and seating with backs, arrangements for preparing/eating meals - with means of boiling water.*
- *An adequate standard of lighting, heating and ventilation should be provided for the facilities.*
- *If appropriate, separate facilities would be necessary for men and women.*
- *Provision for first-aid treatment should be made.*

2. A project involves the construction of a concrete structure on a brownfield site, including the installation of drains. **Outline** the topics that site inductions should cover. **(8)**

Site inductions on a brownfield site should include:

- *Welfare provisions, this should include the location of toilets, showers, rest areas and first aid facilities.*
- *The importance of good personal hygiene, as the work is to take place on a brown field site and involve drains.*
- *Site rules, to include parking arrangements, signing in and out and the use of PPE.*
- *Emergency procedures to deal with, for example, fire or a serious accident. This should include details of the alarm and the location of fire assembly points.*
- *First-aid arrangements.*
- *Procedures for reporting accidents, incidents, ill health and hazards.*
- *Identification of major hazards, which might include the proximity of railway lines and schools.*
- *Means of controlling hazards, including the use of permits to work.*
- *The arrangements for ensuring the safe movement of vehicles, such as the need to keep heavy plant away from excavations and people.*
- *Notification of any restricted areas and the reasons restrictions are in place.*
- *The role of specified site staff, such as Site Contracts Manager/supervisors, Safety Representatives and Safety Specialists.*
- *Any specified waste management and environmental policies and procedures covering the site*
- *Drugs and alcohol policy.*

3. Construction work is about to start on a disused airfield site in a rural location. **Identify** the factors that the principal contractor would have to consider when deciding appropriate first-aid arrangements. **(8)**

Factors to be considered by the principal contractor for first-aid include:

- *The maximum number of persons on site at any one time.*
- *The number and type of contractors involved.*
- *The types of hazard and level of risk present on site.*
- *The likely types of injuries and work related ill-health.*
- *Work patterns and the need to ensure that all shifts are adequately covered.*
- *The need for first-aiders with specialist training, for example, in the use of defibrillators.*
- *The first-aid facilities to be provided, in terms of the number and contents of first-aid boxes.*
- *The need for first-aid rooms, which could be dependent on the proximity of the site to emergency medical services.*
- *The provision of continued cover for sickness, leave and other absences of firs-aiders.*

4. A disused factory that has stood empty for several years is to be demolished to make way for a new shopping centre.

    (a) **Identify** factors related to the history of the site that should be considered when carrying out the initial site assessment. **(4)**

    (b) **Identify** factors, other than the site history, that should also be considered. **(4)**

a) During an initial site assessment the factors to be addressed relating to the history of the site include:

- *The presence of hazardous materials, for example, asbestos or chemical contaminants that were used in the manufacturing processes.*
- *Lack of recent maintenance of the site might mean that some of the structure has deteriorated and become unstable.*
- *Machinery, equipment and heavy plant or debris may be located on upper floors adding an extra weight to a structure that may have deteriorated.*
- *Services relating to the factory and equipment may still be 'live', for example, electrical services.*
- *Many industrial towns were heavily bombed, the geographical location of the site might suggest an increased chance of unexploded bombs.*
- *There may be biological hazards, caused by the presence of vermin, pigeons and any evidence of drug use.*
- *There may be people occupying the buildings, for example, people sleeping rough.*
- *Proximity of roads and traffic that could be at risk if parts of the building collapsed before or during demolition.*

b) Other factors to consider include:

- *The existence of any natural obstacles, for example, rivers and streams.*
- *The local road network would need to be considered. There may be narrow lanes or fast dual carriageways or low bridges that could make access to the site difficult.*
- *Similarly, there may be residential areas with schools and hospitals close by.*
- *There may be railways and overhead power cables close by, which would restrict the positioning of cranes and other mobile plant.*
- *The presence of sewers, underground services, cellars, voids and existing ground conditions.*

ELEMENT 3

1. **Outline possible control measures for plant, machinery and vehicles used on construction sites. (8)**

Control measures for the use of the equipment would include:

- *The proper selection of equipment for the work, ensuring that the equipment is capable of moving the maximum foreseeable load.*
- *Ensuring the competency of drivers and operators, by checking licences/certificates, and the experience they have of construction sites.*
- *Where necessary, ensuring the use of competent banksmen.*
- *The need to ensure that dangerous parts of machines are properly guarded.*
- *Providing a regime of planned inspections and maintenance, with procedures for reporting defects.*
- *The need to ensure good all-round visibility for drivers and operators.*
- *Site control measures to support the use of the equipment include:*

- *Planning and maintenance of traffic routes to segregate pedestrians and vehicles.*
- *Imposing and enforcing speed restrictions in respect of vehicles.*
- *Preventing the unauthorised use or movement of plant and vehicles.*
- *Ensuring good standards of lighting and adequate signage.*
- *Avoiding vehicles reversing where possible.*
- *Providing competent supervision to ensure equipment is used properly and for its proper purpose.*
- *Providing awareness training for all workers on site, covering the hazards associated with the use of plant, machinery and vehicles and the precautions that must be observed.*
- *Providing workers with high visibility clothing.*

2. (a) **Identify FOUR** reasons why a dumper truck used on a construction site may overturn. **(4)**

   (b) **Outline** practical measures that could be taken to minimise the risk of a dumper truck overturning when used on construction sites. **(4)**

a) *Overturn can occur if a dumper truck is:*

- *Being driven over obstacles, uneven or unstable ground, on or across slopes or too close to an excavation or embankment.*
- *Poorly maintained with tyres that are not inflated to the recommended pressure.*
- *Overloaded or the bucket may be unevenly loaded.*
- *Driven by people who are not competent or experienced at driving on a construction site, particularly if they drive at excessive speeds round corners or if they fail to avoid the many obstacles that are found on a construction site.*

b) *Practical measures that could be taken to minimise the risks of a dumper truck overturning include:*

- *Use of trucks with a wide wheel base and a low centre of gravity.*
- *Carrying out regular maintenance with particular attention being given to brakes, steering and tyre pressures and arranging for drivers to carry out pre-use checks.*
- *Providing designated traffic routes, which are kept free from obstructions.*
- *Providing edge protection around excavations.*
- *Setting and enforcing speed limits.*
- *Ensuring that the loads carried by trucks are within their safe working loads.*
- *Ensuring the driver's line of sight is not impaired in any way to avoid sudden steering adjustments.*
- *Avoiding driving across slopes.*
- *Using trained, competent and experienced drivers and monitoring their performance on a regular basis.*
- *Traffic routes positioned not too close to excavations.*
- *Installing smooth roads at the earliest opportunity to avoid rough terrain.*

3. Reversing vehicles within a construction site can be hazardous. **Outline** the means by which the risk of accidents from reversing vehicles can be reduced. **(8)**

When reducing the risk of accidents from reversing vehicle consider:

- *Avoiding the need for vehicles to reverse if possible, by provision of one way systems and good signage.*
- *Where this is not possible then a banksman should be used to ensure the area is clear and to control the reversing activity.*
- *Providing high visibility clothing for those people who need to work in areas where vehicles reverse, for example, a banksman.*
- *Providing physical separation of vehicles and pedestrians in areas where vehicles reverse frequently, for example, by means of barriers.*
- *Providing audible alarms and visual warnings on vehicles to warn of their presence.*
- *Ensuring vehicles are fitted with mirrors or other reversing aids to assist the driver in manoeuvring, particularly providing a view of the rear of the vehicle.*
- *Providing mirrors at blind corners.*
- *Providing a refuge for pedestrians to enable vehicles to pass when space is restricted.*
- *Providing good lighting for the area where vehicles reverse, well directed lighting so that it avoids glare in the mirrors of the vehicles and shadows in the area being reversed into.*
- *Providing training for drivers (for example, the use of a banksman) and pedestrians (for example, the need for restricted access to revering areas), signage and enforcement of site rules.*

4. Many construction workers are involved in work-related driving on public roads as part of their work activities. **Outline** the factors associated with this driving that increase the risk of an incident occurring. **(8)**

The factors that increase risks related to work-related driving include:

- *Distance - that the greater the distance of the journey (i.e. the duration of exposure to the hazard) the greater the risk.*
- *Driving hours - if driving hours related to construction activities are excessive the driver is likely to become fatigued, their attention and reaction levels will fall and they are at increased risk of making errors. The hours may be excessive because the driver has been driving too long without a break, their cumulative hours in a day have become too much or their rest period between days has become too short. For some drivers the driving hours are in addition to other work hours, for example, for someone travelling to a meeting at a site these cumulative hours can have a significant effect on fatigue.*
- *Work schedules - work schedules that are badly organised can put increased pressure on drivers to be in a place by a given time. This can lead to them being tempted to increase speed and take abrupt action to change lanes to improve their progress. This risky action can lead to higher risk of collision and reduced stopping distances.*
- *Amount of traffic and delays - driving-related stress is likely to be experienced when the demands of the road/traffic environment exceed the driver's ability to cope with or control that environment. A person in this situation may resort to irrational behaviour in order to avoid certain situations or events that are putting them under pressure.*
- *Weather conditions - Weather conditions have a significant impact on the risks of driving. Sudden rainfall or snow and fog can lead to poor visibility and sudden breaking. Snow and surface water conditions can increase stopping distances. Even good weather can have a negative effect as glare from the sun can limit visibility. This is particularly the case in early morning or evening and is most significant during the winter when the sun is lower in the sky for longer.*

3. **Outline** the practical measures that could be used to protect pedestrians on a construction site where segregation of people and vehicles is not possible. **(8)**

The practical measures to protect pedestrians on a construction site where segregation of people and vehicles is not possible include:

- *Where vehicles share the same workspace as pedestrians it is important to mark the work area as separate from vehicle routes to warn drives to adjust their approach, be aware of pedestrians and give priority to pedestrians.*
- *Removable barriers or hi-vis tape and signs can be used to indicate work areas that are shared by vehicles.*
- *The use of high visibility clothing by pedestrians will assist drivers to see them.*
- *Drivers should have a clear view at all times, including the use of mirrors or similar devices.*
- *Audible and visual warnings fitted to vehicles would also assist.*
- *The reversing of vehicles should be done with the use of a banksman.*
- *Providing mirrors at blind corners.*
- *Providing a refuge for pedestrians to enable vehicles to pass when space is restricted.*
- *Providing good general lighting.*
- *Workers and drivers should be briefed on the hazards and control measures, including at site inductions.*
- *Signage, such as speed limit reductions, should also be used.*
- *A higher level of supervision than usual will be required.*

ELEMENT 4

1. A welfare unit is to be lifted from the vehicle trailer it is being delivered on to its location on the construction site. **Outline** what the person appointed to have overall control of this operation would have to ensure so that lifting operations are conducted safely. **(8)**

The person appointed to control the lifting operation would need to ensure:

- *An initial assessment of the operation was carried out, considering access to where the lift was to take place, restriction affecting siting of the crane and movement of the jib when lifting, and ground conditions.*
- *That the lifting appliance and the associated equipment were suitable for lifting the load (for example, the load carrying capacity and reach of the jib) and were marked with their safe working loads. Suitability would include the stability of the crane when lifting, for example, its need for outriggers.*
- *Documentary evidence to show that the required examinations, inspections and maintenance had been carried out on the crane and accessories.*

- *Following consultation with everyone involved, that a plan was in place to enable effective co-ordination of the lifting operation.*
- *That all people involved, including the crane driver, slinger and banksman, were competent to carry out their duties and fully conversant with the hand signals or other means of communication that were to be used.*
- *Systems for control of the lifting area were put in place, including demarcation of it, and supervising the lifting operation.*
- *Lifting points on the welfare unit and lifting accessories were suitable to enable the lift to take place safely and not damage the welfare unit.*
- *A systems for reporting defects and incidents was put in place.*
- *Adverse weather conditions were taken into account, especially the presence of high winds which would have an effect on the control of the load.*

2. A 100 metre long section of a footpath in a residential area with a speed limit of 30mph is to have the kerbstones replaced.

    (a) **Identify** the hazards that could affect the health and safety of the employees involved in this process. **(4)**

    (b) **Outline** the control measures that could be put into place to reduce the risk. **(4)**

a) The hazards involved in this activity include:
- *Being struck by other road vehicles.*
- *Frequent handling of the heavy kerbs in an awkward position.*
- *Dropping heavy kerb stones onto fingers or toes.*
- *Silica dust from cutting kerbs to size.*
- *Noise from road traffic and the range of tools being used.*
- *Vibration from prolonged use of saws and other hand held power tools.*
- *Wet cement used to bed the kerbstones in may cause cement burns and dermatitis effects.*

b) Control measures will include:
- *The development of a traffic management plan to provide a safe working area.*
- *Ensuring the use of mechanical aids to transport the kerbs or even using lighter kerbs stones (a range is available made from plastic). At worst, using team lifting techniques.*
- *All employees should be trained in manual handling.*
- *Good welfare facilities should be provided so that hygiene standards can be maintained.*
- *Providing tools with in-built suppression methods (water and/or on tool extraction) to prevent/control dust.*
- *Maintaining the tools used so that cutting blade remain sharp.*
- *Safe systems of work may also be considered to reduce vibration exposure, for example job rotation.*
- *The employees should be issued with a range of PPE, such as safety boots to protect from dropped kerbs, hearing protection, dust masks and hi visibility clothing.*

3. **Identify** factors relating to the condition of lifting accessories that could form part of a pre-use checklist. **(8)**

The factors relating to the condition of lifting accessories that could be included in a pre-use check list include:
- *Abrasion or cuts on fibre rope slings.*
- *Stretched fabric of fibre rope slings.*
- *Broken wires or kinks in wire ropes and slings.*
- *Deformed hooks.*
- *Deformed, stretched and cracked links in chains.*
- *Damaged or missing safety clips from hooks and slings.*
- *Evidence of corrosion or misalignment.*
- *Evidence of alterations to accessories, such as shortening or joining items together and adaption of shackles by using bolts to replace shackle pins.*
- *Marking of accessories with their safe working loads.*

4. **Identify** the requirements for thorough examinations of lifting equipment to be carried out to meet the requirements of the Lifting Operations and Lifting Equipment Regulations (LOLER). **(8)**

The Lifting Operations and Lifting Equipment Regulations require that lifting equipment must be thoroughly examined:
- *Before being put into use for the first time.*

- *After assembly and before being taken into use where the safety of the equipment depends on the installation conditions, for example, a tower crane.*
- *Every six months in the case of accessories.*
- *Every six months in the case of equipment used for lifting persons.*
- *Every twelve months for other lifting equipment.*
- *When exceptional circumstances have occurred which could jeopardise the safety of the equipment.*

5. **Identify** the measures that should be taken to reduce the risk of a rough terrain fork-lift truck overturning. **(8)**

The measures to take to reduce the risk of a rough terrain fork-lift truck overturning include:

- *Driver training and experience with the use of rough terrain fork-lift trucks.*
- *Control measures to deter excessive speed, such as rules, signs and enforcement of a speed limit through supervision and monitoring.*
- *Pre-use checks by the vehicle driver.*
- *The vehicle tyres should be fully inflated.*
- *A maintenance programme to ensure the tyres have no punctures/cuts and are replaced before they become to worn.*
- *Driver training to prevent travelling with the load raised.*
- *Ensuring the vehicle is not overloaded.*
- *Ensuring that the load is stable on the forks.*
- *Traffic routes positioned not too close to excavations.*
- *Avoiding driving across slopes.*
- *Installing smooth roads at the earliest opportunity to avoid rough terrain.*
- *Ensuring the driver's line of sight is not impaired in any way to avoid sudden steering adjustments.*

6. Manual handling operations during construction activities can cause injuries.

   (a) **Identify TWO** types of injury that may be caused by the incorrect manual handling of loads. **(2)**

   (b) With reference to the work environment related to construction manual handling activities, **outline** means of reducing the risk of injury during manual handling operations. **(6)**

a) Potential injuries include:

- *Spinal disc compression or prolapsed disc.*
- *Strains to tendons or muscles.*
- *Hernia or ruptures.*
- *Cuts and broken bones, for example affecting the feet.*

b) Means of reducing the risk of injury during manual handling operations include:

- *Ensuring work positions, workstations or work surfaces are at the optimum heights to avoid unnecessary stooping and reaching.*
- *Ensuring the surface of the floor is flat, clear of obstruction and without changes in level so that the employee does not stumble or have to step over objects when carrying loads.*
- *Ensuring the lighting is suitable and sufficient so that employees can see what they are doing and can see how best to grip and move the load.*
- *Controlling the work temperature to avoid excess cold, which reduces dexterity, and excess of heat, which may cause the hands to sweat and lose grip.*
- *Ensuring sufficient space, so that the employee can adopt kinetic handling techniques.*

ELEMENT 5

1. The Provision and Use of Work Equipment Regulations 1998 require that work equipment used in hostile environments is inspected at suitable intervals.

   Identify the items on a 360° tracked excavator that should be subject to inspection. **(8)**

Items for inspection include:

- *The provision and condition of roll over protection, for example, the cab.*
- *The provision and condition of driver restraints, for example, seats belts.*
- *The seats for the security of their fittings, function of vibration attenuation and condition for comfort.*
- *The condition of the bodywork, for damage that could affect motion or be a problem to pedestrians.*
- *Windscreens and windscreen cleaning equipment.*

- *The condition of rear view and other mirrors.*
- *The condition of lights and warning devices.*
- *The condition of the tracks and linkages.*
- *The effectiveness of the braking system and steering.*
- *The condition of the hydraulic arm and bucket for signs of overloading damage.*
- *The performance of the bucket release and tilt mechanisms.*
- *The integrity of fuel, oil and hydraulic systems and the legibility of labels and signs.*

2.   **Outline** practical control measures for reducing the risk to employees when using a bench mounted electrical powered circular saw on site. **(8)**

The control measures to take to reduce the risks of using a circular saw include:

- *Ensuring the saw bench is set up on level ground and secured against movement.*
- *Ensuring guards are in place on the circular saw and correctly adjusted for protection against moving parts, particularly the saw blade.*
- *Using a reduced voltage of 110 volts for the circular saw and connecting it to the supply through a residual current device (RCD).*
- *Using heavy duty cables or cable covers to provide protection against moving vehicles or similar damage.*
- *Placing materials close to the saw bench to minimise the amount of manual handling to be carried out.*
- *Providing local exhaust extraction to reduce the dust created by the cutting operation.*
- *The use of appropriate personal protective equipment, including hearing and eye protection and gloves to counter the noise, dust and wood splinters.*
- *The provision of information and training to users, supervisors, those that maintain the equipment and workers in the area it operates on the health and safety risks involved and the precautions to be taken.*
- *Restriction of use of the circular saw to suitable and competent people, trained and experienced in the specific risks of the equipment.*
- *Ensuring that the saw is not overloaded when cutting and that the manufacturer's instructions with regard to use are followed, particularly for feeding wood to the saw blade, a push stick may be required.*
- *Providing a good level of supervision to ensure the precautionary measures are followed.*

3.   **Outline** the control measures that should be used to reduce risks when cutting concrete kerbstones with a petrol disc cutter. **(8)**

The control measures that should be used to reduce the risks when cutting concrete kerbstones include:

- *The selection of suitable equipment and its inspection prior to use.*
- *The provision of information on and training in safe use of the equipment and manual handling for users of the equipment, those that supervise them and other workers that could be affected by the hazards of the cutting activity.*
- *Restriction of use of the petrol disc cutter to competent people, trained and experienced in the specific risks of the equipment.*
- *The use of a competent person to change the disc of the disc cutter when needed.*
- *The provision of an adequate top guard for the disc cutter.*
- *Dust suppression by wet cutting and dust extraction to control dust.*
- *Using the equipment in a ventilated area away from other operations.*
- *Stopping the engine and applying the brake when the cutter is not being used or when it is being carried.*
- *Maintaining the disc cutter so that the cutting blade remain sharp.*
- *Protecting the operator against HAVS by, for example, the provision of insulation for the handle and introducing job rotation.*
- *Safe systems of work may be used to reduce vibration exposure, for example, job rotation.*
- *Ensuring a safe system of work for refuelling and keeping the minimum amount of fuel on site.*
- *The provision and use of appropriate personal protective equipment, including goggles, hearing protection, gloves, respiratory protection and safety boots.*
- *Good welfare facilities should be provided so that hygiene standards can be maintained.*
- *Providing a good level of supervision to ensure the precautionary measures are followed.*

4.   **Identify** ways in which accidents can occur from the use of cartridge-operated nail guns on a construction site. **(8)**

The ways accidents can occur when using cartridge-operated nail guns includes:

- *The nail may penetrate right through the material and injure other workers behind the material due to:*
- *The charge strength of the explosive cartridge may be too much for the material the nail is to be fixed to causing.*

- *The charge may be correct, but the where the nail is being fixed may be a weak area in the material or there may be a void behind it.*
- *The material being fixed to may be too thin or thinner than expected.*
- *The operator of the gun or other workers may hold material being fixed, putting their hand too close to the gun or the nail may penetrate the operators hand behind the material.*
- *The nail may ricochet and injure the operator of the gun or other workers near-by.*
- *The nail may strike a particularly hard part of the material it is being fixed to, for example, a reinforced rod or hard aggregate.*
- *The operator may attempt to fire a nail into a hole of a previous attempt at fixing, where the material is damaged and fragile.*
- *Attempting to fix a nail too near an edge of the material, causing the material to break away and deflecting the nail.*
- *Firing a nail into material that is too hard for the charge used and the nail selected.*
- *Not firing the nail square to the material causing it to travel at an angle and bounce of the surface of the material.*

A misfire of the cartridge may occur and the cartridge might explode while someone is attempting to remove it forcibly from the gun.

When a misfire occurs an operator may look at the front of the gun, where the detonation is delayed it could fire the nail into the face of the operator.

Strain injuries may be caused by the recoil of the gun at time of explosion of the cartridge and operators might lose their footing and fall.

5. (a) **Identify** and **give an example for each** of **FOUR** mechanical hazards of construction machinery. **(4)**

   (b) **Outline** the advantages and limitations of using a fixed guard to protect people from mechanical hazards of construction machinery. **(4)**

a) Mechanical hazards of construction machinery include (four only required):
- *Entanglement, for example, the rotating chuck of a drilling machine.*
- *Friction and abrasion, for example, the wheel of a bench grinding machine.*
- *Cutting, for example, the blade of a circular saw.*
- *Shear, for example, the scissor mechanism of a scissor lift mobile elevating work platform (MEWP).*
- *Stabbing and puncture, for example, the nail fired from a nail gun.*
- *Impact, for example, contacted by the moving arm of an excavator.*
- *Crushing, for example, between the folding arms of a MEWP.*
- *Drawing in, for example, the rollers of a surface roller.*
- *Injection, for example, high pressure oil ejected from the hydraulic system of a rough terrain fork-lift truck.*
- *Ejection, for example, dust particle ejected from a disc cutter.*

b) The advantages and limitations of a fixed guard include:

Advantages
- *Create a physical barrier.*
- *Require a tool to remove.*
- *No moving parts - therefore they require very little maintenance.*
- *Can be designed to enable visibility through clear panels or mesh.*
- *Suitable for adverse environments.*

Limitations
- *Do not disconnect power when not in place, therefore the machine can still be operated without the guard being fitted.*
- *May cause problems with visibility for inspection.*
- *If enclosed, may create problems with heat which, in turn, can increase the risk of explosion.*
- *May not protect against non-mechanical hazards such as dust/fluids which may be ejected.*

ELEMENT 6

1. **Explain** how the following two protective measures reduce the risk of electric shock **AND**, in **EACH** case, give an example of their use in construction activities.

    (a) Reduced low voltage. **(4)**

    (b) Double insulation. **(4)**

a) *'Reduced low voltage' involves the reduction of mains voltage by a transformer to a lower, safer voltage - typically 110 volts. Any shock voltage can be restricted to 55 volts by means of a transformer that is centre tapped to earth. Reduced voltage systems are commonly used for portable electrical hand tools on construction sites. Additionally, safety extra low voltage (SELV) - a voltage less than 50 volts - is used in hand lamps.*

b) *In 'double insulation' equipment internal live parts of a piece of equipment have two layers of insulation around them, which prevent the live parts contacting exposed conductive parts, such as the outer metal casing of the equipment. Consequently, an internal electrical fault condition cannot make any part of the casing live and pass current to the user. Double insulation is used on portable electrical hand tools.*

2. A fire has started on a construction site immediately adjacent to a bench mounted electric circular saw.

    (a) **Outline** how the saw's electrical power system may have caused the fire. **(4)**

    (b) **Outline** the possible effects of an electric shock to the saw operator. **(4)**

a) *The saw's electrical power system could cause a fire by:*
- *Arcing or sparking from the motor inside the saw body may have resulted in wood dust igniting.*
- *Alternatively the cables from the power source to the saw may have been left tightly coiled and the electrical resistance generated has built up sufficient heat to ignite.*
- *The power cables could have become damaged so that there was a short circuit, which caused heat sufficient to ignite the cable insulation and wood dust.*
- *The connection of the power cable into the saw may have become loose because of vibration and other movement causing a poor connection that created heat and ignition of wood dust.*

b) *The possible effects of an electric shock to the saw operator includes:*
- *The operator may experience muscular contraction in the hand and be unable to break the grip of the equipment.*
- *The operator could experience respiratory arrest as electricity interferes with the muscles that enable breathing.*
- *The operator could experience cardiac arrest or interruption of the heart beat rhythm, fibrillation.*
- *The heat generated by the body's resistance to the flow of electricity can cause burns that may be internal or external to the body, for example, at the point of contact with the electricity.*
- *The electric shock may also cause secondary injuries, for example, amputation of fingers if the saw blade is still running and the operator comes into contact with it.*

3. A road is being resurfaced in an area that has overhead power lines crossing it. The work involves the use of tipper vehicles, excavators and a road planning machine that has an extended jib.

    Outline control measures to reduce the risk from contact with the overhead power lines. **(8)**

The control measures that should be used to reduce the risks from contact with the overhead power lines include:
- *Consulting the electricity supply company with a view to making the lines dead and obtaining written confirmation that isolation has been achieved.*
- *If isolation was not possible, advice should be obtained from the supply company on a safe working distance and precautions introduced to maintain this distance, for example, the erection of goalpost barriers and warning signs.*
- *Controlling access to the area to ensure only authorised vehicles and other equipment are allowed access and the rules are known by their drivers/operators.*
- *Fitting plant with height restrictors, coupled with audible warnings in the cab.*
- *Designating areas for dropping materials and ensuring that spoil heaps are positioned away from the overhead lines.*
- *Using competent drivers and banksmen.*
- *Communicating the safety precautions to the operatives by means of, for example, tool box talks.*

4.   (a)   **Outline** the control measures that should be used by someone using a hand-held electric drill on a construction site to reduce the risk of electric shock. **(4)**

      (b)   Other than electricity, **identify FOUR** hazards associated with the use of hand-held electric drills on construction sites. **(4)**

a)   *Control measures to reduce the risk of electric shock include:*
■   *A pre-use check of the equipment by user, including of the general condition of the drill for damage, the condition of both plug and socket, evidence of overheating or burning, the integrity of the cables, the rating of the fuse.*
■   *The use of reduced low voltage where possible.*
■   *The provision of a residual current device.*
■   *The siting and protection of cables from damage by vehicles and people.*
■   *Keep drill and cables/connectors out of and protect them from water.*
■   *Positioning the cable so that it does not get damaged in use or when the drill is put down.*
■   *Check for evidence that a portable appliance test (PAT) has been carried out.*

b)   *Other hazards associated with the use of the drill include:*
■   *Entanglement with the chuck or bit.*
■   *Stabbing or puncture by the drill bit.*
■   *Cuts from waste metal from the drilling operation.*
■   *Noise from the drill cutting material.*
■   *Hot surfaces from the heat generated by the drill's cutting process.*
■   *Tripping hazards associated with trailing cables.*

5.   (a)   **Explain** why a fuse fitted to hand-held electrical power tools only provides limited electric shock protection to the user of the tool. **(2)**

      (b)   **Explain** the advantages using a residual current device provides users of hand held electrical power tools from electric shock. **(4)**

      (b)   **Outline** the advantages of double insulation for hand-held electrical power tools. **(2)**

a)   *A fuse protects the equipment rather than the user. This is because it responds at current levels that are often fatal, for example, 3 amperes and above. They are also relatively slow to react to a fault and isolate the flow of current. The time taken to react may be long enough to cause fibrillation in a person in contact with the fault current.*

b)   *The advantages of a residual current device are that it operates at low levels of current, for example, 30 mA and provides rapid isolation from the current, for example, within 30ms. This sensitivity means that it responds to a fault at lower current thresholds and faster than a fuse, limiting the duration of electric shock, making it less likely that the current will cause fibrillation in someone in contact with the fault. In addition, they are difficult to override, can be portable and easy to test.*

c)   *The advantages of double insulation hand-held electrical power tools are that the internal live parts of a hand-held electrical power tool have two layers of insulation around them, which prevent the live parts contacting exposed conductive parts, such as the outer metal casing of the equipment. Consequently, an internal electrical fault cannot make any part of the casing live and pass current to the user.*

ELEMENT 7

1.   Arson is the single greatest cause of fire.

      (a)   **Identify** factors that make some construction sites vulnerable to arson attacks. **(4)**

      (b)   **Outline** control measures that can be taken to reduce the risk of arson on a construction site. **(4)**

a)   *Factors that may make some construction sites might be vulnerable to arson attacks include:*
■   *A lack of or damaged perimeter fencing.*
■   *Inadequate supervision of visitors to the site.*
■   *Failure to provide CCTV or security guards during non-working hours.*
■   *A poor standard of housekeeping with combustible materials allowed to accumulate and the use of open skips.*
■   *A failure to store flammable materials in a secure store when work has finished for the day.*
■   *The location of the site, perhaps in socially deprived areas or areas with a history of vandalism.*

- *A failure to engage with the local community, in particular schools, to encourage fire prevention.*

b) *Control measures that can be taken to reduce the risk of arson include:*
- *Erecting and maintaining an effective perimeter fence.*
- *Controlling the entry of persons to the site, such as visitors, sub-contractors and ex-employees.*
- *Providing security lighting and using security guards/CCTV during non-working hours.*
- *Ensuring combustible waste does not accumulate or is in skips that are secured when not being used.*
- *Ensuring flammable materials are kept in a secure storage area.*
- *Erecting warning signs and liaising closely with local police and neighbouring schools.*

2. Liquefied petroleum gas (LPG) is often stored on construction sites. **Identify** control measures for the safe storage of LPG on construction sites. **(8)**

Factors for the safe storage of LPG on construction sites include:
- *Storage in a clear open space.*
- *Secured compound.*
- *2m high fencing.*
- *Safe distance from toxic, corrosive and combustible substances.*
- *Kept away from exit routes.*
- *Stored in well ventilated areas.*
- *Oxygen cylinders, if stored, is at least 3m away.*
- *Protected from sunlight.*
- *Empty containers stored separate to full ones.*
- *An appropriate fire extinguisher nearby.*

3. Fire is a significant hazard on refurbishment projects that involve hot works.

    (a) **Identify THREE** activities that can be considered as 'hot works'. **(3)**

    (b) **Outline** the precautions that may be taken to reduce the risk of a fire occurring during 'hot works'. **(5)**

a) *Activities that are considered to be 'hot works' include (three only required):*
- *Cutting operations, for example, during the removal of structural steels.*
- *When welding operations are taking place, for example, steel fabrications.*
- *During plumbing operations, for example, where boilers are connected to water distribution systems.*
- *Activities that could create sparks, for example, grinding activities using portable angle grinders.*

b) *Precautions to reduce the risk of fire from 'hot work' include:*
- *The use of permits to work for 'hot work'.*
- *Arranging for combustible and flammable materials to be removed from the immediate area where 'hot work' takes place. For example, removing accumulated rubbish and the proper storage of flammable materials away from the 'hot work'.*
- *Organising work that involves flammable materials in the area of 'hot work' does not take place at the same time as 'hot work'.*
- *Ensuring the area where 'hot work' is to take place is well ventilated after work that involves flammable materials.*
- *Covering combustible materials that cannot be removed easily with non-combustible sheets.*
- *Provision of someone to watch for and respond to possible ignition of combustible and flammable materials.*
- *Provision of fire-fighting equipment, for example, portable extinguishers and fire blankets.*
- *Supervision of work activities that follow the 'hot work' to ensure combustible and flammable materials are not placed where the 'hot work' took place until the areas affected are sufficiently cool.*
- *A check of the 'hot work' area for a period of time after the work is completed to check for possible fires.*

4. **Outline** the factors that would need to be covered in the induction training of workers to enable their response to a fire emergency on a construction site. **(8)**

Factors for fire emergency training on a construction site include:
- *Location and operation of call-points and other means of raising the alarm.*
- *How the fire service is called.*
- *Recognition of fire alarms and the actions to be taken.*
- *Understanding the emergency signs, particularly those that show exit routes and the assembly point.*
- *The importance of maintaining emergency lighting to be available.*
- *Location of fire escape routes and assembly points.*

- *Requirements for safe evacuation (for example, non-use of lifts, do not run etc.).*
- *Consideration of people with special needs.*
- *Location, use and limitations of fire-fighting equipment.*
- *Identity and role of fire marshals.*
- *Arrangements to resume work.*

5. **Outline** the factors to be considered when assessing fire risks and the effects on the current fire risk reduction measures of a major refurbishment project on one floor of an occupied multi-floor office block. **(8)**

Factors to assess include:

- *Sources of ignition - increase in power tools, extension leads, sources of heating and lighting, grinding and welding activities.*
- *Potential sources of fuel - increase in combustible materials in the form of wood, packaging, flammable liquids, located/stored in large volume and in corridors and on stairs.*
- *Sources of oxygen - potential for oxyacetylene equipment.*
- *Effects on structural integrity of the building - fire doors removed or held open, deconstruction of partitioning, openings created in compartmentalised areas.*
- *Fire detection - false alarms due to dust rather than fire, some detectors covered or taken out of use, arrangements for when doing hot work.*
- *Fire warning - possibility of it being decommissioned on the floor being renovated and specific sections of the floor affected directly by the refurbishment work.*
- *Fire extinguishing - need to isolate sprinkler system on floor being refurbished to do certain work, new partitions etc. affecting effectiveness of system.*
- *Fire escape routes and assembly points - may be blocked by materials and contractors' equipment.*
- *Requirements for safe evacuation (for example, non-use of lifts, do not run etc.) - contractors may change and there would be a need to keep them all informed of requirements.*
- *Consideration of people with special needs - occupants of the building that may be affected by the availability of means of escape.*
- *The need for fire marshals to ensure contractor evacuation.*

ELEMENT 8

1. Insulation board tiles that contain asbestos are to be removed from the ceiling of a storage area located within a high street department store.

   Outline measures that should be taken into consideration when planning the work to minimise the risks from asbestos. **(8)**

Measures to be taken to minimise asbestos risks include:

- *Consideration of the condition of the tiles and the type of asbestos, in part, this would determine whether the work is notifiable to the HSE. A survey may be required to determine this.*
- *The possibility that asbestos might be present in the storage area in other forms than the tiles and that it might become disturbed by the work.*
- *Preventing access to the storage area by isolating the storeroom and locking the door if the condition of the tiles is poor.*
- *Provision of information to the department store staff regarding risks from asbestos and the measures being take.*
- *The appointment of a licensed contractor for the removal of the asbestos.*
- *Ensuring that, if the work is notifiable, HSE is given fourteen days' notice of the work to be carried out.*
- *The contractor's need to erect sheeting to contain the asbestos during its removal and dependent on the removal method and the condition of the tiles, the need to maintain the sheeted enclosure under negative pressure.*
- *The contractor's need to have a controlled route in and out of the storage area that prevents asbestos escaping.*
- *The contractor's provision and siting of their decontamination and welfare facilities.*
- *The arrangements for independent monitoring of airborne fibre levels during the operation and for carrying out an air clearance test and the issue of a certificate when the work is completed.*
- *The arrangements for the safe disposal of the asbestos waste by means of a licensed carrier.*

2. Exposure to cement dust can lead to adverse health effects if breathed in, for example, irritation of the nose and throat.

    (a) **Give** the meaning of the term 'workplace exposure limit'. **(2)**

    (b) **Outline** control measures that could be considered to control levels of cement dust in the workplace. **(6)**

a) *A workplace exposure limit defines the maximum permitted concentration of an airborne hazardous substance averaged over a specified period of time (eight hours or fifteen minutes) and referred to as a time weighted average.*

b) *Measures to be taken to minimise cement dust in the workplace include:*
■ *Having the process that produces the dust carried out off site in a controlled environment.*
■ *Providing materials that contain cement in a wet form for distribution round the site.*
■ *Providing the cement in hoppers that can more carefully control the amount of cement provided when putting it into containers for mixing, avoiding the use of bags that have residual dust in them.*
■ *Suppressing the cement dust as it arises with water sprays.*
■ *Enclosing processes that require dry cement to be added for mixing and installing local exhaust ventilation on these mixing processes.*
■ *Carrying out processes that create cement dust, for example, drilling, using wet dust suppression or on tool local exhaust ventilation.*
■ *Changing processes, for example, using a block splitter instead of a cut-off saw.*
■ *Removal of cement (and materials that contain cement) spills/residue before it dries.*
■ *Introducing a high standard of housekeeping using a vacuum cleaning system as opposed to hand sweeping.*

3. **Identify FOUR** hazardous substances that are widely encountered in the construction industry **AND give** an associated health risk for **EACH**. **(8)**

Hazardous substances widely encountered include (four only required):
■ *Silica - inhalation of silica may result in silicosis, which is a fibrosis of the lung.*
■ *Cement - prolonged or repeated exposure to cement dust can lead to dermatitis. Continuous contact with wet cement may cause burns or skin ulcers. Prolonged or repeated breathing of cement dust can lead to silicosis in the lungs.*
■ *Wood dust - inhalation of the dust arising from sanding or cutting of wood may cause allergic or non-allergic respiratory symptoms and cancer (depending on the type of wood).*
■ *Solvents - inhalation of vapours from organic solvents, for example, trichloroethylene, can cause drowsiness, it can depress the central nervous system and may lead to liver failure.*
■ *Isocyanates - inhalation of vapours, particularly when the substance is sprayed, can lead to allergic respiratory symptoms, for example, occupational asthma.*
■ *Lead - lead poisoning results from the inhalation of fumes produced from the heating of lead, for example, when oxyacetylene cutting of metal coated with lead paint.*
■ *Asbestos - asbestos fibres readily become airborne when disturbed and can enter the lungs where they can cause asbestosis, mesothelioma (cancer of the pleural lining of the lungs) and thickening of the pleural lining.*

4. **Identify** the information that should be included in a safety data sheet (SDS) for hazardous chemicals. **(8)**

The safety data sheet for chemicals should include:
■ *Identification of the substance/mixture and of the company/undertaking, including the product identifier shown on the label, its recommended use and contact information for the supplier, including for emergencies.*
■ *Hazards identification, including signal words, hazard statements and precautionary statements – the pictogram of hazard symbols may be provided.*
■ *Composition/information on ingredients.*
■ *First-aid measures for initial care must be described in a way that can be understood by an untrained responder. Whether medical attention or special treatment is required, including the urgency with which it may be needed and symptoms of any effects.*
■ *Firefighting measures, including suitable media, hazards of combustion and advice to firefighters.*
■ *Accidental release measures for non-emergency responders and emergency responders, including spills containment and cleaning up.*
■ *Handling and storage, including any incompatibilities and the effects of things like weather.*

- *Exposure controls/personal protection, including workplace exposure limit values and requirements for such things as local exhaust ventilation and specific personal protective equipment (PPE).*
- *Physical and chemical properties, such as odour, flash point, vapour pressure.*
- *Stability and reactivity, including conditions to avoid, for example, heat or incompatible materials.*
- *Toxicological information, including the health hazards, for example, carcinogenicity, route of entry, symptoms and the effects, including delayed and immediate effects from short and long-term exposure.*
- *Ecological information, in order to evaluate the environmental impact of dealing with spills and arrangements for waste.*
- *Disposal considerations, including methods and properties that may affect landfill or incineration.*
- *Transport information, including UN number and transport hazards.*
- *Regulatory information, including relevant national information on the regulatory status of the chemical where it is being supplied.*
- *Other information, including the date the SDS was prepared, changes from previous versions and advice on training appropriate for workers to ensure protection of human health.*

5. (a) **Identify FOUR** forms of chemical agents that might be found in construction workplaces. **(4)**

   (b) **Outline** the differences between the acute and chronic effects from exposure to chemical agents. **(4)**

a) *Dusts (silica), fibres (asbestos), fumes (welding), vapours (solvent), gases (carbon monoxide), liquids (sulphuric acid), solids (lead), mists and aerosols (sprayed isocyanates) (four only required).*

b) *The differences between acute and chronic effects are:*

- *Acute health effects from exposure to chemical agents include an immediate or rapid adverse effect, following a single or short-term exposure. The effects are usually reversible.*
- *Chronic effects from exposure to chemical agents produce a gradual response and they may not be recognised for a number of years. The effects appear after prolonged or repeated exposure to chemical agents and are often irreversible.*

ELEMENT 9

1. A noise survey carried out on a building site identified that noise exposure action values given in the Control of Noise at Work Regulations 2005 were being exceeded.

   (a) **Identify** the lower **AND** upper noise exposure action values defined in the Control of Noise at Work Regulations 2005. **(2)**

   (b) **Outline** the control measures an employer is required to take by the Control of Noise at Work Regulations 2005 when employees are exposed to noise at or above the upper noise exposure action value. **(6)**

a) *The lower noise exposure action value is 80 dB(A) daily average noise exposure measured over an 8hr period and the upper noise exposure action level is 85 dB(A).*

b) *Control measures required include:*

- *The elimination of noise at source or its reduction to as low a level as reasonably practicable by implementing a programme of organisational and technical measures.*
- *The control of exposure to noise by the application of the general principles of prevention.*
- *The designation and marking of hearing protection zones.*
- *Provide employees who are exposed to noise above the upper action level with personal hearing protectors.*
- *Ensure, so far as is reasonable practicable, that employees entering hearing protection zones wear hearing protection.*
- *The provision to employees of information, instruction and training on the risks of exposure to noise and the controls that are introduced.*
- *Undertaking health surveillance where a risk assessment indicates that this is necessary.*

2.   **Outline** the work-related issues that might increase the levels of occupational stress amongst workers on a construction site. **(8)**

The issues that could increase the level of stress include:

- *Demands of the work - workload and work patterns, stress may be due to an individual not being able to cope with the demands of the job, for example, the expectation of working of excessively long hours or to demanding schedules. If the work pattern or job demands are such that the worker does not get adequate breaks this can also lead to stress. In addition, the worker may have to work unsociable working hours, which can increase the risk of stress.*
- *Demands of the work environments - excessive noise levels, poor levels of lighting, inadequate welfare facilities and the poor standard of housekeeping.*
- *Control - if a construction worker has little control over the pace and manner they work this can create stress.*
- *Support - if a construction worker perceives a lack of encouragement or resources provided by the organisation, line management or co-workers a feeling of remoteness can be created. Failure to provide adequate resources and properly maintain equipment can increase the risk of stress. Failure to provide good levels of communication, seek the views of employees, involve them in decisions and recognise good performance when it occurs can also lead to stress.*
- *Work relationships - failure to introduce procedures and implement policies to cover harassment, discrimination, violence and to investigate complaints can increase the risk of stress.*
- *Role - if workers do not understand their role in the organisation, or have conflicting roles, this can increase the potential for stress.*
- *Change - if the management of organisational change is not conducted or communicated well, individuals can be confused or feel threatened by the change and this could lead to stress.*

3.   As part of major football stadium refurbishment, seat anchors are to be installed by workers using hand-held powered percussive equipment that produce high levels of vibration.

    (a)   **Identify** possible health effects due to exposure to vibration. **(4)**

    (b)   **Outline** control measures that could be used to reduce the risk of health effects due to vibration in this refurbishment work. **(4)**

a)   Effects of vibration could include:

- *Numbness, tingling and blanching of the fingers.*
- *Swollen and painful joints.*
- *A reduction in strength, grip, dexterity and in sensory perception.*
- *Involuntary muscular movement.*

b)   Control measures to consider would be:

- *Elimination of the vibration producing task by considering an alternative means of fixing.*
- *Substituting the percussion tools with lower vibration equipment.*
- *Reducing the time of exposure of the workers using the percussion equipment by providing frequent breaks and/or job rotation.*
- *Modifying the equipment to improve the grip on the tools to reduce the vibration transmitted.*
- *Introducing a planned maintenance programme for the tools.*
- *Providing appropriate personal protective equipment, including gloves to keep the hands warm.*
- *Introducing a programme of health surveillance.*
- *Providing the workers with information, instruction and training on the hazards associated with the use of the tools and the control measures that should be taken.*

4.   (a)   **Identify TWO** types of ionising radiation that workers in construction activities might encounter. **(4)**

    (b)   **Identify TWO** types of non-ionising radiation that workers in construction activities might encounter. **(4)**

    (b)   **Outline** the range of health effects of exposure to non-ionising radiation. **(4)**

a)   Two types of ionising radiation are:

- *Gamma rays and x-rays used to check welds or the integrity of structures.*

b)   Two types of non-ionising radiation are (only two required):

- *Microwaves (for example, from equipment on the roof of office buildings).*
- *Lasers (used for levelling and measurements).*
- *Ultraviolet light (from sunlight and arc welding).*

- *Infrared (from portable lighting).*
- c) *The range of health effects from exposure to non-ionising radiation include:*
- *Heating of the surface of the skin or deeper levels, depending on the energy of the radiation.*
- *Burns to the skin or eyes, for example, sun burn from exposure to ultraviolet light.*
- *Eye damage, for example, the retina from lasers and cataracts from infrared and ultraviolet light.*
- *Skin cancer, from ultraviolet light.*

ELEMENT 10

1. Scaffolding that incorporates a powered hoist has been erected to the outside of an office block in order to undertake repairs to the external cladding of the building.

   Outline factors that could affect the stability of the scaffold. **(8)**

The factors that could affect the stability of the scaffold include:
- *The design of the scaffold could have an effect on its stability, for example, whether the scaffold extends round more than one side of the building or the arrangements made for ground floor access points in to the office building.*
- *Erecting the scaffold on soft or inadequately consolidated ground or without sound foundations, for example, sole boards and base plates.*
- *Inadequate bracing.*
- *Insufficient ties or an inappropriate mix of ties.*
- *Erecting the scaffold using incompetent workmen, for example, building it with an inadequate number of standards and poorly fitted couplings.*
- *The use of defective materials and incorrect components.*
- *The unauthorised removal of ties by workers.*
- *Adverse weather conditions that might overload the scaffold, for example, high winds and heavy rain or snow.*
- *Overloading of the scaffold with people, tools, equipment and materials.*
- *Inadequate strength of scaffold, bracing and ties in the location where the hoist is fitted.*
- *Overloading the hoist with materials.*
- *The scaffold being struck by vehicles.*
- *The scaffold being undermined by excavation work done near to it.*

2. A flat roof of a shop in a busy town centre is to be repaired while the shop remains open.

   Outline the measures that could be taken to reduce the risk to workers involved in the roof repair work and others who may be affected by the work. **(8)**

The measures that could be taken include:
- *Assessing the condition of the roof with regard to its safe working load and possible fragile materials.*
- *The erection of barriers and signs at ground level to prevent access to the working area by unauthorised persons.*
- *The provision of safe means of access to the working area for people and materials, for example, by the use of a scissor lift (mobile elevating work platform).*
- *Segregation of the area where the scissor lift is operating.*
- *Provision of a landing place at the level the roof so that people can get safe access to the roof.*
- *Provision of fall protection at the roof edge and landing place, for example, double guard rails and toe boards.*
- *Provision of barriers, including guard rails and toe boards, at any openings in the roof where someone could fall.*
- *Provision of fall arrest equipment where necessary.*
- *Precautions to be observed in the use of a LPG heated bitumen boiler, including with regard to the risk of fire and hot boiling liquid spills.*
- *Control of the removal of materials from the roof, for example, using the scissor lift and/or chutes.*
- *Control of placing and storage of vehicles, materials and waste at ground level so that it does not present a risk to pedestrians or other vehicles, including using barriers, signs and lighting.*
- *Control of work at ground level so that it does not obstruct fire exits form the shop or other buildings.*
- *The provision and use of personal protective equipment, for example, head protection, eyes, hands and feet. Special protection of the body will be required for those handling hot bitumen.*
- *The employment of competent workers who are fully aware of the risks associated with the work and the precautions that should be taken.*

- *First aid provision and procedures to be followed in the event of an emergency.*
- *Ensuring the occupiers of the shop understand the risks and precautions to be observed.*

3.   **Outline** factors to consider when conducting a working at height risk assessment. **(8)**

The factors to be considered in a working at height risk assessment include:

- *Determining whether the work at height could be avoided.*
- *The nature and duration of the task.*
- *Arrangements for planning and supervising the work.*
- *The suitability and state of repair of the access equipment.*
- *The level of competence and training of the workers involved.*
- *The prevailing weather conditions.*
- *Means of access and egress, including the use of access boards or platforms provided with guard rails and toe boards or fencing.*
- *The use fall arrest systems, for example, harnesses.*
- *The use of personal protection, for example, hard hats.*
- *The arrangements for emergency rescue.*
- *Evaluation of any health conditions of the workers involved in the work, for example, vertigo, heart or balance problems.*

4.   **Outline** safe working practices associated with the use of a mobile elevating working platform. **(8)**

Safe working practices which should be adopted include:

- *The use of competent persons to operate and work from the platform.*
- *Using a MEWP that has received a thorough examination no more than 6 months before use.*
- *Using a MEWP that has had periodic inspections and a pre-use check before use.*
- *Its use only on firm level ground.*
- *Checking for the presence of buried services, drains and overhead obstructions.*
- *The use of outriggers for stability.*
- *The fitting of guard rails and toe boards to the platform, if they are not an integral part of the MEWP.*
- *The use of harnesses by workers on the platform.*
- *The erection of barriers around the area where the platform is to be sited and used.*
- *Ensuring the platform is not overloaded with people, materials and equipment.*
- *Securing all tools and equipment before the platform is elevated.*
- *Not moving the location of the MEWP when it is elevated or with people in it.*
- *Developing and introducing emergency rescue procedures.*

5.   **Outline** safe working practices associated with work over water. **(8)**

Safe working practices which should be adopted include:

- *The provision of barriers, including guard rails and toe boards where practicable.*
- *The provision of fall arrest equipment, for example, safety nets and/or harnesses.*
- *Provision of personal buoyancy aids.*
- *Provision of a safety boat.*
- *Placing safety nets or safety lines across fast flowing water for people to hang on to until rescued.*
- *Close supervision and checks to ensure no one is missing.*
- *Workers working in pairs or larger groups where practicable.*
- *Developing and introducing emergency rescue procedures.*
- *Equipment for raising the alarm.*
- *Provision of rescue lines.*
- *Provision of communication equipment between rescue boats and the shore.*

ELEMENT 11

1.   **Identify** the main hazards associated with excavation work adjacent to a busy dual carriageway with a speed limit of 40mph. **(8)**

The hazards associated with the excavation work include:

- *Collapse of the sides of the excavation.*
- *The effect of the excavation work on adjacent structures, including the road, leading to collapse of the structure.*

- *Water ingress into the excavation, following adverse weather conditions or due to a low water table, causing flooding and a risk of drowning.*
- *Ill health effects due to coming into contact with hazardous substances in contaminated land.*
- *Possible presence of an unexploded bomb.*
- *Contact with buried services, for example, gas, electricity and water.*
- *Possible chemical asphyxiation due to a build-up of carbon monoxide in the excavation from vehicles, including work vehicles.*
- *Lack of oxygen due to a build-up in carbon dioxide in the excavation from chalk deposits.*
- *Fire and explosion from flammable substances.*
- *Movement of excavation machinery, including contact people and overhead lines.*
- *The risk of vehicles, people or materials falling into unprotected excavations.*
- *Biological hazards, for example, leptospirosis.*
- *High noise levels from the vehicles on the duel carriageway.*
- *Being struck by vehicles on the duel carriage way.*

2.   **Outline** the control measures that could be considered for excavation work on a construction site. **(8)**

The control measures for excavation work include:
- *Identification/detection and marking of buried services.*
- *Safe digging methods for where buried services are identified.*
- *Support of the sides of the excavation, for example, shoring by using sheets or using support boxes.*
- *Support for structures where their stability may be affected by the excavation.*
- *Means of access to and out of the excavation.*
- *Crossing points to get from one side of the excavation to the other.*
- *Barriers around the excavation area.*
- *Lighting of the excavation area and signs to warn of its presence.*
- *Safe positioning and storage of spoil from the excavation and material to go in it.*
- *Prevention of water ingress and de-watering, for example, by means of pumps.*
- *Positioning and routing of vehicles and other equipment to avoid collapse of the excavation and build-up of carbon monoxide in the trench.*
- *Provision of personal protective equipment.*
- *Provision of welfare facilities to assist with maintaining hygiene, for example, washing hands.*
- *Checking the atmosphere where there is a risk of flammable/toxic substances or asphyxiation.*
- *Controlling the movement of excavation machinery to avoid contact people and obstructions.*

3.   (a)   **Identify FOUR** examples of a confined space that may be encountered in construction activities. **(4)**

       (b)   **Identify FOUR** hazards associated with work in a confined space encountered in construction activities. **(4)**

a)   *Examples of confined spaces in construction activities include (four only required):*
- *Sewers - brick or concrete structures for carrying liquid waste.*
- *Tunnels - for access purposes or movement of liquids or other materials.*
- *Trench/excavations and pits - areas where earth has been removed.*
- *Tanks - storage tank, for example, a fuel storage tank.*
- *Chambers - an interception chamber for water/waste.*
- *Silos - may be an above ground structure for storing material, for example, cement or mortar.*
- *Cellars - an enclosed low level room or space below ground level usually found in old buildings.*
- *Well - a deep source of water.*

b)   *The hazards associated with confined space work include (four only required):*
- *Flammable or explosive gases or vapours.*
- *High temperatures that could cause loss of consciousness.*
- *Gases, fumes and vapours that could cause loss of consciousness.*
- *Lack of oxygen that could cause loss of consciousness.*
- *Ingress of liquid that changes the level of liquid in the confined space leading to a risk of drowning.*
- *Free flowing solids that could move when stood on, causing a person to be trapped in the solids and become asphyxiated, for example, in a silo.*
- *Falls of materials, particularly during tunnelling work.*
- *Contact with the structure of the confined space due to restricted space, particularly the head.*
- *Claustrophobic effects.*
- *Biological hazards arising from the presence of vermin.*

4.   A leaking underground petrol tank has been emptied so that it can be visually inspected internally prior to repair.

   Outline the features of a safe system of work for the inspection team in order to satisfy the requirements of the Confined Spaces Regulations 1997. **(8)**

A safe system of work for the internal inspection of the tank would include:
- *Control of the activity by a competent person.*
- *A preliminary remote inspection, followed by the completion of a risk assessment.*
- *Planning and preparation, including establishing a health and safety method statement that requires the use of a permit to work system for confined space entry.*
- *The issue of a confined space entry permit to work by a competent person.*
- *Confirmation of isolation and lock off of fuel supply and other relevant services.*
- *The provision of safe means of access and egress.*
- *The stipulation of a minimum number in the work team, at least three workers, one of them should remain outside the confined space.*
- *The selection and training of workers for the working in a confined space.*
- *The provision of monitoring of the atmosphere inside the tank while the work is in progress.*
- *The provision of adequate and suitable lighting and ventilation.*
- *Arrangements for the installation of an effective means of communication between those inside and outside the tank.*
- *The provision of a rescue plan, including raising the alarm, equipment required and getting extra assistance.*
- *The provision of rescue equipment, for example, breathing apparatus, resuscitation equipment and a tripod hoist to assist in the removal of the workers in the event of an emergency.*
- *The provision and use of personal protective equipment such as hard hats, goggles and overalls.*
- *The provision of a harness to assist with emergency escape and consideration of a life line.*

ELEMENT 12

1.   A multi-storey car park in a city centre is to be demolished.

   (a)   **Identify FOUR** possible hazards to the environment that could be caused by the demolition. **(4)**

   (b)   **Outline** measures to reduce the risk to the environment during the demolition work. **(4)**

a)   Possible hazards to the environment include:
- *Airborne dust, fumes and fibres.*
- *Noise.*
- *Spilled fuel.*
- *Silt affecting the drainage systems.*
- *Mud and debris being deposited on adjacent roads.*
- *Congestion of surrounding roads due to site traffic.*

b)   Control measures to consider include:
- *Consideration of the method of demolition.*
- *Damping down the structure and debris to reduce the production of dust.*
- *Sheeting vehicles leaving the demolition site with waste material.*
- *Providing wheel wash facilities and washing down vehicles leaving the demolition site.*
- *Using street cleaners to remove dust, debris and mud from the roads.*
- *Providing noise controls to minimise noise at source, for example, the use of acoustic covers and exhaust silencers on equipment. Orientation of equipment so that noise is directed away from sensitive areas.*
- *Providing noise controls to minimise noise travelling outside the site, for example, sound absorbent barriers, using spoil heaps and stores/welfare facilities to provide an acoustic barrier and distance from the noise to sensitive areas.*
- *Fitting filters or stoppers to site drain gullies.*
- *Bunding fuel tanks and introducing effective controls for waste, including the prohibition of burning rubbish on site.*

2. **Outline** the control measures that should be considered when demolishing a group of ten terraced houses in a series of twenty terraced houses in an occupied street. **(8)**

Control measures for the demolition activity would include:
- *Control of the activity by a competent person.*
- *A preliminary survey, followed by the completion of a risk assessment. Including the identification of hazardous substances, for example, asbestos and lead.*
- *Planning and preparation, including establishing a health and safety method statement that requires a systematic approach to the demolition which maintains the structure of the other properties.*
- *Perimeter fencing/barriers around the demolition area.*
- *Re-routing pedestrians and vehicles away from the demolition area.*
- *Means of access to and out of the demolition area, for equipment and workers.*
- *Checking properties for vagrants, possible drug users or children and securing access to the buildings not yet demolished to prevent re-entry.*
- *Identification and isolation of services to the properties to be demolished.*
- *Provision of shoring of the other properties.*
- *Liaising with the occupants of the other houses, including agreeing when noisy operations could take place.*
- *Giving consideration to relocating the people in the houses most affected by the work.*
- *Safe positioning and storage of material from the demolition.*
- *If demolition is to be done by hand, safe means of access to height, for example, by the provision of independent scaffolds.*
- *Prevention of materials falling from height by provision of toe boards, mesh guards, nets and fans.*
- *Selection and use of suitable demolition machinery that provides protection to the user from falling materials.*
- *Controlling the movement of demolition machinery to avoid contact with people and obstructions.*
- *Site security at night.*
- *Provision of personal protective equipment, including hard hats, goggles, gloves and boots.*
- *Provision of welfare facilities to assist with maintaining hygiene, for example, washing hands.*
- *Control of dust caused by the demolition process, for example, by wetting down.*

3. **Outline** the main issues to be addressed in a pre-demolition survey of a three storey office block in a city centre. **(8)**

The main issues to be addressed in a pre-demolition survey would include:
- *The location and nature of adjacent properties.*
- *Methods used in the construction of the office block including any pre-tensioned or post-tensioned structural items.*
- *Review of drawing available for the building.*
- *The need for structural calculations to be made.*
- *The extent of dilapidation of the structure.*
- *The presence of retaining walls and attendant structural issues.*
- *Specific risks that may need to be considered in the demolition process, for example, removal of lift machinery or heavy water tanks.*
- *The presence of underground cellars.*
- *The potential for asbestos to be present.*
- *The location and condition of existing services, including gas, electricity and sewers.*
- *The need for and provision of temporary services to the site based on what is in place.*
- *Fire risks that would need to be managed during the demolition.*
- *Restrictions of means of access and egress to the site.*
- *Unauthorised use of the site, including the possibility of vagrants, drug users or children using the building and how to secure access to the building before being demolished, to prevent re-entry.*
- *Security issues due to its proximity in a city.*
- *Environmental issues such as noise, vibration and dust caused by the demolition process and the presence of any protected species, for example, bats.*
- *Evidence of biological hazards such as the presence of vermin, including rats and pigeons.*
- *The proximity of the building to roads and pathways.*
- *The proximity of the building to watercourses.*
- *The existence of a health and safety file.*

4.   A steel framed warehouse that was part of a large factory is to be demolished. **Identify** the main control measures to be included in a demolition method statement. **(8)**

Control measures for the demolition method statement would include:
- *Control of the activity by a competent person.*
- *The demolition sequence and the methods of work to be used.*
- *The isolation of unnecessary existing services.*
- *The provision of temporary services to the site.*
- *The control and protection of the employees working on the factory site and the public by means, for example, of creating exclusion zones and erecting perimeter fencing.*
- *Provision of access and egress to the site for vehicles, other equipment and workers (including separation).*
- *Soft strip requirements.*
- *The stability of adjacent buildings.*
- *The use of temporary shoring to prevent premature collapse of the structure.*
- *Controlling the movement of demolition machinery to avoid contact with people and obstructions.*
- *Working at height, including access, for example, by scaffold or MEWP.*
- *The control of noise and dust.*
- *The precautions to be taken in dealing with hazardous materials, for example, asbestos, lead, paints and solvents.*
- *The temporary storage and removal of waste from the site.*
- *The control, communication and co-ordination of site activities.*
- *Procedures for reporting hazards that are identified.*
- *The competencies of the workers to be involved in the demolition operation.*
- *Provision of personal protective equipment, including hard hat, goggles, gloves and boots.*
- *Provision of welfare facilities to assist with maintaining hygiene, for example, washing hands.*
- *Procedures to be followed in the event of an emergency.*

Revision and examination guidance

Content

Revision and examination guidance 452
How to study 452
Approaching the time of the examination...454
The lost art of written communications 454
NEBOSH National Certificate in Construction - Examination 454
Revision checklist...458

Revision and examination guidance

Being successful in exams means having more than an in-depth knowledge of the subject matter, it means also having the necessary exam technique. Studying and revising are activities in their own right and there are tips and techniques that you can adopt which will help you to be more effective and give yourself a greater chance of success.

This section is aimed at providing some useful advice on how to improve your study skills and how to revise. It will also advise you on exam technique and help you to organise your time.

Finally, it will explain what to expect on the day of the exam.

How to study

Time management

Most people live busy lives and finding time to study and take exams can be difficult. So, do not commit to study 'all day'. Make a study plan. Be realistic and disciplined - don't plan a schedule you can't manage.

Remember, too much work can be as unproductive as too little work. A good way to start is to work for 50 minutes, then give yourself a 10 minute break. Also remember to allow breaks in your day for food, relaxation and exercise, but not all at once. Physical exercise will help to increase your concentration. Even a short, brisk walk will improve your attention span.

The best time to do difficult tasks is when you are at your most productive so schedule these topics at the start of your study period. Decide on the time of day when your concentration is at its best; for some this might be first thing in the morning, so consider rising earlier and study before going to work; for others it may be late in the evening, but always remember most people's day jobs are demanding and you may well be too tired!

Another consideration might be to plan to do some work at lunch time, whatever you decide, aim to work to a regular regime that suits you and your family. Try to give each subject equal time; do not concentrate on one subject at the expense of another.

Don't be a slave to the plan, be flexible - you never know when an emergency will crop up - and always leave time at the end for reviewing what you have done and what you must still do.

Finding a suitable environment

It is important that you work in comfortable surroundings. Your study environment should be calm and quiet and free from distraction (i.e. mobile phone, family, TV, facebook).

Ensure your room has adequate lighting to prevent eye strain, is at a comfortable temperature and is well ventilated with plenty of fresh air to keep you awake.

You should also ensure that you have a good chair (an upright chair is better than an armchair) and a spacious desk to take all your books and other study aids.

Revision and exam technique

It may have been some time since you last prepared for and took a professional exam. Remember, success in an exam depends mainly on:

- **Revision** - your ability to remember, recall and apply the information contained in this book.
- **Exam technique** - your ability to understand the questions and write good answers in the time available.

Revision and exam technique are skills that can be learned. We will now deal with both of these skills so that you can prepare yourself for the exam. There is a saying that 'proper planning and preparation prevents a poor performance'. This was never truer than in an exam.

Revision tips

You should recognise the knowledge that you already possess that is relevant to the syllabus. Don't underestimate the importance of this. But, it is never too early to start revising!

Throughout the course or learning you should have been thinking about this and noting the topics that you are finding it difficult to deal with.

- Simply reading this publication repeatedly will not normally help you to remember the information; from the start of your study revisit each days study and abstract (handwritten preferred) the essence of the subject. This process will ensure greater retention and recall because we remember better that which we do, rather than that which we have just read. This process will identify any ambiguity you might have, early in the study period and enable you to seek clarity from your tutor before training is complete.

- As the course progresses, condense the information you have abstracted on to revision cards. This is a revision technique in itself. It means that you can carry a lot of information with you and read them in a spare moment.

Other techniques, which you may consider worth trying, include: mind maps, key words and mnemonics.

Mind maps/key words

Mind maps (often referred to as a spider gram) is a powerful graphic technique which provides a universal key to unlock the potential of the brain. It uses the visualisation part of the brain to retain information in such a way that it can be quickly recovered when required. Tony Buzan is recognised by many as the inventor of mind maps in the 1960's.

Mind maps are best used for a single topic, such as learning a language, the technique is used to identify all the components necessary to achieve this and possibly the order in which they should be carried out. This part is an essential aspect of revision; the fact that you have abstracted that which is required will imbed the information into the brain and enable threads of connectivity to be established simplifying recall in the future.

The mind map should start in the centre of a blank page turned sideways. The blank page, does not restrict the brain to one dimension, as with lined paper, thus enabling the brain to work in a two dimensional way and to spread out in all directions.

Connect the main branches to the centre start point, avoid straight lines and use lines which are curved as this increases the brains attention. The brain works best by association so that when the lines are connected to the second and third level branches you will understand and remember a lot more easily. Use images or sketches and colours throughout to make this more interesting for you and increase the brains stimulation and retention.

Use one key word per line; single key words give your mind map more power and flexibility. An example of an approach to learning a foreign language is illustrated in **figure REG-1 below**:

Figure REG-1: Learning a language mind map.   *Source: Tony Buzan.*

Mnemonics

The use of mnemonics is another brain association technique to aid revision and memory recall. The technique relies on the use of key words to trigger memory recall, often when there are several key headings which require recall to fully answer a question.

Commonly encountered mnemonics are often used for lists and in auditory form, such as short poems, acronyms, or memorable phrases.

- I before E, except after C.
- And 'weird' is just weird.

A common acronym used in health, safety and the environment, is the definition of a safe system of work, PEME.

The acronym PEME is sufficient to trigger the answer, thus:

- A safe system of work involves the combination of People, Equipment, Materials and Environment in the correct way to ensure a safe outcome.

Approaching the time of the examination

As the exam gets nearer, you will need to think about organising all the information from the course in preparation for revision.

We recommend that you refer to the revision checklist located at the end of this section, which contains the syllabus for your exam. If a topic is in the syllabus then it is possible that there will be an examination question on that topic.

You can assess your level of knowledge and recall against the revision checklist. Look at the content listed for each element in the revision checklist. Ask yourself the following question:

> "If there is a question in the exam about that topic. Could I answer it?"

This technique will help you to identify the areas of weakness and then to prepare a plan of work which concentrates on the knowledge that you need to develop.

You can rate your current level of knowledge for each topic in each element of the syllabus guide by using the categories 'High', 'Medium' and 'Low'. Use your ranking as an indication of your personal strengths and weaknesses.

For example, if you scored 'High' for the topic, then there is little work to do on that subject to complete your understanding. However, if you scored yourself as low for the subject then you have identified an area of weakness to focus upon.

The lost art of written communications

From the start of your revision it is essential to practice hand writing whenever possible. Most people have become so used to using personal computers (PC's) and mobile phones for written or text communications, that they experience real difficulty in writing on the day of the exam. Do not underestimate the effort required to handwrite text continuously for two hours for each of the exams. When using a PC you can write whatever you wish in any order and then re-organise the text easily into a logical sequence; this is not possible with the written word on paper in a NEBOSH answer book. You must plan your answer or approach before you commence writing. It is important to provide sufficient written material in your answer, the examiner cannot award marks for that which is not there; again, the use of e-mails has encouraged us to use as few words as possible, leaving the reader to fill in the gaps; the examiner will not fill in the gaps, they will only mark that which is written and developed.

Attempt the questions provided within the assessment section and answer within the exam time frame (10 minutes for a short question, 30 minutes for a long question) without reference to your notes or the suggested answer. This will enable you to get an idea of working under exam conditions. You will need to practice writing answers in, for example, black ink, write your answer on lined paper, but leave each alternate line free. When you have finished; review your answer with your study book and annotate your work with, for example, a *green ink* pen, and use the lines left free in your answer. The *green ink* annotations will help with that which you may have missed or remind you of the detail not covered sufficiently. This way of doing things will help you to build understanding and memory retention.

NEBOSH National Certificate in Construction - Examination

There is a single written examination which lasts two hours and the exam paper consists of; one long answer question 1 (20 marks), and ten short answer questions 2 to 11 (8 marks each).

Exam technique

Make sure that you study the past exam questions and suggested answers that are in your study book. These are produced to help students and tutors in future exams. They are intended to be constructive and warn of the common mistakes made by people sitting these exams. A common fault is that candidates fail to pay attention to the command word in each question.

Understanding the command words

The phrase 'command word' is used to refer to the words specifically associated with the learning outcomes and assessment objectives of the NEBOSH Certificate qualifications.

The syllabus learning outcomes are concerned with what students can do at the end of a learning activity, to assess this command words used are action (active) verbs.

The most common 'command words' used in certificate examination questions are:

Command word	Definition
Identify	To give reference to an item, this could be its name or title. NB: Normally a word or phrase will be sufficient, provided the reference is clear.
Give	To offer for consideration, acceptance, or use of another. NB: Give an example of; Give the meaning of.
Outline	To indicate the principal features or different parts of. NB: An exhaustive description is not required. What is sought is a brief summary of the major aspects of whatever is stated in the question. May often need to give the 'Why' in the answer.
Describe	To give a detailed written account of the distinctive features of a subject. The account should be factual, without any attempt to explain. When describing a subject (or object) a test of sufficient detail would be that another person would be able to visualise what you are describing.
Explain	To provide an understanding. To make an idea or relationship clear. NB: This command word is testing the candidate's ability to know or understand why or how something happens. Is often associated with the words 'how' or 'why', an example may be useful.

Source: NEBOSH Guidance on command words used in learning outcomes and question papers - Certificate qualifications.

Certificate questions will predominantly assess **knowledge, application and comprehension**.

Knowledge requires an ability to recall or remember facts without necessarily understanding them. Command words used in knowledge based questions include **IDENTIFY**. **Application** is the skill of being able to take knowledge and apply it in different contexts and circumstances in order to understand why and where problems and issues arise.

The important thing to remember is that, whatever the context - a transport company, a communications centre or an oil refinery - the principles being assessed are the same, but will have different implications given the different industry or issue being considered. Command words used to assess application include **OUTLINE** and **EXPLAIN**. **Comprehension** requires an ability to understand and interpret learned information. Command words used in comprehension based questions include **EXPLAIN**.

In every question the skills required by the specific command words are also shown in the marks allocated for the question. In general there are going to be more marks available for application and comprehension skill questions than for knowledge based questions.

It is important to read the whole question and to understand what the question requires as the command word on its own will need to be reinforced by the remainder of the question. The need to understand the meaning of the 'command word' and to read the question carefully is emphasised in the comments below that are taken from some recent examiner's reports:

"It was disappointing to note that some candidates again misread the question and provided outlines of the duties of employers rather than employees."

"While answers to this question were generally to a reasonable standard, many were too brief to attract all the marks that were available."

"Some answers were extremely brief and candidates should remember that one-fifth of the marks for the entire paper are available for answers to this question (question 1). Answers are expected to be proportionate to the marks available."

Source: NEBOSH examiners report.

Time management

Good time management during the examination is an essential component for success.

There are 11 questions in total on each paper:

- Question 1 = 20 marks and questions 2-11 = 8 marks each.

You should allow yourself about twenty-five to thirty minutes for the twenty mark question and eight to ten minutes for the short answer questions. There will be a clock in the room but most delegates often find it useful to take their own watch into the exam and have it visible on their desk to help keep track of time. NEBOSH questions are often split into parts to help signpost the answer required and to give you an idea of how much time should be spent on each part of the question.

An easy rule is to allow one minute for each mark available. This is not a precise calculation but, in summary, if you allocate about 10 minutes to each of the short questions and about 25-30 minutes to the long question, this straightforward approach gives sufficient time to plan and write a good answer and not run out of time.

Attempt all questions

Good exam technique includes making sure you attempt all the questions to maximise your chances of a pass grade.

If you **DO NOT** attempt all the questions and you average 50% of the available marks for those attempted, as you can see from the table below, your margin for a pass is significantly reduced.

No. of questions attempted:	For example:	If you only average 50% of the total available marks this will equal:
11	One 20 mark + Ten 8 mark questions	50 marks - Pass
10	One 20 mark + Nine 8 mark questions	46 marks - Pass
8	One 20 mark + Eight 8 mark questions	42 marks - Referred

The fewer the questions attempted, the higher the average mark for each must be obtained for a pass grade to be achieved. It is important to remember that most marks are achieved in the earlier part of the available time spent on any question; do not spend too much time on any one question, certainly do not exceed the time available for each.

If you finish with time to spare go back over the questions and add extra material if you feel it is relevant.

Attempting questions

You must attempt all 11 questions but you may answer them in any order, however, it is advisable to enter question numbers into the answer book, in numerical order before you begin. Allow two pages for question 1 and one page for questions 2 to 11. If you choose to answer in a different order simply write your answer on the appropriate pre-numbered page. This will clearly identify to you that all 11 questions have been attempted and that you have not missed any because you chose not to answer in a numerical order. If you make a mistake and enter the answer on the wrong page of the answer book, simply change the question number, but remember to change the page number of the one not used. Make sure that you read each question very carefully. Read through the whole question before you begin your answer. With questions that comprise of more than one part, it is normal for the parts to be related and you must make sure that you do not answer the sections in the wrong order. It is not uncommon for candidates to miss marks simply by failing to answer the question that was set.

Examiners comment that:

> "Some candidates fail to answer the question set and instead provide information that may be relevant to the topic but is irrelevant to the question and cannot therefore be awarded marks."

So, be sure that you answer the question that has been asked and not the one that you wish had been asked!

Make it easier for the examiner

Make it as easy as possible for the examiner to find places to award you marks. Keep writing legible - remember the examiner cannot award marks for that which cannot be read. If a question consists of different sub-sections then ensure each sub section is correctly numbered and answered against the appropriate number, within your answer. Do not expect the examiners to give marks if the appropriate number and answer are not clearly connected. A general all-embracing answer, may cover the question requirements, but it is not the examiners job to make it fit any specific question numbering or example requirements. Beware, this is a common trap that students fall into when rushing through the exam questions. Take care with abbreviations;

PPE, SSW, explain the words at least once using brackets to introduce the abbreviation first before using again, for example, personal protective equipment (PPE), safe system of work (SSW). This rule applies for each question answered.

Marks will not be awarded if the examiner cannot make sense of the sentence that you have written, poor grammar or spelling will not be penalised, as long as your answers are clear and can be understood. It often helps to keep sentences relatively short, but take care not to assume that the examiner will fill in any gaps in the information provided. As discussed earlier avoid using generic references such as, train, monitor, risk assess, etc. An example is often required: *'train all workers'*, would communicate better if it were more specific to the question, such as *'workers should be trained in the correct disposal technique for waste oil, including hazards that are present and control measures that are in place'*. Pay close attention to the number of marks available for each question or part of a question - this usually indicates how many key pieces of information the examiner expects to see in your answer.

Give examples, wherever possible, based either on your own personal experience or things you have read about. An example can be used to illustrate an idea and demonstrate that you understand the requirements of the question. If you start to run out of time, write your answers in bullet point or checklist style, rather than failing to answer a question at all.

Here is an exercise which will help you to develop your answers to ensure that you address the command word. Questions which require: *outline, describe or explain*; always make sure that your answer gives the 'why'.

Your answer	Too general	Better, but generic	Clear explanation of type	Why given	Improved	Done
Provide PPE	X	X				
Provide suitable PPE	X					
Provide eye protection		X				
Provide chemical resistant goggles			X			
Provide chemical goggles to protect the worker				X		
Provide chemical goggles to protect the worker from chemical splash					√	
Provide chemical goggles to protect the worker from chemical splash when dispensing acid from a container						√

Use a similar approach to develop the following statements:

■ Provide training.
■ Provide supervision.
■ Provide safe access and egress.
■ Provide suitable fire extinguishers.

Finally:

Before the exam you should check the following:

■ Know where the exam is to take place.
■ Arrive in good time.
■ Bring your examination entry voucher, which includes your candidate number. The invigilator will have a seating plan and your place in the examination room is allocated to you.
■ Bring photographic proof of identity.
■ Bring pens, pencils, ruler, etc. (Remember these must be in a clear plastic bag or wallet).
■ Bags, books, reference materials must be left out of reach to the side, rear or front of the room.
■ Mobile phones or any other electronic devices may *NOT* be used. Please ensure devices are switched off and placed in your bag (out of reach) or handed to the invigilator to keep for the duration of the examination.

- Know that translation dictionaries (in paper format, with no personal annotations) approved by NEBOSH may be used.
- Know that water will be provided, but you may bring soft drinks and sweets (silent type, no crisps) if you wish.

Good luck, but always remember:

> "The greatest barrier to success is the fear of failure."

Source: Sven Goran Eriksson.

Revision checklist

The revision checklist is designed to help those wishing to take the NEBOSH National Certificate in Construction. By now you should have been trained in the requirements necessary to fulfil the syllabus requirements and have a good understanding of the command words, which are used at examination.

The following revision checklist is taken from each element of this publication. The purpose of the checklist is for you to review the topics against the command words. Column one is the element and sub element number. Column 2 is the element and sub element topics. Column 3 and 4 are for you to identify if you are generally comfortable at that level (ok) or not (require more revision - rev).

The NEBOSH learning outcomes are stated at the start of each element in the book. For each learning outcome of the sub element, the appropriate command word is stated and column 5 identifies the Command Word (CW) by initial, for that sub element of the syllabus.

- I - Identify.
- G - Give.
- O - Outline.
- D - Describe.
- E - Explain.

These command word cross references are provided to indicate the depth of understanding that is required for that part of the sub element, with **Explain** requiring greater depth of understanding than say for **Outline**.

If the requirement for understanding is **Explain**, then this does not mean all questions for this sub element will require an explanation. All or part of a question may also use the lesser demanding command words as well, for example, **Identify** or **Give**.

	Element topics	Ok	Rev	CW
	Unit NCC1 - Managing and controlling hazards in construction activities			
1.0	**Construction law and management**			
1.1	Scope, definition and nature of construction activities			I
	Types of work			
	Range of activities			
	Meaning of construction terms			
	Particular construction issues			
1.2	Consequences of failing to manage health and safety			O
	General argument			
	Size of the construction health and safety 'problem'			
1.3	Construction (Design and Management) Regulations (CDM) 2015			O
	Scope and application			
	Duties			
	Appointment and competence required of relevant parties			
	Notification of projects			
	Preparation of pre-construction information			
	The construction phase plan			
	Provision of appropriate and relevant information to all parties			

	Element topics	Ok	Rev	CW
	Preparation of the health and safety file			
	Application to domestic clients			
1.4	Sources of external construction health and safety information			I
	Sources external to the organisation			
2.0	**Construction site - hazards and risk control**			
2.1	Initial site assessment			E
	Factors to consider in site assessments			
2.2	Appropriate general site control measures			E
	Site planning			
	Site preparation for specialist activities			
	Site security and means of protecting the public			
	Arrangements with client/occupier of premises			
	Arrangements for site inductions			
	Working in occupied and unoccupied premises			
2.3	Health, welfare and work environment requirements			I
	Provision of health and welfare facilities			
	Sunlight, inclement weather and extreme temperatures			
2.4	Violence at work			E
	Hazards relating to violence at work			
	Control measures to reduce risks from violence at work			
2.5	Substance misuse at work			E
	Types of substances misused at work			
	Hazards of alcohol and drugs at work			
	Control measures for the misuse of alcohol and drugs at work			
2.6	Safe movement of people on construction sites			E
	Hazards to pedestrians			
	Control measures for pedestrian hazards			
	Maintenance of a safe workplace			
	Working on public highways			
3.0	**Vehicle and plant movement - hazards and risk control**			
3.1	Safe movement of vehicles within a construction environment			E
	Hazards from workplace vehicles and plant			
	Control measures to reduce risks from the movement of vehicles and plant			
3.2	Driving at work			O
	Extent of work-related road injuries			
	Factors that increase risks of a road traffic incident			
	Managing work-related road safety			
	Risk assessments for work-related driving			
	Control measures to reduce work-related driving risks			
4.0	**Musculoskeletal hazards and risk control**			

Element topics		Ok	Rev	CW
4.1	Musculoskeletal and work-related upper limb disorders			E
	Meaning of musculoskeletal and work-related upper limb disorders			
	Examples of repetitive construction activities			
	The ill-health effects of poorly designed tasks and workstations			
	Factors contributing to ill-health conditions			
	Appropriate control measures			
4.2	Manual handling hazards and control measures			E
	Common types of manual handling injury			
	Assessment of manual handling risks			
	Avoiding or minimising manual handling risks in construction activities			
	Efficient movement principles for manually lifting loads			
4.3	Lifting and moving equipment			E
	Hazards and controls for mechanically operated load handling equipment			
	Hazards and control measures for manually operated load handling aids			
	Requirements for lifting operations			
	Visual inspection and statutory thorough examination and inspection			
5.0	**Work equipment - hazards and risk control**			
5.1	General requirements for work equipment			O
	Scope of work equipment			
	Suitability as it relates to provision of equipment			
	Requirement to restrict the use and maintenance of equipment			
	Information, instruction and training			
	Equipment to be maintained and maintenance conducted safely			
	Visual inspection and statutory thorough examination and inspection			
	Importance of operation and emergency controls, etc			
	Responsibilities of users			
5.2	Hand-held tools			O
	Hand tools			
	Common portable power tools used in construction			
	Suitability for location			
	Procedures for defective equipment			
5.3	Machinery hazards			D
	Main mechanical and non-mechanical hazards			
	Hazards presented by a range of equipment			
5.4	Control measures for machinery hazards			E
	Machinery guarding			
	The principles, merits and limitations of protection methods			
	Application of protection methods to a range of equipment			
	Basic requirements for guards and safety devices			
6.0	**Electrical safety**			

	Element topics	Ok	Rev	CW
6.1	Hazards and risks associated with electricity			O
	Principles of electricity			
	Risks of electricity			
	High risks associated with electricity			
6.2	Control measures			O
	Selection and suitability of equipment for use in construction activities			
	Electrical systems on site			
	Advantages and limitations of protective systems			
	Use of competent persons			
	Use of safe systems of work			
	Inspection and maintenance strategies			
	Emergency procedures following an electrical incident			
6.3	Control measures for working near overhead power lines			O
	Control measures			
7.0	**Fire safety**			
7.1	Fire initiation, classification and spread			D
	Basic principles of fire			
	Classification of fires			
	Principles of heat transmission			
	Reasons why fires spread			
	Common causes and consequences of fire during construction activities			
7.2	Fire risk assessment			O
	Requirement and matters to be addressed in carrying out the assessment			
	Factors to be considered in carrying out the risk assessment			
	Additional risk assessment factors related to construction			
7.3	Fire prevention and prevention of fire spread			O
	Control measures to minimise the risk of fire in a construction workplace			
	Storage of small quantities of highly flammable/flammable liquids			
	Structural measures to prevent spread of fire and smoke			
	Use of suitable electrical equipment in flammable atmospheres			
7.4	Fire detection, fire alarm and firefighting equipment			I
	Common fire detection and alarm systems			
	Portable firefighting equipment			
	Extinguishing media			
	Access for fire and rescue services and vehicles			
7.5	Means of escape			O
	General requirements for means of escape			
7.6	Evacuation of a construction workplace			O
	Emergency evacuation procedures			
8.0	**Chemical and biological health - hazards and risk control**			

	Element topics	Ok	Rev	CW
8.1	Health risks from hazardous substances			O
	Forms of chemical agent			
	Forms of biological agents			
	Main classification of substances hazardous to health			
	Difference between acute and chronic health effects			
8.2	Assessment of health risks			E
	Routes of entry of hazardous substances into the body			
	Factors to be taken into account when assessing health risks			
	Sources of information			
	Role and limitations of hazardous substance monitoring			
	Basic monitoring equipment			
8.3	Workplace exposure limits			E
	Purpose of workplace exposure limits			
	Long-term and short-term exposure limits			
	Significance of time weighted averages			
	Limitations of exposure limits			
	Application of relevant limits			
	Reducing exposure levels			
8.4	Control measures			O
	Duty to prevent exposure or adequately control it			
	Ensuring the workplace exposure limit is not exceeded			
	Principles of good practice as regards control of exposure			
	Common measures used to implement the principles of good practice			
	Control of substances with specific effects			
8.5	Specific agents			O
	Health risks and controls associated with other specific agents			
	Generation and control of dust on a construction site			
	Health risks and controls associated with asbestos			
	Duty to manage asbestos			
8.6	Safe handling and storage of waste			O
	Basic environmental issues relating to waste disposal and effluent			
9.0	**Physical and psychological health - hazards and risk control**			
9.1	Noise			O
	Physical and psychological effects on hearing of exposure to noise			
	The meaning of common sound measurement terms			
	Assessment of noise exposure			
	Basic noise control measures			
	Personal hearing protection			
	The role of monitoring and health surveillance			
9.2	Vibration			O

	Element topics	Ok	Rev	CW
	The effects on the body of exposure to vibration			
	The need for assessment of exposure, including limit and action values			
	Basic vibration control measures			
	Role of monitoring and health surveillance			
9.3	Radiation			O
	Differences between non-ionising and ionising radiation			
	Types of non-ionising radiation			
	Types of ionising radiation			
	Typical occupational sources of non-ionising and ionising radiation			
	The basic means of controlling exposures to ionising and non-ionising radiation			
	The basic means of controlling exposures to radon			
	Basic radiation protection strategies			
	The role of monitoring and health surveillance			
9.4	Stress			O
	Introduction and meaning of 'work-related stress'			
	Causes of stress			
	Effects of stress			
	Control measures			
10.0	**Working at height - hazards and risk control**			
10.1	Working at height hazards and risks			E
	Work activities involving a risk of injury from falling from height			
	Basic hazards and factors affecting the risk from working at height			
	Methods of avoiding working at height			
	Main precautions necessary to prevent falls and falling materials			
	Emergency rescue			
	Measures to minimise distance and consequences of a fall			
	Requirements for head protection			
	Inspection requirements for work equipment			
10.2	Safe working practices for access equipment and roof work			E
	Scaffolding			
	Mobile elevating work platforms			
	Ladders			
	Other techniques for working at height			
	Fall arrest equipment			
	Roof work			
10.3	Protection of others			O
10.4	Working over or near water			O
	Prevention of drowning			
	Additional control measures			
11.0	**Excavation work and confined spaces - hazards and risk control**			

Element topics		Ok	Rev	CW
11.1	Excavations hazards and assessment			E
	The hazards of work in and around excavations			
	Risk assessment			
11.2	Control measures for excavation work			E
	Controls			
	Particular requirements for contaminated ground			
	Inspection requirements for excavation support systems			
11.3	Confined spaces hazards and risks			E
	Introduction and meaning of the term 'confined space'			
	Typical confined spaces found during construction activities			
	Hazards and risks associated with confined spaces			
11.4	Control measures for confined space working			O
	Precautions for safe entry			
	Monitoring arrangements			
	Emergency arrangements			
12.0	**Demolition and deconstruction - hazards and risk control**			
12.1	Demolition and deconstruction hazards and risk			I
	The meaning of terms			
	The selection of the appropriate method			
	Hazards relating to deconstruction and demolition			
12.2	Control measures			O
	Control measures for deconstruction and demolition work			
12.3	Pre-demolition, deconstruction or refurbishment surveys			I
	Purpose and scope of surveys			
	Duties of the property owner for carrying out a pre-demolition survey			
	Competent person to carry out investigations			
	Identification of features of the structure			
	Review of factors affecting the structure			
12.4	Method statements			O
	Control measures that a method statement should include			

Index

A

Abrasion, 129
Absorption, 262
   noise, 262
   skin contact, 185
Access, 325
   means of, 25, 292, 325, 333
   working at height, 354
Access and egress, 50
   from site, 349
Access equipment
   poorly maintained, 283
   safe working practices, 289
Access from site, 349, 356
Accessories, 101
Accidental release - principles of protection, 252
Accidents, 31
   electrical, 152
Accommodation for clothing, 34
ACOP, 17
Action in the event of a fire, 197
Action values
   noise, 260
   vibration, 266
Activities
   construction, 3
   hazards to public, 46
   non-construction, 23
   range of, 4
   repetitive, 76
   specialist, 29
   temporary nature of, 5
Acute health effects, 207
Acute toxicity, 203
Adequate control of exposure, 222
Adjacent structures, collapse, 318
Adjustable Guard, 138
Advantages
   portable appliance testing (PAT), 165
   protective systems, 158
Adverse weather conditions, 285
Agents
   body response to, 210
   chemical, 201
Aids, load handling, 102
Air
   bags, 307
   exhaust, 262
   monitoring asbestos, 250
Alarm, 190
Alcohol, 42, 69
Allergic contact dermatitis, 209
Alpha particles, 271
Alteration
   works, 3
Amplitude, 257
Apparatus
   defective, 152
Application
   CDM 2015, 8
   domestic clients, 17
   types of PPE, 263
Appointment of relevant parties, 12
Approved code of practice, 17
APS, 19
Area of site, 23
Arrangements
   client/occupier of premises, 31
   site access, 26
   site inductions, 32
   site risks, 15
   training, 356
   welfare, 356
Arson, 182
Asbestos, 356
   accidental exposure, 248
   air monitoring, 250
   controls, 245
   disposal, 250
   duty to manage, 245

   exposure, 248
   health risks, 244
   identification, 246
   licence, 249
   medical surveillance, 250
   procedure for discovery, 248
   removal, 248
   respiratory equipment, 249
   survey, 246
   surveyors, 350
Asbestosis, 211
Asphyxiating atmospheres, 319
Aspiration hazard, 207
Assembly points, 196
Assessment
   excavation, 317
   fire risk, 177
   health risks, 208
   manual handling risks, 81
   noise exposure, 258
   pedestrian risks, 46
   sites, 23
   vibration, 266
Association of Project Supervisors (APS), 19
Asthma, occupational, 237
Atmospheres
   exposure, 330
   flammable and explosive, 189
   toxic and asphyxiating, 319
Atmospheric testing, 333
Attenuation factors
   personal hearing protection, 264
Automation, 87
Avoidance, 344
   adverse weather conditions, 285
   height, 284
   manual handling risks, 85
   premature collapse, 344
   where possible, 331
   working near overhead power lines, 166
Awkward movements, 90

B

Bacteria, 202
Banksman, 31, 61
Barrier, 64, 310, 325
   ground level, 166
Base plate, 291, 292
Basic circuitry, 147
Battering, 324
Behavioural effects of stress, 276
Bench-mounted circular saw, 141
Bench-top grinder, 141
Beta particles, 271
Biological
   agents, 201
   monitoring, 236
Blood borne viruses, 237
Boarding, 293
Boatswain's chair, 304
Bodies, professional, 18
Body
   protective mechanisms, 210
   response to agents, 210
Brace, 291
Bracing, 292
Breathing apparatus, 232
Brick guards, 294
Bricklaying, 76
Brickwork/blockwork, 188
British standards, 18
Building
   materials, 188
   works, 3
Building structure, absence of compartments, 174
Buncefield, 176
Buoyancy aids, 312
Buried services, 162, 317
   detection, 322
   identification, 321

marking, 321
presence of, 26
Burns, electrical, 151

C

Cable avoidance tool (CAT), 162
Cables, 154
Caissons, 318
Call points, 190
Cantilevered scaffold, 291
Capability of equipment, 155
Captor system, 229
Carbon dioxide, 239
    extinguishing media, 193
Carbon monoxide, 2401
Carcinogenic, 202, 205, 236
Cardiac arrest, 149
Carpel tunnel syndrome, 77
Carrying, 84
Cartridge nail gun, 126
Causes
    electrical fires, 151
    fire, 175
    stress, 275
    vehicles overturning, 57
CDM 2015
    appointment and competence, 12
    clients' duties, 9
    construction phase plan, 14
    contractors, 11
    description of project, 13
    designers' duties, 10
    duties, 9
    exemption of domestic clients, 17
    health and safety file, 14, 16
    management of the work, 15
    notification of projects, 12
    pre-construction information, 12
    principal contractors' duties, 11
    principal designer' duties, 10
    regulations, 344
    scope and application, 8
    site risks, 15
CE Marking, 114
CECA, 18
Cellar, 329, 347
Cellular mechanisms, 211
Cement, 241
    dust, 244
    mixer, 142
Chainsaw, 127
Chamber, 329
Changes
    level, 61
    workplaces, 179
Changing workplace, 5
Chapter 8 of the 'Traffic Signs Manual', 52
Chartered Institute of Building (CIOB), 18
Chemical agents, 201
Chemicals, securing, 30
Chilblains, 39
Chisels, 124
Choice of equipment, vibration, 267
Choosing health risk controls, 225
Chop saw, 125
Chronic health effects, 207
CIOB, 18
Circuitry, 147
Civil Engineering Contractors Association (CECA), 18
Civil engineering, 3
Classification
    explosive atmospheres, 189
    fire, 171, 173
    substances hazardous to health, 202
Classification Labelling and Packaging of Substances (CLP) EC
    Regulation, 360
Classified workers, 274
Cleaning requirements, 50
Cleaning, 5
Clearance - site, 4
Client
    arrangements with, 31
    time pressures, 6
Clients' duties, 9
Close boarded excavation, 324
Close sheeting, 324
CNWR, 261
Cofferdams, 318
Cold
    environments, 40
    stress, 39
Collapse, 344

adjacent structures, 318
deliberate controlled, 339
explosive, 340
premature, 340
sides, 317, 318
Collisions
    fixed objects, 58, 92
    moving vehicles, 45
    other vehicles, 58, 92
    pedestrians, 58, 92
Column, 292
Combustible materials
    storage, 181
    use, 181
Commercial properties, 25
Communications, 356
Compatibility, guards, 143
Competence
    asbestos surveys, 246
    relevant parties, 12
    workforce, 346, 355
Competent people, 108
Competent persons, 161
    carry out investigations, 350
    training, 333
    use of, 333
Compressed air, 130
Compressor, 142
Concrete slabs, 76
Condition
    roadways, 349
    structures, 349
Conditions
    ground, 23
    weather, 68
Conduction, 173
Conductors, protection, 154
Confined spaces
    control measures, 331
    hazards, 329
    meaning of, 329
    risks, 329
Confined Spaces Regulations (CSR) 1997, 329, 330, 333, 334, 362
Conformity with standards, 114
Consequences
    failing to manage, 6
    fall, 286
    fire, 176
    health and safety, 6
Considerations
    environmental, 61
    ergonomic, 115
Construction
    issues, 5
    method of, 346
    phase, 14
    size of 'problem', 7
    sources of information, 17
    terms, 5
Construction (Design and Management) Regulations (CDM) 2015, 4, 5, 6, 8, 9, 10, 11, 12, 13, 14, 15, 16, 17, 363
Construction activities, 3
    definition of, 3
    hazards to public, 46
    nature of, 3
    procedure for discovery of asbestos, 248
    repetitive, 76
    scope of, 3
    selection of equipment, 154
    suitability of equipment, 154
    typical confined spaces, 329
Construction environment, 57
    safe movement of vehicles, 57
Construction site
    control of dust, 244
    generation of dust, 244
    safe movement of people, 44
Consultation with service provider, 166
Contact dermatitis, 209
Contaminated ground, 319
    particular requirements, 327
Contents
    construction phase plan, 14
    health and safety file, 16
    pre-construction information, 14
Contractor
    principal, 10
Contractors' duties, 11
Contributory factors
    hand-arm vibration, 266
Control
    dangers on public highways, 31

exposures to radiation, 272
exposures to radon, 273
ignition sources, 181
site risks, 15
stress, 275, 277
Control measures
asbestos, 245
cartridge nail gun, 126
chain saw, 127
chop saw, 125
confined space working, 331
construction site machinery, 133
cut off saw, 125
deconstruction and demolition work, 344
disc cutter, 125
driver, 71
electric drill, 125
electrical safety, 154
excavation work, 321
excavator, 97
fire, 181
fork lift trucks, 92
gin wheel, 103
hand tools, 123
health risk, 222
hoists, 98
identified hazards, 356
journey, 71
lifting operations, 104
lifts, 98
machinery, 135
maintenance work, 52
maintenance, 117
manual handling hazards, 80
method statement, 354
misuse of alcohol and drugs at work, 44
mobile and tower designs, 101
movement of vehicles and plant, 60
musculoskeletal disorders, 79
noise, 262
not to increase risk, 227
office machinery, 131
pallet truck, 103
pedestrian hazards, 46
pneumatic drill/chisel, 124
pneumatic nail gun, 126
sack truck, 102
sander, 126
scissor lift, 100
site, 26
stress, 276
telehandlers, 96
vehicle, 71
vibration, 267
violence at work, 41
wheelbarrow, 102
when segregation is not practicable, 63
working near overhead power lines, 166
working over/near water, 312
work-related driving risks, 71
workshop machinery, 132
Control of Artificial Optical Radiation at Work Regulations (CAOR) 2010,
    372
Control of Asbestos Regulations (CAR) 2012, 33, 245, 356, 372
Control of exposure, 222
    health risks, 224
Control of Lead at Work Regulations (CLAW) 2002, 228
Control of Noise at Work Regulations (CNWR) 2005, 258, 261, 262, 263,
    265, 266, 375
Control of Substances Hazardous to Health Regulations (COSHH) 2002,
    17, 133, 213, 220, 221, 222, 223, 226, 230, 231, 235, 236,   377
Control of Substances Hazardous to Health (Amendment) Regulations
    (COSHH) 2004, 381
Control of Vibration at Work Regulations (CVWR) 2005, 266, 267, 268,
    269, 381
Control of water, 326
Control proportional to health risk, 224
Control systems, 121
Control, loss of, 57
Controls, 121
    emergency stop, 119
    excavation work, 321
    ionising radiation, 273
    non-ionising radiation, 272
    stop, 119
Convection, 173
Cooling, 171
Co-operation, 31
Coordination of work activities, 357
Correct clearance distances, 166
Corrosive, 202
Coupling, 59

CPL Regulation, 212
Cracking of walls, 352
Cradles, 305
Cranes, 100
Crash decks, 307
Crawling boards, 310
Crossing points, 325
Crushing, 129
Current, 147
    use, 23
    path, 150
Cut off saw, 125
Cutting, 129
CVWR, 266

D
Damping, 262
Dangerous parts of machinery, 135
Dangerous Substances and Explosive Atmospheres Regulations
    (DSEAR) 2002, 189, 382
Dangers, public highways, 31
Data, manufacturers', 17
Data sheets, health and safety, 213
dB(A)/dB(C), 258
Dead electrical supplies, 153
Deafness, 257
Debris netting, 294
Decayed floorboards, 352
Decibel scale, 257
Decommissioning, 3
Deconstruction, 339, 350
    control measures, 344
    hazards, 340
Decoration, 5
Defective apparatus, 152
Defective equipment, 128
    fire, 175
Defects, roof, 353
Definition
    common sound measurement terms, 257
    confined space, 329
    construction activities, 3
    construction, 5
    deconstruction, 339
    demolition, 339
    flammable, 186
    flashpoint, 186
    scaffolding, 291
Deliberate
    controlled collapse, 339
    ignition, 175
Demarcating safe areas, 309
Demarcation, 310
Demolition, 339
    control measures, 344
    deliberate controlled collapse, 339
    exclusion zone, 340
    hazards, 339
    investigation, 346
    piecemeal, 339
    risk, 339
    selection of the appropriate method, 340
Depth of the excavation, 320
Dermatitis, 209
Description of project, 14
Design, 86
    loading platforms, 296
    scaffolding, 289
Designated walkways, 47
Designers' duties, 10
Detection
    buried services, 322
    fire, 190
Detectors, 322
Deterioration of materials, 283
Device
    trip, 138
    two-hand control (2HC), 138
Dewatering, 326
Differences
    non-ionising and ionising radiation, 269
Digging, 76
    methods, 322
Dilapidation, 343
    structure, 351
Dilution ventilation, 230
Direct
    burning, 173
    shock, 150
Directional signs, 195
Disabled, fire, 198
Disc cutter, 125

Dismantling, 4
    scaffolds, 76
Disorders
    musculoskeletal, 75
    work-related upper limb, 75
Display screen equipment - use of, 77
Disposal
    off-site, 349
    waste, 251
    waste off site, 355
Distance, 67
    guard, 136
    travel, 194
Diversion of supply, 166
Document shredder, 141
Domestic clients, application, 17
Doors, 195
Dose, 208
Double insulation, 160
Drainage, 47
Drawing-in, 130
Drawings, 353
Drills - fire, 197
Drinking water, 33
Driver
    competence, 66
    identification, 66
    management systems, 66
    selection, 65
    training, 66
Driving
    at work, 66
    hours, 67
    risk assessments, 69
Drowning prevention, 311
Drugs, 43, 69
Dry powder, extinguishing media, 192
Dumper trucks, 97
Duration, 150
Dust, 51, 201, 341, 345
    cement, 244
    on a construction site, 244
    sampler, 218
    total inhalable and respirable, 193
    wood, 244
Duties
    CDM 2015, 9
    client, 9
    contractors', 11
    designer, 10
    manage asbestos, 245
    principal contractors', 11
    principal designer, 10
    property owner, 350

E

Ear muffs, 263
Ear plugs, 263
Earthing, 159
Eating facilities, 34
Economic effects, fire, 176
Edge protection, 304, 309
Effective guards and devices, 142
Effectiveness of controls, 225
Effects
    acute, 207
    chronic, 207
    exposure to vibration, 265
    extreme temperatures, 38
    health, 207
    inclement weather, 37
    materials, 297
    stress, 276
Efficient movement principles for manually lifting loads, 88
Effluent waste, 251
Egress and access, 50
Egress from site, 349, 356
EH40, 213
Ejection, 130
Electric drill, 125
Electric shock, 148
    direct, 150
    effect on the body, 148
    indirect, 150
    severity of effects, 149
Electrical accidents, 152
Electrical burns, 150
Electrical Equipment, 152
    flammable atmospheres, 189
    flammable/explosive environments, 154
    poorly maintained, 153
    wet environments, 154

Electrical fires, 151
    common causes, 151
Electrical generators, 142
Electrical incident, emergency procedures, 165
Electrical safety, control measures, 154
Electrical supplies, live, 153
Electrical systems, progressively extending, 155
Electrical work, 161
Electricity, 342
    hazards, 147
    high risks, 153
    principles, 147
    risks, 148
    secondary effects, 152
Electricity at Work Regulations (EWR) 1989, 153, 161, 384
Electrons, 270
Elimination of substance, 225
Emergency
    arrangements, 334, 355
    controls, 119
    lighting, 195
    plans, 181
    rescue, 286, 308
    stop controls, 120
Emergency procedures, 308
    electrical incident, 165
    evacuation, 196
Employees
    fatal injury, 7
    major injury, 7
    protection of, 32
    specified injury, 7
Enclosure of health hazards, 228
Engineering
    civil, 3
    construction works of, 3
Engineers, structural, 350
Ensuring stability, 297
Entanglement, 128
Environment, 78, 86
    construction, 57
    manual handling factors, 82
    protection, 345
    wet, 154
    work requirements, 32
Environmental
    considerations for vehicles, 61
    considerations, 50
    issues, 251
Environmental harm, fire, 176
Epicondylitis, 78
Equipment, 79, 356
    capability, 155
    falls of, 317
    firefighting, 191
    mechanical, 320
    monitoring substances, 216
    overturning, 341
    positioning and routing of, 327
    reach, 167
    respiratory protective, 232
    selection, 94, 154
    siting, 344
    stability, 105
    strength, 104, 155
    suitability, 105, 154
    unsuitable, 152
Erecting scaffolds, 76
Ergonomic considerations, 115
Escape, 194
European standards, 18
Evacuation procedures, 196
Examination, statutory, 109, 118
Excavation, 4
    assessment, 317
    control measures, 321
    depth, 320
    falls of equipment, 317
    falls of material, 317
    falls of persons, 317
    hazards, 317
    inspection requirements, 328
    meaning of, 5
    type of soil, 320
    underground power cables, 153
Excavators, 97
Excessive driving time, 71
Exclusion zone, demolition, 340
Existence of services such as gas, electricity and water, 342
Existing premises, maintenance, 3
Exit signs, 195

Explosive atmospheres, 189
    exposure to, 330
Explosive collapse, 340
Explosive environments, electrical equipment, 154
Exposure
    adequately control, 223
    asbestos materials, 248
    control, 224
    duty to prevent, 223
    explosive atmospheres, 330
    ionising and non-ionising radiation, 272
    levels, 220
    limitations, 219
    not exceeded limit, 223
    oxygen deficient atmospheres, 330
    routes, 224
    toxic atmospheres, 330
Exposure action/limit values
    noise, 261
    vibration, 267
Extent of dilapidation of the structure, 351
External burns, 150
External sources of information, 17
Extinguishing media, 192
Extreme temperatures, 38
Eye irritation, 204
Eye protection, 233

F

Fabrication, 4
Facilities
    changing clothing, 33
    eating, 34
    first aid, 35
    health and welfare, 32
    rest, 34
    shared, 31
    washing, 33
    welfare, 328
Factors
    affecting the structure, 353
    fire risk assessment, 177
    manual handling, 81
    musculoskeletal ill-health conditions, 78
    site assessments, 23
Fall
    arrest equipment, 306
    arresting systems, 287
    consequences, 286
    from height, 45
    of materials, 285
    of people, 285
    on the same level, 44
    prevention, 286
    protection, 344
Falling
    from height, 281
    materials, 284, 341
    objects, 45
    protection, 63, 344
Falls, 341
    from height, 281
    into excavation, 317
Fans, 290
Fatal injury
    workers, 7
Fatality
    asbestos, 212
    fire, 175
Fencing, 48
    perimeter, 30
Fibres, 201, 243
Fibrillation, 149
File, 124
    health and safety, 15
Filling in, 327
Financial, 6
Finishing
    of concrete slabs, 76
Fire
    action, 197
    alarm, 190
    arson, 181
    assembly points, 196
    building materials, 188
    classes, 192
    classification, 171, 173
    colour code of extinguishers, 192
    combustible materials, 181
    common causes, 175
    compartments, 174
    consequences, 176

    detection, 190
    disabled and infirm, 198
    doors, 195
    drills, 197
    electrical, 151
    emergency lighting, 195
    emergency plans, 181
    evacuation procedures, 196
    exit and directional signs, 195
    explosive atmospheres, 189
    extinguishing media, 192
    fire marshals, 196
    flammable atmospheres, 189
    flammable materials, 181
    flammable, 186
    flashpoint, 186
    gases in cylinders, 184
    hazards, 178
    hot work, 181
    housekeeping, 185
    initiation, classification and spread, 171
    inspections, 185
    instruction notices, 197
    means of escape, 194
    openings and voids, 189
    passageways, 195
    permit to work, 183
    portable fire fighting equipment, 191
    prevention, 181
    principles, 171
    refuge, 198
    risk assessment, 177
    risk reduction, 179
    roll call, 197
    signs, 195
    smoking, 182
    sources of fuel, 172
    sources of ignition, 171
    sources of oxygen, 172
    spread of fire and smoke, 188
    spread, 171, 174
    stairs, 195
    structural measures, 188
    systems of work, 182
    training, 191, 197
    travel distances, 194
    triangle, 171
    zoning, 189
Fire Safety (Scotland) Regulations (FSSR) 2006, 176, 386
Fire (Scotland) Act (FSA) 2005, 176, 386
Firefighting equipment
    training requirements, 191
First-aid, 31
    facilities, 35
Fit for purpose, 114
Fitness to drive, 69
Fixed guards, 136
Fixed objects
    collisions, 58, 92
Fixing
    plasterboard, 76
Flammable, 186
    atmospheres, 189
    environments, 154
    liquids, 186
    materials, 181
    substances, 27
Flat roofs, 308
Floorboards
    decayed, 352
Flue, 329
Fluid injection, 130
Foam
    extinguishing media, 192
Foot protection, 234
Footpaths, 24
Force reduction, 262
Fork-lift trucks, 90
    control measures, 92
    hazards, 90
    over balancing, 91
    overturning, 91
    parking areas, 93
Form FOD ASB5, 250
Formal
    inspection, 163
    tests, 163
Format
    pre-construction information, 14
Forms
    biological agents, 201
    chemical agent, 201

Foundations
  unstable, 353
Fragile roofs, 282
Free-flowing solids, 331
Frequency, 150, 257
  inspection, 164
  testing, 164
Friction, 129
Frostbite, 39
Frost-nip, 39
Fuel sources, 172
Fumes, 201, 341, 345
Fungal growth, 352
Fungi, 201
Fuses, 158

G

Gamma rays, 271
Gas, 342
Gases in cylinders, 184
Gases, 201
Generators, 157
Genetic damage, 237
Germ cell mutagenicity, 204
Gin wheel, 103
Glass, 188
Gloves, 233
Goal posts, 166
Gradients, 61
Ground
  conditions, 23
  consolidation equipment, 142
  contaminated, 319
  level barriers, 166
  probing radar, 322
Growth
  fungal and harmful, 352
Guard
  adequate strength, 143
  adjustable, 138
  allow maintenance without removal, 143
  compatibility with process, 143
  distance, 136
  effective, 142
  fixed, 136
  interlocking, 137
  maintained, 143
  not easily by-passed, 143
  not increase risk or restrict view, 143
  rail, 292
  self adjusting, 137
Guarding, 48
  machinery, 135
Guardrails, 293, 325
Guidance notes, 17
Guidelines for assessment of manual handling operations, 84

H

Hammers, 123
Hand fed power planner, 141
Hand tools, 113, 123
Hand/arm protection, 233
Hand-arm vibration, 265
  contributory factors, 266
Hand-held tools, 123
Handling while seated, 84
Harmful growth, 352
Harmful, 202
Harmonised warning pictograms, 212
Harnesses, 306, 308
Hazard statements, 212
Hazardous substance monitoring, 215
Hazardous substances, 208, 342, 347
  health risks, 201
  minimising emission, release and spread, 223
Hazardous Waste (England and Wales) Regulations (HWR) 2005 (as amended), 387
Hazards
  alcohol and drugs at work, 43
  cartridge nail gun, 126
  chain saw, 127
  chop saw, 125
  confined spaces, 330
  construction site machinery, 133, 135
  cut off saw, 125
  deconstruction, 340
  demolition, 339, 340
  disc cutter, 125
  dumper trucks, 97
  electric drill, 125
  electricity, 147

excavation, 317
excavators, 97
fire, 178
fork lift trucks, 90
gin wheel, 103
hand tools (non-powered), 123
hoist, 98
lifts, 98
machinery, 128, 135
maintenance, 116
mechanical, 128, 319
mechanically operated load handling equipment, 90
mobile and tower designs, 100
non-mechanical, 131
non-vehicle movement related, 58
office machinery, 131
overhead power lines, 320
overhead, 319
pallet truck, 103
pedestrians, 44
pneumatic drill/chisel, 124
pneumatic nail gun, 126
sack truck, 102
sander, 126
scissor lifts, 100
telehandlers, 96
to general public, 46
violence at work, 41
wheelbarrow, 102
work equipment, 131
working at height, 281
workplace vehicles and plant, 57
workshop machinery, 132
Hazards identified
  control measures, 356
Head protection, 233, 288, 311
Health and safety
  affecting structure, 353
  consequences, 6
  data sheets, 213
  file, 15
  management, 6
  size of problem, 7
  sources of information, 17
Health and Safety at Work etc. Act (HASAWA) 1974, 17, 50, 66, 108, 114, 116, 123, 128, 141, 161, 213
Health and safety data sheets, 213
Health and Safety (Display Screen Equipment) Regulations (DSE) 1992 (as amended), 389
Health and Safety Executive (HSE), 8, 15, 192, 250
Health and Safety (First-Aid) Regulations (FAR) 1981 (as amended), 31, 390
Health and Safety (Miscellaneous Amendments) Regulations (MAR) 2002, 390
Health and Safety (Miscellaneous Repeals, Revocations and Amendments) Regulations (MRRA) 2013, 392
Health and Safety (Safety Signs and Signals) Regulations (SSSR) 1996, 49, 61, 392
Health effects, 207
  infrared, 270
  ionising radiation, 271
  microwaves, 270
  radio frequency, 270
  ultraviolet, 269
  visible light, 269
Health requirements, 32
Health risks, 245
  asbestos, 244
  assessment, 208
  hazardous substances, 201
  principles to control exposure, 223
  specific agents, 237
Health surveillance, 235, 264, 268, 274, 328
Heat, 330
  exhaustion, 40
  stress, 39
  stroke, 40
  transmission, 173
Heating, 35, 50
Helmets, 233
Hepatitis, 238, 243
Hierarchy of measures for dangerous parts of machinery, 136
High pressure fluid injection, 130
High risks - electricity, 153
High visibility, 50
Highways
  dangers, 31
  working on, 52
HIV, 237
Hoists, 98, 103
  scaffold, 296
Holders, 139

Hold-to-run, 139
Hood, 229
Hot
    environments, 41
    work, 181
Hours
    driving, 67
Housekeeping, 185
    requirements, 50
HSE
    guidance note EH40, 213
    publications, 17
Hum detectors, 322
Human harm - fire, 176
Hydrogen sulphide, 243
Hygiene - personal, 235
Hypothermia, 39

I

ICE, 18
Identification
    asbestos, 246
    buried services, 321
    features of the structure, 351
    key structural elements, 351
    location, 351
    services, 347
    structure, 351
    type of services, 351
Identified hazards - control measures, 356
Ignition sources, 171
IIRSM, 19
Illegal drugs, 43
Ill-health
    incidence of, 7
    conditions, 78
    effects, 777
Immersion foot, 39
Impact, 129
    vehicles, 297
Inadequate maintenance, 152
Incident report, 71
Inclement weather, 37
Incompatible waste streams, 252
Increased distance, 273
Independent tied scaffold, 289
Indirect shock, 150
Individual, 86
    manual handling capability, 82
Induction, site arrangements, 32
Industrial properties, 25
Information
    external sources, 17
    health, 226
    pre-construction, 14
    providing to all parties, 15
    work equipment, 115
Information sources
    health, 212
    limitations in assessing risks to health, 214
    supplier, 214
Information, 50
    fork-lift trucks, 95
Infrared, 270, 272
    possible sources, 270
    potential health effects, 270
Ingestion, 208
Ingress
    water, 318
Inhalable dust, 193
Inhalation, 208
Initial site assessment, 23
Initiation of fires, 171
Injection, 210
    high pressure fluid, 130
Injuries
    work-related road, 66
Injury
    fatal, 7
    non-fatal, 7
    Inspection, 109
    fire equipment, 191
    formal, 163
    frequency of, 164
    LEV, 228
    records of, 164
    strategies, 162
    visual, 163
Inspection requirements
    excavation support systems, 328
    scaffolding, 298
    work equipment, 288

Installation
    extending electrical system, 155
    lifting equipment, 105
Installation, removal and maintenance of services, 5
Institute of Civil Engineers (ICE), 18
Institution of Occupational Safety and Health (IOSH), 19
Instruction, 50, 288
    notices, 197
    work equipment, 115
Insulation, 262
    double, 160
Intensity, 257
Interlocking guards, 137
Internal burns, 151
International Institute for Risk and Safety Management (IIRSM), 19
International standards, 18
Investigations
    competent person to carry out, 350
Involving the workforce, 87
Ionisation, 270
Ionising radiation
    health effects, 271
    sources, 272
    types, 270
Ionising Radiation Regulations (IRR) 1999, 274, 392
IOSH, 19
Irritant contact dermatitis, 209
Irritant, 202
Isocyanates, 240
Isolation, 117, 161, 262, 354
    substance, 225
    supply, 159, 166
Issues
    construction, 5
IT sources, 18

J

Jet silencers, 262
Jigs, 139
Journey, 71

K

Kerb laying, 76
Key structural elements, identification, 351
Kinetic handling principles, lifting techniques, 88

L

Labels, 212
Labour Force Survey (LFS), 7, 76
Ladders, 300
    step, 302
Landscaping, 5
Lead, 240
Leading edge protection, 309
    systems, 304
Leads, 154
Leaning walls, 352
Ledger, 292
Legal, 6
    drugs, 42
    effects of fire, 176
    responsibilities of individuals on public roads, 69
Legionnaires' disease, 242
Legionnella, 242
Legislation, 17
Leptospira, 242
LEV, 228
Licence for asbestos removal, 248
Licensed carrier, 250
Licensed disposal site for asbestos, 250
Lifting accessories, 101
Lifting and moving equipment, 81
Lifting equipment
    installation, 105
    lifting persons, 109
    positioning, 105
    stability, 105
    strength, 104
    suitability, 105
Lifting operations, 104, 106, 107
Lifting Operations and Lifting Equipment Regulations (LOLER) 1998, 104,118, 394
Lifting persons
    special requirements, 109
Lifting techniques using kinetic handling principles, 88
Lifting, 29, 84
Lifts, 98
    scissor, 100

Lighting, 28, 35, 51, 122, 311, 325
    emergency, 195

Limit values
noise, 260
Limitations
dilution ventilation, 230
exposure limits, 219
hazardous substance monitoring, 215
health information, 214
portable appliance testing (PAT), 165
PPE, 263
protective systems, 158
Limiting exposure
vibration, 267
Liquefied petroleum gas, 184
Liquids, 201
highly flammable, 186
Literacy
workers, 6
Live electrical
supplies, 153
work, 161
Load, 85
handling aids, 102
handling equipment, 90
manual handling factors, 82
manually operated, 102
Loading, 4, 58
platforms, 296
unloading and storage of materials, 4
unloading, 27
Local
effect, 208
exhaust ventilation, 228
Locating buried services, 162
Lock-out, 117
Lock-off, 333
Long-term
exposure limits (LTEL), 219
samplers, 218
Low voltage systems, 159
Lower exposure action values - noise, 261
LPG, 184
LTEL, 219

M

Machinery, 113
dangerous parts, 135
guarding, 135
hazards, 128
information, 140
instruction, 140
protection methods, 135
supervision, 140
training, 140
work equipment, 116
Mains electrical supplies, 153
Maintenance
conducted safely, 117
control measures, 117
existing premises, 3
fire equipment, 1901
hazards, 116
inadequate, 152
personal hearing protection, 264
safe workplace, 50
services, 5
strategies, 162
vehicles, 62
vibration, 267
without guard removal, 143
Maintenance work
control measures, 52
vehicle, 59
Major Contractors Group (UKCG), 19
Management
construction phase plan, 15
failing, 6
health and safety, 6
of vehicle movements, 60
of work, 15
waste, 349, 355
Management of Health and Safety at Work Regulations (MHSWR) 1999,
6, 123, 181, 394
Management systems
driver competence, 66
Managing, work related road safety, 68
Manual handling, 341, 345
assessment of risks, 81
guidelines for assessment, 84
hazards, 80
injuries, 80
operations

Manual Handling Operations Regulations (MHOR) 1992 (as amended),
82, 84, 398
Manual handling risks, avoiding, 85
Manually lifting loads, movement principles, 88
Manually operated
hoists - gin wheel, 103
load handling aids, 102
Manufacturers'
data, 17
health and safety data sheets, 213
Marked
safe working load, 106
Markings, 64, 311
buried services, 321
CE, 114
services, 162
work equipment, 122
Marshals
fire, 196
Mast climbing work platform, 304
Materials, 321
construction terms, 5
deterioration, 283
excavation, 5
fall of, 285, 317
falling, 341
inappropriately stored, 174
loading, 4
musculoskeletal disorders, 75
storage, 4, 326
structure, 5
unloading, 4
work related upper limb disorders, 75
Meaning of
common sound measurement terms, 257
confined space, 329
construction activities, 3
construction, 5
deconstruction, 339
demolition, 339
flammable, 186
flashpoint, 186
scaffolding, 291
Means of
access, 25, 295, 309, 325, 333
controlling dangers on public highways, 31
escape, 194
protecting the public, 30
securing plant, chemicals, etc, 30
Measures
consequences of a fall, 286
preventative, 40
Mechanical equipment, excavation, 320
Mechanical hazards, 128, 319
Mechanically operated load handling equipment, 90
Mechanisation, 87
Media, extinguishing, 192
Medical surveillance, 250
Mesothelioma, 212
Metal detectors, 322
Method, demolition and deconstruction, 340
Method of construction, 346
Method statements, 354
control measures, 354
Methods of supporting excavations, 323
Microwaves, 270, 273
possible sources, 270
potential health effects, 270
Minimise distance of a fall, 286
Minimising emission, 223
Mists, 201
Misuse
hand tools (non-powered), 123
substance at work, 42
Misusing equipment, fire, 175
Mitigating distance, 286
Mobile
cranes, 100
elevating work platforms, 299
tower scaffolds, 291
Monitoring, 264, 268, 274
arrangements, 334
asbestos, 250
biological, 236
equipment, 215
performance, 68
substance, 215
Moral, 6
Movement
awkward, 90
of people on construction sites, 44
of vehicles, 57

© RMS

plasterboard, 76
principles for manually lifting loads, 88
repetitive, 89
Moving and lifting equipment, 90
Moving objects, 45
Moving vehicles
collisions, 45
MSDs, 75
Multi-lock system, 161
Musculoskeletal disorders, 75
control measures, 79
factors causing ill-health conditions, 78
Mutagenic, 202

N

Nature
activities, 5
construction activities, 3
workers, 5
Neutrons, 270
New Roads and Street Works Act (NRSWA) 1991, 52, 399
Nitrogen, 240
Noise, 51, 257, 342, 345
action values, 260
control measures, 262
exposure, assessment of, 258
exposure level, 262
exposure limit values, 261
induced hearing loss (deafness), 257
limit values - noise, 260
lower exposure action values, 261
physical effects, 257
psychological effects, 257
units, 258
upper exposure action values, 261
Non-mechanical hazards, 131
Non-vehicle movement related hazards, 58
Non-construction activities, 23
Non-English speaking workers, 6
Non-ionising radiation
controls, 272
sources, 269
Notices, fire instruction, 197
Notification
asbestos removal, 248
projects, 12
Number
fatal injury to workers 7
major injury to employees, 7
specified injury to employees, 7

O

Occupational
asthma, 237
sources of ionising radiation, 270
Occupied premises, 3, 31, 32
Off site disposal - waste management, 349
Office machinery
control measures, 131
hazards, 131
Offices, 28
One meter rule, 259
On-site segregation - waste management, 349
Open air storage of flammable liquids, 188
Open sheeting, 324
Openings, 189
Operation controls, 119
Operations - lifting, 104
Organic solvents, 239
Organisations
external sources of information, 17
trade, 18
Over balancing - fork-lift trucks, 91
Overalls, 233
Overhead
cables - protection, 162
hazards, 319
services - presence of, 26
Overhead power lines, 153
avoidance, 166
consultation with service provider, 166
control measures, 166
correct clearance distances, 167
diversion of supply, 166
goal posts, 166
ground level barriers, 166
hazards, 320
isolation of supply, 166
pre-planning, 166
restriction of equipment/vehicle reach, 167

Overturning
equipment, 341
fork-lift trucks, 91
plant, 341
vehicles, 57, 341
Oxygen
deficient atmospheres - exposure to, 330
sources, 172

P

Pallet truck, 103
Parking - fork-lift trucks, 93
Passageways, 195
Past structural alterations, 354
Pedestal drill, 141
Pedestrians
collisions, 58, 92
control measures, 46
hazards, 44
segregation, 63
People
fall of, 285, 317
movement on construction sites, 44
protective measures, 64
Perimeter fencing, 30
Peritendinitis, 78
Permit to dig, example, 323
Permit-to-work
confined spaces, 332
document, 332
fire, 183
procedures, 156, 332
requirements, 156
Person, competent, 161, 350
Personal
fall protection systems, 287
samplers, 218
Personal hearing protection, 263
application of various types, 263
attenuation factors, 264
limitations of various types, 263
maintenance, 264
purpose, 263
selection, 263
use, 263
Personal hygiene and protection regimes, 235
Personal protective equipment, 49, 327, 334, 225
environmental waste, 252
machinery, 140
use of, 49
Personal Protective Equipment at Work Regulations (PPER) 1992 (as amended), 49, 400
Phase, construction, 14
Photocopier, 141
Physical effects
noise, 257
stress, 276
Pictograms, 213
Piecemeal demolition, 339
Piling, 29
Pit, 330
Pitch, 257
Plan - construction phase, 14
Planning
confined spaces, 331
prevent falls, 285
Plant, 356
hazards, 57
overturning, 341
positioning and routing of, 327
securing, 30
Plasterboard
fixing of, 76
movement, 76
Plate compactor, 142
Platforms, staging, 303
Pneumatic
drill/chisel, 124
nail gun, 126
Policy
driving, 68
violence at work, 41
Poor posture, 88
Poorly
designed tasks - ill-health effects, 77
designed workstations - ill-health effects, 77
maintained electrical equipment, 153
Portable
appliance testing (PAT), 165
circular saw, 142
electrical equipment, 152
firefighting equipment, 191

power tools, 124
Positioning of,
   lifting equipment, 105
   vehicles, plant and equipment, 327
Power
   cables, 153
   lines overhead, 153, 167, 320
   tools, 113, 124
Precautionary
   measures, vibration, 267
   statements, 212
Precautions for safe entry, 331
Pre-construction information, 14
Pre-deconstruction, 346
Pre-demolition, 350
   survey - duties of the property owner, 350
Premature collapse, 340
   avoidance, 344
Premises
   client/occupier arrangements, 31
   occupied, 3, 32
   unoccupied, 3, 32
Preparation
   construction phase plan, 14
   health and safety file, 16
   of site for specialist activities, 29
   pre-construction information, 14
   site, 29
Pre-planning - working near overhead power lines, 166
Presence of
   cellars, 347
   public, 321
Pressures - time, 6
Preventative measures
   extremes of temperature, 40
   inclement weather, 40
   vibration, 267
Preventing falls, 286
Prevention
   falling materials, 285
   falls, 285
   fire, 181
   of drowning, 311
   of exposure, 222
Previous/current use, 23
Principal contractor, 10
   duties, 11
   time pressures, 6
Principal designers' duties, 10
Principles
   efficient movement for manually lifting loads, 88
   electricity, 147
   fire, 171
   heat transmission, 173
   kinetic handling, 88
   of good practice, control of exposure, 223
   of good practice, health risk, 223
   of protection, accidental release to environment, 252
Problem, size of, 7
Procedures
   defective work equipment, 116
   permit-to-work, 156
Product labels, 212
Professional bodies, 18
Progressively extending electrical systems, 155
   installation, 155
   planning, 155
Project
   description, 14
   notification, 12
Properties
   commercial, 25
   industrial, 25
   of common building materials, 188
   residential, 25
Property owner - duties, 350
Protecting the public, 30
Protection
   against overhead cables, 162
   driver, 62
   falling materials, 63, 344
   falls, 344
   from impact of vehicles, 297
   openings and voids, 189
   other employees/visitors, 32
   regimes, 235
Protection of
   conductors, 154
   public, 354
   surrounding structures, 354
   the environment, 345
   third parties, 354

Protection of others
   barriers, 310
   demarcation, 310
   head protection, 311
   lighting, 311
   marking, 311
   sheeting, netting and fans, 311
   signs, 310
   tunnels, 310
   working at height, 310
Protective
   clothing, 250
   equipment and clothing, 232
   measures - for people and structures, 64
   mechanisms, 210
   overalls, 233
Protective systems
   advantages, 158
   limitations, 158
Protons, 270
Provision
   disabled, 198
   equipment, 113
   health and welfare facilities, 32
   information and training, 226
   information to all parties, 15
   of work equipment to prevent falls, 286
   utility services, 28
Provision and Use of Work Equipment Regulations (PUWER) 1998 (as amended), 113, 401
Proximity of
   roadways, 320, 349
   structures, 320, 349
Psychological effects - noise, 257
Public
   hazards caused by construction activities, 46
   highways, 31, 52
   presence of, 321
   protecting, 30, 354
   roads - legal responsibilities of individuals, 69
   supply, 157
Publications - HSE, 17
Pulling, 84
Puncture, 129
Purpose
   construction phase plan, 14
   health and safety file, 16
   personal hearing protection, 263
   pre-construction information, 14
   surveys, 350
Pushing, 84
Push-sticks, 139
Putlog, 292
   scaffold, 290

R
Radiation, 269
   differences, 269
   types, 269
   of heat, 173
Radiation protection
   advisers (RPA), 274
   strategies, 273
   supervisor, 274
Radio frequency, 270, 273
   detectors, 322
   possible sources, 270
   potential health effects, 270
Radon, 271
   controlling exposures, 273
Railways, 24
Range of activities, 4
Rate
   fatal injury to workers, 7
   major injury to employees, 7
   specified injury to employees, 7
Registration, Evaluation, Authorisation and Restriction of Chemicals (REACH) EC Regulation, 213, 403
Records of
   inspection, 164
   testing, 164
Reduced time, 273
   exposure, 227
   voltage systems, 159
Reducing exposure levels, 221
Reduction of exposure, 225
Refresher, training, 66
Refuge, 198
Refurbishment systems, 350
Regulatory Reform (Fire Safety) Order (RRFSO) 2005, 176, 406
Release
   of hazardous substances, 223

to environment, 252
Relevant parties, 12
Reliability of controls, 225
Remediation works, 28
Removal
    asbestos, 248
    of services, 5
Renovation, works, 3
Repetitive
    construction activities, 76
    movements, 89
Reported
    major injury to employees, 7
    specified injury to employees, 7
Reporting of Injuries, Diseases and Dangerous Occurrences Regulations
    (RIDDOR) 2013, 68
Reproductive toxicity, 205
Requirements
    for disposal, 250
    for lifting persons, 109
    for scaffold erectors, 295
    for temporary electrical supplies, 157
    guards and safety devices, 142
    health, welfare and work environment, 32
    lifting operations, 104
    means of escape, 194
    permit-to-work, 156
    persons accidentally exposed to asbestos materials, 248
    removal of asbestos, 248
    work equipment, 113
Residential properties, 25
Residual current device (RCD), 159
Resistance, 147, 150
Resistant slip, 47
Respirable dust, 193
Respirator, 231
Respiratory
    failure, 149
    protective equipment, 231
    sensitisation, 204
Responsibilities
    individuals on public roads, 69
    users of work equipment, 123
Rest facilities, 34
Restraint systems, 62
Restricted space, 331
Restriction
    of equipment/vehicle reach, 167
    site, 23
    use and maintenance of work equipment, 115
Reveal pin, 292
Reversing, warnings, 65
Review
    control measures for health risks, 225
    fire risk assessment, 180
    means of escape, 196
    of factors affecting the structure, 353
Reviewing - risk assessments, 84
Risk
    activities in construction, 266
    confined spaces, 330
    demolition, 339
    electricity, 148
    of electricity, 148
    reduction - fire, 179
    road traffic incident, 67
    site, 15
    violence at work, 41
    working at height, 281
Risk assessment, 46
    confined spaces, 331
    driving, 70
    excavation, 320
    factors to consider, excavation, 320
    fire, 177
    guidelines for manual handling operations, 84
    reviewing, 84
    the vehicle, 70
    vibration, 266
Road, 23, 26
    injuries, work-related, 66
    marking equipment, 142
    safety, systems, 68
    safety, 68
    traffic incident risks, 67
Road Traffic Act (RTA) 1991, 407
Roadways, 26
    condition of, 349
    proximity of, 320, 349
Role
    call, 197
    fire marshals, 196

hazardous substance monitoring, 215
    of health surveillance, 274
    of monitoring, 274
    over, 62
    stress, 276, 277
Roof
    defects, 353
    lights, 282
    work, safe working practices, 289
    work, 308
Roofs, 282
    flat, 308
    sloping, 309
Rope, 308
    access, 306
Routes
    of entry, 208
    of exposure, 224
Routing of vehicles, plant and equipment, 327
Rules
    for vehicles on site, 65
    safe operation of cranes, 107
    site, 31

S

Sack truck, 102
Safe
    areas, 309
    digging methods, 322
    entry, precautions, 331
    handling and storage of waste, 251
    handling, 251
    movement of vehicles, 57
    place of work, 122
    storage of spoil, 325
    system of work, 4, 161
    viewing points, 30
    working load (SWL), 101, 106
    working practices, 289
    workplace, 50
Safety
    boats, 312
    features, 292
    helmets, 233
    nets, 307
Samplers, 216
Sandblasting, 52
Sander, 126
Sanitary conveniences, 33
Saw
    chop, 125
    circular, 141
    cut off, 125
Scaffold
    erecting/dismantling, 76
    erectors - requirements, 295
    hoists, 296
Scaffolding, 289
    design features, 289
    inspection requirements, 298
    safety features, 292
    terms, 291
    working at height, 354
Schools, 25
Scissor lifts, 100
Scope
    CDM 2015, 8
    of construction activities, 3
    of surveys, 350
    work equipment, 113
Screwdrivers, 124
Seated, manual handling, 84
Seating, 34
Secondary effects of contact with electricity, 152
Securing
    chemicals, 30
    loads, 58
    plant, 30
    site, 30
Segregation
    on-site segregation, 355
    on-site, 349
    pedestrians and vehicles, 63
    people, 228
    process, 228
Selection, 65
    drivers, 65
    equipment, 94
    equipment, construction activities, 154
    equipment, flammable atmospheres, 189
    operators, 95
    personal hearing protection, 263

respiratory protective equipment, 231
Self
  adjusting guard, 137
  employed, fatal injury, 7
Sensitisation dermatitis, 209
Sensitising, 202
Sensitive protective equipment, 138
Serious eye damage, 204
Service provider - consultation, 166
Services, 321, 354
  buried, 26, 317
  electricity, 342
  gas, 342
  identification of, 347
  installation, 5
  maintenance, 5
  marking, 162
  overhead, 26
  removal, 5
  temporary, 354
  type, identification, 351
  utility, 28
  water, 342
Sewer, 330
Shared
  facilities, 31
  workplaces, fire, 180
Sharp items, treading on, 46
Shear, 129
Sheeting, 59, 297
Shielding, 273
Shock, electric, 148, 150
Shoring, 324
Short term
  exposure limits (STEL), 219
  samplers, 216
Sides, collapse, 317
Significance
  of the structure, 351
  of time weighted averages, 227
Significant - site risks, 15
Signs, 28, 30, 49, 65, 310, 325
  use of, 49
Silencing, 262
Silica, 243
Silo, 330
Single-stage alarm, 190
Site
  access, 349, 356
  area of, 23
  arrangements, 26
  assessments, factors, 23
  clearance, 4
  control measures, 26
  egress, 349, 356
  history, 23
  inductions, arrangements, 32
  means of protecting the public, 30
  movements, 4
  other (non-construction) activities, 23
  planning, 26
  preparation for specialist activities, 29
  restrictions, 23
  risks, 15
  rules, 31, 65
  security, 30
Site Waste Management Plans Regulations (SWMP) 2008, 307
Siting, 344
Skin
  contact, absorption, 185
  corrosion, 203
  irritation, 203
  sensitisation, 204
Slabs, concrete, 76
Slip
  resistant surfaces, 47
  same level, 44
Sloping roofs, 282, 309
Smoke, 201
  detection, 190
  structural measures, 188
  seals, 188
  tubes, 218
Smoking, 182
Smothering, 171
Soft
  fall beanbags, 307
  landing systems, 307
  strip requirements, 354
Soil
  testing, 328
  type, 320

Sole boards, 292
Solids, 201
  free-flowing, 331
Solvents, 43, 239
Sound
  measurement terms, 257
  power, 257
  pressure, 257
Sources
  fuel, 172
  ignition, 171
  infrared, 270
  microwaves, 270
  of information, external, 17
  of information, health, 212
  of ionising radiation, 270, 272
  of non-ionising radiation, 269, 271
  oxygen, 172
  radio frequency, 270
  ultraviolet, 269
  visible light, 269
Spanners, 124
Spillage control and drainage, 47
Spindle moulding machine, 141
Spoil, safe storage of, 325
Spread
  fire, 171
  of hazardous substances, 223
Stabbing, 129
Stability, 122
Staff alarm, 191
Staging platforms, 303
Stairs, 195
Standards, British/European/International, 18
Start controls, 120
Static, samplers, 218
Statutory thorough examination, 109, 118
Steelwork, 29, 188
STEL, 219
Step ladders, 300
Stop controls, 120
Storage, 26
  flammable and combustible materials, 181
  flammable substances, 27
  highly flammable/flammable liquids, 186
  inappropriately, 174
  incompatible waste streams, 252
  liquefied petroleum gas, 184
  of materials, 4
  of waste, 251
Strength
  guards, 143
  of equipment, 155
Stress
  behavioural effects, 276
  causes of, 275
  change, 276, 278
  cold, 39
  control measures, 276
  control, 275, 277
  demand, 275, 277
  due to traffic, 67
  effects of, 276
  heat, 39
  physical effects, 276
  role, 276
  support, 275, 277
  work relationships, 275, 277
Striking
  against fixed objects, 46
  against stationary objects, 46
  by objects, 45
Structural
  alterations, past, 354
  calculations, 353
  condition, 347
  engineers, 350
  measures, fire and smoke, 188
Structure
  condition of, 349
  dilapidation of, 351
  factors affecting, 353
  identification of, 351
  identify features, 351
  meaning of, 5
  protective measures, 64
  proximity of, 320, 349
  significance of, 351
  type, 346
Substance misuse at work, 42
Substances
  classification, 202

duty to prevent exposure or control it, 223
excavations, 327
flammable, 27
hazardous to health, 201
hazardous, 342, 349
monitoring, 215
principles to control exposure, 223
reducing exposure levels, 221
routes of entry, 208
with specific effects, 236
Suitability
for location, work equipment, 128
of equipment - construction activities, 154
provision of equipment, 113
traffic routes, 60
Suitable
electrical equipment, 189
strong, and stable lifting equipment, 104
Sump points, 326
Superficial mechanisms, 210
Supervision
prevent falls, 285
Supplier information sources, 214
Supply of Machinery (Safety) Regulations (SMSR) 2008, 17, 114, 409
Support
equipment, 321
stress, 275, 277
systems, excavations, 328
Supporting excavations - methods, 323
Surface
condition, 61
slip resistant, 47
Surrounding structures, protection of, 354
Surroundings, 23
Surveillance
health, 328, 235
medical, for asbestos, 250
Survey, 346
asbestos, 246
pre-demolition, 350
purpose of, 350
scope of, 350
Surveyors, 350
Suspension
from cradles, 305
trauma, 308
Systemic effect, 208
Systems
for control of work equipment, 121
management of driver competence, 66
road safety, 68

T

Tag out, 117
Tank, 330
Target
organs, 208
systems, 208
Task, 78, 86
manual handling factors, 82
poorly designed, ill-health effects, 77
Telehandlers, 96
Temperatures, 36
Temporary
electrical supplies, 157
nature of activities, 5
services, 354
workplaces, 179
Tendinitis, 78
Tenosynovitis, 76
Terms
common sound measurement terms, 257
confined space, 329
construction activities, 3
construction, 5
deconstruction, 339
demolition, 339
flammable, 186
flashpoint, 186
scaffolding, 291
Testing, 66, 163
atmospheric, 333
frequency of, 164
portable appliance. 165
records of, 164
soil, 328
Tetanus, 243
The Workplace (Health Safety and Welfare) Regulations (WHSWR) 1992, 33, 40, 50
Third parties, protection of, 354
Ties, 292
Timber, 188

Time
exposed to health risks, 227
pressures, 6
weighted average (TWA), 192, 197
Tinnitus, 257
Toe boards, 292
Tools
hand-held, 113, 123
portable power, 124
power, 113
Topography, 23
Total inhalable dust, 193
Tower
cranes, 100
scaffolds, 291
Toxic, 202
asphyxiating atmospheres, 319
atmospheres - exposure to, 319, 330
Toxicity, 208
Trade organisations, 18
Traffic
routes - sufficiency and suitability, 60
signs manual, chapter 8, 52
stress, 67
Training, 50, 66, 288
arrangements, 356
asbestos, 250
competent persons, 333
drivers, 66
fire equipment, 191
fire, 197
fork-lift trucks, 95
health, 226
manual handling, 87
refresher, 66
work equipment, 115
Transitory nature of workers, 5
Transom, 292
Transport - liquefied petroleum gas, 184
Travel distances, 194
Treading on sharp items, 46
Trench, 330
box, 324
foot, 39
Trestles, 303
Trip device, 138
Trips, 44
Truck
fork-lift, 90
pallet, 103
sack, 102
Tubes, smoke, 218
Tunnels, 310
Twisting, 84
Two meter rule, 258
Two-hand control (2HC) device, 138
Two-stage alarm, 190
Types of
ionising radiation, 270
structure, 346
work, 3
Typical confined spaces found during construction activities, 329

U

UK Contractors Group (UKCG), 19
Ultraviolet, 269, 272
possible sources, 269
potential health effects, 269
Underground power cables, 153
Unloading, 4, 58
loading, 27
Unoccupied premises, 3, 32
Unprotected edges, 283
Unstable
access equipment, 283
foundations, 353
Unsuitable equipment, 152
Upper
exposure action values - noise, 261
limb disorders, 75
Use
competent persons, 333
dilution ventilation, 230
electrical equipment in flammable atmospheres, 189
flammable and combustible materials, 181
liquefied petroleum gas, 185
of caissons, 318
of cofferdams, 318
personal hearing protection, 263
previous/current, 23
signs and personal protective equipment, 49
User checks, electrical, 163

Utility services, provision of, 28

V

Vapour, 201
Vat, 330
Vehicle, 321
    collisions, 58, 92
    condition, 69
    hazards, 57
    impact, 297
    maintenance work, 59, 62
    movement management, 57, 60
    overturning, 57, 341
    positioning and routing of, 327
    protective measures for people and structures, 64
    reach, restriction, 167
    segregation, 63
    siting, 344
    warnings, 65
Ventilation, 34
    dilution, 230
    local exhaust, 228
Vertical distance, 282
Vibration, 265, 342, 345
    choice of equipment, 267
    control measures, 267
    effects of exposure, 265
    exposure action values, 267
    exposure - assessment of, 266
    exposure limit values, 267
    hand-arm, 265
    limiting exposure, 267
    maintenance, 267
    precautionary measures, 267
    preventive measures, 267
    risk assessment, 266
    whole body, 266
Viewing points, 30
Violence at work, 41
Viruses, 202, 237
Visibility, 61
    high, 50
Visible light, 269, 272
    possible sources, 269
    potential health effects, 269
Visibly marked, 106
Vision, 69
Visitors, 32
Visual inspection, 109, 118, 163
Voids, 189, 283
Voltage, 147, 150

W

Work at Height Regulations (WAH) 2005, 284, 286, 288, 410
Walkways, 47
Walls
    cracking, 352
    leaning, 352
Warning, 122
    of vehicle approach, 65
    pictograms, 213
    reversing, 65
Washing facilities, 33
Waste
    disposal, 251
    effluent, 251
    streams storage, 252
Waste management, 349
    off-site disposal, 349, 355
    on-site segregation, 349, 355
Water, 331, 342
    control, 326
    drinking, 33
    extinguishing media, 192
    ingress, 318
Waterways, 24
Weather, 283, 297, 231
    conditions, 6, 63, 68
    inclement, 37
Weighting scales - dB(A), dB(C), 258
Weils disease, 24
Welding, 181, 186
Welfare
    arrangements, 356
    facilities, 328
    requirements, 32
WELs, 213
Wet environments - electrical equipment, 154
Wheelbarrows, 102
Whole body vibration (WBV), 266
Wood dust, 244

Work
    activities, coordination, 357
    driving, 66
    environment requirements, 32
    hot, 181
    maintenance, 52
    management, 15
    platform, mast climbing, 304
    platforms, 299
    progression, fire, 180
    relationships, stress, 275, 277
    schedules, 67
    type, 320
    types of, 3
    vehicle maintenance, 59
Work equipment
    controls, 121
    emergency stop controls, 139
    general requirements, 113
    hazards, 131
    information, instruction and training, 115
    inspection, 118, 288
    lighting, 122
    maintained, 116
    maintenance conducted safely, 117
    markings and warnings, 122
    procedures for defects, 116
    restriction on use and maintenance, 115
    scope, 113
    stability, 122
    statutory thorough examination, 118
    suitability for location, 128
    suitability, 113
    users responsibilities, 123
    workspace, 122
Workers
    effects of extreme temperatures, 38
    effects of inclement weather, 37
    fatal injury, 7
    literacy of, 6
    non-english speaking, 6
    transitory nature of, 5
Workforce competence, 346, 355
Working
    environment, 82
    occupied premises, 32
    on public highways, 52
    over/near water, 311
    platforms, 293
    unoccupied premises, 32
Working at height, 281
    access, 354
    adverse weather conditions, 285
    avoiding, 284
    consequences of a fall, 286
    deterioration of materials, 283
    effectiveness of design, 281
    emergency rescue, 286
    falling materials, 284
    hazards, 281
    instruction, 288
    other techniques, 304
    protection of others, 310
    provision of work equipment, 286
    risks, 281
    roofs, 282
    scaffolding, 354
    training, 288
    unprotected edges, 283
    vertical distance, 282
    voids, 283
    weather, 284
Workplace
    changes to, 179
    constantly changing, 5
    electrical equipment, 152
    evacuation, 196
    exposure limits (WELs), 213, 223
    shared, fire, 180
    storage flammable liquids, 187
    temporary nature of, 5, 179
    vehicles and plant - hazards, 57
Workplace (Health, Safety and Welfare) Regulations (WHSWR) 1992, 33, 40, 50, 412
Work-related
    driving risks - control measures, 71
    road injuries, 66
    upper limb disorders, 75
Works, 3
    alteration, 3
    building, 3

    of engineering construction, 3
    remediation, 28
    renovation, 3
Workspace, work equipment, 122
Workstations, poorly designed, ill-health effects, 77
WRULDs, 75, 77

X
X-rays, 271

Z
Zones, 189